PRENTICE HA

MIDDLE GRADES
Mathematics
An Interactive Approach

Course **2**

anne H. **Chapin**

ark **Illingworth**

Marsha **Landau**

Joanna O. **Masingila**

Leah **McCracken**

PRENTICE HALL

Middle Grades Mathematics
An Interactive Approach

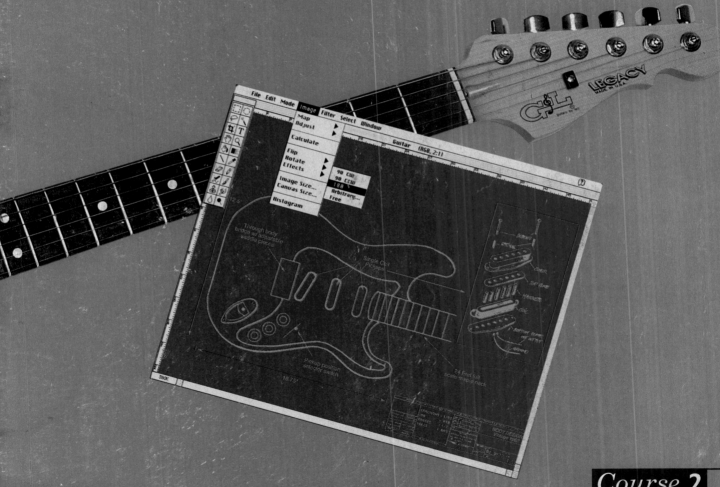

Course 2

Needham, Massachusetts
Englewood Cliffs, New Jersey

The authors and consulting authors on *Prentice Hall Mathematics: An Interactive Approach* team worked with Prentice Hall to develop an instructional approach that addresses the needs of middle grades students with a variety of ability levels and learning styles. Authors also prepared manuscript for strands across the three levels of Middle Grades Mathematics. Consulting authors worked alongside authors throughout program planning and all stages of manuscript development offering advice and suggestions for improving the program.

Authors

Suzanne Chapin, Ed.D., Boston University, Boston MA; Proportional Reasoning and Probability strands

Mark Illingworth, Hollis Public Schools, Hollis, NH; Graphing strand

Marsha S. Landau, Ph.D., National Louis University, Evanston, IL; Algebra, Functions, and Computation strands

Joanna Masingila, Ph.D., Syracuse University, Syracuse, NY; Geometry strand

Leah McCracken, Lockwood Junior High, Billings, MT; Data Analysis strand

Consulting Authors

Sadie Bragg, Ed.D., Borough of Manhattan Community College, The City University of New York, New York, NY

Vincent O'Connor, Milwaukee Public Schools, Milwaukee, WI

ISBN 0-13-031121-9
Printed in the United States of America
3 4 5 98 97 96 95

Reviewers

We are grateful to our reviewers who read manuscript at all stages of development and provided invaluable feedback, ideas, and constructive criticism to help make this program one that meets the needs of middle grades teachers and students.

All Levels

Ann Bouie, Ph.D., Multicultural Reviewer, Oakland, CA

Mary Lester, Dallas Public Schools, Dallas, TX

Dorothy S. Strong, Ph.D., Chicago Public Schools, Chicago, IL

Course 1

Darla Agajanian, Sierra Vista School, Canyon Country, CA

Rhonda Bird, Grand Haven Area Schools, Grand Haven, MI

Leroy Dupee, Bridgeport Public Schools, Bridgeport, CT

Jose Lalas, California State University, Dominguez Hills, CA

Richard Lavers, Fitchburg High School, Fitchburg, MA

Course 2

Raylene Bryson, Alexander Middle School, Huntersville, NC

Sheila Cunningham, Klein Independent School District, Klein, TX

Natarsha Mathis, Hart Junior High School, Washington, DC

Jean Patton, Sharp Middle School, Covington, GA

Judy Trowell, Little Rock School District, Little Rock, AR

Course 3

Michaele F. Chappell, Ph.D., University of South Florida, Tampa, FL

Bettye Hall, Math Consultant, Houston, TX

Joaquin Hernandez, Shenandoah Middle School, Miami, FL

Dana Luterman, Lincoln Middle School, Kansas City, MO

Loretta Rector, Leonardo da Vinci School, Sacramento, CA

Anthony C. Terceira, Providence School Department, Providence, RI

Prentice Hall dedicates this interactive mathematics series to all middle level mathematics educators and their students.

TABLE OF CONTENTS

Interpreting Data

border

denomination

Look for photos with captions that bring math to life in every chapter!

Children between the ages of 4 and 12 influenced about $132 billion worth of purchases in 1990, according to James MacNeal of the Texas A&M Marketing Department.

✳ *Hot Page™ Lesson*

CHAPTER 2 **G**eometry

ROLL

Look for the Flashback (just-in-time review) features in every chapter!

✳ FLASHBACK

Perpendicular lines are lines that intersect to form right angles.

Look for photos with captions that bring math to life in every chapter!

Physical therapists use goniometers to measure the amount of motion a person has in a joint, like an elbow or a knee. The goniometer has a built-in protractor.

Source: *Scholastic Dynamath*

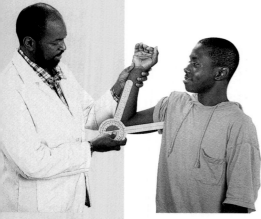

YAW   PITC

center of gravity

Applications of Decimals

Through THE Hoop

Look for the Who?, What?, Why?, When?, Where?, and How? features in every chapter!

An adult human heart weighs about 0.656 lb and pumps about 656.25 gal of blood per hour. **Find the number of gallons of blood a heart pumps in 1 day.**

Source: *Reader's Digest's ABC's of the Human Body*

CHAPTER 4 Introduction to Algebra

▶ **L**ook for newspaper clippings that bring math to life in every chapter!

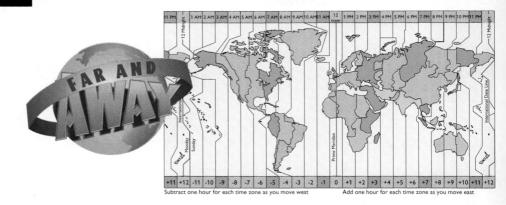

Subtract one hour for each time zone as you move west   Add one hour for each time zone as you move east

The Red Planet

In 1971, the unmanned spacecraft Mariner 9 transmitted pictures and other data as it passed near Mars. Scientists learned that the temperature of Earth's nearest planetary neighbor ranged from 68°F below zero during the day to 176°F below zero at night. The planet has a red, stony, desert landscape, much like what scientists and science fiction writers had imagined for years.

CHAPTER 5

Measurement

wetwells

aerated grit tanks
380 g/min

primary
clariflocculators
261,538 g/h

sewage

grit washer

to landfill

flotation
thickeners

Look for frequent use of real data in every chapter!

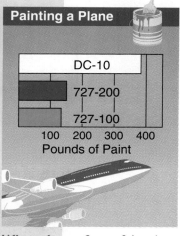

Painting a Plane

| DC-10 |
| 727-200 |
| 727-100 |

100   200   300   400
Pounds of Paint

When the surface of the plane is painted, each pound of paint adds $30 a year to fuel costs. **Estimate the increased yearly costs for each type of plane.**

Source: American Airlines

Look for relevant quotations in every chapter!

66 ———————

The most beautiful thing in the world is, precisely, the conjunction of learning and inspiration.
—Wanda Landowska
(1879-1959)

99

✳ *Hot Page*™ *Lesson*

CHAPTER 6 Patterns and Functions

Look for Problem Solving Hints in every chapter!

Problem Solving Hint
Use Guess and Test.

Look for long term investigations in every chapter!

Mission: Take the following measurements of each member of your group: height; distance from (1) fingertip to fingertip (arms spread), (2) wrist to elbow, and (3) ankle to kneecap. Find relationships among the following pairs of measurements: height/fingertip to fingertip; height/wrist to elbow; height/ankle to kneecap.

✴ *Hot Page™ Lesson*

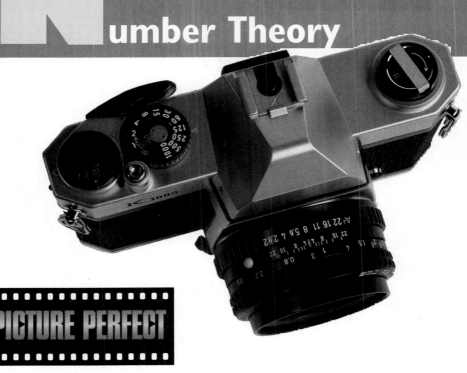

CHAPTER 7 Number Theory

PICTURE PERFECT

Look for Great
Expectations career
letters throughout the
book!

GREAT EXPECTATIONS

✷ *Hot Page™ Lesson*

CHAPTER 8

Fraction Applications

Look for **What You'll Need** materials lists in every chapter!

WHAT YOU'LL NEED

✓ Colored Pencils

✓ Ruled Paper

✓ Pattern blocks

✓ Calculator

Look for photos with captions that bring math to life in every chapter!

Of the world's tallest skyscrapers $\frac{1}{3}$ are in Chicago. About $\frac{1}{6}$ are in New York City and $\frac{1}{7}$ are in Houston.

Source: *The World Book Encyclopedia*

CHAPTER 9

Reasoning with Proportions

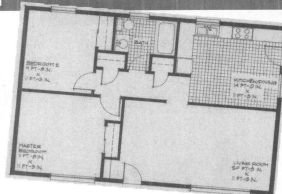

Look for frequent use of real data in every chapter!

1991 World Production of Automobiles

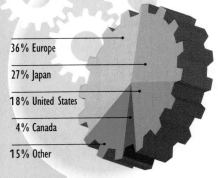

36% Europe

27% Japan

18% United States

4% Canada

15% Other

World Total: 48,400,000

CHAPTER 10 Probability

Look for the World View feature in every Data File!

WORLD VIEW

There are 92 countries that have birth rates higher than India, and 134 countries that have birth rates higher than China. However, $\frac{1}{3}$ of the world's births occur in these two countries.

✳ *Hot Page™ Lesson*

Look for Mixed Review in every lesson to maintain problem solving and computational skills!

Mixed REVIEW

1. How long is a diagonal of a 5 m × 12 m rectangle?

Write the prime factorization.

2. 625   **3.** 7,200

The rule for a function is $f(n) = -2n - 4$. Find:

4. $f(-3)$ **5.** $f(2)$

6. What is the probability of rolling a number less than 5 on a number cube?

CHAPTER 11

Graphing in the Coordinate Plane

✳ *Hot Page™ Lesson*

Look for the Who?, What?, Why?, When?, Where?, and How? features in every chapter!

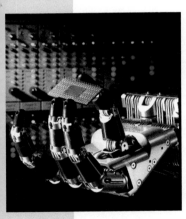

 By the year 2000 there may be over 60,000 robots in use in the United States.

Source: *Robotics*

Data File 1

A matter of MONEY

WORLD VIEW

In the 14th century, the Chinese issued the *kwan* note. It measured 9 in. x 13 in. The kwan was 72 times larger than the bani note issued in Romania in 1917.

Source: *Usborne Book of Countries of the World Facts*

DOLLAR DETAILS

The dollar bill in your wallet today measures 6.14 in. x 2.61 in. It is about 0.0043 in. thick. The eight-digit serial number is preceded and followed by a letter. The serial numbers follow a pattern A 00000001 A, A 00000002 A, etc.

OUR PAPER MONEY

The Bureau of Engraving and Printing in Washington, D.C. is responsible for printing all United States paper money. Money is printed on 16 presses that print 8,500 bills per hour. Some presses operate 24 h/d.

Federal Reserve banks issue bills to the public. A letter printed in large type as part of the Federal Reserve Seal tells which bank issued the note.

federal reserve seal

serial numbers

security thread

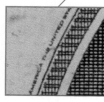

microprinting

portrait

treasury seal

WHAT YOU WILL LEARN

- how to collect, record, and interpret data
- how to construct, read, and interpret tables, charts, and graphs
- how to use technology to analyze data
- how to use logical reasoning to solve problems

All in a Day's Work

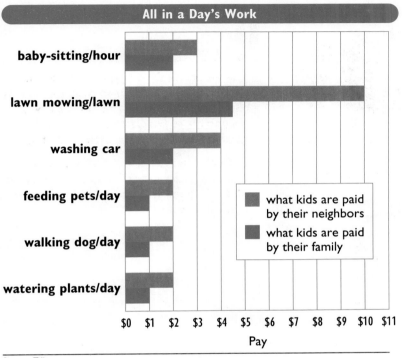

baby-sitting/hour

lawn mowing/lawn

washing car

feeding pets/day

walking dog/day

watering plants/day

Legend:
- what kids are paid by their neighbors
- what kids are paid by their family

Pay: $0 $1 $2 $3 $4 $5 $6 $7 $8 $9 $10 $11

Source: *Zillions*

Average Interest Rates

Year	Savings Account	Certificate of Deposit
1985	5.99%	9.66%
1986	5.00%	7.60%
1987	4.95%	7.66%
1988	4.96%	8.11%
1989	5.02%	8.30%
1990	4.93%	7.71%
1991	4.39%	6.83%

Source: *Statistical Abstract of the United States*

border

denomination

Spending Your Hard Earned Money

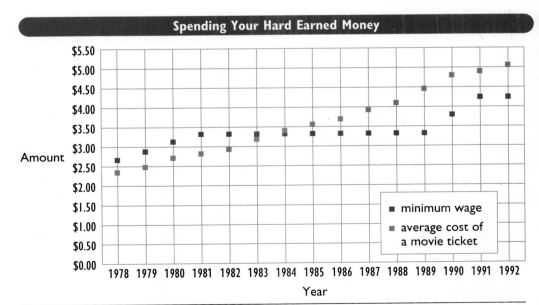

Amount: $5.50 $5.00 $4.50 $4.00 $3.50 $3.00 $2.50 $2.00 $1.50 $1.00 $0.50 $0.00

Year: 1978 1979 1980 1981 1982 1983 1984 1985 1986 1987 1988 1989 1990 1991 1992

Legend:
- minimum wage
- average cost of a movie ticket

Source: *Statistical Abstract of the United States; Variety; U.S. News & World Report*

investigation

Memo

People's ages are not good indicators of their heights. Children grow at about the same rate for the first few years of their lives but soon begin to grow at greatly differing rates. At age 20 an American male is as likely to be 5 ft 6 in. tall as he is to be 6 ft tall. Worldwide the differences are even greater. How about weights? Are they good indicators of people's heights?

Mission: Answer this question: Can you estimate a person's height if you know their weight? If your answer is yes, explain how you can use a person's weight to estimate his or her height. If it is no, explain why.

LeADs tO FOLLow

✓ What relationships among weight and height can you find for people in your family?

✓ What data or information can help you answer the question?

✓ Could you identify an animal if you were given a weight?

Reporting Frequency

WHAT YOU'LL NEED

✓ Graph paper

Number of Children	Tally	Frequency
1	||	2
2	⊞⊞ ||||	9
3	⊞⊞	5
4	||||	4
5	|||	3
6	||	2

THINK AND DISCUSS

When you collect information about a group, you are collecting *data*. Data can be presented in many ways. One way to present data is in a *frequency table*. A **frequency table** lists each piece of data together with the number of times it occurs. The sum of the *tally marks* is the frequency of each data item. Consider the table at the left. Twenty-five adults were asked how many children were in their families when they were growing up.

1. What number of children was most common? least common?

Example 1   Display the data from the frequency table at the left above in a *line plot*.

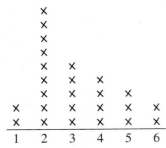

For each response, put an ✕ above the number of children in the family.

2. What information does a frequency table give you that a line plot does not?

The **range** of a set of numerical data is the difference between the greatest and least values in the set.

Example 2   Find the range of the following new car prices.

$8,750 $24,560 $16,230 $26,990 $12,400

• 26,990 − 8,750 = 18,240   Subtract the least value from the greatest value.

The range is $18,240.

3. Earth Science What is the range of the data given below?

Alaska mountain heights (ft): 16,390   14,573   20,030
16,550   15,885   14,163   14,831   16,237   15,638   16,286
17,400   14,730   14,530

WHERE? Every day over 11,000 babies are born in the United States. That is more than 450 babies each hour. **About how many babies are born each minute?**

Source: *The World Almanac*

How Many Baseball Cards Do You Have?

11	I	21	I
12	ﬀﬀ	22	IIII
13	II	23	
14	I	24	III
15	IIII	25	I
16	I	26	
17	II	27	III
18		28	I
19		29	
20	IIII	30	ﬀﬀ II

When the range of a set of data is large, it is helpful to divide the data into *intervals* of equal size. To avoid duplicating data, intervals must not overlap.

Forty children who collect baseball cards told how many they had. Their responses are noted in the table at the left.

4. a. Hobbies How many children have 17 baseball cards?

   b. How many children have 23 baseball cards?

5. What is the range of the number of baseball cards collected?

6. a. Would intervals of 0–10, 10–20, and 20–30 be appropriate for the data? Why or why not?

   b. Give two possible choices of intervals for the data.

A **histogram** is a special type of *bar graph* used to show frequency. The height of each bar gives the frequency of the data. There are no spaces between consecutive bars. The histogram below shows the data from the table at the left above.

How Many Baseball Cards Do You Have?

Frequency vs. Number of Baseball Cards

Interval	Frequency
11–12	6
13–14	3
15–16	5
17–18	2
19–20	4
21–22	5
23–24	3
25–26	1
27–28	4
29–30	7

7. What is the interval in the histogram?

8. Which interval has the greatest frequency? the least frequency?

9. Would you look at the histogram or the table to find how many children have more than 22 cards? Explain.

10. a. Redraw the histogram using intervals of a different size.

   b. How did the overall look of the histogram change?

WHAT? The most valuable baseball card is one of the six known baseball series cards of Honus Wagner. It was sold at Sotheby's in New York City for $451,000 in March, 1991. Honus Wagner's claims to fame include 10,427 at bats and 703 bases stolen.

Source: *The Guinness Book of Records* and *The World Almanac*

Work in groups of four. Ask about eight people (everyone in your group plus everyone in another group) one of the questions shown at the right.

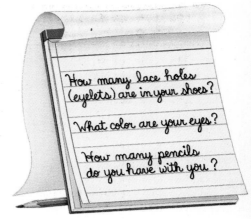

11. Record the responses in a frequency table.

12. Create a line plot or a histogram for your data.

13. What response was most frequent? least frequent?

TRY THESE

14. a. How many data items does the line plot at the right show?

b. What does each data item or × represent?

c. Which response had the greatest frequency?

15. Nutrition Emma surveyed a group of students at Midtown Middle School about their favorite fruit. Eight said they liked apples best, six said they preferred oranges, four chose bananas, five chose peaches, and one said she preferred kiwi fruit to all others.

a. Create a frequency table for the data.

b. Make a line plot and histogram to show the data.

c. What similarities do you see between the line plot and the histogram?

How Many Pairs of Red Socks Do You Own?

```
          ×
          ×
          ×
     ×    ×
     ×    ×    ×
     ×    ×    ×    ×
     ×    ×    ×    ×    ×
    ─────────────────────
     0    1    2    3    4
```

ON YOUR OWN

16. Entertainment Fifty people responded to the question "How many movies did you see in a theater in July?" The histogram at the right shows their responses.

a. About how many of the people surveyed did not go to the movies during July?

b. What was the most frequently seen number of movies? How many people gave that response?

c. How many more people went to three movies than went to five movies?

d. How many people saw two or more movies in a theatre?

How Many Movies Did You See in a Theater in July?

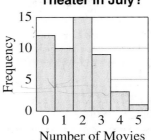

Compare.
Use <, >, or =.

1. 10 + 2 ■ 15 − 3
2. 7 × 2 ■ 5 × 3

Use mental math.

3. 594 + 406
4. 702 − 212

5. Replace each ■ with
+, −, ×, or ÷.

  4 ■ 6 ■ 3 = 7 ■ 3

17. Ms. Blumberg asked twenty-five of her math students what color their winter jackets were. Seven had red jackets, two had pink jackets, three had green jackets, nine had blue jackets, and four had multicolored jackets.

   a. Create a frequency table for the data.

   b. Make a histogram for the data.

   c. What is the difference between the number of jackets of the most common color and the number of jackets of the least common color?

18. Business Estelle works at the local bookstore. She keeps track of the number of books people buy. At the right is the line plot she made Friday morning.

```
                              ×
              ×       ×
              ×   ×   ×
              ×   ×   ×                   ×
              ×   ×   ×   ×   ×   ×
            ┌───────────────────────────
              1   2   3   4   5   6
```

   a. How many more people bought two books than bought four books?

   b. How many people bought more than three books?

19. Health Gabriel asked 16 people about the time they get up in the morning. The table at the left shows their responses.

5:30	6:45	5:45	6:15
6:25	6:20	7:15	7:45
8:00	7:00	8:00	7:30
6:00	7:10	7:50	6:10

   a. Make a frequency table and a histogram for the data. Use half-hour intervals such as 6:00–6:29 and 6:30–6:59.

   b. What half-hour interval is the most common?

20. Money Fifty people counted the pennies in their pockets. The frequency table at the left shows how many each had.

Number of Pennies	Frequency
1–5	12
6–10	6
11–15	10
16–20	7
21–25	5
26–30	6
31–35	0
36–40	4

   a. Can you tell from the table how many people had 17 pennies in their pockets? Why or why not?

   b. How many more people had 1–5 pennies than had 26–30 pennies?

   c. Create a histogram from the data. Use the intervals in the table.

21. Writing Would you prefer to use a histogram or a line plot to display 100 pieces of data? Explain your choice.

 22. Investigation (p. 4) Obtain a growth chart for babies. You can locate one in a book on baby care or obtain one from a pediatrician. Explain how to interpret the chart. Describe any relationships that you see between height and weight.

1-2 **U**sing a Computer to Graph Data

What's Ahead

• Using a spreadsheet to generate graphs

• Choosing the best graph for a given purpose

■ **WHAT YOU'LL NEED**

✓ **Computer**

✓ **Spreadsheet software**

T H I N K A N D D I S C U S S

The table below shows the amount of money made by three movies in the United States over four weekends. The table was made on a computer with a *spreadsheet* program. A spreadsheet is a tool for organizing and analyzing data.

1. **a. Discussion** How is the spreadsheet organized? What information does it show?

   b. What do you notice about the amount of money each movie made over the four weekends?

Money Made (Millions of Dollars)

	A	B	C	D	E
1	**Movie**	**August 6–8**	**August 13–15**	**August 20–22**	**August 27–29**
2	**The Secret Garden**		4.6	4.3	3.3
3	**Jurassic Park**	5.1	4.3	3.8	2.9
4	**Free Willy**	5.4	4	3.1	2.3

Source: *Hollywood Reporter*

A **cell** is the box where a row and a column meet. For example, column C and row 2 meet at the shaded box above. The name of this box is *cell C2*. The *value* in cell C2 is 4.6.

2. **a.** What is the value in cell D3?

   b. What does the number mean?

3. What cells are in row 1? in column E?

4. What cell has the value 5.4?

5. Why do you think cell B2 is blank?

After 16 weeks in the theaters, "Jurassic Park" passed "E.T." to become the top money-making movie of all time.

Source: *Variety*

Spreadsheets can save you a lot of time and effort when you want to make a graph. A **bar graph** compares amounts. The bar graph below was made from one of the rows of the spreadsheet, but the title of the graph is missing.

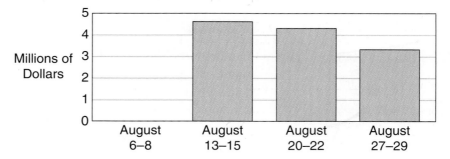

6. **a. Critical Thinking** Which movie does the bar graph represent? Explain how you know.

   b. During which weekend did the movie make the most money?

To show how an amount changes as time goes by, you can make a **line graph.** The line graph below shows the same data as the bar graph above, but the line helps your eye focus on changes and trends.

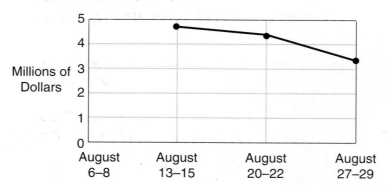

7. **a.** Suppose you wanted to predict the amount of money the movie would make the weekend after August 27–29. Which graph would you use? Why?

   b. Use the graph you chose to make a prediction.

8. **Discussion** These two graphs show the same information in two different ways. Is it always appropriate to show the same data in a bar graph and a line graph?

9. **a.** What do the spreadsheet below and the bar graph at the right show?

b. Why would a line graph of the same data *not* make sense?

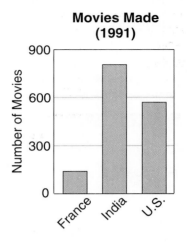

Movies Made (1991)

	A	B
1	**Country**	**Movies in 1991**
2	France	133
3	India	806
4	United States	578

Source: *Encyclopedia Britannica Yearbook*

Would you use a line or a bar graph to display each of the following? Why?

10. the population in Alaska in 1950, 1960, 1970, 1980, and 1990

11. the number of boys and the number of girls at your school

Computer **For Exercises 12 and 13, use a computer or make the graphs by hand.**

12. Make a line graph of the money made during August by *Jurassic Park* or *Free Willy*. Describe the trend you see in your graph.

13. Make a bar graph comparing the money made by *Jurassic Park* and *Free Willy* during the weekend of August 6–8.

14. **Writing** Is the graph below appropriate for the data? Use the definitions for bar graph and line graph in your answer.

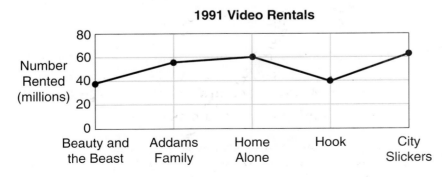

1991 Video Rentals

Mixed REVIEW

Ages of Students in Mr. Harris's Class

Age	Number of Students
14	IIII
13	HHT HHT HHT I
12	HHT HHT II

1. How many students are in the class?

2. Make a line plot and a histogram from the data.

3. What is the range of ages of the students?

4. What age is the most common?

Calculate.

5. 4 × 27   6. 18 ÷ 3

Making Data Displays

T H I N K A N D D I S C U S S

You use different types of graphs to display different types of data. **Double line graphs** compare changes over time of two sets of data. The graph below compares record high temperatures in Juneau, Alaska, for the first eight days of September, to record low temperatures in Key West, Florida, for the same period. The **legend,** or key, identifies the lines.

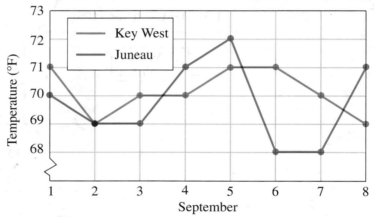

Record Highs In Juneau Compared to Record Lows in Key West

Source: *Juneau and Key West Chambers of Commerce*

1. **Weather** What is the highest temperature shown on the double line graph? Was it for Key West or Juneau?

2. Give the date(s) when the difference in the recorded temperatures is the greatest.

3. Was the record high in Juneau ever the same as the record low in Key West on the same day? If so, on what date(s)?

4. **a.** On what date(s) is the record high in Juneau lower than the record low in Key West?

   b. On what date(s) is the record high in Juneau higher than the record low in Key West?

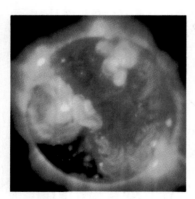

 Temperatures at the core of the Sun reach about 27,000,000°F. If the heat from the core were to stop suddenly, it would be 10 million years before the surface of the Sun began to cool and before the Earth was affected.

Source: *Did You Know?*

You can use **double bar graphs** to compare two sets of data. Double bar graphs can be either horizontal, like the one at the right, or vertical, like the one in the Work Together activity.

5. In the graph at the right, which zoo has the greatest number of mammals? of reptiles?

6. Which zoo has more reptiles than mammals?

WORK TOGETHER

The double bar graph below compares the 1992 circulation of adults' books and children's books at four libraries. Work with a partner to study the graph and answer the questions.

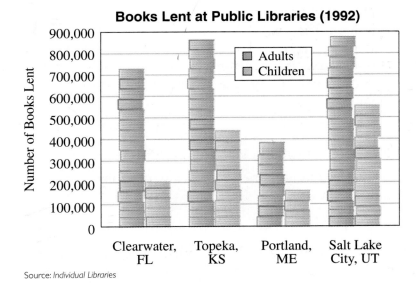

Source: *Individual Libraries*

7. Which library lent the most children's books?

8. Which libraries lent about the same number of adults' books?

9. a. Which library lent almost 400,000 adults' books?

b. Which library lent about 400,000 children's books?

10. a. Which library had the greatest difference between the number of adults' books and children's book lent?

b. Suppose you were the librarian in that community. About how many adults' books would you buy for every children's book?

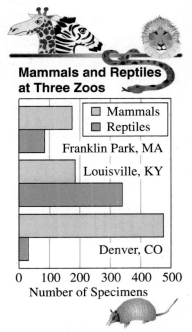

Mammals and Reptiles at Three Zoos

Mammals ☐
Reptiles ☐

Franklin Park, MA

Louisville, KY

Denver, CO

0 100 200 300 400 500
Number of Specimens

Source: *Individual Zoos*

M*i*x*ed* REVIEW

	A	B
1	Month	Income
2	Jan	$550
3	Feb	$680
4	Mar	$720

Use the data in the spreadsheet above.

1. Which column shows the monthly income?

2. What is the value in cell B4?

3. Display the data in a bar graph.

4. Display the data in a line graph.

5. What is the range of monthly income?

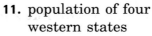
Decide whether a double bar or a double line graph is appropriate for the given data. Draw the graph.

11. population of four western states

Population		
State	1980	1990
ID	943,935	1,006,749
NV	800,493	1,201,833
OR	2,633,105	2,842,321
WA	4,132,156	4,866,692

Source: *The Information Please Almanac*

12. Education nationwide SAT scores

Year	Verbal	Math
1970	460	488
1975	434	472
1980	424	466
1985	431	475
1990	424	476

Source: *The World Almanac*

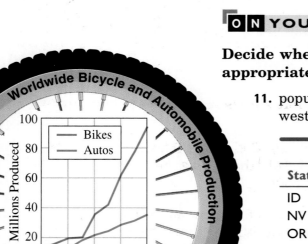

Source: *Worldwatch Institute*

13. Business The double line graph at the left shows the difference between bicycle and automobile production over several years. After what year do the two lines begin to separate widely? What do you think could account for this?

14. Data File 7 (pp. 278–279)

a. Which type of camera sold the most in 1981? in 1991?

b. About how many more 35-mm cameras than instant cameras were sold in 1991?

15. Writing Cut out at least one line graph or bar graph from a newspaper or magazine. Write a summary of the data shown.

CHECKPOINT

	A	B	C
1	St	Bush	Clinton
2	IA	37	44
3	NE	47	29
4	NY	34	50
5	TN	43	47

1. Choose A, B, C, or D. Which rows of the spreadsheet at the left most likely generated the double bar graph at the right?

A. rows 2 and 3   **B.** rows 3 and 4

C. rows 2 and 4   **D.** rows 3 and 5

2. Make a frequency table and a line plot of the data below.

5 7 8 3 5 4 6 7 8 9 1 2 5 4 2 1 3

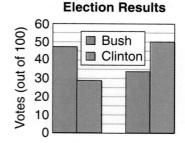

1992 Presidential Election Results

PROBLEM SOLVING STRATEGIES

Make a Table
Use Logical Reasoning
Solve a Simpler Problem
Too Much or Too Little Information
Look for a Pattern
Make a Model
Work Backward
Draw a Diagram
Guess and Test
Simulate a Problem
Use Multiple Strategies
Write an Equation

Solve. The list at the left shows some possible strategies you can use.

1. In a yard full of two-legged kids and four-legged dogs, the number of legs is 14 more than twice the number of heads. Find the number of dogs.

2. Use each of the digits 1 to 5 once to make a two-digit number and a three-digit number that have the greatest possible difference.

3. **Nutrition** Valerie was given three bags of fruit, one labeled "peaches," one labeled "plums," and one labeled "peaches and plums." Each label was incorrectly placed. Valerie reached into one bag and pulled out a peach. She was then able to identify the fruit in each bag.

   a. Into which bag did Valerie reach?

   b. How was each bag of fruit labeled?

4. Popsville is 20 mi from Topsville. Mopsville is 5 mi from Popsville along the same road. How far could Mopsville be from Topsville?

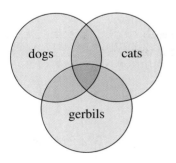

5. Fifty students were surveyed about their pets. The following results were confusing to them. Use a Venn diagram like the one at the left to determine how many students had no pets.

   • Of the 50 students surveyed, 30 had cats and 25 had dogs.

   • Sixteen students had both cats and dogs, but no gerbils.

   • Although 5 reported that they had only gerbils, 4 noted they had both dogs and gerbils, while 2 had both cats and gerbils.

   • Only 1 student had all three pets mentioned.

6. Ahmed had 10 loose identical red socks and 10 loose identical blue socks in his sock drawer. One morning the electricity was out, and since Ahmed got up before dawn, he couldn't see the colors of his socks. How many socks did he have to remove from the drawer to have a matched pair?

Mean, Median, and Mode

THINK AND DISCUSS

To make a general statement about a set of data, you can find the *mean,* the *median,* and the *mode* of the data.

To find the **mean** of a set of numbers, find the sum of the numbers and divide the sum by the number of items in the group. The mean is often referred to as the *average.*

	20 Responses to "How Many Times a Day Do You Drink from the Water Fountain?"	
0	1	1
5	2	10
2	3	5
1	5	2
2	3	4
3	5	5
2	2	

Example 1
Twenty students were asked how many times a day they drank from the water fountain. Their responses are at the left. Find the mean of the data.

• 63 ÷ 20 = *3.15*

The mean is 3.15. On average, these students drink from the water fountain about three times a day.

1. Earl conducted the survey, but he forgot to include his own response. How does the fact that he did not drink from the water fountain affect the mean?

The **median** is the middle value in a set of numbers arranged in numerical order. If there is an even number of data items, the median is the mean of the two middle items.

Example 2
Find the median of the given data.

• 0 1 1 1 2 2 2 2 2 2 3 3   Arrange the data in
  3 4 5 5 5 5 5 10   order.

• 0 1 1 1 2 2 2 2 2 2 3 3   The two middle
  3 4 5 5 5 5 5 10   items are 2 and 3.

• 2 + 3 = 5
  5 ÷ 2 = 2.5

The median is 2.5.

2. Find the median of the data at the left.

The Number of Letters in a Bowl of Alphabet Soup

46 65 37 35 47 55 62

If one data item is much higher or lower than the rest of the data, it is called an **outlier.**

3. What is the outlier of the water fountain data?

4. Suppose the student who drank 10 times a day from the water fountain had been absent the day of the survey.

   a. What would have been the mean of the data? the median?

   b. How did the outlier affect the data?

WHAT? The amount of water (H_2O), the most common chemical compound on Earth, has remained the same since the creation of the planet about 4.6 billion years ago.

Source: *Did You Know?*

The data item that occurs most often is the **mode.** A set of data may have more than one mode. If you have a set of data where the items are not numbers, you can still talk about the mode.

Example 3   Find the mode of the water fountain data.
   • 0 1 1 1 2 2 2 2 2 2 3 3 3   2 occurs six times.
     4 5 5 5 5 5 10
   The mode is 2.

5. What is the mode of the data at the right?

Number of People in Mr. Singh's Yoga Classes
12 8 10 7 8 9

Example 4   Would you use the mean, the median, or the mode to describe each situation? Explain.

   a. the favorite book of the third grade

   Mode; use the mode when the data are not numerical.

   b. the number of students in each class at school

   Mean or median; use the mean when there are no outliers to distort the data.

   c. the number of pets your classmates have

   Median; use the median when an outlier may distort the data. Someone may have many pets.

WORK TOGETHER

Work with a partner to collect data on one of the topics at the right or a topic of your own. Collect at least 10 pieces of data.

6. Find the mean, median, and mode of the data.

7. Which measurement best describes the data you collected?

DATA CHOICES
• Number of buttons on people's clothing
• Number of pages in a book

Do You Return Aluminum Cans?

Response	Frequency
Give them to a charity	1
Never	4
Sometimes	12
Always	33

8. **Environment** Fifty people who live in a state where there is a deposit on aluminum cans were asked if they returned their cans. At the left is a table of the responses.

   a. What was the mode?

   b. Suppose you were working on a bill to require a deposit on aluminum cans in a state with no deposit. How could you use the data in the table in a campaign?

9. Roll one number cube 20 times. Keep track of the number you roll each time. Find the mean, median, and mode of your data. What conclusions can you draw?

Find the mean, median, and mode of the given data.

10. hours of homework at night

    1.5   2   3   2.5   2   3.5   1.75   3.25

11. daily low temperatures (°F) for a week of variable weather

    55.2   58   62.3   62.3   65.6   67   72

12. number of seconds for the 50-yd dash

    27   30   25   28   29   33   32   25   25   35

13. a. The total weight of all the students in a class is 2,825 lb. The mean is 113 lb. How many students are in the class?

    b. The median weight is 125 lb. Exactly 3 students weigh 125 lb. How many students weigh more than 125 lb?

Grade	Tally
60	|
78	|||
80	ﬀ ||
81	||
85	ﬀ |||
87	||
91	|
94	|

14. **Education** The Jonesberg Middle School seventh grade math class took the test for Chapter 4 recently. The class scores are shown in the tally table at the left.

    a. Find the mean, median, and mode of the data.

    b. What is the outlier in this set of data?

    c. Does the outlier raise or lower the mean?

    d. Which measure—the mean, the median, or the mode—most accurately reflects how the class did as a whole? Give evidence to support your answer.

Birthday Bash

Last Sunday 7 people at the Rose Hill Retirement Home celebrated their birthdays. Mrs. Ullsca turned 102, while the "baby" of the group, Mrs. Hansen, turned a mere 62.

Family members and friends gathered at the home for a party that included cake and singing. Other birthdays being celebrated included Mr. Harlem, 75; Mr. Joyla, 84; Mr. Kuggles, 63; Miss Rugas, 71; and Mrs. Saeger, 63.

15. a. Find the mean, median, and mode of the data. Round the mean to the nearest whole number.

b. Is there an outlier? If there is, identify it and explain how it affects the data.

c. What is the range in ages of the Rose Hill residents celebrating birthdays?

16. Writing Ten people were surveyed about the number of times someone should brush his/her teeth each day. Their responses are shown in the table at the right. Explain why the mean is not a good representation of this data.

How Many Times a Day Should You Brush Your Teeth?

Response	Frequency
3 times	9
10 times	1

17. Dominic hopes to have a 90 average on tests for his Spanish class. His test grades so far are 89, 94, 76, 84, 91. The maximum grade on any one test is 100.

a. What is Dominic's average now?

b. Critical Thinking There is one more test left in the grading period. Will it be possible for Dominic to have a 90 average? Support your answer by giving examples.

18. Data File 10 (pp. 416–417)

a. Calculate the mean life expectancy for the animals in the table. Round to the nearest tenth.

b. What is the median life expectancy? the mode?

c. Can you accurately represent the data using the measures of mean, median, and mode? Explain.

19. Investigation (p. 4) Gather data on the weights and heights of at least 10 seven-year-olds you know. Find the mean, median, and mode of the data.

M̲i̲x̲e̲d̲ REVIEW

	A	B	C
1	10	12	120
2	6	9	54
3	2	6	12

Compare.
Use <, >, or =.

1. C3 ▪ B1

2. B2 ▪ A1

3. What patterns do you see in the data?

Estimate.

4. 197 × 3   5. 42 × 19

Exploring Scatter Plots

┌THINK AND DISCUSS

Sometimes you may find that two sets of related data cannot be easily compared in a double line or a double bar graph. In a **scatter plot,** these related sets are graphed as points, but the points are not connected.

The scatter plot below shows the relationship between the age of red maple trees and their diameters.

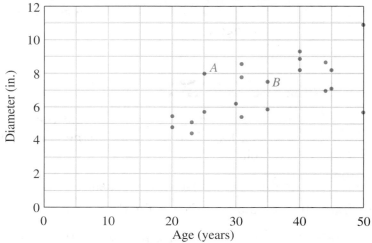

Age and Diameter of Red Maple Trees

Source: *USDA Forest Service*

The largest red maple tree in the United States is located in St. Clair Country, Michigan. This giant tree has a diameter of 70.5 in. about 4.5 ft from the ground.

Source: *The Guinness Book of Records*

1. **a. Life Science** How old is a tree with a diameter of about 5 in.?

   b. About how great is the diameter of a 40-year-old tree?

2. **a.** How old is the tree shown by point *A*?

   b. About how great a diameter does the tree shown by point *B* have?

3. About how great is the greatest diameter in this scatter plot?

4. What is the range of diameters shown in the scatter plot?

5. What general statement can you make about the relationship between the age of red maple trees and their diameters?

As you examine a scatter plot, you may notice that the data points show a trend, or *correlation*. The three scatter plots below show the types of relationships two sets of data may have.

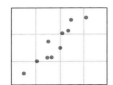 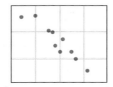 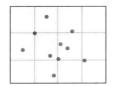

Positive correlation
In general, as the values of one set of data increase, the values of the other set increase also.

Negative correlation
In general, as the values of one set of data increase, the values of the other set decrease.

No correlation
The values of one set of data are not related to the values of the other set.

6. What correlation do you see in the scatter plot of the red maple trees on page 20?

WORK TOGETHER

The table at the right shows bookbag weights and the number of books in each bag. Work with a partner to graph the data on a scatter plot.

Bks	Wt (lb)	Bks	Wt (lb)
3	6	6	8
3	8	6	12
4	6.5	7	9.5
4	7	7	11
4	9	7	16
5	7	8	12
5	10	8	12.5
6	7.5	8	16.5

7. a. What labels did you choose for the axes?

   b. What intervals did you choose for the axes?

8. What sort of correlation do you see between the number of books in a bag and its weight?

ON YOUR OWN

Tell what correlation you would expect to see in scatter plots comparing the following sets of data. Explain your reasoning.

9. the number of children in a family and the number of pets

10. hours spent watching TV and hours spent studying

11. area of a state and the number of governors the state has had

Moose and Wolf Populations on Isle Royale, Michigan

Year	Wolf	Moose
1979	50	664
1980	30	650
1981	14	700
1982	23	900
1983	24	811
1984	22	1062
1985	20	1025
1986	16	1380
1987	12	1653
1988	11	1397
1989	15	1216
1990	12	1313
1991	12	1600
1992	13	1880

Source: *National Park Service, Isle Royale, Michigan*

Mixed REVIEW

Grades on the science test were 100, 85, 90, 100, 90, 80, 95, 85, 70, 85, 100, 85, 75, 30, 90.

1. Find the mean, the median, and the mode.

2. What is the outlier and how did it affect the mean?

3. Six students from a class of 25 play only tennis and 8 play only baseball. Nine students play neither sport. How many play both?

12. Biology In the late 1970s, Isle Royale in Lake Superior had the world's highest density of wild wolves. That means there were more wolves per square mile on Isle Royale than there were anywhere else in the world. Because of this, and because Isle Royale had a stable moose population at the same time, a great deal of information was collected on the relationship between the moose and the wolves on the island. The data at the left show the populations from 1979 to 1992.

a. Is the moose population increasing or decreasing? what about the wolf population?

b. Make a scatter plot to compare the moose (along the side of the graph) and wolf (along the bottom) populations.

c. What conclusions can you draw from the data as displayed on the scatter plot?

13. Space The space shuttle *Columbia* has made 13 trips into space. The table at the right shows the number of crew members and the length in days of each trip.

Days	Crew
2	2
2	2
8	2
6	7
5	5
11	5
7	2
5	4
10	6
8	7
9	7
14	7
14	7

a. Plot the data on a scatter plot.

b. Writing Examine your scatter plot. Do you see a correlation? Support your answer.

14. Choose A, B, or C. Carmella created a scatter plot comparing the daily temperature and the number of people at a beach. Which of the three scatter plots below most likely represents the data? Explain your choice.

A.
People / Temperature

B.
People / Temperature

C.
People / Temperature

15. Investigation (p. 4) Make a scatter plot of the data on weights and heights that you collected in Lesson 1-4. What conclusions can you draw?

What's Ahead

1-6 **L**ogical Reasoning

READ · PLAN · LOOK BACK · SOLVE

• Solving problems using the strategy of logical reasoning

In 1991, more than 1.8 million immigrants came into the United States. Immigrants bring with them different languages and cultures, making the United States the richly diverse country it is.

Source: *The Information Please Almanac*

Eve, Frieda, Pascal, Walter, and Mika are each taking an intensive foreign language course. Each person is taking a different course. One day, Mr. Sanchez, a neighbor of Mika's, asked about the classes. Mika gave him the following information.

• The woman studying Italian is not Eve. Also, Eve is not studying German.

• Frieda and Pascal do not study Mandarin Chinese, but one of them takes French.

• Eve, Frieda, and Walter drive to their classes together on Tuesday nights. One of them takes German, one takes Spanish, and one takes Italian.

Mr. Sanchez thought for a while, took out a paper and pencil, and told Mika exactly what language each person was taking. Who is taking which language?

READ ▶

Read the problem and analyze the given information.

1. Think about what you are being asked and the information you are given.

   a. What information are you given?

   b. What information do you need to find?

PLAN ▶

Decide on a strategy to solve the problem.

Logical reasoning is a strategy that can help you eliminate impossibilities, organize alternatives, and find a solution. Begin by considering the first clue.

2. a. Could Eve be studying Italian? Could she be studying German?

   b. Could she be studying French? What piece of information tells you the answer?

   c. What language is Eve studying? Which clues did you use?

Construct a logic table to help you organize your thoughts as you consider each piece of information separately. Continue until you have gathered all the information you need.

	French	German	Italian	Mandarin Chinese	Spanish
Eve	×	×	×	×	●
Frieda	■	■	■	■	×
Mika	■	■	■	■	×
Pascal	■	■	■	■	×
Walter	■	■	■	■	×

3. a. There is an × in every box but one of Eve's row. Why?

   b. There is an × in every box but one of the column for Spanish. Why?

   c. What is the significance of the blue dot in the box where Eve's row and the column for Spanish meet?

4. Who do you know is *not* studying Italian? How can you use this knowledge in your table?

5. Copy and complete the table. Use an × for an impossibility, and a dot when you know what language that person is taking.

To solve this problem, you considered the information you were given and eliminated impossibilities.

6. How did the table help you solve this problem?

TRY THESE

Use logical reasoning to solve.

7. Skye's class is selling pencils to raise money for a field trip. The top four pencil sellers in the class were Skye, Amalie, Leonard, and Scott. Skye sold more pencils than Amalie but fewer than Leonard. Scott also sold more than Amalie, but he sold fewer than Skye. Amalie sold the fewest pencils. Who sold the most pencils in the class?

Julia B. Robinson, a mathematician, was the first woman elected to the National Academy of Sciences. She used number theory to solve logic problems.

Source: *The Book of Women's Firsts*

8. **Sports** You oversee the three lockers that contain the school's basketballs, footballs, and soccer balls. Each locker is labeled and contains only one type of ball. Unfortunately, the lockers were moved recently, and now the labels are all incorrect. Your job is to tell which locker has which balls so they can be relabeled. You are given one chance to open a locker and pull out a ball. You reach into the locker marked "footballs" and pull out a basketball. Which balls are in the locker labeled "basketballs," and which are in the locker labeled "soccer balls"?

ON YOUR OWN

Use any strategy to solve each problem. Show your work.

9. Which number in the group at the right is described below?
   - the sum of the digits of the number is 14
   - the number is even
   - the number is a multiple of 5
   - the number is in the thousands
   - the number is less than 2,220

10. Daphne has the same number of sisters as she has brothers. Her brother Tomas has twice as many sisters as he has brothers. How many children are there in Daphne and Tomas's family?

11. **Money** Before he got his allowance on Monday, Hugh was broke. Tuesday he spent $1.25. Wednesday his sister paid him back the dollar she owed him. How much is Hugh's allowance if he now has $3.25?

12. Find the median of all the positive even multiples of 7 that are less than 105.

13. How many different ways can you arrange 36 square ceramic tiles to form a rectangle?

14. **Cars** To save gas, Mr. Mews, Ms. Rose, and Ms. Trang carpool to go to work. So far this month Ms. Trang drove 10 mi more than Mr. Mews. Mr. Mews drove 3 times as far as Ms. Rose. Ms. Rose drove 5 mi. How far did they drive altogether?

Daily Homework

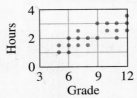

Use the scatter plot.

1. What correlation do you see in the scatter plot?

2. How many students were surveyed?

Estimate.

3. 122 + 237

4. 393 − 27

5. 48 × 4   6. 9 × 119

1-7 **M**aking Stem-and-Leaf Plots

New Jersey Devils

Player	Pts
Chorske	36
Driver	42
Kasatonov	40
Lemieux	68
McKay	33
Richer	64
Stastny	62
Stevens	59
Todd	63
Vilgrain	46
Weinrich	32
Zelepukin	31

Source: *Sports Illustrated Sports Almanac*

THINK AND DISCUSS

The table at the left shows data on the top 12 scorers for the New Jersey Devils during the 1991–92 hockey season. To compare the scores, you can make a *stem-and-leaf plot*. A **stem-and-leaf plot** is a display that organizes your data by showing each item in order.

To choose the *stems,* look at the greatest and least data items. The greatest value is 68. The least value is 31. The *stems* represent, in this case, the tens' place. Write the stems in a column. Draw a line to their right, as shown below.

In this case, the *leaves* are the ones' digits associated with the tens' values. A stem is the digit or digits remaining when the leaf is dropped. A leaf is always one digit, the number's last digit on the right. Write the values of the leaves to the right of the stems.

```
3 | 6  3  2  1
4 | 2  0  6
5 | 9              ← leaves
6 | 8  4  2  3
```

Arrange the leaves from least to greatest. Include a *key* to explain what your stems and leaves represent.

```
3 | 1  2  3  6
4 | 0  2  6
5 | 9
6 | 2  3  4  8
         3 | 1 means 31  ← key
```

1. a. What number has stem 5 and leaf 9?

  b. What number has stem 6 and leaf 8?

It is easy to find the median and mode of data displayed in a stem-and-leaf plot. The median is the middle leaf and its stem, or the mean of the two middle leaves and their stems. To find the mode, look for the greatest number of repeated leaves on one stem.

Example   Use the data at the right to create a stem-and-leaf plot for women's 80-m hurdle times at the Olympic Games. Find the median and the mode.

- 10 | 3 5 7 8 9
  11 | 2 7 7

  10 | 3 means 10.3

- 10.8 + 10.9 = 21.7   **Find the mean of the two**
  21.7 ÷ 2 = 10.85   **middle data items.**

- The only number that occurs more than once is 11.7.

The median is 10.85. The mode is 11.7.

Women's 80-m Hurdles	
Year	Time(s)
1932	11.7
1936	11.7
1948	11.2
1952	10.9
1956	10.7
1960	10.8
1964	10.5
1968	10.3

Source: *The Information Please Almanac*

2. The stem-and-leaf plot at the right shows the miles nine cars got per gallon of gasoline.

a. Find the mode.

b. Find the median.

c. Find the mean.

1 | 6
2 | 4 8
3 | 2 5 5 9
4 | 3 5

1 | 6 means 16

WORK TOGETHER

In 1990, the National Assessment Governing Board administered a national math test to eighth graders across the United States. The average scores of students in nine midwestern states are listed in the table at the right. Work with a partner to create a stem-and-leaf plot for the data.

3. What did you choose for the stems?

4. Find the median and the mode of the data.

5. The national average score on the test was 261. Find the mean of the given data. Round to the nearest whole number. Compare it to the national average. Which is greater? Explain any differences you see in the two averages.

National Math Test Scores, 1990	
(greatest possible score: 350)	
Illinois	260
Indiana	267
Iowa	278
Michigan	264
Minnesota	276
Nebraska	276
North Dakota	281
Ohio	264
Wisconsin	274

Source: *The World Almanac*

Create a stem-and-leaf plot for each set of data. Find the median and the mode.

6. ball players' salaries (millions of dollars)

    1.3   1.4   2.3   1.4   2.4   2.5   3.9   1.4   1.3   2.5   3.6   1.4

7. daily high temperatures (°F)

    98   99   94   87   83   74   69   88   78   99   100   87   77

The stem-and-leaf plot at the left shows kilometers walked during a benefit walk. Use it for Exercises 8–11.

```
16 | 1  1  2  3  5  5
17 | 0  2  2  4
18 | 4  5  8  9
19 | 3  6  7  9  9  9
        19 | 3 means 19.3
```

8. What numbers make up the stems?

9. What numbers make up the leaves for the first stem?

10. How many people walked more than 19 km?

11. Find the mean, median, mode, and range.

Use the stem-and-leaf plot at the left for Exercises 12–16.

```
4 | 3  6  7
5 | 1  2
6 | 1  7
7 | 1  8
8 | 2  6  8
      8 | 2 means 82
```

12. How many data items are there?

13. What is the least measurement given? the greatest?

14. How many measurements are greater than 65?

15. Find the median and range.

16. **Choose A, B, C, or D.** Which of the following is most likely the source of the data in the stem-and-leaf plot? Why?

    A. test scores

    B. average monthly temperatures in Dallas (in °F)

    C. depth of 12 swimming pools (in feet)

    D. numbers of books in libraries throughout New York City

17. **Writing** Explain how to find the median in a stem-and-leaf plot. Consider both stem-and-leaf plots with an odd number of data items and stem-and-leaf plots with an even number of data items.

18. Sports The ten women and ten men who have won the most golf tournaments during their careers as of 1993 are listed in the table below along with the number of wins.

Women Golfers		Men Golfers	
Name	**Career Wins**	**Name**	**Career Wins**
Kathy Whitworth	88	Sam Snead	81
Mickey Wright	82	Jack Nicklaus	70
Patty Berg	57	Ben Hogan	63
Betsy Rawls	55	Arnold Palmer	60
Louise Suggs	50	Byron Nelson	52
Nancy Lopez	44	Billy Casper	51
JoAnne Carner	42	Walter Hagen	40
Sandra Haynie	42	Cary Middlecoff	40
Carol Mann	38	Gene Sarazen	38
Babe Zaharias	31	Lloyd Mangrum	36

Source: *Sports Illustrated Sports Almanac*

a. Create a stem-and-leaf plot of the data for all the golfers.

b. Find the median, mode, and range of the data.

CHECKPOINT

Find the mean, median, mode, and range of the data below. Identify any outliers and tell how they affect the mean.

1. words in some of Shakespeare's sonnets

122 114 113 116 120 123 119 117 123 111

2. gymnastics scores (out of 10)

7.09 8.002 7.6 6.98 3.6 8.9 7.085 7.5 8.65

3. Create a scatter plot of the data at the right. What conclusions can you make from the graph?

4. Elsa, Keiko, and LaTonya went to the beach. Each girl carried a towel and something else. The girl who carried the pink towel carried the beach ball. The girl who carried the iced tea had a striped towel. Keiko carried the sandwiches. Elsa carried neither the iced tea nor the blue towel. Which girl had which towel, and what else did she carry?

Compare.
Use <, >, or =.

1. 12×3 ■ $45 - 9$

2. $24 \div 2$ ■ 3×6

Complete each number pattern.

3. 1 2 4 7 11 ■ ■

4. 1 4 9 16 ■ ■ ■

5. The director of a rafting club needs an average of 12 people on each trip. The first four trips one day had 10, 14, 9, and 12 people. How many must take the last trip for the average to be 12?

Movie Attendance

Year	Cost (dollars)	People (millions)
1982	2.94	1,175
1984	3.36	1,199
1986	3.71	1,017
1988	4.11	1,085
1990	4.75	1,057
1992	5.05	964

Source: *Motion Picture Association of American*

Practice

Display the data at the right in the form requested.

	Responses to "How Many Minutes Did You Exercise Today?"

1. line plot   2. frequency table   3. stem-and-leaf plot

4. Find the mean, median, and mode of the data.

5. What was the range of exercise times?

6. How many people exercised for more than 20 minutes?

Responses to "How Many Minutes Did You Exercise Today?"

10, 20, 35, 12, 17, 14, 16, 12, 15, 14, 23, 19, 11, 10, 26, 11, 12, 15, 27, 21, 38

Exercises 7–10 refer to the graph below.

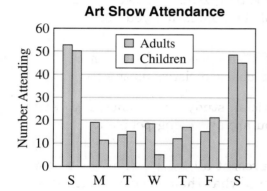

Art Show Attendance

7. On what day was there the greatest difference in admission figures between adults and children?

8. On what day did the most adults attend the art show?

9. About how many children attended the art show on the weekend?

10. About how many more adults attended the art show on Wednesday than on Thursday?

The stem-and-leaf plot at the right shows wind speeds recorded during a storm.

11. Create a frequency table for the data.

12. Create a line plot for the data.

13. Find the mean, median, mode, and range of the data.

```
0 | 9
1 | 4  6  8
2 | 5  5  9
3 | 0  3  4  4  8
        3 | 0 means 30
```

The line plot below shows the number of bids six items received at an auction.

```
   ×
   ×              ×
×  ×        ×  ×
×  ×  ×  ×  ×  ×
445 446 447 448 449 450
```

14. How many data items are represented?

15. How many more bids did the most popular item receive than the least popular?

What's Ahead

- Identifying a representative sample
- Writing survey questions

1-8 Representative Samples and Surveys

THINK AND DISCUSS

Statisticians are people who collect and study information about specific groups, or *populations*. The most accurate way to collect data is to gather information from the whole group. This is usually impractical. A *sample* of the *target group* can often provide enough information to draw conclusions.

1. Suppose you are a statistician studying the eating habits of college students. What question could you ask to decide if Joe Smith is a member of the population you are studying?

A **representative sample** is a group selected from the population that has the same characteristics as the population.

2. Suppose you are a statistician studying the snacking habits of teenagers in Idaho. You are surveying people as they walk along the street.

   a. Would your sample represent all teenagers if you asked five teenagers in a group what their favorite snack was? Why or why not?

   b. Would your sample represent all teenagers if you asked all the teenagers who passed you as you stood for three days on the corner of Main Street in Boise, Idaho? Why or why not?

   c. What are some ways you could find a representative sample of the population?

A sample is a **random sample** if each object in the population has an equal chance of being included.

3. a. Where would you go to obtain a representative sample of people visiting Yosemite National park?

   b. Suppose you decided to hand out flyers from one location within the park. Would you reach a random sample of visitors? Why or why not?

Every 10 years since 1790, the United States government has geared up for the census. In 1990, over 300,000 workers and $3 billion went into finding out about citizens like you. The 1990 population of the United States was 248,709,893. **About how much did the government spend per person to take the census?**

Source: *Scholastic Update* and *The World Almanac*

From age 2 to age 11, the average child in the United States watches almost 32 h of television per week. **About how many hours per day does the average child spend watching TV?**

Source: *The Guinness Book of Records*

Biased questions are unfair questions. They can make assumptions about you that may or may not be true. Biased questions can also make one answer seem better than another.

4. **Discussion** Which of the following questions is biased? Which is fair? Why?
   - "Is there violence in Saturday morning cartoons?"
   - "Do you think the extreme violence on all Saturday morning cartoons affects young, impressionable children?"

WORK TOGETHER

Work in groups of four. Design two survey questions, one fair and one biased.

5. What populations are your questions aimed at?

6. How could you select a random sample of the population to answer the questions?

DECISION-MAKING

 Buying Control Index

Do you decide what cereals your family purchases? If you do, you have *buying control* for cereal. Advertisers are interested in finding out who has buying control for different items.

COLLECT DATA

1. **a.** With your group, brainstorm at least six items for which students your age are likely to have buying control.

   b. Design and conduct a survey to determine the buying control of your friends for the items. Your group should survey at least 25 people. Be sure to include a question asking the gender of your survey participants.

ANALYZE DATA

To compare buying control for different items, you can develop a *buying control index*. The sample shows how to change your survey data into index numbers.

Tell whether the following questions are biased or fair.

7. Which do you think is cozier, a down comforter or a woolen blanket?

8. Is the soft, luxurious feel of a down comforter cozier on a cold winter night than the scratchy feel of a woolen blanket?

9. Do you prefer rock music or jazz?

10. Do you prefer the loud, harsh discords of rock music or the soothing, mellow sounds of jazz?

11. **Engineering** Jeremy is an urban planner. He is interested in how the city's bus drivers are affected by work crews in the streets. How can he be sure to survey a random sample?

12. **Writing** Suppose you are a statistician studying the earning potential of high school dropouts. How would you select a representative sample?

M**i**x**e**d REVIEW

Use the following stem-and-leaf plot of Trinh's exercise program.

Miles Biked per Day

0	5 5 7 8 8 9 9
1	0 0 0 1 2 7 8
2	2 5 8 8 9 9

2 | 5 means 25

1. What number has stem 1 and leaf 0?

2. Find the mean, median, mode, and range.

3. Which measure in Exercise 2 could be used to convince Trinh's parents that she has plenty of time left for her homework?

Sample Thirty-four students out of 45 have buying control over purchasing cassettes or CDs.

$$34 \; \boxed{\div} \; 45 \; \boxed{\times} \; 100 \; \boxed{=} \; 75.5$$

Round the calculator result to the nearest whole number. The index for the cassettes and CDs is 76.

2. Use the data you collected to create buying control indexes for male participants, female participants, and all participants in the survey.

M**AKE DECISIONS**

3. Suppose you are in charge of contacting stores in your community to sell advertising in the school newspaper. You want to show store managers that it is to their advantage to buy advertising space. Construct a poster with appropriate charts to show the buying control of the students at your school.

Children between the ages of 4 and 12 influenced about $132 billion worth of purchases in 1990, according to James MacNeal of the Texas A&M Marketing Department.

Using Statistics to Persuade

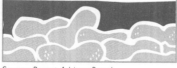

PEANUT FACTS

Average farm: 100 acres
100 lb of peanut seeds per acre are needed.
Average yield: 2,705 lb/acre
Cost of seed: $.70/lb
Average profit: $63 per acre
30,000 peanut butter sandwiches can be made from 1 acre of peanuts.
548 peanuts make one 12-oz jar of peanut butter.
210 calories in 2 oz of peanut butter
0 mg cholesterol in 100 g of peanut butter
8 g fat in 1 oz of peanut butter
800,000,000 lb of peanut butter are expected to be consumed each year.

Source: *Peanut Advisory Board*

WORK TOGETHER

You and your partner have been struggling to make ends meet on a peanut farm. Finally, you decide to look for outside investors, and you compile the statistics at the left. Decide how you will go about convincing people to invest in your peanut farm.

1. Which statistics would you present to a bank when applying for a loan?

2. Which statistics would you *not* present to possible investors?

3. One of your investors claims to have heard that peanut butter is high in cholesterol. How would you respond to this?

THINK AND DISCUSS

Statistics are a powerful tool. You can use statistics to influence a friend. Companies use statistics to present their best image. Advertisers use statistics to influence you about what to buy.

Sometimes people present accurate data in a misleading manner to encourage the conclusions they support. Both graphs below show the price of gold over several months in 1993.

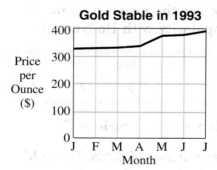

Source: *Business Week*

The symbol ⟩ near the corner of the graph on the right indicates that some values have been left out along the price scale.

4. What is different about the graphs on page 34? the same?

5. Business Suppose you are the owner of Vinny's Gold and Jewel Emporium. You are explaining to a customer why your prices are now so high. Which graph would you show? Why?

6. Suppose you are Ace Jackson, a newspaper reporter doing an article on the recent change in prices at Vinny's Gold and Jewel Emporium. Which graph would you show? Why?

7. Which of the two graphs is misleading? What makes it misleading?

Some persuasive tactics may be subtle. The poster at the right is part of an ad campaign at Harry's Hamburger Heaven. The table below shows the data from Harry's.

Item	Calories	Fat (g)	Number Sold Tuesday
Kiddie Burger	480	35	80
Hamburger Plus	575	42	68
Health Burger	580	40	65
Golden Fried Hamburger	660	57	43
Burger Deluxe	700	55	75

8. Nutrition What is the average number of calories in a hamburger at Harry's Hamburger Heaven?

9. How is the poster misleading?

Example The data below show the number of movies filmed on location in Washington state over five years. Would the tourism office use the mean, median, or mode to advertise its popularity with Hollywood?

Year	1988	1989	1990	1991	1992
Number of Movies	6	7	3	7	4

• mean = 5.4   median = 6   mode = 7

The mode is the greatest number of films. It would be used to promote Washington to film makers.

10. Film crews made four movies in Washington in 1987. Would this data item change which measure the tourism office would use? Explain.

1990 Population (thousands)

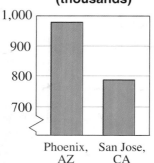

Phoenix, AZ   San Jose, CA

Source: *The World Almanac*

TRY THESE

11. Environment Kano asked 100 people "Should the beautiful mountains of New York's Adirondack Park be preserved in their natural, wild state?" Of the 100 responses he received, 80 were "yes." Do you think Kano's results were unbiased? Explain why or why not.

Use the bar graph at the left for Exercises 12 and 13.

12. At first glance, this graph gives the impression that Phoenix has twice the population of San Jose. Explain why this impression is incorrect.

13. Redraw the graph accurately.

ON YOUR OWN

14. a. Sports Use the data at the right to create a line graph that shows a great increase in the number of people running in the Boston Marathon.

b. Sports Create a second line graph showing little increase in the number of people running the Boston Marathon.

Boston Marathon Entrants

	Women	Men
1983	725	5,949
1988	1,093	5,665
1993	1,861	7,069

c. Advertising Suppose you were a Boston Marathon promoter. Which graph would you show to convince companies donating prize money that they should increase the prize money because participation has increased?

15. Education Liberty has the following scores on exams in her geography class.

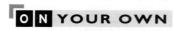

93   83   76   92   76

a. Find the mean, median, and mode of the exam scores.

b. Should Liberty use the mean, median, or mode to display her impressive knowledge of geography?

c. Should her teacher use the mean, median, or mode to encourage Liberty to study harder?

Mixed REVIEW

Explain why you would or would not expect to see a trend in the scatter plots described below.

1. height of a person and his/her income

2. the number of years of education and income

3. Is the question "Do you prefer spring or fall?" biased?

Calculate.

4. 127 × 33

5. 144 ÷ 16

6. Replace each ▓ with +, −, ×, or ÷.

6 ▓ 2 ▓ 3 = 20 ▓ 5

16. Hobbies Use the data in the table at the right to create two different histograms. One will show that there is little difference between income and hours of television watched. The other will show that there is a great deal of difference between hours of television watched and income.

17. Writing Find a graph in a newspaper or magazine. Describe the data presented. Tell whether the graph is misleading or fair, and how you know.

18. Nutrition Farnaz asked 50 boys and 50 girls at her school, "What's your favorite pizza topping?" She wrote an article for the school newspaper and included the double bar graph below. Explain why the graph is misleading. Redraw the graph accurately, and include a new title.

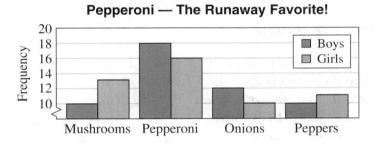

Annual Income	Hours of TV per Week
Under $30,000	53
$30,000 to $39,999	49
$40,000 to $49,999	48
$50,000 to $59,999	47
$60,000 and more	46

Pepperoni — The Runaway Favorite!

19. Data File 1 (pp. 2–3) Draw a double line graph for interest rates from the point of view of a bank manager who wants to focus attention on how much greater the interest rate is for a certificate of deposit than for a savings account.

20. Medicine The graph below and the data at the right show measles cases in the United States over five years.

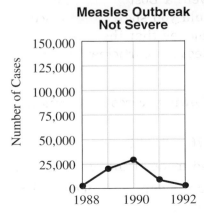

Measles Outbreak Not Severe

a. Does the graph give an accurate representation of the data? Why or why not?

b. Redraw the graph with a maximum of 30,000 cases. Create a title for your graph. Is your graph more accurate than the one at the left? Why or why not?

Measles Cases Reported in the United States	
1988	3,396
1989	18,193
1990	27,786
1991	9,643
1992	2,237

Source: *Centers for Disease Control*

Wrap up

Collecting and Reporting Data 1-1

To organize data, you can make a frequency table and use it to create a histogram or line plot. The *range* of the data is the difference between the greatest and least elements.

Cooked	Frequency
0	11
1	8
2	4
3	2
4	1
5	0

1. Frances surveyed her classmates to see how many times a week each cooked dinner at home. The frequency table at the right shows their responses. Make a line plot and a histogram for the data.

Displaying Data 1-2, 1-3

Spreadsheets can be useful tools for organizing data. You can create graphs from a spreadsheet. A *bar graph* compares amounts and a *line graph* compares changes in data over time.

2. Refer to the spreadsheet below.

   a. What is the value in cell B3?

   b. Which cell has the value 6.8?

   c. Make a double bar graph to show the data.

	A	B
1	3.5	3.8
2	6.8	6.1
3	2.1	0.9

3. a. Data File 9 (pp. 362–363) Would you use a bar graph or a line graph to show changes in household size from 1930 to 1991?

   b. Make the graph.

4. Data File 10 (pp. 416–417) Why is the data on life expectancies displayed in a double bar graph?

Mean, Median, and Mode and Using Statistics 1-4, 1-9

The *mean, median* and *mode* of a set of data, along with any *outliers,* reflect the characteristics of the data.

5. Meredith is learning to play the French horn. She kept a record of her daily practice time in minutes for two weeks.

   a. Find the mean, median and mode of the data.

   b. What are the outliers? How do they affect the mean?

   c. Meredith wants to impress her teacher with her dedication. Will she show her teacher the mean, median, or mode of her daily practice time?

Practice Record			
Week 1		Week 2	
20	40	10	60
15	65	0	40
35		20	
15		15	
15		35	

Scatter Plots and Stem-and-Leaf Plots 1-5, 1-7

Scatter plots show the relationship between two sets of data.
You can use stem-and-leaf plots to organize a set of data.

Weights and Pulse Rates of 10 Animals

Animal	Weight (lb)	Pulse (beats/ min)
carp	17	59
cat	9	130
cod	11	48
fox	10	240
mink	2	340
porcupine	15	300
rabbit	3	150
salmon	6	38
squirrel	1	390

6. **Choose A, B, or C.** Which of the scatter plots below shows a positive correlation?

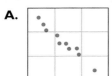

A.   **B.**   **C.**

7. Make a scatter plot for the data at the right.

   a. What type of correlation do you see in the graph?

   b. What conclusions can you draw from the graph?

8. Make a stem-and-leaf plot to display the Ski Team's times on their preliminary runs. Find the median and mode.
   times in minutes: 3.1   2.4   4.6   3.2   3.1   2.7

Surveys and Representative Samples 1-8

9. **Writing** The editor of the school newspaper has asked you to do an article on how students get to school and what improvements students would like to see in the bus service.

   a. Write a fair question for your survey.

   b. How would you choose your representative sample?

Solving Problems with Logical Reasoning 1-6

10. Sam, Katie, and Martin went to a costume party as a spider, a fox, and a fish. Each brought a treat to the party. The fish did not bring oatmeal cookies. The spider brought apples. Martin was the fox, and Katie made popcorn. Who wore what costume and took which treat?

GETTING READY FOR CHAPTER 2

1. Name the geometrical shapes in the design at the right.

2. Describe each of the following as completely as you can.

   a. triangle   b. rectangle   c. parallelogram

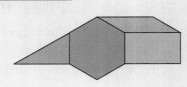

PUTTING IT ALL TOGETHER

 **ollow Up**

Weights and Heights

Is a person's weight a good indicator of the person's height? Look at the answer you gave at the beginning of the chapter. Revise or expand on it based on your study of the chapter. Then use statistics to answer the question persuasively. You may write a report, create a poster or display, or give an oral presentation. The following suggestions may help.

✓ Use a scatter plot.
✓ Use measures of central tendency.
✓ Use an appropriate data display.

The problems preceded by the magnifying glass (p. 8, # 22; p. 19, # 19; and p. 22, # 15) will help you complete the investigation.

Excursion: Meg guessed that people's shoe sizes would generally increase as their heights increased. A scatter plot showed that she was right. What other characteristics of a person might increase as the person's height increased? What might decrease?

Where Were You Born?

Some of your classmates were born nearby, while others may have been born in another state or country. Collect data about how far from school your classmates were born.

✍ Make a map with a point for each student.
✍ Find the mean and median distances from school to where people were born.
✍ Draw a circle with the school as the center. Use either the mean or median as the radius. Explain your choice of radius.
✍ How many students fall inside the circle?
✍ How many outside?
✍ Did anyone fall on or close to the circle's circumference?

HAPPY BIRTHDAY TO US!

What is the "birthday" of your class? To find out, find the number of days each student has been alive. Then average the number of days you have each lived. With this average, work backward to find the average date of birth for your class. Plan a celebration for the "class birthday."

GOING TO THE DOGS

Dogs are very popular pets around the world. The American Kennel Society recognizes dozens of different breeds of dogs. The heaviest breeds of dogs are the St. Bernard and Old English Mastiff. Both breeds regularly run 170 lb–200 lb. The smallest breeds are the Miniature Yorkshire Terrier, Miniature Chihuahua, and Toy Poodle. Find out today's top five most popular dog breeds. Compare their average weights. Find out how much it would cost to feed each breed for a week. Make a chart of your findings.

Piece of Pie

Pie is a popular dessert. Everyone has a favorite kind.

- Make a survey of your family and friends to find each person's favorite kind of pie.
- Make a chart showing the different choices.
- Use pictures rather than words to display your data.

Big Feet?

Can you predict a person's height from their shoe size? Survey a number of people you know asking their height and shoe size. Make scatter plots for the data you collect. Use one graph for males and one for females. Do you see a pattern? Can you predict a person's shoe size from their height? Explain.

1. Twenty people were asked about the amount of time it takes them to commute to work.

"How Many Minutes Do You Spend Commuting to Work?"			
30	60	25	10
15	45	35	30
25	50	90	20
35	10	60	30
40	30	50	45

   a. Make a frequency table for the data.

   b. Make a histogram of the data. Use 10-min intervals.

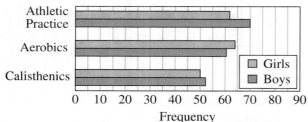

Teenagers' Preferred Exercise

2. Use the graph above to answer the following questions.

   a. Who gets the most exercise through athletic practice?

   b. Who gets less of their exercise through calisthenics?

   c. Which form of exercise do teenagers do most?

   d. About how many girls were surveyed?

3. The Summer Street School holds a crafts fair every year. Their profits for the last 5 years are $425, $355, $390, $400, and $360. Make a line graph representing the profits.

4. **Choose A, B, or C.** To best describe the favorite subject of seventh grade students, which measurement would you use?

   A. mean   **B.** median   **C.** mode

5. Mark Lenzi and Tan Liangde were the front-runners at the 1992 Summer Olympic men's diving competition. Use the scores to create an appropriate graph to compare the two divers' scores for the first five dives of the finals. Round the scores if necessary.

Dive	Lenzi	Tan
1	36	43.74
2	45.03	43.89
3	48	55.44
4	52.92	39.36
5	45	51.03

6. Find the mean, median, mode, and range of the weights, in ounces, of one-month-old hamsters: 1.25, 2, 3.25, 2.25, 2.5, 3.5, 1.75, 1, 1.75, 2, 1.5, 2.

7. Ella, Sara, and Tim have the last names Syrio, Ellis, and Trag. Syrio is Trag's nephew. No one has a first and a last name that begin with the same letter. What is the full name of each person?

8. Create a stem-and-leaf plot for the following junior league bowling scores: 45, 56, 34, 55, 78, 21, 38, 66, 56, 41.

9. Suppose you are a statistician conducting a survey on how long people wait in doctors' offices. Would you reach a representative sample if you called all of Dr. Lopez's patients? Explain.

10. **Writing** Explain how someone could use a misleading graph.

Choose A, B, C, or D.

1. Use the line plot to determine the number of families that own at least two bicycles.

```
                    ×
            ×   ×   ×
            ×   ×   ×
    ×   ×   ×   ×   ×   ×
    ×   ×   ×   ×   ×   ×
    0   1   2   3   4   5
```

A. 4   **B.** 11   **C.** 15   **D.** 19

2. What is the range of the data in the stem-and-leaf plot?

```
 8 | 8
 9 | 1  6
10 | 3  4  4  5
11 | 0
          8 | 8 means 88
```

A. 88   **B.** 22

C. 104   **D.** 110

3. What could the data in the stem-and-leaf plot above most likely represent?

  A. High temperatures for 8 days

  B. Number of hours spent watching television in one day

  C. Weight in pounds of Chicago Bears football players

  D. Number of books read in one week by members of the Mystery Club

4. Which symbol makes the sentence true?

$$3 \times 5 - 2 = 7 + (3 \; \blacksquare \; 2)$$

  A. ×   **B.** ÷   **C.** +   **D.** −

5. What is the mode of the data set 3, 7, 7, 9, 2, 4, 3, 8, 8, 7, 0, 6?

  A. 6.5   **B.** 7   **C.** 8   **D.** 9

6. What is the best estimate of 12×37?

  A. 200   **B.** 300   **C.** 400   **D.** 500

7. When the soccer team stopped for lunch, eight players ordered pasta and salad while three players ordered salad only. There are 20 players on the team, and each player ordered at least one of these two items. How many players ordered pasta but no salad?

  A. 5   **B.** 12   **C.** 9   **D.** 17

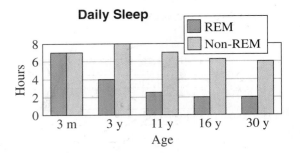

Daily Sleep

8. Use the bar graph to compare the total number of hours slept daily by a 3-month-old to the total hours slept by a 30-year-old.

  A. about half as much

  B. about twice as much

  C. about the same

  D. about three times as much

9. Use the bar graph to estimate the REM sleep for each age group. What is the mean of the data?

  A. 3.5   **B.** 2   **C.** 5   **D.** 2.5

10. In the bar graph, about how many more hours does a 3-month-old spend in REM sleep than a 30-year-old?

  A. 2   **B.** 3   **C.** 4   **D.** 5

Geometry

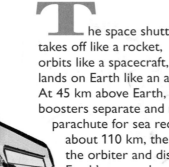

The space shuttle takes off like a rocket, orbits like a spacecraft, and lands on Earth like an airplane. At 45 km above Earth, the solid rocket boosters separate and return to Earth by parachute for sea recovery. At an altitude of about 110 km, the external tank separates from the orbiter and disintegrates upon reentry into Earth's atmosphere. Engineers designed the orbiter for use in up to 80 missions. The solid rocket boosters should last for about 6 flights each.

Source: Alabama Space Science Exhibit Commission

Data File 2

When Science World polled its readers asking, "What exciting space discoveries will be made in the next century," they got some pretty wild answers. The circle graph shows what the 9,000 respondents predicted.

WORLD VIEW

On June 16, 1963 Valentina Tereshkova became the first woman in space. She spent 70 h 50 min in space in the Soviet spacecraft, *Vostok 6*.

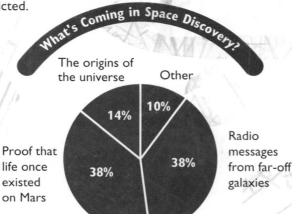

What's Coming in Space Discovery?

The origins of the universe — 14%

Other — 10%

Proof that life once existed on Mars — 38%

Radio messages from far-off galaxies — 38%

Source: *Science World*

+Y

+X

WHAT YOU WILL LEARN

- how to classify geometric figures
- how to use tools to draw geometric figures
- how to use technology to explore circles
- how to solve problems by drawing diagrams

The space shuttle has 3 body axes. There is a different name for rotation around each axis.

X—Roll   Y—Pitch   Z—Yaw

Astronauts control rotation along each axis with a rotational hand controller (RHC). Each RHC has a maximum angle, called *hardstop*, through which it can pivot. It also has an angle after which the RHC becomes difficult to move. This is called *softstop*. Softstop warns the astronaut when hardstop is being approached.

Source: Alabama Space Science Exhibit Commission

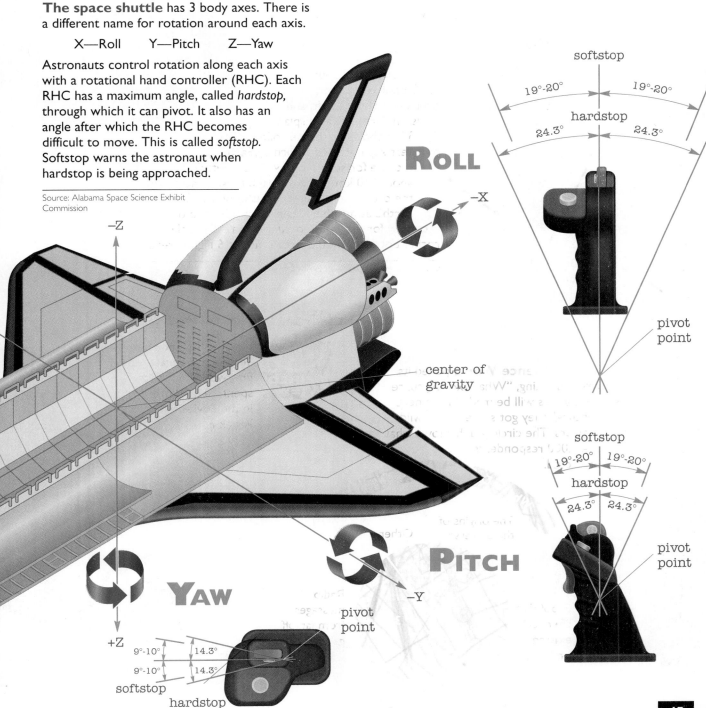

ROLL

softstop

19°-20°   19°-20°

hardstop

24.3°   24.3°

pivot point

center of gravity

PITCH

softstop

19°-20° | 19°-20°

hardstop

24.3° | 24.3°

pivot point

YAW

+Z

9°-10° | 14.3°

9°-10° | 14.3°

softstop

hardstop

pivot point

−Z

−X

−Y

investigation

Memo

The Electronics Emporium has always used the same advertising firm to create newspaper ads that promote their products. Lately, the Emporium's sales have been slipping due to increased competition from other electronic stores. The owners of the Emporium have decided that they should change advertising firms. They have invited several firms, including the one you work for, to submit sample newspaper ads advertising a new line of electronic products.

Mission: Design a sample ad for the Electronics Emporium. You may use paper, pens, pencils, straightedges, and/or compasses. Your ad should promote a television set, a VCR, a CD player, and a speaker system. You should write your own promotional copy and determine the cost of each product.

LeADs tO FoLLow

✓ Think about a newspaper ad that you like. What is there about the ad that you like best?

✓ What is there about the ad that might convince you to visit the store to see the product?

2-1

Exploring Visual Patterns

WORK TOGETHER

1. a. What would be the next figure for the pattern shown? Sketch it.

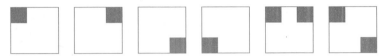

b. What might be the eighth and ninth figures in the pattern? Can you sketch more than one possibility?

2. a. Sketch the next two figures for the pattern.

b. What might be the ninth and tenth figures in the pattern?

THINK AND DISCUSS

Many patterns involve geometric figures. Describe the next two figures for each pattern below.

3.

4.

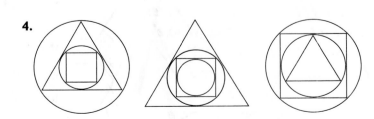

Shown above are three parts of a quilt square called Dutchman's Puzzle. **Draw the design that completes the quilt square.**

Source: *The Quilt ID Book*

1. Find the mean.

2. Find the mode(s).

Use the graph for
Question 3.

3. Does Brand M cost
twice as much as Brand N?
Explain.

4. Thieu worked 3 h a day
on a jigsaw puzzle. It took
him 13 h to complete the
puzzle. If he started the
puzzle on Saturday, what
day did he finish the
puzzle?

ON YOUR OWN

5. **a.** Draw the next two figures for the pattern.

b. **Writing** Describe the twentieth figure for the pattern.

Choose the figure that continues each pattern.

6.

A. **B.** **C.**   **D.**

7.

A. **B.** **C.** **D.**

8. Copy the first four figures for the patterns in the Work
Together activity. Decide on a way to continue the pattern
that is different from Questions 1 and 2. Draw at least the
next four figures in your pattern.

9. Copy the figures on dot paper. Draw two figures that might
continue the pattern. Then try to find a different way to
continue the pattern.

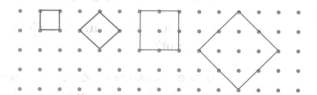

2-2 **A**ngles

WHAT YOU'LL NEED

✓ Protractor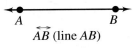

WORK TOGETHER

Study the pairs of angles shown below, along with their measures. Some pairs are *complementary angles* and some are not. Work with your group to develop a definition of *complementary angles.*

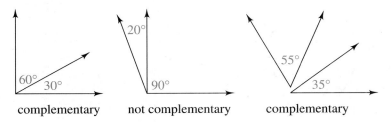

complementary   not complementary   complementary

Work with your group to develop a definition of *supplementary angles.*

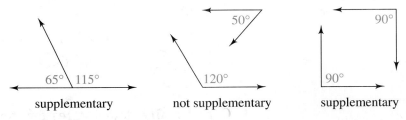

supplementary   not supplementary   supplementary

FLASHBACK

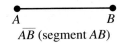

$\overleftrightarrow{AB}$ (line *AB*)

$\overline{AB}$ (segment *AB*)

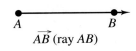

$\overrightarrow{AB}$ (ray *AB*)

$\overrightarrow{BA}$ (ray *BA*)

THINK AND DISCUSS

An **angle** is made up of two rays (the *sides* of the angle) with a common endpoint (the *vertex* of the angle). You can call the angle shown ∠*DCE*, ∠*ECD*, ∠*C*, or ∠1.

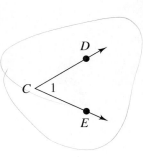

1. Can you call the angle ∠*CDE*? Why or why not?

2. If the measure of ∠1 is 56°, what is the measure of a complementary angle? of a supplementary angle?

3. Draw a large angle.

   a. Place the center point of your protractor on the vertex of the angle.

   b. Make sure that one side of the angle passes through zero on the protractor scale.

   c. Read the scale where it intersects the second side of the angle. What is the measure of the angle?

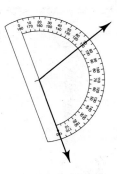

4. How would you measure an angle with sides that do not extend to the scale of the protractor?

5. Use your protractor to draw a 140° angle.

You can classify angles according to their measures.

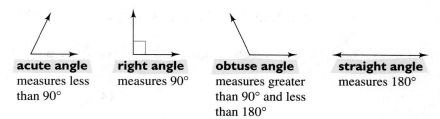

acute angle
measures less than 90°

right angle
measures 90°

obtuse angle
measures greater than 90° and less than 180°

straight angle
measures 180°

6. Classify the angle you drew in Question 5.

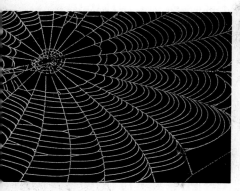

A spider makes adjacent angles as it constructs the spokes that form the bridge for its web. After constructing the bridge, a spider spins a thread joining the spokes to form a spiral.

Two **adjacent angles** share a vertex and one side but have no common interior points. ∠ABD and ∠DBC are adjacent angles.

7. Are ∠ABD and ∠ABC adjacent angles? Why or why not?

8. Draw two intersecting lines and number the nonstraight angles as shown.

   a. Name the pairs of adjacent angles.

   b. Two pairs of numbered angles are not adjacent. They are *vertical angles.* Name the pairs of vertical angles.

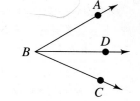

   c. Use your protractor to measure your numbered angles. What seems to be true of vertical angles?

You can use the notation $m\angle A$ to write *the measure of $\angle A$.*

Example Find the measures of $\angle 1$, $\angle 2$, and $\angle 3$ if $m\angle 4 = 128°$.

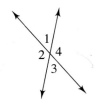

$m\angle 1 = 180° - 128°$ $\angle 1$ and $\angle 4$ are
$m\angle 1 = 52°$ supplementary.
$m\angle 2 = 128°$ $\angle 2$ and $\angle 4$ are vertical.
$m\angle 3 = 52°$ $\angle 1$ and $\angle 3$ are vertical.

T R Y THESE

9. $\angle A$ and $\angle B$ are supplementary angles. If $m\angle A = 15°$, what is $m\angle B$?

10. $\angle C$ and $\angle D$ are complementary angles. If $m\angle C = 50°$, what is $m\angle D$?

11. $\angle 1$ and $\angle 2$ are vertical angles. If $m\angle 1 = 75°$, what is $m\angle 2$?

Estimate the measure of each angle. Then classify the angle.

12.   **13.**   **14.**

15. a. Name two adjacent angles.

  b. If $m\angle ADB = 20°$ and $m\angle BDC = 55°$, then $m\angle ADC = $ ■.

  c. Could you name any of the angles shown at the right with a single letter? Why or why not?

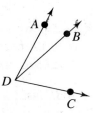

O N YOUR OWN

Classify each angle as acute, right, obtuse, or straight.

16. $m\angle A = 45°$ **17.** $m\angle B = 180°$

18. $m\angle C = 90°$ **19.** $m\angle D = 150°$

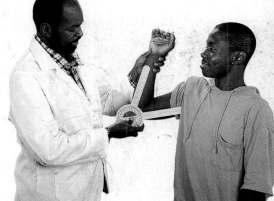

Physical therapists use goniometers to measure the amount of motion a person has in a joint, like an elbow or a knee. The goniometer has a built-in protractor.

Source: *Scholastic Dynamath*

2-2 Angles   **51**

Mixed REVIEW

Compute mentally.

1. 803 + 997
2. 14 + 36 − 11

Draw a line plot for each set of data.

3. 9, 13, 12, 12, 10, 13, 11
4. 7, 2, 4, 3, 6, 5, 6, 2, 4, 7
5. Draw the next figure in the pattern.

6. How many rectangles are in the figure below?

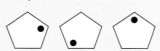

Tell whether the estimate for each angle measure is reasonable. If it is not reasonable, give a better estimate.

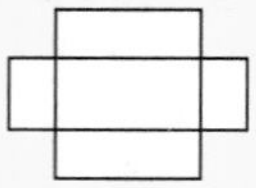

20. 120°

21. 60°

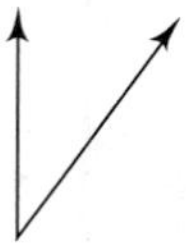

22. 45°

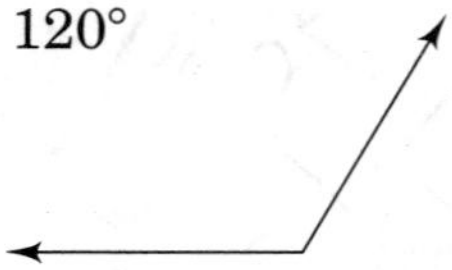

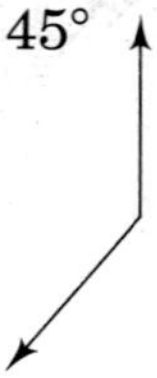

23. Writing One student measured $\angle ABC$ and said that $m\angle ABC = 60°$. Explain the mistake that was made.

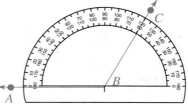

Use the figure below to name the following.

24. four lines

25. three segments

26. four rays

27. four right angles

28. two pairs of adjacent supplementary angles

29. two pairs of obtuse vertical angles

30. two pairs of complementary angles

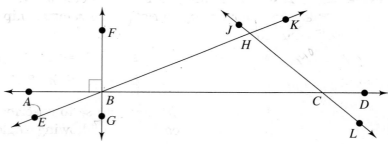

31. Use a protractor to draw two complementary angles, one of which has measure 25°.

32. Use a protractor to draw two supplementary angles, one of which has measure 55°.

33. Use a protractor to find $m\angle A$, $m\angle B$, $m\angle C$, and $m\angle D$.

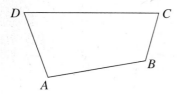

34. These are photocopies of two ivory tusks. Identify which comes from a mammoth and which comes from an elephant.

a.

b.

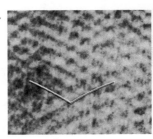

35. a. Draw vertical angles, ∠1 and ∠2, that are supplementary.

   b. Draw vertical angles, ∠3 and ∠4, that are complementary.

Use dot paper or graph paper to draw angles with the following measures *without* using a protractor.

36. 90°   **37.** 180°   **38.** 45°   **39.** 135°

40. a. Data File 2 (pp. 44–45) If an astronaut wishes to raise the nose of the space shuttle, around which axis will the astronaut rotate?

   b. When the astronaut raises the nose of the space shuttle, through what angle measure will the rotational hand control move before it becomes difficult to move?

41. Choose A, B, C, or D. ∠1 and ∠2 are supplementary. ∠1 and ∠3 are complementary. What is the relationship between ∠2 and ∠3?

   A. $m\angle 2 = m\angle 3$ **B.** $m\angle 2 = m\angle 3 + 90°$

   C. $m\angle 3 = m\angle 2 + 90°$ **D.** $m\angle 2 + m\angle 3 = 180°$

42. Critical Thinking Use *acute, right,* and *obtuse* to describe the possible kinds of angles in each of the following angle pairs.

   a. two supplementary angles   **b.** two adjacent angles

   c. two complementary angles   **d.** two vertical angles

43. If $m\angle XYZ = 87°$ and $m\angle 1 = 34°$, what is $m\angle 2$?

Ivory ID

Ed Espinoza of the United States Fish and Wildlife Service has found a way to identify whether ivory tusks are from prehistoric mammoths or from elephants. Ivory smugglers try to slip illegal elephant ivory into the United States by labeling the ivory as mammoth tusks.

On the flat edges of tusks are distinctive markings. Ed Espinoza and a team of scientists photocopied and measured these markings. They found that markings from mammoth tusks create angles that are 90° or less. Markings from elephants create angles that are 115° or more.

2-3  **Triangles**

WORK TOGETHER

Begin with a paper triangle that is a different shape from those of the other members of your group.

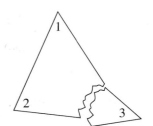

• Number the angles of the triangle and tear them off the triangle.

• Place the three angles side-by-side so that pairs of angles are adjacent and no angles overlap. What seems to be true?

• Compare your results with those of your group. Make a conjecture.

FLASHBACK

Congruent segments are segments that have the same length. Congruent angles are angles that have the same measure.

THINK AND DISCUSS

You can classify triangles by the number of congruent sides or by angle measures.

scalene triangle
no congruent sides

isosceles triangle
at least two
congruent sides

equilateral triangle
three congruent sides

right triangle
one right angle

acute triangle
three acute angles

obtuse triangle
one obtuse angle

1. Classify each triangle by its sides.

a.   b.   c.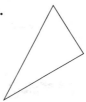

2. Classify each triangle in Question 1 by its angles.

3. Is an equilateral triangle also an isosceles triangle? Why or why not?

4. a. Fold a paper equilateral triangle so that one side matches another side. What is true of the angles that match?

   b. If you fold the triangle so that a different pair of sides match, do you get the same result? What is true of the three angles of an equilateral triangle?

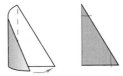

In the Work Together activity you discovered that the following statement is true for all triangles.

The sum of the measures of the angles of a triangle is 180°.

5. Can you find the measure of each angle of an equilateral triangle? Explain.

6. Begin with a paper isosceles triangle that is not equilateral. Fold the triangle so that one side lies on another side. Repeat two more times so that different sides are paired. What do you discover?

If you know the measures of two angles of a triangle, you can find the measure of the third angle.

Example   Find the measure of ∠C.

$$53° + 61° = 114°$$
$$180° - 114° = 66°$$
$$m∠C = 66°$$

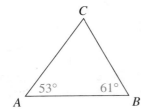

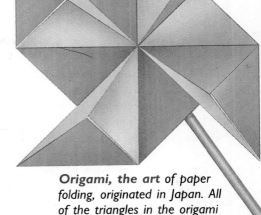

Origami, the art of paper folding, originated in Japan. All of the triangles in the origami pinwheel have the same size and the same shape.

7. Judging by appearance, classify each triangle by its sides. Name any congruent sides.

a.

b.

c.

d.

8. Classify each triangle in Exercise 7 by its angles. Name any obtuse or right angles.

Find each missing angle measure.

9.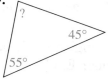

10.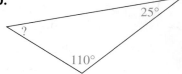

Find each missing angle measure.

11.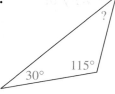

12.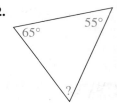

In an orchestra, a triangle is a percussion instrument. It is made of a thin steel rod. The triangle is held in the air by a string, and it is struck with a small metal stick. **Does a musical triangle look like a scalene triangle, an isosceles triangle, or an equilateral triangle?**

Source: *Encyclopedia Americana*

13. Use your protractor to draw a triangle with angles measuring 75°, 45°, and 60°. Label the angle measures.

14. a. Writing Can an equilateral triangle be a right triangle? Why or why not?

b. Can an obtuse triangle have a right angle? Why or why not?

15. Choose A, B, C, or D. The measures of two angles of a triangle are 35° and 50°. Classify the triangle.

A. acute

B. right

C. obtuse

D. cannot be determined

Find the missing angle measures for each isosceles triangle.

16.

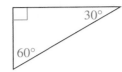

2 cm   80°   2 cm

?   ?

17.

70°   25 mm

?   ?

25 mm

18. The triangles shown below are all right triangles.

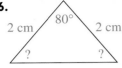 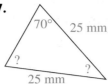

30°

60°

35°   55°

45°

45°

a. What is the sum of the measures of the two acute angles in each triangle?

b. What is the relationship of the two acute angles in these triangles? Is this true for all right triangles? Explain.

19. **Critical Thinking** The measures of the angles of a triangle are 50°, 60°, and 70°.

a. Classify the triangle by its angles.

b. Can the triangle be equilateral? Why or why not?

c. Can the triangle be isosceles? Why or why not?

d. Can you classify the triangle by its sides? Why or why not?

CHECKPOINT

1. Draw the next figure for the pattern at the right.

Classify the angle with the given measure.

2. 23°   **3.** 117°   **4.** 90°

Judging by appearance, classify each triangle by its sides and angles.

5.   **6.** 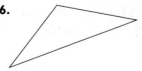   **7.**

2-4 **D**raw a Diagram

Drawing a diagram can help you visualize the relationships described in a problem.

> One angle of an isosceles triangle measures 50°. What are the measures of the other two angles?

1. Think about the information you are given and what you need to find.

   a. What is the measure of one angle of the triangle?

   b. What kind of triangle is involved in this problem?

   c. What is special about this kind of triangle?

   d. Summarize the goal of this problem.

A good strategy to use here is to *draw a diagram*. Although you are given the measure of one angle of the triangle, you do not know which angle. In particular, you do not know if this angle is one of the two congruent angles in an isosceles triangle or if this angle is the angle that is not congruent to another angle.

2. Draw a diagram that shows the 50° angle as one of the two congruent angles.

   a. What is the measure of the angle that is congruent to the given angle?

   b. What is the measure of the third angle?

3. Draw a diagram that shows the 50° angle in a different location. What are the measures of the other angles?

4. Are there any other ways an isosceles triangle can have a 50° angle? Why or why not?

5. Write a solution to the original question by summarizing what you have found.

6. Describe how drawing a diagram helped you solve the problem.

◀ **LOOK BACK**

Think about how you solved the problem.

▀T▀R▀Y THESE

Draw a diagram to help you solve each problem.

7. Each morning Jacob walks to school. At 8:20 he passes a stoplight that is two blocks from home. He reaches the town library at 8:24. At this point he is three blocks from school and half the way there. If Jacob walks at the same pace all the way to school, at what time does he arrive at school? Explain your answer.

8. At the first meeting of the Table Tennis Club, the seven members decided to have a tournament in which every player will play a game against every other player. How many games will there be in the tournament?

According to Professor Michael Hill of the University of Minnesota, the average woman walks 256 ft/min. The average man walks about 245 ft/min. **Find out how far you walk in a minute.**

▀O▀N YOUR OWN

Use any strategy to solve each problem. Show all your work.

9. Suppose you buy several pencils at a discount store. All the pencils are the same price, and you buy as many pencils as the cost (in cents) of each pencil. The pencils cost a total of $1.44. How many pencils did you buy?

10. The diagram shows part of a design made by using toothpicks to form triangles. The top level uses three toothpicks. The second level uses six toothpicks. The third level uses nine toothpicks, and so on.

   a. If you decide to continue the design so that it has seven levels, how many toothpicks do you need altogether?

   b. Which level will use 24 toothpicks?

11. Find all the combinations of six whole numbers greater than zero that you can add to get a sum of 12.

3. Find the mean, the median, and the mode of the following scores: 98, 85, 87, 85, 78.

4. Three test scores are 88, 92, and 85. What must the fourth score be to make the mean 90?

Use the diagram for Exercises 5 and 6.

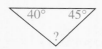

5. Find the missing angle measure.

6. Classify the triangle by its angles.

7. Find two whole numbers that have a sum of 166 and a difference of 32.

12. Shana climbed a set of stairs and stopped at the middle step. She then walked down 2 steps, up 4 steps, down 3 steps, and up 5 steps, and she was at the top of the stairs. How many steps are in the set of stairs?

13. Raphael has only dimes and quarters. His coins total $1.55. Find all the possible combinations of dimes and quarters that Raphael might have.

14. **Data File 4 (pp. 142–143)** Karen lives in London. Some of her relatives live in Phoenix and some live in Singapore. When Karen calls her brother at 10 A.M. London time, it is 5 P.M. where he lives. Does he live in Phoenix or Singapore?

15. **Gardening** Each year Brandon plants tulip bulbs in a square flower bed. (Three examples of square flower beds are shown below.) This year Brandon's flower bed has 29 more bulbs than it had last year. If the flower bed is still square, how many tulip bulbs are in it this year?

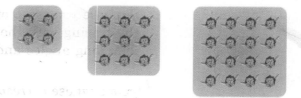

16. Rosa, Carlos, and Maria are in a band together. They play guitar, piano, and drums. Carlos is the cousin of the guitar player. Rosa lives next door to the drum player and two blocks from the guitar player. Who plays which instrument?

17. The Molinos have two children. The sum of their ages is 21 and the product of their ages is 110. How old are the children?

18. How many angles are shown? How many of them are obtuse?

19. Three angles have the same vertex but no common interior points. Together they measure 180°. The sum of the first and second angles is 88°. The sum of the second and the third angles is 120°. Find the measure of each angle.

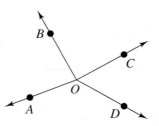

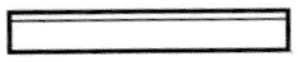

2-5

Congruent Triangles

THINK AND DISCUSS

Figures that have the same size and shape are **congruent.**

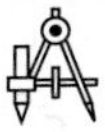

1. Name the pairs of figures that appear to be congruent.

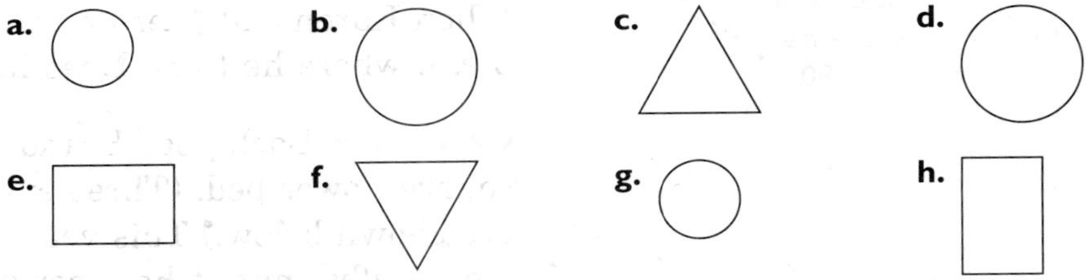

a.   b.   c.   d.

e.   f.   g.   h.

2. How could you check that two figures are congruent?

3. Suppose you trace one of two congruent polygons and match the tracing with the second polygon. What is true of the matching angles and segments?

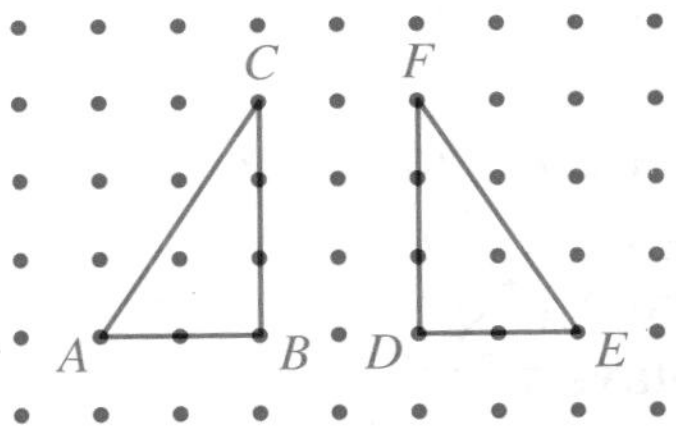

Polygons whose *corresponding parts* (sides and angles) are congruent are called **congruent polygons.** If you match vertices A and E, B and D, and C and F, then the corresponding sides and angles of the two triangles shown will be congruent. You can write this as follows, using the symbol ≅ for "is congruent to" and △ for "triangle."

$$\overline{AB} \cong \overline{ED} \qquad \angle A \cong \angle E$$
$$\overline{BC} \cong \overline{DF} \qquad \angle B \cong \angle D$$
$$\overline{CA} \cong \overline{FE} \qquad \angle C \cong \angle F$$
$$\triangle ABC \cong \triangle EDF$$

Note that you name corresponding vertices in the same order.

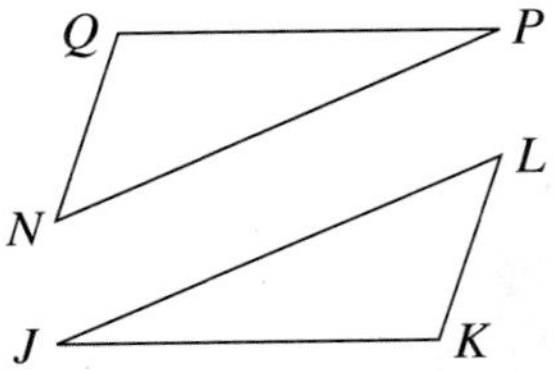

4. The triangles shown at the left are congruent.

   a. Which vertex corresponds to vertex J? to K? to L?

   b. Complete.

$$\triangle JKL \cong \ \blacksquare$$

$$\overline{JK} \cong \blacksquare \qquad \overline{KL} \cong \blacksquare \qquad \overline{LJ} \cong \blacksquare$$

$$\angle J \cong \blacksquare \qquad \angle K \cong \blacksquare \qquad \angle L \cong \blacksquare$$

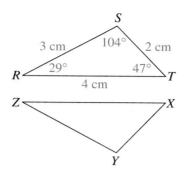

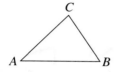

Example $\triangle XYZ \cong \triangle TSR$

a. Write six congruences involving corresponding parts of the triangles.

$$\angle X \cong \angle T \qquad \angle Y \cong \angle S \qquad \angle Z \cong \angle R$$
$$\overline{XY} \cong \overline{TS} \qquad \overline{ZY} \cong \overline{RS} \qquad \overline{ZX} \cong \overline{RT}$$

b. Find $m\angle X$ and the length of $\overline{ZY}$.

- Because $\angle X \cong \angle T$, $m\angle X = m\angle T = 47°$.
- Because $\overline{ZY} \cong \overline{RS}$, the length of $\overline{ZY}$ is 3 cm.

WORK TOGETHER

Draw a large scalene $\triangle ABC$. Work with your group to construct the following triangles, using only a compass and straightedge.

5. a. Follow Steps 1–3 below to construct $\angle D$ congruent to $\angle A$. In Step 1 you draw a ray with endpoint D. Then you put the tip of the compass at point A and draw an arc that intersects the sides of $\angle A$. Keeping the compass open to the same width, put the tip of the compass at D and draw an arc. Now complete Steps 2 and 3.

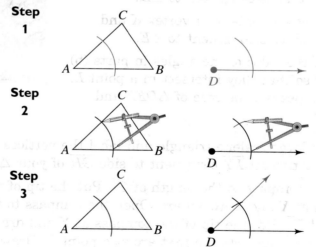

b. Put the tip of the compass at A and open the compass wide enough so that you could draw an arc through B. Use that compass opening to construct $\overline{DE}$ on one side of $\angle D$ so that $\overline{DE} \cong \overline{AB}$. On the other side of $\angle D$ construct $\overline{DF}$ congruent to $\overline{AC}$. Draw $\overline{EF}$.

c. What appears to be true of $\triangle ABC$ and $\triangle DEF$?

6. a. △DEF ≅ ▪

b. △EFD ≅ ▪

c. △DFE ≅ ▪

d. Name six congruences involving corresponding sides and angles.

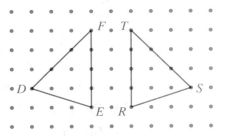

7. Critical Thinking Suppose you know that △ABC ≅ △ZXY. What can you conclude about the angles and sides of △ZXY? Why?

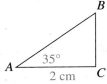

8. a. Draw a large scalene triangle and label the vertices *D, E,* and *F.* Construct $\overline{JK}$ congruent to side $\overline{DE}$ of your △DEF.

b. Construct an angle with vertex *J* and side $\overrightarrow{JK}$ that is congruent to ∠D.

c. Construct an angle with vertex *K* and side $\overrightarrow{KJ}$ that is congruent to ∠E.

d. Extend the sides of the angles in parts (b) and (c) so that they intersect in a point *L.* What appears to be true of △DEF and △JKL?

9. a. Draw a large scalene triangle and label the vertices *G, H,* and *I.* Construct $\overline{XY}$ congruent to side $\overline{GH}$ of your △GHI.

b. Open the compass to the length of $\overline{GI}$. Put the tip of the compass at *X* and draw an arc. Open the compass to the length of $\overline{HI}$. Put the tip of the compass at *Y* and draw an arc that intersects the first arc at a point *Z.* Draw $\overline{XZ}$ and $\overline{YZ}$.

c. What appears to be true of △GHI and △XYZ?

10. Critical Thinking In △ABC and △PQR, $\overline{AB}$ and $\overline{PQ}$ are the same length. $\overline{BC}$ and $\overline{QR}$ are the same length. Must $\overline{AC}$ and $\overline{PR}$ be the same length? Why or why not?

*The **Amundsen-Scott** South Pole Base, when completed, will house the Earth's best observatory. The average temperature is −72°F. The low temperature reduces the air pressure. The low air pressure and the flattening of the atmosphere at the poles allows the telescopes great views of the sky. **Describe the congruent triangles in the design of the structure.***

Source: *Omni*

11. List the pairs of triangles that appear to be congruent.

a.   b.   c.

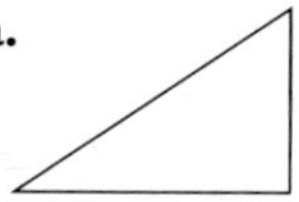

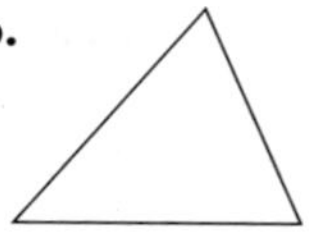

d.   e.   f.

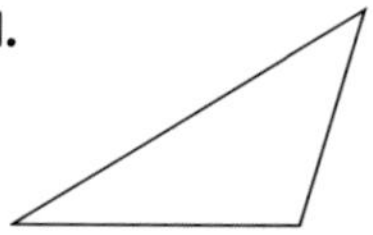

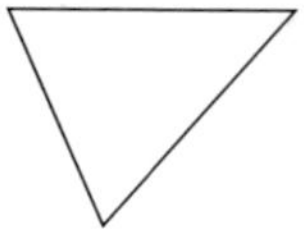

12. Complete. (Be sure that you name corresponding vertices in the same order.)

a. △ABC ≅ ■   b. △ABC ≅ ■   c. △ABC ≅ ■

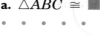
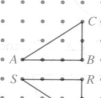

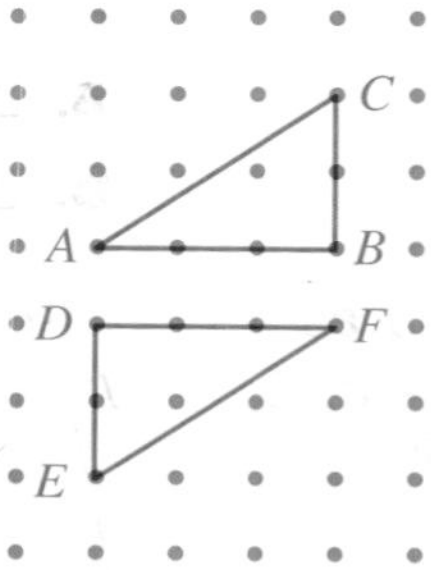

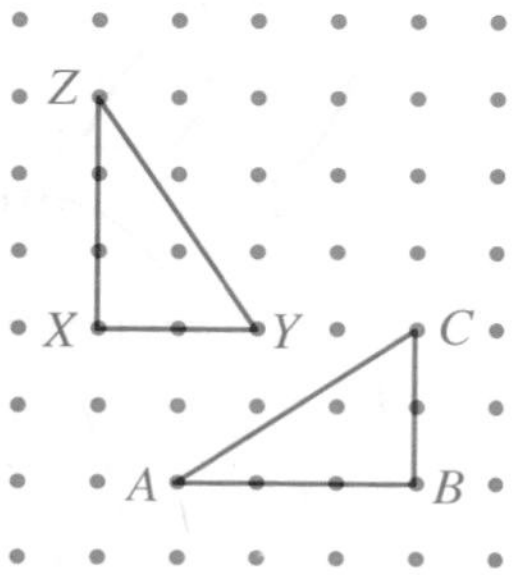

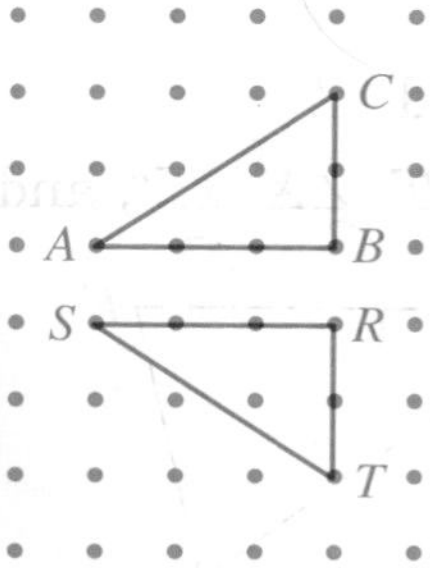

Henry Ford
*revolutionized
industry by using
the concept of congruence
when he used the assembly-line
method to mass produce his
Model T automobile. Ford first
produced the Model T in 1908.
With mass production, the cost
of a Model T dropped from
$950 in 1909 to $360 in
1926.*

13. △DEF ≅ △CLK

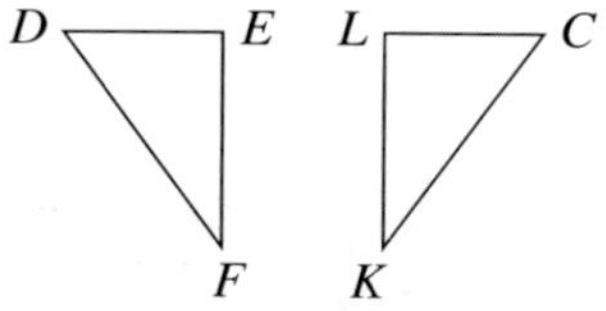

a. ∠D ≅ ■   b. ∠E ≅ ■
c. ∠F ≅ ■   d. $\overline{DE}$ ≅ ■
e. $\overline{EF}$ ≅ ■   f. $\overline{DF}$ ≅ ■

14. Assume that △XYZ ≅ △RBP.
Write six congruences
involving corresponding
sides and angles.

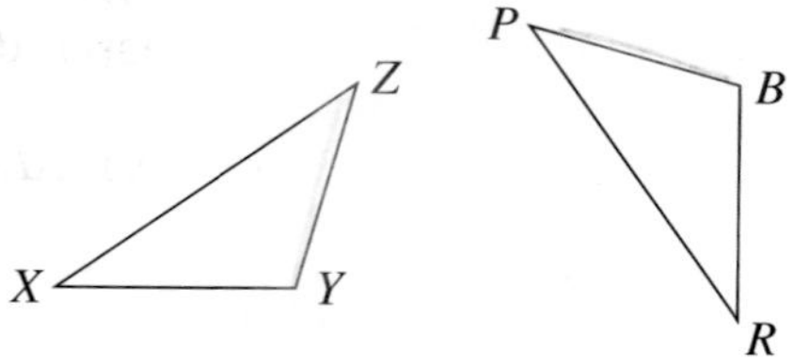

15. Draw a segment and label it as $\overline{AB}$.

a. Construct a segment, $\overline{XY}$, that is congruent to $\overline{AB}$.

b. Construct a segment, $\overline{CD}$, that is twice as long as $\overline{AB}$.

16. Draw an obtuse angle, ∠E. Construct an angle, ∠F, that is congruent to ∠E.

17. a. Draw a large scalene triangle, $\triangle RST$. Use a straightedge and compass to construct a $\triangle XYZ$ that is congruent to $\triangle RST$.

b. Writing Explain how you constructed $\triangle XYZ$ in part (a).

18. Complete in as many correct ways as you can: $\triangle ABC \cong$ ■

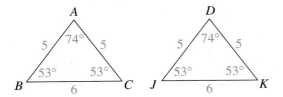

19. Choose A, B, C or D. $\triangle RST$ and $\triangle XYZ$ are congruent equilateral triangles. Which angle or angles must be congruent to $\angle R$?

A. $\angle X$ only

B. $\angle S$ and $\angle T$

C. $\angle X$, $\angle S$, and $\angle T$

D. $\angle S$, $\angle T$, $\angle X$, $\angle Y$, and $\angle Z$

20. $\triangle RST \cong \triangle EFG$. Find as many angle measures and side lengths for $\triangle EFG$ as you can.

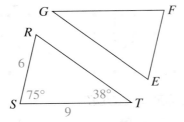

21. a. Use dot paper or graph paper to draw $\triangle XYZ$ and $\triangle JKL$ so that $\triangle XYZ \cong \triangle JKL$.

b. Sketch two *noncongruent* triangles that have three pairs of congruent corresponding angles.

22. Is $\triangle ABC$ congruent to $\triangle DEF$? Why or why not?

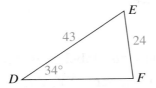

23. Investigation (p. 46) Because illustrations are eye-catching, they often appear in advertisements. Find at least two examples of illustrations in ads. For each example, explain why the ad designer might have chosen the illustration.

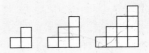

What's Ahead

- Classifying polygons and identifying regular polygons
- Working with special quadrilaterals

 The Pentagon, built between 1941 and 1945, is the headquarters for the U.S. Department of Defense. When it was built, the Pentagon was the largest office building in the world. It covers 34 acres and has 3,700,000 ft² of office space.

FLASHBACK

Two lines are parallel if they lie in the same plane and do not intersect. Segments are parallel if they lie in parallel lines.

THINK AND DISCUSS

You name *polygons* by the number of sides.

triangle   quadrilateral   pentagon

hexagon   octagon   decagon

1. How many sides does a pentagon have? a hexagon? an octagon? a decagon?

A **regular polygon** has all sides congruent and all angles congruent.

2. Which of the polygons above appear to be regular?

3. What is another name for a regular triangle?

Some quadrilaterals have special names.

A **trapezoid** has exactly one pair of parallel sides.

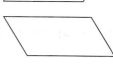

A **parallelogram** has both pairs of opposite sides parallel.

A **rectangle** is a parallelogram with four right angles.

A **rhombus** is a parallelogram with four congruent sides.

A **square** is a parallelogram with four right angles and four congruent sides.

4. What is another name for a regular quadrilateral?

Every quadrilateral has two pairs of opposite sides and two pairs of opposite angles.

5. Name two pairs of opposite sides.

6. Name two pairs of opposite angles.

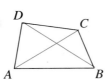

The *diagonals* of quadrilateral *ABCD* are $\overline{AC}$ and $\overline{BD}$.

What road hazard is the Australian road sign warning drivers about? Write all the names that can be used for the shape of the top sign. **What is the best name?**

Start with a parallelogram that is a different shape from those of the other members of your group. Draw one diagonal of your parallelogram. Cut out the parallelogram and then cut along the diagonal.

7. a. Are the two triangles that are formed congruent? Why or why not?

b. Were the opposite sides of your parallelogram congruent? Why or why not?

c. What have you shown about the opposite angles of your parallelogram? Suppose you had cut along the other diagonal. What do you think would have been the result?

8. Compare your results with those of your group. What can you conclude about parallelograms? Does your conclusion also apply to rectangles, squares, and rhombuses? Why or why not?

The shell of the hatchling turtle shows the occurrence of polygons in nature. **What polygons do you see on the turtle's shell?**

You can use the fact that the opposite sides of a parallelogram are congruent and parallel to draw parallelograms on dot paper or graph paper.

Example   Draw each of the following figures on dot paper.

a. parallelogram *ABCD* that is not a rectangle or a rhombus

b. rhombus *EFGH* that is not a square

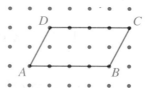   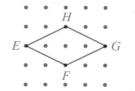

T R Y THESE

Judging by appearance, classify each quadrilateral. Then name the congruent sides and angles.

9.

10.

11.
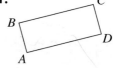

O N YOUR OWN

Classify each polygon by the number of sides. Then state whether it appears to be a regular polygon.

12.

13.

14.

15.

Judging by appearance, state all correct names for each quadrilateral. Then circle the best name.

16.

17.

18.

19.

Use dot paper to draw each of the following.

20. a rectangle

21. a square

22. a rhombus that is not a square

23. a trapezoid with two right angles

24. a regular quadrilateral

25. **Critical Thinking** Can a quadrilateral be both a rhombus and a rectangle? Explain.

26. **Writing** Write a sentence that uses the word *all* and some of the following words: trapezoids, parallelograms, rectangles, rhombuses, squares. Repeat for the word *some* and then for the word *no*.

27. a. Draw a quadrilateral with exactly one pair of opposite angles that are congruent.

b. Draw a quadrilateral with exactly one pair of opposite sides that are congruent.

28. **Choose A, B, C, or D.** Which statement or statements are false?

     I. Every trapezoid is a quadrilateral.

     II. Every rectangle is a square.

     III. Every parallelogram is a rhombus.

A. II only   **B.** III only

C. II and III   **D.** I, II, and III

List all additional side lengths and angle measures you can find for each quadrilateral.

29. parallelogram $ABCD$, length of $\overline{AB}$ is 6 cm, $m\angle A = 65°$

30. square $EFGH$, length of $\overline{EF}$ is 3 m

31. rhombus $WXYZ$, length of $\overline{WX}$ is 4 cm

32. rectangle $JKLN$, length of $\overline{JK}$ is 5 in.

33. trapezoid $PQRS$, length of $\overline{PQ}$ is 10 cm, $m\angle Q = 65°$

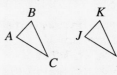
Problem Solving Hint

Draw a diagram.

What's Ahead

• Identifying parts of circles and working with inscribed quadrilaterals

2-7

Circles

WHAT YOU'LL NEED

✓ Computer

✓ Geometry software

✓ Protractor

THINK AND DISCUSS

Even a Frisbee™ can benefit from a computer. Some engineers use computers to streamline these plastic discs so they will soar farther and more smoothly. Others use computers to help produce high-quality Frisbees more quickly and cheaply.

Graphic designers use computers to make the flying toys look great. To do that, a graphic designer might use a *circle* and other geometric figures to model the design on the top of the Frisbee, as shown below.

A circle is a set of points on a plane that are all the same distance from a given point, called the *center*. You name a circle by its center. Circle *O* is shown below.

A **radius** is a segment that has one endpoint at the center and the other endpoint on the circle.

$\overline{OB}$ is a radius of circle *O*.

A **diameter** is a segment that passes through the center of a circle and has both endpoints on the circle.

$\overline{AC}$ is a diameter of circle *O*.

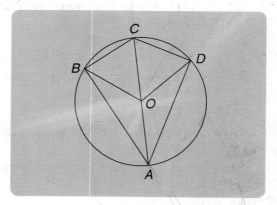

A **central angle** is an angle with its vertex at the center of a circle.

$\angle AOB$ is a central angle of circle *O*.

A **chord** is a segment that has both endpoints on the circle.

$\overline{AD}$ is a chord of circle *O*.

1. What geometric figures do you see in the design on the previous page?

2. Name the isosceles triangles in the design. How do you know they are isosceles?

3. **a.** Estimate the measures of the following angles. Record your estimates.

$\angle BOC$ $\angle COD$ $\angle BOA$ $\angle DOA$

$\angle CBA$ $\angle BAD$ $\angle ADC$ $\angle DCB$

   b. Measure the angles listed above. Compare each measure to your estimate.

4. Name all the obtuse triangles and right triangles in the design.

5. Name any congruent triangles in the design.

An **arc** is part of a circle. A **semicircle** is half a circle. You use three letters to name a semicircle. The first and third letters name the endpoints of the semicircle.

6. **a.** Is $\overset{\frown}{ADC}$ (read "arc *ADC*") a semicircle of circle *O*?

   b. Why do you need to use three letters to name a semicircle?

7. $\overset{\frown}{AB}$ is one arc of circle *O*. Name two more arcs that are shorter than a semicircle.

8. Which of the following appear to be arcs?

   a.   **b.** **c.** **d.** **e.**

9. One chord of circle *O* is $\overline{AD}$. Name the other chords shown.

10. **Language** An analogy is one way to express a comparison. Complete this analogy.

   Chord is to *Arc* as *Diameter* is to ■ .

You call a polygon whose sides are the chords of a circle an **inscribed** polygon.

11. Name a polygon that is inscribed in circle *O*.

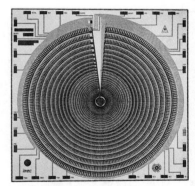

WHAT? This is a picture of a microchip used for robotic vision. Computer scientists at the University of Pennsylvania designed the chip. The chip simulates light-sampling abilities like those found in the human eye. In the center, there are 102 photocells that act like the area on the human retina where vision is the sharpest.

Source: *Discover*

12. What is true of all the vertices of an inscribed polygon?

13. Name the pairs of opposite angles of quadrilateral *WXYZ*.

14. Do any sides of quadrilateral *WXYZ* appear to be congruent? How could you use a compass to check whether they are congruent?

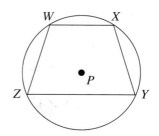

WORK TOGETHER

Computer Make a conjecture about the sum of the measures of the opposite angles of an inscribed quadrilateral. Test your conjecture by trying it with different circles and different quadrilaterals.

ON YOUR OWN

Name each of the following for circle *O*.

15. two chords

16. three radii

17. a diameter

18. a central angle

19. a semicircle

20. two arcs

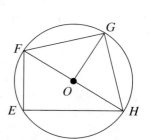

21. the longest chord shown

22. an inscribed quadrilateral

23. an inscribed triangle

24. a. Draw a design for a round belt buckle that includes an inscribed quadrilateral.

   b. Writing Describe your design so someone could draw it without looking at your drawing.

   c. Ask a family member or friend to use your description to draw your design. Compare the results to your design and rewrite the description of your design if necessary.

1. Make a histogram for the following record high temperatures: 100°, 127°, 134°, 118°, 100°, 118°, 117°, 122°, 119°, 116°, 118°, 114°.

2. Draw an octagon.

3. Draw a trapezoid.

4. Bicycling burns 11 calories/min. Running burns 14 calories/min. Dancing burns 8 calories/min. Would you burn more calories by running for 15 min 3 days a week or bicycling 40 min 2 days a week?

25. Choose A, B, C, or D. Which of the following is *not* an inscribed polygon?

 A. B. C. D.

Computer **Make and test a conjecture about each of the following.**

26. an inscribed quadrilateral whose vertices are the endpoints of two diameters

27. an inscribed triangle that has a diameter as one of its sides

28. the nonparallel sides of an inscribed trapezoid

Computer Graphics

The computer is quickly becoming the paintbrush of the movie and advertising industries. Animators and commercial artists use software graphics programs to shape three-dimensional objects that look very realistic.

One type of program allows an artist to create images as wire frames. These frames are composed of intersecting lines. Using a more complex program, an artist can create a figure using many polygons, much like a wire net. Each point of a polygon can be stretched to allow the shaping and shading of the figure.

The computer helps advertisers create such images as cars turning into tigers and moviemakers to show images like the blood of a Klingon floating across the movie screen. Using the computer as a canvas, artists are changing the way we see the world.

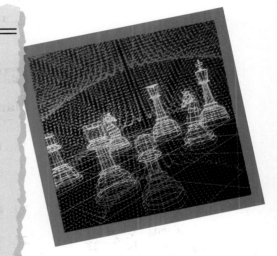

29. When you finish this exercise, you will see how artists can use straight lines to give the feeling of a curve. Draw two perpendicular lines and mark them as shown at the right. Using a straightedge, join the letters that are the same.

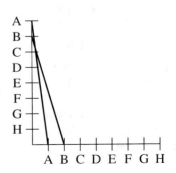

 30. Investigation (p. 46) Conduct a survey to determine features that other students respond to positively in ads and features that they respond to negatively.

Draw the next figure for the pattern.

1.

2.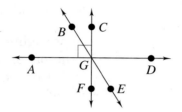

Classify each angle as acute, right, obtuse, or straight.

3. $m\angle A = 36°$ **4.** $m\angle B = 102°$ **5.** $m\angle C = 180°$ **6.** $m\angle D = 143°$

Name each of the following.

7. two lines   **8.** two segments

9. two rays   **10.** two right angles

11. a pair of vertical angles

12. a pair of complementary angles   **13.** a pair of supplementary angles

Find each missing angle measure. Then classify each triangle by its angles.

14.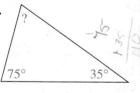

15.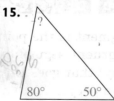

16.

17.

△ABC ≅ △DEF. Complete each statement.

18. $\angle A \cong$ ■   **19.** $\angle C \cong$ ■

20. $\overline{AB} \cong$ ■   **21.** $\overline{BC} \cong$ ■

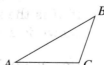
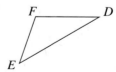

22. Draw a circle O. Draw, label, and identify three radii, a diameter, an inscribed quadrilateral, and five chords.

Draw each of the following polygons on dot paper.

23. a right triangle   **24.** an isosceles triangle   **25.** a rhombus that is not a square

26. a hexagon   **27.** a pentagon   **28.** a regular quadrilateral

Constructing Bisectors

WHAT YOU'LL NEED

✓ Tracing paper

✓ Compass

✓ Straightedge

WORK TOGETHER

Use a straightedge to draw a segment, $\overline{AB}$, on tracing paper. Fold the paper so that point A lies on point B. Unfold the paper and label the intersection of $\overline{AB}$ and the foldline as point M.

1. Compare your result with a partner's.
   a. What is the relationship between $\overline{AM}$ and $\overline{MB}$?
   b. What kind of angles does the foldline make with $\overline{AB}$?

Use a straightedge to draw an angle, $\angle CDE$, on tracing paper. Fold the paper so that $\overrightarrow{DC}$ lies on $\overrightarrow{DE}$. Unfold the paper. Label any point of the foldline that lies inside $\angle CDE$ as point F. Draw $\overrightarrow{DF}$.

2. Compare your result with your partner's. What is the relationship between $\angle CDF$ and $\angle FDE$?

THINK AND DISCUSS

FLASHBACK

Perpendicular lines are lines that intersect to form right angles.

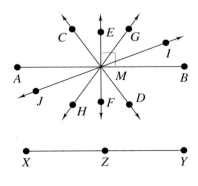

The **midpoint** of a segment is the point that divides the segment into two congruent segments. A **segment bisector** is a line (or segment or ray) that goes through the midpoint of the segment. A line that is perpendicular to a segment at its midpoint is the **perpendicular bisector** of the segment.

3. If M is the midpoint of $\overline{AB}$, which of the segment bisectors shown is a perpendicular bisector?

4. How many bisectors does a given segment have?

5. If you draw a segment, $\overline{XY}$, on a sheet of paper, how many perpendicular bisectors of $\overline{XY}$ can you draw?

6. Point Z is the midpoint of $\overline{XY}$.
   a. If $\overline{XY}$ is 38 mm long, what is the length of $\overline{XZ}$? of $\overline{ZY}$?
   b. If $\overline{XZ}$ is $\frac{3}{4}$ in. long, what is the length of $\overline{ZY}$? of $\overline{XY}$?

You can use a compass and straightedge to construct the perpendicular bisector of a given segment.

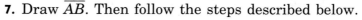

7. Draw $\overline{AB}$. Then follow the steps described below.

   Step 1   Open the compass to more than half the length of $\overline{AB}$. Put the tip of the compass at A and draw an arc intersecting $\overline{AB}$.

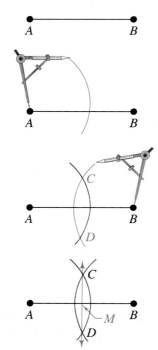

   Step 2   Keeping the compass open to the same width, put the tip at B and draw another arc intersecting $\overline{AB}$. Label the points of intersection of the arcs as C and D.

   Step 3   Draw $\overleftrightarrow{CD}$. Label the intersection of $\overline{AB}$ and $\overleftrightarrow{CD}$ as point M.

   You have constructed the perpendicular bisector, $\overleftrightarrow{CD}$, of $\overline{AB}$. Point M is the midpoint of $\overline{AB}$.

8. Describe how to construct $\overline{AB}$ so that point M is the midpoint of $\overline{AB}$.

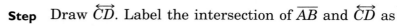

9. Suppose you want to construct a line through point F that is perpendicular to $\overleftrightarrow{EF}$. Describe how you might start.

The **bisector** of an angle is the ray that divides the angle into two congruent angles.

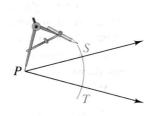

10. Draw a large $\angle P$. Then follow the steps below to construct the angle bisector of $\angle P$.

    Step 1   Put the tip of the compass at P and draw an arc that intersects the sides of $\angle P$. Label the points of intersection as S and T.

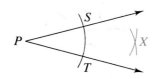

    Step 2   With the compass tip at S and then at T, and with the same compass opening, draw intersecting arcs. Label the point where the arcs intersect as X.

Step 3 Draw $\overrightarrow{PX}$.

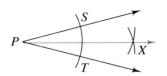

You have constructed the bisector, $\overrightarrow{PX}$, of $\angle SPT$.

ON YOUR OWN

11. Draw a segment. Then construct its perpendicular bisector.

12. Draw an acute angle. Then construct its angle bisector.

13. The bisector of $\angle JKL$ is $\overrightarrow{KN}$. If the measure of $\angle JKN$ is 66°, what is the measure of $\angle JKL$?

Problem Solving Hint

Draw a diagram.

14. Point A is the midpoint of $\overline{XY}$. Point Y is the midpoint of $\overline{XZ}$. Point Z is the midpoint of $\overline{AB}$. If $\overline{XA}$ is 2 cm long, how long is $\overline{XB}$?

Construct a segment congruent to $\overline{CD}$ on your paper.

15. Construct and label the following.

   a. a segment half as long as $\overline{CD}$

   b. a segment one fourth as long as $\overline{CD}$

   c. a segment $1\frac{1}{2}$ times the length of $\overline{CD}$

16. a. Construct a 90° angle.

   b. Construct a 45° angle.

   c. Construct a triangle with a side congruent to $\overline{CD}$ included between a 45° angle and a 90° angle. What is the measure of the third angle? Can you draw any conclusions about the other sides?

17. Construct a rectangle with two sides congruent to $\overline{CD}$ and two sides half as long as $\overline{CD}$.

18. Draw an obtuse angle, $\angle ABC$. Then construct and label the following two angles.

   a. an angle with measure one fourth the measure of $\angle ABC$

   b. an angle with measure three fourths the measure of $\angle ABC$

Mixed REVIEW

Make a stem and leaf plot for each set of data.

1. 43, 46, 51, 56, 55, 59, 56, 63, 61, 56, 45, 63

2. 209, 208, 221, 213, 222, 218, 241, 225, 211, 212

True or false?

3. A central angle of a circle has its vertex at the center of the circle.

4. An inscribed polygon has diameters of a circle as its sides.

5. A 160° angle is bisected. One of the bisected angles is bisected. This continues until a 10° angle is formed. How many angles were bisected?

Restricting geometric constructions to those that can be made with a straightedge and a compass dates to the time of Euclid, a Greek mathematician who lived about 300 B.C. In his book called the *Elements*, Euclid organized the mathematical knowledge about geometry that had been developed in the previous 300 years.

Source: *An Introduction to the History of Mathematics*

19. Writing How are a segment bisector and an angle bisector alike?

20. Choose A, B, C, or D. $\overrightarrow{AD}$ is the bisector of $\angle BAC$. $\overleftrightarrow{AD}$ is the perpendicular bisector of $\overline{BC}$. Which of the following must be true?

    I. $\angle BAD \cong \angle CAD$ II. $\overline{AD} \cong \overline{AD}$

   III. $\overline{BD} \cong \overline{CD}$ IV. $\angle BDA \cong \angle CDA$

A. I and III   **B.** I, II, and III

C. I, II, and IV   **D.** I, II, III, and IV

CHECKPOINT

Find the measure of each numbered angle.

1. $\triangle BCD \cong \triangle SRT$

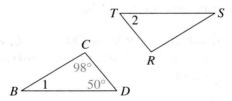

2. $\triangle EFG \cong \triangle UVW$

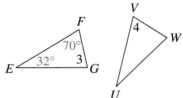

Draw each of the following polygons.

3. a square   **4.** a trapezoid   **5.** a rhombus   **6.** a hexagon

Name the following for circle *O*.

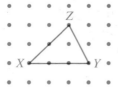

7. all radii   **8.** all diameters   **9.** all semicircles

10. all chords   **11.** all inscribed quadrilaterals

12. Draw a segment. Construct the perpendicular bisector of the segment. Then bisect one of the angles formed by the segment and its perpendicular bisector.

13. Choose A, B, C, or D. Which triangle is not congruent to $\triangle XYZ$?

A.   **B.**   **C.** 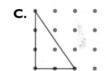   **D.**

PROBLEM SOLVING STRATEGIES

Make a Table
Use Logical Reasoning
Solve a Simpler Problem
Too Much or Too Little Information
Look for a Pattern
Make a Model
Work Backward
Draw a Diagram
Guess and Test
Simulate a Problem
Use Multiple Strategies
Write an Equation

Use any strategy to solve each problem. Show all your work.

1. The Martin Luther King School library has 8 tables and 42 chairs. There are several small tables with 4 chairs each and some large tables with 6 chairs each. How many tables of each type are in the library?

2. A display of oil cans in an auto parts store is stacked so that each row has one less can than the row below it. If there are 21 cans in the display, how many rows of cans are there?

3. There are 30 students in Ms. Valdez's seventh-grade class. For every 3 girls in the class, there are 2 boys. How many girls are in the class?

4. Counting numbers like 6, 7, 8, 9, and 10 are called *consecutive.* Find six consecutive counting numbers with a sum of 81.

5. How many triangles are shown?

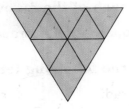

 Fifteen-year-old Mary Buchannan won the largest radio prize ever awarded on November 21, 1980. Her prize, from radio station WKRQ in Cincinnati, is $25,000 a year for 40 years. **If Mary receives her prize money each November 21st, what is the total amount of money she has received by today's date?**

Source: *Guinness Book of Records*

6. Ms. Johnson fills her car with gas every sixth day. Mr. Martinez fills his car with gas every eighth day. They both filled their gas tanks today. How many days will it be until they next fill their cars on the same day?

7. **Business** A radio station gave free T-shirts to listeners during a three-day promotion. The disk jockey gave away half of the shirts plus one during the first day, half of the remaining shirts plus one during the second day, and half of the remaining shirts plus one during the third day. At the end of the third day there was one shirt remaining. How many shirts were there at the beginning of the promotion?

What's Ahead

- Identifying and drawing three-dimensional figures

2-9 Three-Dimensional Figures

THINK AND DISCUSS

What geometric figures do you see in the entrance to the Louvre? in the Jomo Kenyatta Conference Center in Nairobi, Kenya? in the United Nations Building? Figures, such as these buildings, that do not lie in a plane are *space figures,* or *three-dimensional figures.*

Some three-dimensional figures have only flat surfaces. The flat surfaces, called *faces,* are shaped like polygons.

— face

1. Which of the buildings have faces?

Prisms are three-dimensional figures with two parallel and congruent polygonal faces, called *bases.* A prism is named by the shape of its bases.

WHO? Architect I. M. Pei designed the glass and steel entrance of the Louvre, the French national art museum. Originally a royal palace, the Louvre was built in the 14th and 15th centuries. Through his design, Pei connected ancient Egypt with a modern structure that is in harmony with the Renaissance palace.

2. Match each prism with one of the following names: triangular prism, rectangular prism, hexagonal prism.

a.   b.   c.

3. Each segment formed by the intersection of two faces is an *edge*. Why are some of the edges of the prisms in Question 2 dashed?

4. A *cube* has six congruent faces. What is another name for a cube?

5. a. Name two edges of the rectangular prism that are perpendicular to $\overline{AE}$ at A.

b. Name two edges that are parallel to $\overline{AB}$.

c. Even though $\overline{AB}$ and $\overline{HG}$ do not lie in the same face of the rectangular prism, there is a plane that contains them. Because they lie in *coplanar* lines that do not intersect, $\overline{AB}$ and $\overline{HG}$ are parallel. Name two other segments that are parallel even though they do not lie in the same face.

d. Lines that are not parallel and do not intersect are **skew** lines. One pair of skew lines are $\overleftrightarrow{AB}$ and $\overleftrightarrow{EH}$. Name another pair of skew lines.

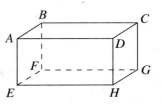

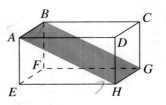

A **pyramid** is a three-dimensional figure with only one base. The base is a polygon and the other faces are triangles. A pyramid is named by the shape of its base.

6. Match each pyramid with one of the following names: triangular pyramid, rectangular pyramid, pentagonal pyramid, hexagonal pyramid.

a.

b.

c.

7. Which of the three-dimensional figures below have bases? Describe the bases.

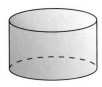

cylinder

cone

sphere

WORK TOGETHER

Work with a partner to draw a rectangular prism. Use a pencil so you can erase. Begin with two congruent rectangles that overlap. Connect the rectangles as shown. Decide which edges should be hidden and make them dashed.

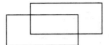 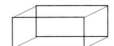 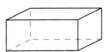

ON YOUR OWN

Give the best name for each of the following.

8.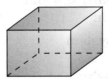

9.

10.

GREAT EXPECTATIONS

Architect

I want to be an architect. This career interests me because I like building things and using math in my work. I want to learn more about architecture because it is fun to build model buildings. My interest in architecture first began when I heard about the computer game Sim City. I started to play it and loved it. My current hobbies include building models. I have about 20. I also build cars, houses, planes, buildings, and things I think up, by using LEGO. So, if I could be anything, I would be an architect.

Matt Brookhart

Give the best name for each of the following.

11.

12.

13.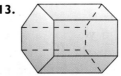

14. **a.** Name three pairs of parallel lines.

b. Name three pairs of skew lines.

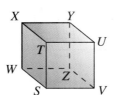

15. Draw a cube.

16. **Writing** How are a cylinder and a cone alike? How are they different?

 17. **Investigation (p. 46)** Use what you have learned about drawing three-dimensional figures to sketch:

a. a television set   **b.** a speaker system

Classify as true or false. If false, explain why.

18. Every rectangular prism is a cube.

19. Some pyramids are prisms.

Dear Matt,

I recall that my reasons for pursuing architecture were very similar to yours. It is important in choosing something as critical as one's life work, that you consider the element of fun. I have fun practicing architecture.

The notion that you can start with a sketch on the back of a napkin and end up with a multi-story, many faceted, extremely complex building, still intrigues me.

As amateur archaeologists, my partner and I have spent numerous hours in the jungles of Central America trying to understand more about the Olmec civilization through the remnants of its architecture. In this sense, architecture provides us with a link to the past as well as a bridge to the future.

Ivenue Love-Stanley, Architect

Wrap Up

1. Draw the next figure in the pattern at the right.

An *angle* is made up of two rays with a common endpoint. You can classify angles according to their measures.

You can use a compass and straightedge to construct congruent figures and the *perpendicular bisector* of a segment or the *bisector of an angle.*

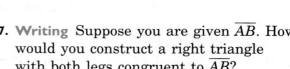

Name a pair of angles for each of the following.

2. vertical angles   3. complementary angles

4. adjacent angles   5. supplementary angles

6. Draw a large triangle *LMN* with an obtuse $\angle L$. Construct the bisector of $\angle L$. Then construct the perpendicular bisector of $\overline{MN}$.

7. **Writing** Suppose you are given $\overline{AB}$. How would you construct a right triangle with both legs congruent to $\overline{AB}$?

You can classify triangles by the number of congruent sides or by the measures of the angles. The corresponding angles and sides of *congruent triangles* are congruent. The sum of the measures of the angles of a triangle is 180°.

All sides and all angles of a *regular polygon* are congruent. Some four-sided polygons (quadrilaterals) have special names.

8. **Choose A, B, C, or D.** In $\triangle DEF$, the $m\angle D$ is twice the $m\angle E$. Which words might describe $\triangle DEF$?

    I. acute   II. obtuse   III. right

A. I and II   **B.** I and III   **C.** II and III   **D.** I, II, and III

9. $\triangle UVW \cong \triangle XYZ$. Write the six congruences involving corresponding angles and sides.

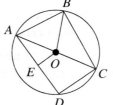

10. Define a trapezoid.　　**11.** Define a rhombus.

Circles and Three-Dimensional Figures　　2-7, 2-9

A *circle* is a set of points on a plane that are all the same distance from a point called the center.

A *prism* is a three-dimensional figure with two parallel bases.

A *pyramid* is a three-dimensional figure with one base.

Name each of the following for circle O.

12. a chord　　　**13.** a semicircle　　　**14.** a central angle

15. an inscribed quadrilateral

16. an arc smaller than a semicircle

17. Writing Describe how a triangular pyramid and a triangular prism are alike. How are they different?

Strategies and Applications　　2-4

You can draw a diagram to help you see the relationships described in a problem.

18. In $\triangle TRI$, $\overline{TR}$ and $\overline{TI}$ are congruent. If $m\angle R = 32°$, find the possible measures of the other two angles of the triangle.

GETTING READY FOR CHAPTER 3

To round a whole number, use the method described below.

Round 12,376 to the nearest hundred.
12,376	3 is in the hundreds' place.
376 → 400	376 is closer to 400 than 300, so round up to 400.
12,376 rounds up to 12,400.	

Round each number to the indicated place.

　1. 1,272 to the nearest hundred　　　**2.** 32,455 to the nearest thousand

　3. 54,671 to the nearest ten　　　**4.** 191 to the nearest hundred

PUTTING IT ALL TOGETHER

follow Up

The Newspaper Ad

On the basis of the sample ads submitted, Electronics Emporium has selected several firms, including your own. From this group, the Emporium will choose its new advertising firm. You now have the opportunity to revise your original ad, based on your study of the chapter, and to submit it for final consideration. The problems preceded by the magnifying glass (p. 65, # 23; p. 73, # 30; and p. 83, # 17) will help you revise your ad.

Advertising is big business in the United States. Companies spend huge amounts of money on advertising, sometimes as much as one-quarter of their budgets. In 1990, manufacturers of electronic entertainment products spent nearly $400 million on advertising.

Excursion: Compare these drawings of a TV set. Which is more realistic? Why?

BOXING SQUARES

This is a game for two people. You need a pencil or pen and a piece of square dot paper at least 6 dots by 6 dots. The players take turns connecting two horizontal or vertical dots on the paper. When a player connects two dots which make the last side of a square, s/he claims that square by putting her/his initial in the box. When all the squares on the paper have been claimed, the player with the most squares is the winner.

Variation 1: Use triangle dot paper to make triangles.
Variation 2: Use triangle dot paper to make parallelograms.

Straw Structures

You can make models of pyramids by using straws as the edges of the structure. Six straws make a tetrahedron, a pyramid with four triangular faces.

You can also construct other types of three-dimensional figures from straws. With your classmates, see how many different kinds of figures you can create. Display them with their proper names for others to see.

read this

There are capital letters in the alphabet that read the same if a mirror is placed above or below them. This horizontal reflection works with the letters in BED but not in BET.

BED   BET
BED   BET

Also, there are capital letters which read the same when a mirror is placed to the right or left of them. This vertical reflection works with the letters in TAX but not in TAB.

TAX | XAT
TAB | BAT

Make a list of letters for each type of reflection. Then make as many words as you can from the letters in each list. How many letters are in the longest word you can make? Can you make a sentence out of words from each list? Are there any words which read the same both horizontally and vertically?

Construction Challenge

Using only a compass and a straightedge there are a number of basic polygons you can construct. You can construct the following regular polygons inscribed in a circle.

Triangle Square Hexagon Octagon

When you have made these constructions, write down step-by-step directions so that a classmate can follow them.

1. Draw the next figure in the pattern.

2. Choose A, B, C, or D. ∠1 and ∠2 are acute vertical angles. ∠1 and ∠3 are adjacent supplementary angles. What must be true?

    I. ∠1 is obtuse.
    II. ∠2 and ∠3 are complementary.
    III. $m\angle 1 = m\angle 3$
    IV. ∠2 and ∠3 are supplementary.

A. I only   **B.** I and II

C. III and IV   **D.** IV only

3. Two angles of a triangle are complementary. What type of a triangle must it be?

4. a. The measures of two angles of a triangle are 54° and 26°. What is the measure of the third angle?

  b. Classify the triangle by its angles.

5. △ABC ≅ △XYZ. Write six congruences involving corresponding sides and angles.

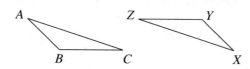

6. Critical Thinking Can a trapezoid have two congruent sides? three congruent sides? four congruent sides? Explain.

7. Construct a 45° angle.

8. △ABC ≅ △EBD. Find as many angle measures and side lengths as you can.

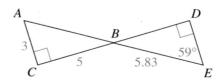

9. Draw a large △ABC with $\overline{AB} \cong \overline{BC}$. Construct the angle bisector of ∠B. Let the angle bisector intersect $\overline{AC}$ at D. What do you think is true of the two smaller triangles? Why?

10. Give the best name for each figure.

a.   **b.**

c.   **d.**

11. Name each of the following for circle O.

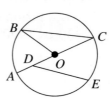

  a. a central angle

  b. two radii

  c. a chord that is not a diameter

  d. a semicircle

12. Writing Write a definition for *square* that uses the word *rhombus.*

Choose A, B, C, or D.

1. Which numbers are all divisible by 9?

   A. 36, 18, 21   **B.** 108, 252, 45

   C. 98, 81, 450   **D.** 120, 180, 267

2. $\angle 1$ and $\angle 2$ are complementary and the measure of $\angle 1$ is four times the measure of $\angle 2$. What is the measure of $\angle 2$?

   A. 18°   **B.** 36°   **C.** 72°   **D.** 144°

3. In the stem-and-leaf plot below, the stem represents the tens' digit. What does the stem and leaf plot *not* tell you?

   $$\begin{array}{c|ccc} 1 & 3 & 4 & 9 \\ 2 & 1 & 2 & 4 & 4 \\ 3 & 0 & 3 \end{array}$$

   A. The greatest number is 33.

   B. The mode is 24.

   C. The median is 22.

   D. There are 12 items of data.

4. Which kind of graph would best show the change in population of the United States from 1930 to 1990?

   A. line graph

   B. bar graph

   C. line plot

   D. stem-and-leaf plot

5. Find the *best* estimate for the perimeter of the shaded region.

   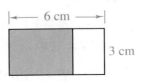

   A. 8 cm   **B.** 14 cm

   C. 12 cm   **D.** 18 cm

6. To find how much time students in your class generally spend on their math homework, which is the best survey question to ask?

   A. How long did the math homework take you last night?

   B. How many hours did you spend on math homework last week?

   C. Which homework takes you more time, math or history?

   D. Did you do last night's math homework?

7. Which figure continues the pattern?

   A. △   **B.** ◁   **C.** ▷   **D.** ▽

8. Two angles of a triangle each measure 36°. Which classification is correct?

   A. acute triangle   **B.** right triangle

   C. obtuse triangle   **D.** scalene triangle

9. In parallelogram $ABCD$, the length of side $\overline{AB}$ is 9. The measure of $\angle A$ is 40°. Which measure *cannot* be found?

   A. length of $\overline{BC}$ **B.** length of $\overline{CD}$

   C. $m\angle C$ **D.** $m\angle D$

10. The mean of six numbers is 9. Five of the numbers are 4, 7, 9, 10, and 11. What is the sixth number?

    A. 6   **B.** 9   **C.** 12   **D.** 13

Applications of Decimals

Through the Hoop

WORLD VIEW

In the 1972 Summer Olympics, the then Soviet Union won the gold medal in basketball. The Soviets were the first team to ever beat the United States Olympic team.

Data File 3

Teresa Edwards' accomplishments include an outstanding basketball career at the University of Georgia, membership on three United States Olympic teams, and three years as a professional in a Japanese women's league. Teresa would have preferred to play in the United States but there was no women's professional basketball league in 1992.

Source: *Sports Illustrated for Kids*

Teresa Edwards' Olympic Statistics

Year	Games	Points	Assists
1984	6	15	8
1988	5	83	17
1992	5	63	27
Totals	**16**	**161**	**52**

Teresa Edwards' Pro Statistics

Season	Games	Points	Assists
1989-1990	15	479	69
1990-1991	15	477	90
1991-1992	15	328	65
Totals	**45**	**1,284**	**224**

Source: *Sports Illustrated for Kids*

Sales of Basketballs (in millions)

Year	Number Sold	Dollars	Year	Number Sold	Dollars
1980	3.2	39.7	1986	3.1	47.5
1981	2.7	38.4	1987	3.5	54.6
1982	2.3	32.6	1988	3.6	60.3
1983	2.4	37.3	1989	3.6	65.5
1984	2.8	45.0	1990	4.0	79.6
1985	2.5	38.5	1991	3.6	64.5

Source: *National Sporting Goods Association*

WHAT YOU WILL LEARN

- how to compute, estimate, and solve problems using decimals
- how to use properties and work with variable expressions
- how to use technology to explore decimal patterns
- how to solve problems with too much or too little information

Number of Titles Won by Major NBA Teams from 1947-1993

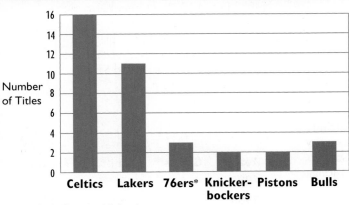

*Formerly the Syracuse Nationals

Source: *1993 Information Please Sports Almanac and NBA*

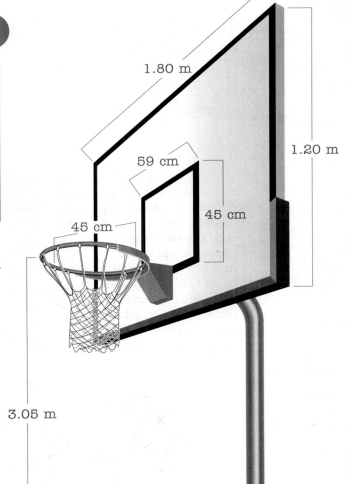

Shaquille O'Neal played basketball at Louisiana State University before becoming a center for the Orlando Magic. In 1991, O'Neal became the first player to lead the Southeastern Conference in scoring, rebounding, field goal percentage, and blocked shots in a single season. His collegiate career single-game highs include 53 points, 24 rebounds, and 12 blocks.

Source: *Louisiana State University*

Shaquille O'Neal's NCAA Statistics

Season	Games	Field Goals/ Attempts	Free Throws/ Attempts	Points	Rebounds	Assists	Blocks
1989/90	32	180/314	85/153	445	385	61	115
1990/91	28	312/497	150/235	774	411	45	140
1991/92	30	294/478	134/254	722	421	46	157

Source: *Sports Illustrated for Kids*

investigation

Project File

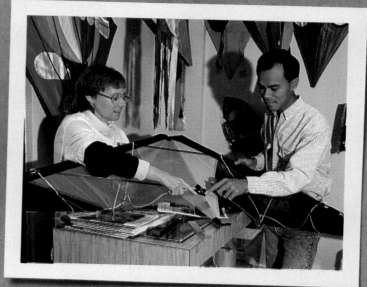

Memo

Have you ever wondered what it would be like to start your own business? Each year thousands of people choose to open their own businesses. They enjoy the independence that having their own business allows them and like making decisions for themselves. Unfortunately, poor planning, changing consumer tastes, fluctuations in the economy, and just plain bad luck cause many of them to fail. According to the Small Business Administration, only 1 in 3 new businesses employing 4 or fewer persons survives for 6 years.

Mission: Decide on a business you would like to start that involves a service to the public or the sale of a product. Describe the operation of the business. How many hours will your business be open each day? What kind of supplies will you need to start your business? What would be a good location for your business?

LeADs tO FoLLow

✓ How can you decide whether there is a need for your business?

✓ What goals should you set for your business?

✓ To whom do you expect to sell your product or service?

• Rounding decimals

• Comparing and ordering decimals

WHAT YOU'LL NEED

✓ Graph paper

hundreds	tens	ones	.	tenths	hundredths	thousandths
1	5	5	.	0	4	6
6	3	3	.	6		

FLASHBACK

Round up if the digit to the right is 5 or greater. Round down if the digit to the right is 4 or less.

WHO? In 1954, Jerrie Cobb set a world speed record for women pilots of 226.148 mi/h. She was the first woman to pass NASA's tests for astronauts (in 1960), although she never went into space.

Source: *The Book of Women's Firsts*

THINK AND DISCUSS

In 1920, a gas-powered Dusenberg set the one-mile speed record in auto racing at 155.046 mi/h (miles per hour). In 1983, a jet-propelled Thrust set an all-time record of 633.6 mi/h.

To read a decimal, you need to know the value of the last digit on the right. You read 155.046 as "one hundred fifty-five *and* forty-six thousandths" because the last digit is in the thousandths' place. ("And" indicates the decimal point.) You read 633.6 as "six hundred thirty-three and six tenths."

1. David read 12.0045 as "twelve and forty-five thousandths." Was he correct? Why or why not?

2. The digit 6 appears three times in the place value chart at the left. What is the value of the 6 each time it appears?

You can round decimals in a way that is similar to the way you round whole numbers.

Example Round 1.73628 to the nearest hundredth.
1
- 1.73628   Look at the digit to the right of the hundredths' place.

- 3 → 4   Since 6 > 5, round up.

- 1.74   Write the rounded number.

To show that 1.73628 is approximately equal to 1.74, you write 1.73628 ≈ 1.74.

3. Shoshana rounded 1.73628 to the nearest thousandth. She wrote 1.736. Was she correct? Why or why not?

You do not write extra zeros at the end of a rounded decimal. The place you are rounding to is the last digit you write.

4. Which number, 1.3760 or 1.37600, is 1.37602 rounded to the nearest ten-thousandth? Why?

Models can help you compare decimals.

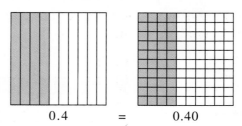

0.4   =   0.40

The numbers 0.4 and 0.40 are **equivalent decimals.** They name the same amount.

5. Draw models of 0.58 and 0.6. Which number is greater?

To order decimals, you can compare them using a number line.

Example 2   Order 0.5, 0.8, and 0.25 from least to greatest using a number line.

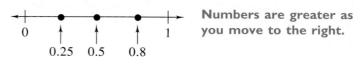

Numbers are greater as you move to the right.

From least to greatest, the numbers are 0.25, 0.5, and 0.8.

Another way to order decimals is to compare place values.

Example 3   Use the data at the left to order the cities according to the average yearly rainfall.

- Compare the decimals 40.24, 40.74, and 40.14. The digits in the tens' and ones' places are the same.

- Compare the digits in the tenths' place.

$$7 > 2 > 1$$

Therefore, $40.74 > 40.24 > 40.14$.

Ranked from greatest rainfall to least rainfall, the cities are Huntington, Galveston, and Cincinnati.

6. Weather The average annual rainfall for Bismarck, North Dakota, is 15.36 in. Denver, Colorado, has an average annual rainfall of 15.31 in. Which decimal place must you use to tell which city has the greater amount of rainfall?

Average Yearly Rainfall

City	Amount (in.)
Galveston, TX	40.24
Huntington, WV	40.74
Cincinnati, OH	40.14

Source: *The World Almanac*

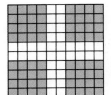
7. **a.** Write the numbers for the shaded area of these models in words and in decimal form.

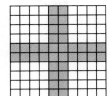 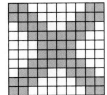

b. Write a statement using <, >, or = that compares the decimals from part (a).

Compare using <, >, or =.

8. 0.167 g � 0.16 g   **9.** 3.09 m ▪ 3.7 m

10. **Biology** The smallest spider is a male *Patu marplesi* that is 0.017 in. across, about the size of a period. The largest spider is a male goliath bird-eating spider that is 11.020 in. across.

a. Write each number in words.

b. Round each number to the nearest hundredth.

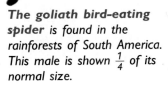

The goliath bird-eating spider is found in the rainforests of South America. This male is shown $\frac{1}{4}$ of its normal size.

ON YOUR OWN

Identify the place value of the underlined digit. Then round each decimal to the indicated place.

11. 0.769<u>4</u>9   **12.** 5.194<u>3</u>8   **13.** 0.56439<u>1</u>8

Write five numbers between the given numbers.

14. 40 and 50   **15.** 18 and 19   **16.** 3.7 and 3.8

17. During last week's math challenge, each group in Suzanne's class earned points.

a. Draw a number line to compare the team points.

b. List the groups from greatest number of points to least.

18. **Writing** Explain how you would determine which decimal number is greater, 16.75 or 16.746.

Last Week's Math Challenge Points	
Ayla's group	9.3
Max's group	8.9
Suzanne's group	9.5
Simon's group	9.2
Terri's group	9

Use this information:
Two angles of a triangle measure 72° and 85°.

1. Find the measure of the third angle.

2. Classify the triangle by its angles.

Write *true* or *false*.

3. A hexagonal prism has 12 edges.

4. A pyramid may have a circular base.

5. Stacy wrote a list of consecutive whole numbers. She began with 1 and ended with 113. How many digits did she write?

19. a. A bowling ball weighs 5.61 kg and a bowling pin weighs 1.57 kg. Round each weight to the nearest kilogram.

b. About how many bowling pins would it take to equal the weight of the bowling ball?

20. Write at least five decimals that round to 7.26.

21. Write the greatest possible decimal less than 1 using each of the digits 4, 7, 0, and 6 once.

22. Sports Six students participated in the long jump on Field Day. The first-place distance was 4.72 m. The last-place distance was 3.5 m. There were no ties. Give possible distances for the other four jumpers.

Sports Use the table below for Exercises 23–25.

Major League Batting Champions				
National League			American League	
Year	Player	Batting Avg.	Player	Batting Avg.
1989	Tony Gwynn, San Diego	.336	Kirby Puckett, Minn.	.339
1990	Willie McGee, St. Louis	.335	George Brett, Kan. City	.329
1991	Terry Pendleton, Atlanta	.319	Julio Franco, Texas	.341
1992	Gary Sheffield, San Diego	.330	Edgar Martinez, Seattle	.343

Source: *The Information Please Sports Almanac*

23. Who had the highest batting average? the lowest?

24. List the players in order from highest to lowest batting average. Who is listed before George Brett? Who follows Tony Gwynn?

25. Critical Thinking Suppose you rounded each batting average to the nearest hundredth. Could you accurately order the players from highest to lowest? Why or why not?

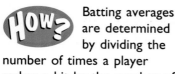 Batting averages are determined by dividing the number of times a player makes a hit by the number of times the player is at bat.

 26. Investigation (page 92) Talk to someone who has started a business. Ask the person to describe the planning he or she did before getting under way. Find out how the actual operation of the business is different from what the person expected.

Estimation Strategies

• Estimating with decimals

Taco $2.39
Grilled Cheese $1.89
Yogurt with
 Granola $1.49
Fruit Cup $1.99
Frozen Juice Bar $1.39
Frozen Yogurt $1.59
Juice sm $.69
 lg $1.29

THINK AND DISCUSS

You want to buy a grilled cheese sandwich, frozen yogurt, and small juice. You only have $6. You can *round* to estimate the total.

$$1.89 + 1.59 + 0.69 \approx 2 + 2 + 1$$
$$= 5$$

The cost is about $5.

1. Is this estimate more or less than the exact cost? How do you know?

Rounding can also help you estimate differences.

Example 1   Estimate the difference between the price of a taco and the price of a grilled cheese sandwich.

$$2.39 - 1.89 \approx 2.5 - 2$$ Round to the nearest
$$= 0.5$$ half-dollar.

A taco costs about $.50 more.

2. About how much more does a large juice cost than a small juice?

You can use *front-end estimation* to estimate sums.

Example 2   Estimate the cost of a taco and yogurt with granola.

$$\left.\begin{array}{r} 2.39 \\ +1.49 \\ \hline 3 \end{array}\right\} \approx 1$$

Add the front-end digits. Adjust the estimate by estimating the sum of the cents.

$$3 + 1 = 4$$

The total cost is about $4.

3. In Example 2, do you get the same answer if you use rounding? Why or why not?

4. About how much do three frozen juice bars cost?

The largest deep-dish pizza was made in Chicago on April 1, 1993. It had a circumference of 37.7 ft, which is about 38 ft. **Which number would you expect to see in a record book? in a newspaper article?**

Source: *Pizza and Pasta*

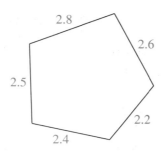

2.8
2.6
2.5
2.2
2.4

When addends *cluster* around a number, you can use that number and multiplication to estimate the sum. Clustering can help you estimate the perimeter of the pentagon at the left.

$$2.8 + 2.6 + 2.2 + 2.4 + 2.5 \approx 2.5 + 2.5 + 2.5 + 2.5 + 2.5$$
$$5 \times 2.5 = 12.5$$

The perimeter of the pentagon is about 12.5 units.

5. Steve bought three paperbacks at a used-book store. They cost $2.53, $2.65, and $2.39.

   a. Explain how you would estimate the total cost.

   b. About how much would each paperback cost?

You can use estimation to find products.

FLASHBACK

Area of a rectangle = length × width

Example 3   Estimate the area of a living room that measures 10.5 ft × 9.25 ft.

      $10.5 \approx 11$ $9.25 \approx 9$ **Round each factor.**

          $11 \times 9 = 99$ **Multiply.**

The area of the living room is about 99 ft².

6. Estimate the area of a rug measuring 3.75 ft × 4.25 ft.

You can estimate quotients using two *compatible numbers*. **Compatible numbers** are numbers that are easy to divide mentally.

CD Price List	
Category	Price
A	$23.95*
B	$15.95
C	$12.95
D	$ 7.95

*Double CD

Example 4   You've saved $50.25. Based on the chart at the left, about how many CDs from Category D could you buy?

   $50.25 \approx 48$ $7.95 \approx 8$ Choose numbers that are close to the actual
        $48 \div 8 = 6$ numbers and are easy to divide.

You can buy at most 6 CDs from Category D.

7. About how many CDs in category B can you buy? Explain your choice of compatible numbers.

   a. Is an estimate of the price good enough to decide if you have enough money to buy the CDs you want? Explain.

   b. Is an estimate of the price good enough when you pay for your CDs? Why or why not?

Work in pairs. Suppose you are building shelves to hold the bookbags described in the table at the right. Each shelf holds 30 kg. Use estimation to answer the following questions.

Bookbag Weights (kg)	
Adam	8.4
Denise	8
Jake	6
Leroy	7.49
Miranda	7.63
Nicola	6.9
Pieter	8.5
Zeke	7.52

8. Is it possible to use only 2 shelves? Why or why not?

9. What is the least number of shelves you would need?

10. Who should share a shelf to distribute the weight as evenly as possible?

TRY THESE

11. In Chicago, Illinois, the average wind speed is 10.4 mi/h. In Great Falls, Montana, the average wind speed is 13.1 mi/h. About how much greater is the average wind speed in Great Falls than in Chicago?

12. It took 75.75 lb of shredded cheese to make the world's largest burrito. Estimate how many 10-lb boxes of shredded cheese the cooks needed.

Chicago, often called the "Windy City," did not get its nickname from the weather but from long-winded politicians of the past.

Source: *The Book of Why*

Estimate. Use any strategy.

13. $3.963 \div 1.79$ **14.** 4.27×1.6 **15.** $9.355 - 0.7$

ON YOUR OWN

Cluster to estimate.

16. $6.3 + 5.9 + 6.09 + 6.33 + 5.68 + 6.1 + 5.821$

17. $\$14.25 + \$13.75 + \$14.53 + \$13.69$

18. Travel A train traveled at an average speed of 42.5 mi/h for 6.75 h. About how far did the train travel?

19. Writing Bill used a calculator to add $362.9 + 42.8 + 35.46$. His answer was 826.36.

   a. Describe how Bill could have gotten this answer.

   b. How could estimation help him discover his mistake?

The world's fastest train is France's TGV (Train à grande vitesse), averaging 132 mi/h. **About how far could this train travel in 4.75 h?**

Source: *The Guinness Book of Records*

M_xed REVIEW

1. Identify the outlier of 8, 5, 10, 15, 7, 9, 3, 30, 3.

Order the numbers from greatest to least.

2. 0.04, 0.040007, 4.004, 0.40, 0.403

3. 7.618, 7.681, 7.6801, 7.0681

Evaluate.

4. 738 + 187 + 232

5. 7083 − 896

6. An electrician cut a 25-ft cable into two pieces. One of the pieces was four times longer than the other. How long were the two pieces of cable?

Although coral can survive in water from 61°F to 97°F, it grows best in temperatures from 73°F to 77°F. The rate of growth for some species is only $\frac{1}{2}$ in./y, but some corals can eventually grow as tall as 15- to 20-story buildings.

Use any estimation strategy to calculate. Tell which strategy you used.

20. 71.43 − 28.098

21. 24.32 × 176.12

22. 345.124 ÷ 8.98

23. 726.27 + 685.8 + 699.05

Use front-end estimation to find each sum.

24. 5.429 + 2.665

25. 3.602 + 2.309

26. 2.174 + 5.891

27. **Choose A, B, C, or D.** Kiah correctly estimated a sum to be 900. Which numbers did she use to get this estimate?

   A. 682.14 + 65.21 + 142.65   **B.** 734.3 + 201.79 + 55.22

   C. 421.5 + 337.948 + 275.801   **D.** 225.06 + 275.8 + 269.7

28. **Money** Apples cost $.69 a pound. Estimate the cost of a 3.75-lb bag.

29. **Entertainment** On March 25, 1992, Mark Pi made 4,096 noodle strings in 54.8 seconds from one piece of dough at a food show in Columbus, Ohio.

   a. Estimate the number of noodles he made per second.

   b. Explain how you found the estimate.

30. **Weather** Seven students measured rainfall at their homes and plotted the data in the stem-and-leaf plot at the right.

Rainfall (in.)			
0	5	9	
1	1	3	6 7
2	4		

2 | 4 means 2.4

   a. Estimate the difference between the greatest and the least rainfall.

   b. Estimate the average rainfall for the area.

31. **Oceanography** The largest independent coral formation in the world is Galaxea Fascicularis off Okinawa, Japan. It measures 7.24 m long and 4.002 m high. About how much longer is it than high?

32. **a.** Data File 3 (pp. 90–91) Find the average number of points Teresa Edwards scored in each game of her professional career.

   b. Check your answer by estimating. Explain how you got your estimate.

3-3   **A**dding and Subtracting Decimals

U.S. Frozen Dessert Production (quarts/person)		
Year	Yogurt	Juice Bars
1987	—	0.7664
1988	—	0.819
1989	1.341	0.8
1990	1.9	0.825
1991	2.39	0.9112

Source: *International Ice Cream Association*

T H I N K   A N D   D I S C U S S

The table at the left shows that the production of frozen yogurt and frozen juice bars is increasing every year. You can add decimals to find the combined frozen yogurt and frozen juice bar production per person in 1991.

$$2.39 \; \boxed{+} \; 0.9112 \; \boxed{=} \; 3.3012$$

In 1991, 3.3012 qt of frozen yogurt and frozen juice bars were produced for each person in the United States.

1. How can you estimate to decide if the sum is reasonable?

2. Isaac reported the number of quarts of frozen yogurt and frozen juice bars produced in 1991 in the local newspaper. Was it necessary for him to report the exact amounts? Explain.

When adding and subtracting decimals with paper and pencil, you must align the decimal points.

Example
1
How much more frozen yogurt was produced per person in 1991 than in 1989?

$$\begin{array}{r} 2.390 \\ -1.341 \\ \hline 1.049 \end{array}$$ **Align the decimal points and annex a zero.**

Frozen yogurt production was up 1.049 qt per person in 1991.

3. How much more yogurt was produced than juice bars in 1989? in 1991?

4. a. Graph the 1989–1991 data on a double bar graph.

b. Explain how the graph helps you see differences in frozen dessert production without calculating.

c. **Critical Thinking** Suppose you had $1,000 to invest in a frozen dessert company. Would you choose a frozen yogurt company or a frozen juice bar company? Explain.

The properties of addition can help when you add decimals mentally. You already know the first property very well.

Identity Property

Adding zero does not change the sum.

Arithmetic   **Algebra**

$5.6 + 0 = 5.6$ $a + 0 = a$

5. How do you use the identity property to find
$5.238 - 5.238 + 17.9$?

Commutative Property

Changing the order of the addends does not change the sum.

Arithmetic   **Algebra**

$1.2 + 3.4 = 3.4 + 1.2$ $a + b = b + a$

Associative Property

Changing the grouping of the addends does not change the sum.

Arithmetic   **Algebra**

$(2.5 + 6) + 4 = 2.5 + (6 + 4)$ $(a + b) + c = a + (b + c)$

Example 2   Use the properties of addition to find the sum
$0.7 + 12.5 + 1.3$ mentally.

$$0.7 + 12.5 + 1.3 = 12.5 + 0.7 + 1.3 \quad \text{Commutative Property}$$
$$= 12.5 + (0.7 + 1.3) \quad \text{Associative Property}$$
$$= 12.5 + 2$$
$$= 14.5$$

6. The commutative property allows you to change the order of the addends in $4.4 + 5.3 + 0.6$. Some possible orders are $0.6 + 5.3 + 4.4$ and $0.6 + 4.4 + 5.3$.

   a. Which of the three orders given above do you prefer to use to find the sum mentally? Explain your answer.

   b. What other property do you use when finding the sum mentally?

   c. What is the sum?

WORK TOGETHER

You and your partner are the town's newest and hottest DJs. Part of your job is to update the radio station's tapes. Today you will be compiling a 15-min tape of music to play on the 4th of July. The list at the right is of the appropriate music available at your station. Choose songs whose combined times will be as close to 15 min as possible without going over. No more than 2 min of empty space can be left at the end of the tape.

4th of July Music Selections

Title	Min
76 Trombones	3.12
Liberty Bell March	3.6
Stars & Stripes Forever	3.52
Born in the USA	4.65
Oklahoma	3.27
Strike Up the Band	2.7
Pennsylvania Polka	2.7
Star Spangled Banner	4.5

7. a. Which songs would you choose?

  b. How much time will they use up?

8. How much time is left at the end of the tape?

9. Can you have six songs on the tape? Why or why not?

TRY THESE

10. Claudine, Aimee, and Claudine's sister Juliet went roller skating. Admission was $3.50 for ages 12 and up, and $1.75 for those under 12. Roller skates were $2.75 a pair. Claudine and Aimee are 13 years old, and Juliet is 10.

  a. How much more did Claudine pay for admission than Juliet?

  b. What was the total cost of admission?

  c. How much did it cost for them all to rent roller skates?

Identify each property shown.

11. $(46.8 + 32.7) + 7.3 = 46.8 + (32.7 + 7.3)$

12. $1.978 + 312.2 - 1.978 = 312.2 + 1.978 - 1.978$

13. $60.2 + 0 = 60.2$

ON YOUR OWN

Mental Math Use the properties of addition to evaluate.

14. $16.2 + 23.5 + 3.8$

15. $24.4 + (5.6 + 11)$

Mixed REVIEW

Complete.

1. A quadrilateral with both pairs of opposite sides parallel and four right angles is a(n) ▇.

2. Another name for a regular triangle is a(n) ▇ triangle.

Estimate. Use any strategy.

3. $198.4 \div 2.03$

4. $348.89 - 49.402$

Calculate.

5. When you join the Teen Tape Club, you receive 6 tapes for 1¢ each. You must then buy 8 more tapes for $7.99 each. What is the average price of each tape?

G gauge   5.3975 cm wide

O gauge   3.175 cm wide

N gauge   0.79375 cm wide

16. The lengths of the sides of a rectangle are 8.7 m and 6.13 m. What is the perimeter of the rectangle?

17. **Cars** The fastest land-speed record by a woman driver in a rocket-engine car was 524.016 mi/h. Kitty Hambleton achieved the record in 1976. Because of wind resistance, her average two-way speed was 512.710 mi/h. How great a difference was there between her fastest speed and her average speed?

18. **Hobbies** The width of the tracks determines the size of model trains. The figures at the left picture model trains and their tracks.

  a. Estimate the difference between the widths of the smallest gauge track and the largest gauge track.

  b. Suppose you plan to buy a train for a 5-year-old child. Which train would you purchase? Why?

19. **Writing** Does the commutative property apply to subtraction as well as addition? Explain why or why not, and give examples.

20. **Investigation (page 92)** Conduct a survey of other students to find out what businesses they'd like to see in the neighborhood of your school.

CHECKPOINT

Order the numbers from greatest to least.

1. 8.05, 8.5, 8.059, 8.049, 8.0499, 8.015

Compare using <, >, or =.

2. 4.406 ■ 4.4060   3. 6.621 ■ 6.612   4. 10.01 ■ 10.101

5. a. Round to estimate $3.07 + $3.48 + $4.25.

  b. Use front-end estimation to find the same sum.

  c. Explain which estimation strategy you would use when buying items at a store.

Find each sum or difference.

6. 2.99 + 3.08 + 18.5642   7. 89.32 − 23.073

3-4 Too Much or Too Little Information

What's Ahead

• Deciding if a problem has too much or too little information

Some problems may not contain enough information for you to solve them. Others may contain more information than you will use. Before you begin any calculations, you must decide whether you can solve the problem and what information you will need.

***People in the United States** use 23,500 bushels of fresh lemons every day. It would take a single lemon measuring 52 ft long and 33 ft high to provide that much lemon juice.*

Source: *In One Day*

Holdfield Middle School is sponsoring a Family Day on Saturday. The seventh grade will be selling lemonade at their booth, and Jerry and Monina are in charge of bringing all the supplies.

Since they hope the class will sell at least 100 cups of lemonade, Jerry and Monina have borrowed four 64-oz pitchers to serve the lemonade. They bought fourteen 12-oz cans of frozen lemonade for $.89 each. Each can makes 48 oz of lemonade. They also bought three packages of 50 paper cups at $1.50 per package.

The class plans to charge $.30 for a cup of lemonade. Each cup will contain 6 oz of lemonade. How much did the seventh grade spend on supplies for the lemonade stand?

READ

Read and understand the given information. Summarize the problem.

1. Think about what you are being asked, the information you are given, and which information you can use.

  a. What do you need to find?

  b. Do you need all the given information to solve the problem? Explain.

PLAN

Decide on a strategy to solve the problem.

To find the total cost of supplies for the lemonade stand, you need to decide what the supplies are, and how much the class spent on them.

2. What information tells you the cost of the lemonade?

3. What information tells you the cost of the other items?

SOLVE

Try out the strategy.

Use the information you collected to solve the problem.

4. **a.** How much did the seventh grade spend on lemonade?

   b. How much did the other items cost?

   c. What was the total cost of supplies for the lemonade stand?

LOOK BACK

Think about how you solved this problem.

To solve the problem, you selected the information you needed and set aside unneeded information.

5. What information didn't you need?

6. Do you have enough information to find the seventh grade's profit for the day? Why or why not?

TRY THESE

Solve if possible. If not, tell what information is needed.

7. A group of friends made a 4-yd long rectangular banner for the gym. They paid $3.75 per yard for the fabric and $9 for the trim to go around the banner's 10-yd perimeter. What was the width of the banner?

8. **Hobbies** The pet store has 32 tropical fish in a tank. The store charges $2.45 per fish and $5.00 for a fish bowl. How much will a fish bowl and some fish cost?

9. **Travel** The four members of the Coy family drove for eight hours a day for three days. What is the average number of miles the family traveled each day?

Mixed REVIEW

Make a stem-and-leaf plot for each set of data.

1. 29, 27, 37, 40, 46, 48

2. 1.3, 2.2, 1.7, 1.4, 1.3, 2.5

Calculate.

3. 52.039 + 12.99

4. 10.98 − 6.018

5. On August 5, 1990, Beth Cornell and a team of helpers created a 100-tier cake, the tallest in the world at 30.85 m. About how tall was each tier?

6. Find 3 consecutive numbers whose sum is 60.

ON YOUR OWN

Use any strategy to solve each problem. Show all your work. If it is not possible to solve a problem, tell what needed information is missing.

10. **Money** Rita sold frozen slush at the fair. She sat at her stand from 12 noon to 5 P.M. She charged $.50 for a small cup of fruit slush and $.75 for a large cup. Twelve children bought a total of 15 small cups and 24 adults bought a total of 28 large cups. How much money did Rita take in?

11. **Biology** The rare and shy giant panda lives alone in the bamboo forests of China. It spends about 10–12 h each day eating. The panda mainly eats bamboo but will also eat berries, flowers, fruit, grasses, bark, and some small wild animals. About every 50 years, bamboo forests flower, seed, and die. When this happens, many pandas die. In 1983, before the most recent bamboo forest die-back, there were an estimated 1,000 pandas alive. How many are left?

12. **Money** Devon earns $25.50 per day working part-time as a sales clerk in a shoe store. As an incentive, his boss pays him an extra $.50 for each package of sports socks Devon sells. After working for 5 days, Devon earned $157.50. How many packages of sports socks did he sell?

13. **Sports** A group of 120 girls between the ages of 6 and 16 voted on their favorite sports. The first four sports received 27, 26, 22, and 21 votes. The four sports to make the top of the list were basketball, volleyball, swimming, and softball. In what order were the sports listed?

   • Softball was not in third place.

   • Basketball came right after softball in popularity.

   • The first place sport is not played with a ball.

14. **Entertainment** The Drama Club put on two presentations of the play *The Wizard of Oz,* one on Friday night and one on Saturday night. Twice as many people came to see the play on Saturday as on Friday. If 495 people saw the play altogether, how many came on each night?

15. **Biology** Each spring, the female crocodile digs a nest in the banks of a river, close enough to the water so that she can watch over the nest, but not so close that it could flood. She lays 30 to 70 eggs and covers them with sand. After 90 days the eggs hatch, and the mother crocodile carries the babies in her mouth to the river. Baby crocodiles are about 12 in. long when they hatch and grow about 10 in. a year. How old is a crocodile that is about 32 in. long?

16. A balance scale balances with 1 green block and 3 red blocks on one side and 3 green blocks on the other side. All blocks of the same color weigh the same amount. Red blocks weigh 0.25 lb. How much do green blocks weigh?

The giant panda is about 6 in. long and weighs about 3 lb at birth. Adult pandas can weigh up to 300 lb and stand 5 ft tall when upright.

HOW? The gender of a crocodile is determined by the temperature of the egg during incubation. Most eggs kept cooler than 90°F hatch into females. Most of those kept warmer than 92°F become males. About half of eggs incubated between 90°F and 92°F become males and half become females.

Source: *Crocodiles & Alligators of the World*

WHAT YOU'LL NEED

✓ **Calculator**

✓ **Graph paper**

3-5 **M**ultiplying and Dividing Decimals

T H I N K A N D D I S C U S S

You can use models to show multiplication of decimals. This model shows that the product of 0.7 and 0.4 is 0.28.

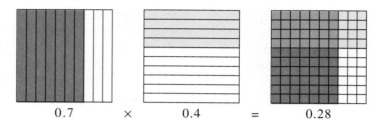

0.7 × 0.4 = 0.28

1. Write 0.7, 0.4, and 0.28 in order from greatest to least.

2. a. Draw a model for the product of 0.2 and 0.9.

   b. Write 0.2, 0.9, and their product in order from greatest to least.

   c. What is true about the product of two numbers less than 1?

**Ways to Write
"Multiply 3.4 by 5"**

3.4 × 5
3.4 • 5
3.4(5)
(3.4)(5)

There are several ways to indicate multiplication. They are listed in the table at the left.

3. Suppose you are indicating multiplication by using a dot. Why is it important to make it a *centered* dot?

When you work on decimal problems, it is a good idea to estimate before you calculate.

**Example
1**

Fish costs $2.58/lb at the supermarket. What is the price of 5.2 lb?

Estimate: 2.58 × 5.2 ≈ 3 × 5 = 15

2.58 **✗** 5.2 **▤** *13.416*   Use a calculator.

13.416 ≈ 13.42   **Round money up.**

13.42 ≈ 15   **Your answer is reasonable.**

The price is $13.42.

4. a. Brian noticed that the decimal point key on his calculator was not working. How could he use estimation to place the decimal point when finding the area of a room that is 12.5 ft × 15.75 ft?

b. Find the area of the room.

Estimation can also help you avoid errors when you are dividing decimal numbers.

Example 2   Suppose you rode your bike 25.75 mi in 2.5 h. Find your average speed in miles per hour.

Estimate: $25.75 \div 2.5 \approx 25 \div 2.5 = 10$

$25.75 \;\boxed{\div}\; 2.5 \;\boxed{=}\; 10.3$ **Use a calculator.**

$10.3 \approx 10$ **Your answer is reasonable.**

You rode an average of 10.3 mi/h.

5. Sue's father is a salesman. Last week he drove 283.4 mi on 16.2 gal of gasoline. Sue found that he averaged about 1.75 mi/gal.

a. Do you agree with Sue's average? Support your answer by showing your work.

b. How could Sue use estimation to check her answer?

The properties of multiplication can help you find products mentally. You are already very familiar with two properties.

Identity Property
The product of 1 and any number is that number.

Arithmetic	**Algebra**
$5 \times 1 = 5$	$a \times 1 = a$

Zero Property
The product of zero and any number is zero.

Arithmetic	**Algebra**
$5 \times 0 = 0$	$a \times 0 = 0$

6. Terry found the answer to $3.625 \times 58.42 \times 0$ in less than 1 second. How did he do it?

Commutative Property
Changing the order of the factors doesn't change the product.

Arithmetic	**Algebra**
$5 \times 2 = 2 \times 5$	$a \times b = b \times a$

On April 17, 1988, about 30,000 people took part in a bicycle parade in San Juan, Puerto Rico. The number of people living in Puerto Rico is about 117.4 times as great as the number who rode in the parade. **About how many people live in Puerto Rico?**

Source: *The Guinness Book of Records*

Associative Property	
Changing the grouping of the factors doesn't change the product.	
Arithmetic	**Algebra**
$(3 \times 2) \times 5 = 3 \times (2 \times 5)$	$(a \times b) \times c = a \times (b \times c)$

Example 3   Evaluate $0.25 \times 3.58 \times 4$.

$$0.25 \times 3.58 \times 4$$

$$= 3.58 \times 0.25 \times 4 \quad \leftarrow \text{Commutative Property}$$

$$= 3.58 \times (0.25 \times 4) \leftarrow \text{Associative Property}$$

$$= 3.58 \times 1 = 3.58 \quad \leftarrow \text{Identity Property}$$

7. What property would you use first when evaluating $4.3 \times 2.5 \times 2$? Explain your reasoning.

WORK TOGETHER

Work with a partner.

• Use a calculator to find each product.

   0.1×0.4 0.6×0.03 0.27×0.35 0.59×0.261

• Copy and complete the table at the left based on your calculations.

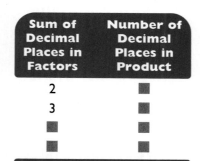

Sum of Decimal Places in Factors	Number of Decimal Places in Product
2	▨
3	▨
▨	▨
▨	▨

8. What do you notice about the relationship between the sum of the decimal places in the factors and the number of decimal places in the product?

9. Predict the number of decimal places in the product of 0.736 and 0.9751. Then compute the product. Was your prediction correct? Why or why not?

10. Write a rule that will help you predict the number of decimal places in a product.

11. a. Find 0.5×0.3 and 0.5×0.5 without a calculator and then with a calculator.

     b. Find 0.5×0.2 and 0.5×0.4 without a calculator and then with a calculator.

     c. When the final digit in a decimal product is a zero, what does your calculator do?

TRY THESE

Use the properties of multiplication to complete. Name the property.

12. $3.6 \times \blacksquare = 0$ 13. $\blacksquare \times 1.5 = 1.5 \times 3.4$ 14. $7.8 \times \blacksquare = 7.8$

15. $(2.5 \times \blacksquare) \times 2.3 = 2.5 \times (1.4 \times 2.3)$ 16. $\blacksquare \times 1 = 25.5$

17. Nikia bought 3.2 yd of fabric for a total price of $13.92. How much did the fabric cost per yard?

ON YOUR OWN

Mental Math Use the properties of multiplication to evaluate.

18. $0.2 \times 3.41 \times 5$ 19. $1.09 \times 23.6 \times 0$ 20. $(2.3 \times 0.5) \times 4$

The answers to the following equations contain decimal errors. Estimate each product or quotient. Rewrite each equation with the decimal point in the correct place.

21. $10.8 \div 4.5 = 24$ 22. $2.7 \times 1.3 = 351$ 23. $11.44 \div 2.6 = 44$

24. Find each quotient.

   a. $75\overline{)300}$ b. $7.5\overline{)300}$ c. $0.75\overline{)300}$

   d. Describe what happens to a quotient when the dividend (300) remains the same and the divisors (75, 7.5, and 0.75) decrease.

25. **Writing** Does the commutative property work for division as well as multiplication? Why or why not? Give examples.

26. **Gardening** After digging up some lilac bushes, Roger used turf to cover the bare dirt. The turf cost $2.25/yd². Roger paid a total of $27.90. How much turf did he buy?

27. **Sports** The International Tennis Federation (ITF) requires that a new tennis ball bounce between 0.53 and 0.58 of its original height when dropped. Determine the range of acceptable heights after the second bounce for a new tennis ball that is dropped from a height of 200 cm. Round your answer to the nearest hundredth.

Round each decimal to the indicated place.

1. 33.51682‾3

2. 0.618‾7368

Tell whether each angle is acute, right, or obtuse.

3. 105°   4. 36°

5. 90°   6. 95°

7. One fourth of the students in the seventh grade are in the class chorus. One third are in the band. Four fifths of the class chorus went to rehearsal on Thursday. How many of the 120 students in the seventh grade went to chorus rehearsal on Thursday?

This new tennis ball was dropped from a height of 150 cm. After its first bounce, it reached a height of 79 cm. **Does this ball meet ITF requirements?**

3-6 Patterns in Quotients

What's Ahead

• Using calculators to find patterns in repeating decimals

• Understanding about division by zero

■ WHAT YOU'LL NEED

✓ Calculator

┌T┐H I N K A N D D I S C U S S

Do you know how your calculator's memory affects the answers it gives you? Try a short experiment.

1. Use mental math to compute.

   a. $6 \div 2 \times 2$ **b.** $8 \div 4 \times 4$ **c.** $15 \div 5 \times 5$

2. If you divide by a number and then multiply by the same number, what happens?

3. **a.** What should your calculator display if you enter

   1 ➗ 3 ✖ 3 ▬ ?

   b. Try it. What do you get?

4. Now try the same calculation in two steps.

   a. Enter 1 ➗ 3 ▬ . Write your result.

   b. Clear the calculator. Enter your result from part (a) and multiply it by 3. What does the display show?

With calculators, what you see is not always what your calculator has in its memory. Most calculators store digits in memory. Calculators use these hidden digits for rounding.

5. When you compute $1 \div 3$ on a calculator, the display shows a series of 3's after the decimal point.

   a. How many 3's do you think you would need to show the exact answer to $1 \div 3$?

   b. Find $1 \div 3$ using paper and pencil.

   c. Will the process stop? Why or why not?

6. **a.** Use your calculator to compute $2 \div 3$. Is the number in the last place of the display the same as the others?

   b. What did your calculator do with the hidden digits?

The Chinese abacus, *one of the earliest mechanical computing devices, dates from about* A.D. *1175. This abacus shows the number 1,532,786.* **How would you show the number 1,175?**

Source: *History of Mathematics*

A **terminating decimal** is a decimal that stops, or terminates. For example, $1 \div 4 = 0.25$. A decimal in which a digit or a sequence of digits keeps repeating is a **repeating decimal.**

$1 \div 3 = 0.333333333 \ldots = 0.\overline{3}$

$1 \div 6 = 0.1666666666 \ldots = 0.1\overline{6}$

$4 \div 11 = 0.36363636 \ldots = 0.\overline{36}$

The bar indicates the digit or digits that repeat.

7. **a.** Use paper and pencil to find $1 \div 7$. What sequence of digits repeats?

   b. Write the quotient of $1 \div 7$ using a bar to show the repeating part of the decimal.

   c. Use a calculator to find $1 \div 7$. How many of the repeating digits can you see in your calculator's display?

8. **a.** Use a calculator to find $9 \div 64$.

   b. Does the quotient of $9 \div 64$ repeat or terminate? Tell how you know.

WORK TOGETHER

Work with a partner. Use a calculator.

9. **a.** Look at the division problems at the right. What pattern do you see in the divisors?

   b. Copy the table. Find the missing divisors. Find each quotient.

   c. As the divisor gets closer and closer to zero, what happens to the quotient? Why?

   d. Discussion Why do you think dividing by zero is referred to as *undefined?*

Dividend		Divisor		Quotient
50	÷	100	=	■
50	÷	10	=	■
50	÷	1	=	■
50	÷	0.1	=	■
50	÷	0.01	=	■
50	÷	0.001	=	■
50	÷	■	=	■
50	÷	■	=	■
50	÷	■	=	■

ON YOUR OWN

Choose Use a calculator, paper and pencil, or mental math to find each quotient. Use a bar to show repeating decimals.

10. $3 \div 8$ 11. $2 \div 7$ 12. $1 \div 0.3$ 13. $155 \div 11$

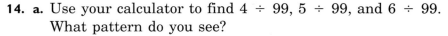

M*i*xed REVIEW

Use a calculator to find each quotient.

1. 2.21 ÷ 1.7

2. 0.75 ÷ 0.5

Use mental math to evaluate.

3. (13 × 0.2) × 5

4. 3 × (1.5 × 6)

5. A penny weighs about 0.1 ounce. How much is a pound of pennies worth?

6010150330
7564014270
2314429524
0643021845
9561814675

 On Nov. 19, 1989, Yasumasa Kanada and Yoshiaki Tamura computed *pi* (π) to 1,073,740,000 places without having it repeat or terminate.

Source: *The Guinness Book of Records*

---

14. **a.** Use your calculator to find 4 ÷ 99, 5 ÷ 99, and 6 ÷ 99. What pattern do you see?

   b. Use your pattern to find 7 ÷ 99, 8 ÷ 99, and 9 ÷ 99 without a calculator.

15. Complete Exercise 14 again, using each number below in place of 99.

   a. 999   **b.** 11   **c.** 33   **d.** 101

16. Divide 1 by each whole number from 10 to 20.

   a. For which divisors do the quotients repeat?

   b. For which divisors do the quotients terminate?

   c. For which divisors can't you tell if the quotient terminates or repeats? Why can't you tell?

17. **Writing** Is the number 3.03003000300003 . . . a repeating decimal? Why or why not?

Slices of Pi

What do circles, computers, and "Star Trek" have in common? They are all linked to a very special number, *pi*.

Pi, or π, defines the relationship between a circle and its diameter. In 1767 a man named Johann Lambert proved that π is an irrational number, a decimal that neither terminates nor repeats.

Because π never ends, the crew of the Enterprise were able to use it to keep a fiendish computer busy until it could be dismantled.

Over the centuries, different approximations of π have been used. The Egyptians believed it to be 256 ÷ 81. Archimedes, a Greek mathematician, proved that π is between 22 ÷ 7 and 223 ÷ 71. Another Greek estimate was 377 ÷ 120. The Chinese used 355 ÷ 113, and one Indian estimate was 62,832 ÷ 20,000. Other early estimates include 3 and 3.16.

Use the article to answer the following questions.

18. Which of the two limits of π given by Archimedes is closer to the value your calculator gives?

19. Find two numbers not mentioned in the article whose quotient is about equal to π.

PROBLEM SOLVING STRATEGIES

Make a Table
Use Logical Reasoning
Solve a Simpler Problem
Too Much or Too Little Information
Look for a Pattern
Make a Model
Work Backward
Draw a Diagram
Guess and Test
Simulate a Problem
Use Multiple Strategies
Write an Equation

This Brazilian stamp was issued in 1967 and shows a one-sided strip called a Möbius strip. You can make this strip by taking a piece of paper and making a half twist. Now tape the ends together. **How can you show that this piece of paper now has only one side?**

Solve. The list at the left shows some possible strategies you can use.

1. The junior high school is having a heritage fair. Ed, Tessa, Joe, and Liz are each presenting an item from the countries of their heritage. The items the students plan to present are maracas from Mexico, a sari from India, a shell from Tahiti, and a ram's horn from Israel. Joe did not bring an item from Tahiti or India. Tessa did not bring in an item from Tahiti. Ed brought maracas. What items did the other students bring?

2. There are 43 students in the school chorus. Ten of the chorus members also belong to the orchestra. There are 52 students in the orchestra. Eight of the orchestra members belong to both the chorus and the chess club. How many students belong to both the orchestra and the chorus but not to the chess club?

3. After Jim woke up Saturday morning, it took him 2 h to shower, dress, and have breakfast. He then went to the baseball field with his friend for 4.5 h. It took him a half-hour to get to the field and a half-hour to return. Jim arrived home at 5:15 P.M. At what time did he wake up?

4. Allen is the youngest in a family of 8 children. He has 5 sisters and 2 brothers. The sum of the ages of Allen and his sister Rachel is 40. The difference of their ages is 16. Rachel got married a few years ago and has 2 children of her own. How old are Allen and Rachel?

5. Carmen has 3 pen pals. She writes back to each pen pal the same week that she gets a letter. Riaz writes every 4 wk. Julia writes every 3 wk. Roy writes every 5 wk. Carmen wrote 3 letters this week. How many weeks will it be before she has to write 3 letters in the same week again?

6. One angle of an isosceles triangle measures 41.35°. What could be the measures of the other angles?

3-7 Using the Distributive Property

WORK TOGETHER

Luther, Pearl, Sundar, Crystal, Stella, and Kip painted scenery screens for the school play. Each screen was a rectangle 9 ft tall that could be combined with other rectangles to make different scenes. Here are three rectangles that are the same shape as the screens.

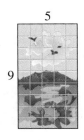
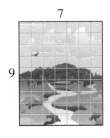

Work in pairs. Use graph paper to draw rectangles that have the following dimensions.

$$9 \times 4 \quad 9 \times 7 \quad 9 \times 6 \quad 9 \times 3 \quad 9 \times 5 \quad 9 \times 8$$

• Cut out the rectangles.
• Find the area of each rectangle.
• Combine any two rectangles and find the combined area.

In June 1993, the AIDS quilt consisted of 2,973 blocks of 8 panels that could be arranged in many different ways. Groups of 4 blocks together are displayed on the ground with a 6-ft walkway around them so people can see each panel clearly.

Source: *The Names Project*

THINK AND DISCUSS

Suppose you combine the 9×3 and 9×4 rectangles. You can multiply to find the area of each separate rectangle. Then you can find the total area by adding.

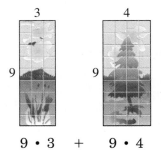

$$9 \cdot 3 \quad + \quad 9 \cdot 4$$

You use the order of operations to know which operation to do first.

Order of Operations

- Do all operations within grouping symbols first.
- Multiply and divide from left to right.
- Add and subtract from left to right.

---

1. a. Using the order of operations, what do you do first to simplify 9 • 3 + 9 • 4? What do you do last?

b. What is the total area?

Another way to find the total area of the combined rectangles is to add the widths and multiply by the length.

2. a. What is the width of the combined rectangles?

b. A numerical expression that describes the area by combining the widths first is 9 • (3 + 4), or 9(3 + 4). Using the order of operations, what should you do first?

c. What is the area of the combined rectangles?

FLASHBACK

$4 \times 5 = 4 \cdot 5 = 4(5)$

You can rewrite 9 • 3 + 9 • 4 as 9(3 + 4) because they are equal expressions. The rewritten expressions illustrate the *distributive property*.

$$9 \cdot 3 + 9 \cdot 4 = 9(3 + 4)$$

Distributive Property

You can multiply each term inside a set of parentheses by a factor outside the parentheses.

Arithmetic	Algebra
6(3 + 2) = 6 • 3 + 6 • 2	$a(b + c) = a \cdot b + a \cdot c$
5(8 − 2) = 5 • 8 − 5 • 2	$a(b − c) = a \cdot b − a \cdot c$

The distributive property can help you multiply numbers mentally. To find 6×53 mentally, think of 53 as $50 + 3$.

$$6(50 + 3) = 6 \cdot 50 + 6 \cdot 3$$
$$= 300 + 18$$
$$= 318$$

3. What steps would you use to find 7×5.9 mentally using the distributive property and subtraction?

4. a. Explain why $3(2.5 + 5) = (2.5 + 5)3$.

    b. Complete: $(2.5 + 5)3 = (2.5)\blacksquare + (5)\blacksquare$

ON YOUR OWN

Write two expressions to find the area of each figure. Find the area.

5. 1   3   8

6. 3   5   5

7. 5   2   3

Find the missing numbers.

8. $4(7 + 8) = 4(\blacksquare) + 4(\blacksquare)$ **9.** $3(8.2 - 1.5) = (\blacksquare)8.2 - (\blacksquare)1.5$

10. $\blacksquare(4.8) = 6(5) - 6(\blacksquare)$ **11.** $\blacksquare(2.8 + 6.5) = 7(2.8) + 7(6.5)$

12. Advertising Sam made a large poster for his school rummage sale. The poster measured 20 in. by 28.5 in.

    a. Use the distributive property to write an equation about the area of the poster.

    b. Evaluate your equation to find the area of Sam's poster.

13. Dustin and his five brothers and sisters went to the Science Museum. The fee for the dinosaur exhibit was $5.25 per person. The planetarium was an extra $4.75 per person.

    a. Show how you would use the distributive property to find how much Dustin and his brothers and sisters paid together to see the dinosaur exhibit.

    b. Use the distributive property to find how much they paid together to see the planetarium show.

    c. How much did Dustin's family pay all together?

Mixed REVIEW

1. Multiply 4.2×10, 4.2×100, $4.2 \times 1,000$. Predict $4.2 \times 1,000,000$.

Find each quotient. Use a bar to show repeating decimals.

2. $5 \div 3$

3. $7 \div 16$

4. $15 \div 18$

5. Carla and Tanya were paid $45.00 for painting a fence. Carla worked 6 h, and Tanya worked 9 h. How much is Tanya's share of the money?

Calculate mentally using the distributive property.

14. 6(3.9) **15.** 10.3(4) **16.** 2(2.6) **17.** 11.6(2)

Insert +, −, ×, or ÷ to make each equation true.

18. 5.2 ▇ 3 + 2.4 = 18 **19.** 23.1 ÷ 7 ▇ 3.3 = 6.6

Place parentheses to make each equation true.

20. 4 + 4 ÷ 4 − 4 = 1 **21.** 4 × 4 ÷ 4 + 4 = 2

22. 4 + 4 + 4 ÷ 4 = 3 **23.** 4 × 4 − 4 + 4 = 4

24. 4 + 4 × 4 − 4 = 28 **25.** 4 + 4 × 4 − 4 = 0

26. Money People buying recycled newspaper to use for other products pay $5 for 1 ton. The United States recycled 6.6 million tons of newspaper during 1991. Use the distributive property to find how much money was made from the sale of recycled newspapers in 1991.

27. Hobbies Elena is making a wooden plaque for her grandfather's birthday. Because her grandfather is Italian, she is using one piece each of walnut, oak, and cherry to represent the three colors of the Italian flag. Each piece of wood measures 6 in. × 4.5 in.

   a. Use the distributive property to find the area of each piece of wood.

   b. Use the distributive property and your answer to part (a) to find the area of the wooden plaque.

28. Money Ione is buying lilies to use in centerpieces for a special dinner. Each centerpiece will have 3 lilies. There are a total of 10 tables. After a discount for buying in bulk, each lily costs $.92. Use the distributive property to figure the cost of the lilies mentally.

29. Money You want to buy 4 notebooks at $.89 each. Use mental math to find the total cost.

30. Writing Explain how you could use the distributive property in at least two different ways to calculate 4(110.5).

31. Investigation (page 92) Design a sales receipt that you could use in your business. Show how typical business transactions would be recorded on the receipts.

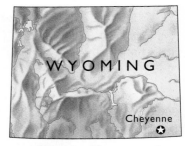

WYOMING

Cheyenne

The state of Wyoming generates the least amount of waste per year, 320,000 tons. Of this amount, three hundredths of every ton is recycled. **How many tons of waste does Wyoming recycle in 1 y?**

Source: *The Information Please Environmental Almanac*

3-8

Exponents

T H I N K A N D D I S C U S S

Luis and Sofia made a bargain with their parents. The conversation went something like this:

"Mom, Dad, we'll wash the dinner dishes from now on without complaining," Luis volunteered.

Sofia nodded in agreement. "Yes, we'll wash the dishes—if you pay us. Pay us 2¢ tonight, and each day pay us twice as much as the day before."

Their parents decided this would be an easy way to have the dishes washed with no complaints, so they agreed. By the end of the second week, however, they were no longer happy with the dishwashing deal.

The table below and the pennies at the left show how quickly numbers increase as you double them.

Day	Cents
one	$2 =$ ■
two	$2 \times 2 =$ ■
three	$2 \times 2 \times 2 =$ ■
four	$2 \times 2 \times 2 \times 2 =$ ■

1. Complete the table above to find how many cents Luis and Sofia were paid each of the first four days.

You can use an *exponent* to write repeated factors.

$$\text{base} \rightarrow 2^4 \leftarrow \text{exponent}$$

The **base** is the number used as a factor. The **exponent** tells how many times the base is used as a factor. You read 2^4 as "two to the fourth power." The *standard form* of 2^4 is 16. The *exponential form* of 16 is 2^4.

Cents	Power of 2
2	■
4	■
8	■
16	2^4
■	■

2. Copy and complete the table at the left.

3. How much did Luis and Sofia get paid on the fifth day?

Their parents paid Luis and Sofia 2^{10}¢ on the tenth day. The $\boxed{y^x}$ key can help you to find how much money 2^{10}¢ is in standard form.

$$2 \;\boxed{y^x}\; 10 \;\boxed{=}\; \textit{1024}$$

Luis and Sofia's parents paid them 1,024¢, or $10.24.

4. **a.** Use a calculator to evaluate 2^{14}. Write your answer in standard form.

   b. How many dollars is that?

   c. Why do you think Luis and Sofia's parents were not happy with the dishwashing bargain anymore?

*Gibraltar is the smallest colony in the world, with an area equal to $(1.5)^2$ mi^2. **What is the area of Gibraltar in standard form?***

Source: *The Guinness Book of Records*

You can use exponents with bases other than 2. This square has sides of 3 units. Its area is $3 \times 3 = 3^2$, or 9 square units.

5. Why do you think we call 3^2 "3 squared"?

You can use the $\boxed{x^2}$ key to square numbers.

$$2.8 \;\boxed{x^2}\; \textit{7.84}$$

6. Which calculator keys would you use to evaluate 2.3^4? Which would you use to evaluate 2.3^2?

To evaluate expressions that contain exponents, you must include exponents in the order of operations.

Order of Operations
• Do all operations within grouping symbols first.
• Do all work with exponents.
• Multiply and divide from left to right.
• Add and subtract from left to right.

Problem Solving Hint

One way to remember the order of operations is with the sentence "Please Excuse My Dear Aunt Sally."

7. **Discussion** Explain how you would find the value of each of the following expressions.

   a. $(3 + 5)^2 \div 4$ **b.** $(3 + 5^2) \div 4$

8. When an exponent is within a set of parentheses, what should you do first?

Your calculator follows the order of operations. To simplify $3^4 \times (5 - 1.2)^3$, use the parentheses keys as needed.

3 $\boxed{y^x}$ 4 $\boxed{\times}$ $\boxed{(}$ 5 $\boxed{-}$ 1.2 $\boxed{)}$ $\boxed{y^x}$ 3 $\boxed{=}$ *4444.632*

9. **a.** In the expression $(7.8 - 2.9)^4$, what is the base? the exponent?

   b. Write $(7.8 - 2.9)^4$ in standard form.

WORK TOGETHER

Work with a partner. Look at the pattern in the powers of 2 below.

Standard form	16	8	4	2	1
Power of 2	2^4	2^3	2^2	2^1	$2^\blacksquare$

10. **a.** What exponent do you think completes the equation below?

$$2^\blacksquare = 1$$

   b. Check your prediction on your calculator.

11. Find 3^0, 4^0, 5^0, 10^0. What do you notice?

12. Choose a number greater than 1,000,000. With that number as the base and 0 as the exponent, what is the value of the expression?

13. Write a general rule to describe your discovery.

ON YOUR OWN

14. **a.** Without calculating, predict which is greater, 2^6 or 6^2.

   b. Find 2^6 and 6^2. Was your prediction correct? Why or why not?

15. **a.** Write $6 \times 6 \times 6 \times 6$ in exponential form.

   b. For the expression you wrote in part (a), what is the base? the exponent?

   c. Write the standard form of the expression.

Legend says the reign of the first emperor of Japan began around 660 B.C., but it probably only began about 40 B.C. Emperor Akihito is the 5^3 descendant to rule Japan. **How many emperors has Japan had?**

Source: *The Guinness Book of Records*

Write each expression in exponential form.

16. $5.2 \times 5.2 \times 5.2$ **17.** $0.3 \times 0.3 \times 0.3 \times 0.3 \times 0.3$

Write each expression as a product of repeated factors and in standard form.

18. 4^5 **19.** 5.2^3 **20.** 13^6 **21.** 0.2^4 **22.** 3.7^3

Choose Use your calculator, paper and pencil, or mental math to evaluate each expression.

23. $2^5 \times 4^0$ **24.** $12 + 5^3$ **25.** $1^3 - 3(1 - 14^0)$ **26.** $3(0.5 + 2.5)^2$

Match the fact with the exponential form of the number.

27. wheels on a unicycle   **a.** 2^5

28. planets in the solar system   **b.** 3^2

29. freezing point of water in °F   **c.** 5^0

30. a. Suppose you had a secret that you told 3 people. They each told 3, and each of those people told 3. Make a chart to show how your secret spread.

     b. Use exponents to write the number of people who learned your secret on the last round.

31. a. Copy and complete the table at the right.

     b. What pattern do you see when you find powers of 10?

     c. Use your pattern, not a calculator, to tell how many zeros are in the standard form of 10^{12}.

32. Writing Find the value of 0.5^2. What happens to the number of decimal places when a decimal between 0 and 1 is squared? Which is greater, the original number or its square? Why is this so?

33. Write two numbers in exponential form that are between the values of 5^2 and 5^3.

34. Trace your foot on graph paper. Estimate its area. Write two numbers in exponential form that the area of your foot falls between.

35. a. Write 81 in exponential form using 3 as the base.

     b. Write 81 in exponential form using 9 as the base.

	Number	Number of zeros
10^0	■	0
10^1	■	1
10^2	■	■
10^3	■	■
10^4	■	■
10^5	■	■

Compare using <, >, or =.

1. 0.168 ■ 0.1680

2. 5.6 ■ 5.592

3. 1.83 ■ 2.032

4. 11.26 ■ 11.206

5. 3.012 ■ 3.12

6. 6.89 ■ 6.51

7. 79.284 ■ 79.28

8. 35.009 ■ 35.01

Order from least to greatest.

9. 0.234, 0.243, 0.23, 0.24

10. 0.368, 0.3681, 0.36792, 0.3

11. 10.2, 10.02, 10.201

**Use a calculator or paper and pencil to find each answer.
Use a bar to show repeating decimals.**

12. 0.213×5.2

13. $5.1 - 2.83$

14. $86.4 \div 27$

15. $6.02 + 5.283$

16. $23.102 - 4.9$

17. $2.8 \div 0.6$

18. $15 \div 0.11$

19. 4.2×3.7

20. $312.6 + 0.835 + 7.26$

21. $70.273 + 6.84 + 3$

22. $290.007 - 95.094$

Mental Math Use the distributive property to evaluate.

23. $4(30 + 8)$

24. $4(90 - 6)$

25. $3(8 - 0.5)$

26. $(5.4)3$

27. $9(19)$

Which operation should you perform first? Explain.

28. $97 - 15 + 42$

29. $14(37 \div 13)$

30. $32 - 4 \cdot 7$

31. $3 + 14^2$

32. $123 + 2 \cdot 0$

33. $39 \div 3 \cdot 6$

34. $47 + 150 \div 15$

35. $164 \div (4 \cdot 4)$

**Choose Use a calculator, paper and pencil, or mental
math to find each value.**

36. 3^4

37. 6^3

38. 170^0

39. 2.7^3

40. 10^9

41. 1.8^2

Estimate Use any method.

42. 6.9×8.92

43. $\$37.63 \div 7.19$

44. $98.52 - 46.9074$

45. $0.167 + 0.902 + 0.55$

46. $\$1.49 + \$2.36 + \$10.98$

47. 10.22×4.908

48. $\$4.29 + \$3.88 + \$1.01$

49. $5.7621 - 2.497$

50. $2.4 + 2.71 + 2.359$

51. $145.9 + 153.29 + 151.2 + 148.008$

52. $22.7 + 23.095 + 19.26 + 18.802$

3-9

Evaluating Variable Expressions

WORK TOGETHER

Work in groups of three. Find the number of times your heart beats in 15 s by taking a 15-s reading of your *pulse.* Each beat corresponds to one beat of your heart. The inside of your wrist and your upper neck are good places to find pressure points.

• Record each person's 15-s rate. Calculate the beats per minute.

• How many times would each person's heart beat in 5 minutes?

• How many times would each person's heart beat in 1 day? in 1 week?

THINK AND DISCUSS

1. Explain how you found the expected number of heartbeats in 5 minutes, in 1 day, and in 1 week.

You can use a **variable,** a symbol that stands for a number, to describe the number of heartbeats in any given number of minutes. Suppose your heart beats 72 times in one minute. The *variable expression* 72*m* represents the number of heartbeats in *m* minutes.

You can *evaluate* the expression by replacing the variable *m* with a number. To evaluate 72*m* for *m* = 3, you replace *m* by 3 to obtain the *numerical expression* 72 • 3.

$$72m = 72 \cdot 3$$
$$= 216$$

For *m* = 3, the *value* of the expression 72*m* is 216.

2. When you replace *m* by 3, why do you need to include a multiplication symbol?

FLASHBACK

65*x* means 65 times *x*.

 An adult human heart weighs about 0.656 lb and pumps about 656.25 gal of blood per hour. **Find the number of gallons of blood a heart pumps in 1 day.**

Source: *Reader's Digest's ABCs of the Human Body*

"Two Thumbs Up!"

"Adventurous!"

THE ADVENTURES OF HUCK FINN

E.T.

The movie "E.T." was released in 1982. Since then it has made over $225,000,000, making it one of the top money-making movies ever produced.

Source: *The Information Please Almanac*

A variable expression may include more than one operation. If you buy 4 video tapes and a $7 cassette tape, the variable expression $4v + 7$ represents the total cost of the purchase.

3. What operations are included in the expression $4v + 7$?

4. Suppose the cost of each video is $19.95. Use the expression $4v + 7$ to find the total cost.

5. Suppose you and a friend take three children to the movies. Let a be the cost of an adult's ticket and let c be the cost of a child's ticket.

   a. What does $2a$ represent?

   b. What does $3c$ represent?

   c. Evaluate $2a + 3c$ for $a = \$6$ and $c = \$3.50$.

Sometimes variable expressions contain exponents.

Example   Evaluate $4n^2 + p^2$ for $n = 3$ and $p = 1.5$.

$$4 \; \boxed{\times} \; 3 \; \boxed{x^2} \; \boxed{+} \; 1.5 \; \boxed{x^2} \; \boxed{=} \; 38.25$$

TRY THESE

6. a. What operation should you do first to evaluate the expression $4 + 0.5n$ for $n = 3$?

   b. Find the value of the expression.

7. Find the value of $12x \div 6y$ for $x = 3$ and $y = 1$.

8. Johann and his friend Kayla collect bottle caps. Johann has s shoe boxes full of bottle caps. Kayla has $2s$ shoe boxes full.

   a. Who has more bottle caps?

   b. If Johann has 1 box, how many boxes does Kayla have?

   c. If Johann has 3 boxes, how many boxes does Kayla have?

ON YOUR OWN

Mental Math Evaluate each expression for $p = 4$ and $n = 6$.

9. $5p + 3$ **10.** $3p + n^2$ **11.** $p \times n$ **12.** $2 + 4n$

13. a. Evaluate $4n - n^2$ for $n = 4$ and then for $n = 2$.

   b. Which expression has a greater value? Explain why.

Tell whether each expression is numerical or variable.

14. $4 + (3 \times 2)$ **15.** $6n + 5$ **16.** $a^2 \div 2$ **17.** $12 \div 6$

18. Writing The expressions $4y^2$ and $(4y)^2$ are different. Explain why by discussing the value of each expression for $y = 5$.

19. Complete the table below. Substitute the value indicated on the left for the variable in the expression at the top of each column. Then evaluate each expression.

	$t + 2$	$2(t - 1)$	$2t^2$	$2(2t)$
$t = 1.7$	■	■	■	■
$t = 2.04$	■	■	■	■

Minty Money

The United States Mint makes all the United States coins at production facilities in Philadelphia, San Francisco, Denver, and West Point, NY. Federal Reserve banks then distribute the coins to the public.

The following numbers of coins were produced in 1991:

9,324,386,076	pennies
1,050,600,678	nickels
1,528,461,114	dimes
1,201,934,693	quarters

Use the article for Exercises 20 and 21.

20. a. The variable expression for the value in dollars of n nickels is $0.05n$. Evaluate the expression using the number of nickels minted in 1991.

   b. Which would you rather have, the dollar value of the pennies or of the nickels minted in 1991? Why?

21. A standard dime is 0.053 in. thick. How could you find if all the dimes minted in 1991, stacked one on another, would reach the moon?

22. Data File 1 (pp. 2–3) How much is a 2-in. stack of one-dollar bills worth?

Mixed REVIEW

Exercises 1 and 2 refer to rectangle PQRS.

1. Find $m\angle R$.

2. True or false? $\overline{SP}$ and $\overline{PQ}$ are parallel.

Write in exponential form.

3. $6 \times 6 \times 6 \times 6 \times 6$

4. $2.4 \times 2.4 \times 2.4 \times 2.4$

5. When Cindy changes the oil in her car, she needs to buy 5 qt of oil. Oil costs $1.09 a quart. How much does it cost to change the oil?

 In 1981, Elizabeth Jones became the first woman chief sculptor—engraver at the United States Mint. She designs and makes special occasion medals and coins. She also makes molds for standard coins.

Source: *The Book of Women's Firsts*

3-10 Writing Variable Expressions

THINK AND DISCUSS

In everyday conversation people use word phrases that express mathematical ideas. As you read the following conversation, notice the use of mathematical expressions.

"Hi, Frank. How was the car wash?"

"Fabulous, Gina! We made twice as much money as we did last year. We washed 80 more cars than last year!"

"Great! That means we'll be able to lower the cost of the band trip by $2 per person."

1. Identify the mathematical phrases in Frank and Gina's conversation.

Even though you don't know how much money the band made last year, you can express the amount they made this year by writing a variable expression.

2. Let m represent the money the band made last year. Then the money they made this year is $\blacksquare m$.

3. Let c represent the number of cars they washed last year. Then the number of cars they washed this year is $c + \blacksquare$.

When you know the value of a variable, you can write a numerical expression.

4. Suppose the band made $240 from last year's car wash. Then the numerical expression for the money they made this year is $\blacksquare \cdot 240$.

5. Suppose they washed 50 cars last year. Then the numerical expression for the cars they washed this year is $50 + \blacksquare$.

6. Suppose t was the cost per person for the band trip before the car wash. Write a variable expression describing the cost of the trip after the car wash.

In one day, Americans spend $2.5 million washing their cars.

Source: *In One Day*

The table at the right shows some of the key words you can use in word phrases for variable expressions.

Example Write each word phrase as a variable expression.

Key Words	Operation
add	+
plus	
sum	
total	
increased by	
more than	
minus	−
difference	
subtract	
less than	
less	
decreased by	
product	×
times	
quotient	÷
divide	

Word Phrases	Variable Expression
"It'll be 20 less." "Decrease that by 20." Find the difference of that number and 20.	$n - 20$
"May I have 10 more?" "Please add 10 to that." "Increase it by 10, please."	$r + 10$
"Double that, please." "I need twice as much as that."	$2x$
"Divide it among the four of you." "What's the quotient of s and 4?" One fourth of the students	$s \div 4$

7. Write a variable expression for "5 less than a number."

8. a. Write a variable expression for the cost of p posters at $4 per poster.

   b. Write a word phrase for your variable expression.

   c. Write a numerical expression for the cost of 50 posters at $4 per poster.

   d. Write a variable expression for "p posters to be divided among 9 students."

9. Discussion How are variable expressions useful?

WORK TOGETHER

Work with a partner. Write each variable expression as a word phrase. Then make up a story using your word phrases.

$3 \div n$ $n \div 3$ $3n$ $3 - n$

TRY THESE

Write a numerical expression for each word phrase.

10. three times seventeen

11. sixty-seven less than eighty

 From 1953 to 1991, Gwilym Hughes of Great Britain saw an average of 528 movies a year. **What variable expression could you write to find approximately how many movies he saw in any given number of years? How many movies did he see in 38 years?**

Source: *The Guinness Book of Records*

This section of a page of a telephone directory shows 11 names in 1 in. Each page has 4 columns and is 11 in. long.
What variable expression could you write to find the approximate number of names in the entire telephone directory?

Write a variable expression for each word phrase.

12. nine less than x

13. four more than s

14. seven increased by y

15. the product of 7 and t

16. Mariko found s shells on the beach. She shared them equally with her brother. Write a variable expression that shows the number of shells each person had.

ON YOUR OWN

Write each variable expression in words.

17. $4 \div n$ **18.** n^2 **19.** $n - 8.2$ **20.** $6.5 - n$

21. a. There are b books on one shelf in the library. Write a variable expression for the books on 275 shelves.

   b. Evaluate your expression for 25 books per shelf.

   c. Critical Thinking Will evaluating the expression give you the approximate number of books in the library or the actual number? Why?

Farmers' Market Produce

Produce	Package
Apples	10 per bag
Daisies	12 per bunch
Peaches	4 per box
Plums	6 per box
Tomatoes	8 per box

Use the data from the sign at the left for Exercises 22 and 23.

22. a. Write a numerical expression to show the number of plums in 5 boxes.

   b. Write a variable expression to show the number of plums in p boxes.

23. Write a variable expression for the sum of the number of apples in a bags and the number of tomatoes in t boxes.

24. In 1926, Gertrude Ederle became the first woman to swim the English Channel. Her time was 2 h faster than the time of any previous swimmer.

   a. Let t be the previous record time. Write a variable expression for Gertrude Ederle's time.

   b. Writing Explain how you decided whether to write a variable expression using addition or using subtraction.

   c. The previous record was 16.5 h. What was Gertrude Ederle's new record time?

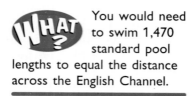

You would need to swim 1,470 standard pool lengths to equal the distance across the English Channel.

25. Choose A, B, C, or D. What will you find in the variable expression for "a number squared increased by three"?

A. multiplication and subtraction

B. multiplication and division

C. exponents and parentheses

D. exponents and addition

26. Erik mows lawns to make money. He can mow 1 lawn each day after school and 2 lawns on Saturday and on Sunday.

a. Write a numerical expression for the number of lawns Erik mows in 1 week.

b. Write a variable expression for the number of lawns he mows in w weeks.

c. Suppose Erik earns an average of $6 for each lawn. Write a numerical expression for the amount of money he makes in 1 week.

d. Write a variable expression for the amount of money he makes in w weeks.

Mixed REVIEW

Estimate each answer.

1. $239.6 - 118.43$

2. $26.92 + 13.267$

Evaluate for $p = 7$.

3. $p^2 - 2p$

4. $4(p - 2)$

5. Nicole has read the first 79 pages of a book. When she has read 17 more pages, she will have read half of the book. How many pages are in the book?

CHECK POINT

1. Choose A, B, C, or D. A used-book store paid $250 for a collection of used books. The store sold the entire collection for $315. What additional information do you need to find how much profit the store made per book?

A. the insured value of the collection

B. the time that passed from when the books were purchased until they were sold

C. the number of books in the collection

D. There is enough information to solve the problem.

Evaluate. Use a bar to indicate repeating decimals.

2. 8.006×2.34 **3.** $20 \div 6$ **4.** $4^2 + 25$

5. $3c - 8$ for $c = 6$ **6.** $5 \times 2n^2$ for $n = 5$ **7.** $6(5.7)$

Write each variable expression in words.

8. $p \times 3$ **9.** $14 + s$ **10.** $7 - t$

3-11 Using Decimals

Appliance	Wattage
Air conditioner	150
Clock	2
Dryer	4,856
Fan	200
Hair dryer	1,235
Iron	1,100
Microwave oven	1,450
Radio	71
Refrigerator	254
Electric stove	12,200
Television	145
Toaster	1,146
VCR	45
Washer	512

THINK AND DISCUSS

The **watt** is a unit of electrical power. The amount of power an appliance uses is called **wattage.** The table at the left lists the average wattage various household appliances use in one hour.

1. How are the appliances that use more than 1,000 watts of power in an hour alike?

2. **Estimation** About how much more wattage does a dryer use than a washer?

3. How can you calculate the wattage a television uses in 3 h?

4. **a.** Write a variable expression that shows how much wattage a television uses in h hours.

   b. Evaluate your expression for $h = 2$, 4.5, and 3.75.

The number of *kilowatt-hours* you use determines how much you pay the electric company. Since a watt is a very small unit of measure, electric companies use *kilowatts* to compute customers' bills. A **kilowatt** (kW) is 1,000 watts. You use this formula to calculate kilowatt hours (kW•h).

$$kW\text{•}h = \frac{\text{wattage} \times \text{hours used}}{1,000}$$

5. Which appliances in the table use at least 1 kW•h each hour that they are on?

6. If the stove has been on for 1 h, how many kilowatt hours has it used?

If you know the electricity cost per kilowatt-hour (electricity rate), you can find how much it costs to run various appliances by using this formula:

$$\text{cost} = kW\text{•}h \times \text{electricity rate.}$$

7. Todd's electricity rate is $.12 per kW•h. How much does it cost to run his electric stove for 1 h?

The greatest power failure in the United States and Canada occurred Nov. 9–10, 1965. An estimated 30,000,000 people lost power. New York City was without power for 13.5 h.

Source: *The Guinness Book of Records*

WORK TOGETHER

Do this activity in a group of three or four.

• Choose three appliances from the appliance table that all the members in your group have in their homes.

• Estimate the number of hours each appliance is on in each person's home in a 24-h period.

• Make a table listing the three appliances. With each appliance, list each person's name and the number of hours the appliance runs in one day.

8. For each appliance your group listed, write and evaluate a numerical expression for the number of kilowatts the appliance uses in 1 h.

9. **a.** For each appliance your group listed, write a variable expression that shows the kilowatts used for operating the appliance for *x* hours.

   b. Evaluate each expression for the number of hours listed for each person in your table.

10. Suppose the electricity rate in your city or town is $.10 per kW•h. What is the cost per day for operating each appliance on your list?

 The largest power plant currently in operation is the Raul Leoni hydro-electric plant in Guri, Venezuela, with a capacity of 10,300,000 kW. Capacity refers to the greatest possible one-day output of the plant, not the regular everyday output. **How long would it take for an electric stove to use 10,300,000 kW?**

Source: *The Guinness Book of Records*

ON YOUR OWN

11. Rachael found that her family used their microwave for about 2 h per week.

   a. How many kW•h is this?

   b. At $.11 per kW•h, what is the weekly cost?

12. Write a variable expression for the cost of using a hair dryer for *d* hours at an electricity rate of $.13 per kW•h.

13. Write a variable expression for the cost of using an electric fan for *f* hours if the electricity rate is $.13 per kW•h.

14. **Writing** Describe how you might conserve electricity in your home. You may want to include ideas about how to use certain appliances so that you don't waste electricity and ideas about using nonelectric appliances.

Mi*x*ed REVIEW

Name the property shown.

1. $8.3 \times 53 = 53 \times 8.3$

2. $89.3 \times 1 = 89.3$

Write a variable expression for each word phrase.

3. *r* divided by eight

4. fifteen less than *c*

5. About 5^3 million Americans tuned in to watch the final episode of M*A*S*H on February 28, 1983. The U.S. population at that time was about 230 million. How many people living in the U.S. did not watch the final episode?

Use the electric bill to answer Exercises 15–17.

For Service to	Joan P. Mayer 367 Livingston Ave. Minnetonka, MN

ELECTRICITY USED THIS PERIOD		COST OF ELECTRICITY	
APR 23 Estimated Read	11742	Basic Monthly Charge	$5.78
MAR 23 Meter Reading	11230	Energy Charge	
		512* kW•h @ $0.106733	▪
kW•h Consumed This Period	512*		
kW•h/DAY - This Period	16.5		
kW•h/DAY - Same Period Last Year	27.2		
Next Scheduled Read	MAY 23	CURRENT CHARGES	▪

*Estimated use

GREAT EXPECTATIONS

Writer

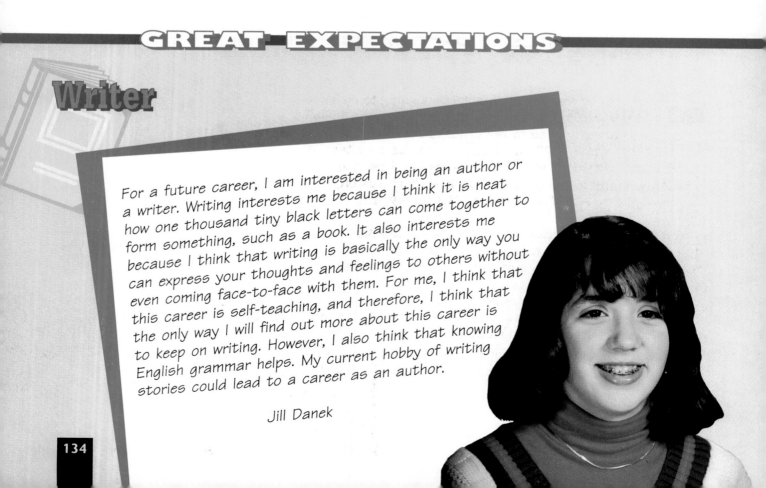

For a future career, I am interested in being an author or a writer. Writing interests me because I think it is neat how one thousand tiny black letters can come together to form something, such as a book. It also interests me because I think that writing is basically the only way you can express your thoughts and feelings to others without even coming face-to-face with them. For me, I think that this career is self-teaching, and therefore, I think that the only way I will find out more about this career is to keep on writing. However, I also think that knowing English grammar helps. My current hobby of writing stories could lead to a career as an author.

Jill Danek

15. **a.** Calculate Joan's energy charge for this period. Round your answer to the nearest cent.

    b. What are the current charges?

    c. What is the average charge per day for Joan's electricity?

16. Compare the number of kilowatt hours used per day during this period with the number of kilowatt hours used per day during the same period last year. What could account for changes in the amount of electricity used?

17. The chart at the right shows how much electricity Joan has used each month for the past year.

    a. Discussion During what season of the year does Joan seem to use the most electricity?

    b. How could where Joan lives affect her electricity use?

18. Research Find out why the electric company includes a basic monthly charge in the bill.

kW•h per Month			
May	500	Nov	691
Jun	513	Dec	709
Jul	558	Jan	715
Aug	595	Feb	725
Sept	542	Mar	625
Oct	526	Apr	512

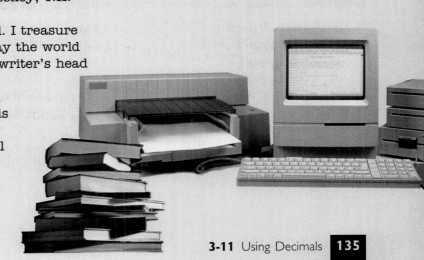

Dear Jill,

When I went off to college, I thought I was going to be a scientist, so I studied astronomy, math, and physics. Even though I had always loved to read, I didn't take courses in literature and writing. When I turned out to be a writer rather than a scientist, my only teachers had been the brilliant ones inside the covers of books—Jane Austen, Charles Dickens, A.A. Milne, Robert McCloskey, T.H. White.

But the science training wasn't wasted. I treasure my understanding, such as it is, of the way the world works. And it's true that everything in a writer's head gets into her books sooner or later. I like your insistence that writing is self-taught, and that the way you will get better at it is by continuing to write. But even more important, I think, is the unconscious skill you acquire by reading. Readers make writers.

Jane Langton
Author

Wrap Up

Estimation Strategies   3-1, 3-2

You can estimate decimals using rounding, front-end estimation, clustering or compatible numbers.

Use any estimation strategy to calculate. Then tell which strategy you used.

1. $50.3 \div 6.9$ **2.** $1.46 + 4.38$ **3.** $8.2 + 7.8 + 8.123 + 8.392 + 7.989 + 8.01$

Properties   3-3, 3-5, 3-7

To evaluate an expression, use the commutative property to change the order. Use the associative property to change the grouping.

To evaluate an expression with parentheses, use the distributive property to distribute a factor to each term inside the parentheses.

Use the properties to find each missing number. Identify the property you used.

4. $6(3.2) = \blacksquare(3) + 6(\blacksquare)$

5. $8.6 + 9.2 = \blacksquare + 8.6$

6. $(3.8 + 2) + 3 = 3.8 + (2 + \blacksquare)$

7. $8.2 \times \blacksquare = 5.9 \times 8.2$

8. $(7 \times \blacksquare) \times 1 = 7 \times (3.2 \times 1)$

9. $5(8.1 + 6.2) = 5(\blacksquare) + 5(\blacksquare)$

Repeating and Terminating Decimals   3-6

A *terminating decimal* is a decimal that stops, or terminates. A decimal in which a digit or sequence of digits keep repeating is a *repeating decimal.*

10. Divide 1 by each whole number from 1 to 10. Which divisors result in quotients that are repeating? Which result in quotients that are terminating?

11. Writing Is 0.05055055505555 . . . a repeating decimal? Explain why or why not.

Exponents 3-8

You use an **exponent** to show repeated multiplication. For example, the exponential form of $2 \times 2 \times 2 \times 2 \times 2$ is 2^5, and the standard form is 32.

Write each expression as a product of repeated factors and in standard form.

12. 2^3 **13.** 9^4 **14.** 3^7 **15.** 0.2^3 **16.** 0.12^2

Variable Expressions 3-9, 3-10

A **variable** is a symbol that stands for a number. A variable expression contains at least one variable. To evaluate an expression, you replace the variable with a number that represents its value.

Evaluate each expression for $x = 3$ and $y = 5$.

17. $6x + 9$ **18.** $3 + 8y$ **19.** $x \cdot y$ **20.** $2x + y^2$

Write a variable expression for each word phrase.

21. n less than 8   **22.** the product of 6 and c **23.** 6 more than twice n

Strategies and Applications 3-4, 3-11

Before you try to solve any problem, you must first decide whether you have enough information, too much information, or too little information.

24. Mona's electricity rate is $.14 per kW•h. How much does it cost to run her refrigerator for 3 hours?

   a. Tell what needed information is missing.

   b. Find the needed information and solve the problem.

GETTING READY FOR CHAPTER 4

Write a variable expression to describe each situation.

1. the cost of c cassettes at $8 per cassette   **2.** $2 more than d dollars for one CD

3. 4 pencils fewer than n pencils in the box   **4.** n pencils distributed among 4 friends

follow Up

Starting a Business

At the beginning of the chapter you chose a business that you would like to start. Now it is time to apply for a bank loan to get your business going. Review your description of the operation of your business. Revise the description, if necessary, based on your study of the chapter. Then prepare a business plan to present to the bank officer who will be reviewing your loan. The following suggestions may help.

✓ Make a graph.
✓ Make a spreadsheet.
✓ Make an oral presentation.

The problems preceded by the magnifying glass (p. 96, # 26; p. 104, # 20; and p. 119, # 31) will help you complete the investigation.

Excursion: Many people who want to go into business for themselves buy franchises. What is a franchise? What must a person do in order to become the owner of a franchise?

Who to Talk to:
• an owner of a local branch of a national chain

Cipher/Decipher

In a cryptarithm, numbers are replaced by letters. Rewrite the cryptarithm below using numbers.

$$\begin{array}{r} HI \\ \times\ NT \\ \hline AT \\ FIN \\ \hline FOOT \end{array}$$

Once you have figured out the numbers for the cryptarithm, make one of your own to share with your class.

It's Paper Thin

Many kinds of paper have been around you throughout your life. Have you ever wondered how thick a piece of paper is? The answer varies depending on the kind of paper you are measuring. Make a plan to measure the thickness of a piece of notebook paper to a thousandth of an inch. When you are sure that your method is reasonable, measure the notebook paper. Compare notebook paper to construction paper, tracing paper, oaktag, newsprint, and pages in a textbook as well as other kinds of paper you may find. Make a chart of the paper you have measured in order of thickness.

Horse Speed

Although the horse is not the fastest animal, man has always had a respect for its speed. What is the fastest that a horse has run? In horse races, the distance is measured in furlongs. Look up the times for horses in the Kentucky Derby. Which horse holds the record? What was the time? Convert this to miles per hour. Round your answer to the nearest tenth of a mile.

GAME-ZERO IN ON THE RANGE

This is a game to play with two players and a calculator.

Player 1 – picks two 4-digit numbers that have a range of 100. For example, 3,500 and 3,600. Write the two numbers down.

Player 2 – picks a two digit number and enters it into the calculator.

Players 1 and 2 take turns multiplying the read-out on the calculator by any whole or decimal number. The first player to get a readout between the two numbers wins. Use your estimation skills–no pencil and paper.

Play Ball

Millions of baseball cards are printed, then sold, and traded each year. On the back of a baseball card you can find the statistics for a player's career. These include batting averages for infield and outfield players and ERA (Earned Run Averages) for pitchers. Find out how these figures are calculated. Make a display comparing former greats with your favorite current players. If you play baseball or softball, keep track of your own statistics during the next season.

1. Round each number to the tenths' place.

   a. 0.571034   **b.** 26.095   **c.** 501.9386

2. On her last bank statement, Rhea Medeiros had a balance of $213.15 in her checking account. She wrote two checks, one for $68.94 and the other for $128.36. What is her current balance?

3. Use front-end estimation to estimate the sum of the following grocery item prices: $7.99, $2.79, $4.15, $2.09.

4. **Estimation** Use any method.

   a. $289.76 - 52$ **b.** $8.7891 - 3.493$

   c. $68.5 \div 7.02$ **d.** $97.60 \cdot 3.4$

   e. $21.15 + 19.38 + 20.046 + 22.07$

5. **Writing** Alison has a choice of two jobs for the summer. She can pump gas at $5.20/h for 18 h/wk or she can babysit at $3.75/h for 25 h/wk. If you were Alison, which job would you choose? Why?

6. Use graph paper to draw models of 0.65, 0.25, and 0.50. Then use $<$, $>$, or $=$ to compare the decimals.

7. Divide. Use a bar to show repeating decimals.

   a. $1.9 \div 1.8$ **b.** $51 \div 3$ **c.** $1.2 \div 0.3$

8. Write a variable expression for each word phrase.

   a. the sum of twice a number and 6.5

   b. 35.9 less than a number

   c. the quotient of r and four

   d. s decreased by x

9. The attendance at a two-day concert doubled on Saturday. Let p represent the number of people who attended the concert on Friday. Write a variable expression for the number of people who attended Saturday's concert.

10. Evaluate $7n^2 - 3y^2$ for $n = 6.8$ and $y = 3.5$.

11. **Writing** Explain how you would teach someone to use the distributive property to multiply 7 by 2.5.

12. Carl's family purchased a 150-watt air conditioner. During a nine-day heat wave, they ran the air conditioner for 8 h each day. The electric rate is $.12/kW•h. How much did it cost to cool their home during the heat wave?

13. **Mental Math** Use the distributive property to evaluate.

    a. 6(10.5)   **b.** 3(98)   **c.** (7.3)6

14. **Choose A, B, C, or D.** The weights of four bags of apples were 3.5, 3.8, 4.2, and 3.5 lb. What was the median weight?

    A. 3.5   **B.** 3.65   **C.** 3.75   **D.** 3.8

15. What information do you need to solve this problem? At the 1992 Summer Olympics, Pablo Morales of the United States swam the 100-m butterfly in 53.32 s to win the gold medal. At the 1972 Summer Olympics, Mark Spitz won the same event. Who had the faster time, and how much faster was it?

Cumulative Review

Choose A, B, C, or D.

1. What variable expression is described by the word phrase "increase r by 2"?

   A. $2r$ **B.** $r - 2$ **C.** $r + 2$ **D.** $r \cdot 2$

2. After rounding, Esther arrived at a sum of 5. What numbers could she have added?

   A. $4.23 + 7.8$ **B.** $3.95 + 2.25$

   C. $2.37 + 2.07$ **D.** $2.35 + 2.73$

3. What's the greatest number of movie tickets you can buy if you have $33.48 and each movie ticket costs $6.75?

   A. 3   **B.** 4   **C.** 5   **D.** 6

4. In the figure at the right, which pair of lines intersect?

   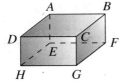

   A. $\overleftrightarrow{AB}, \overleftrightarrow{CG}$

   B. $\overleftrightarrow{DH}, \overleftrightarrow{FB}$ **C.** $\overleftrightarrow{AE}, \overleftrightarrow{AB}$ **D.** $\overleftrightarrow{HG}, \overleftrightarrow{EF}$

5. Name the property of addition illustrated by the equation below.
   $0.8 + (1.6 + 4.2) = 0.8 + (4.2 + 1.6)$

   A. Identity property

   B. Commutative property

   C. Associative property

   D. Distributive property

6. Which pair of numbers is between 6^3 and 6^4?

   A. 3^6 and 4^6 **B.** 5^3 and 5^4

   C. 7^2 and 7^3 **D.** 4^5 and 5^4

7. What is $0.3 \times 0.3 \times 30$?

   A. 30   **B.** 27   **C.** 9   **D.** 2.7

8. In the diagram at the right, which pair of angles are adjacent angles?

   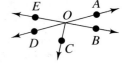

   A. $\angle EOD, \angle DOC$ **B.** $\angle BOC, \angle BOD$

   C. $\angle AOE, \angle BOC$ **D.** $\angle AOB, \angle EOD$

9. What is 64 written in exponential form?

   A. 2^6 **B.** 4^3 **C.** 8^2

   D. All of the above are correct.

10. What information is *not* given by the bar graph below?

    A. There are about the same number of birds as amphibians at the zoo.

    B. There are more farm animals than wild animals.

    C. Reptiles are included in the "other" category.

    D. There are fewer birds than farm animals at the zoo.

    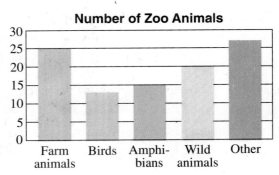

ntroduction to Algebra

Afamily of four spends an average of $189.70 per day while on vacation. They travel an average of 100 mi/da of vacation.

Vacation Spending

$84 Lodging

$96 Meals

$9.70
Gas, oil, and tolls

Source: *AAA World*

Data File 4

Have You Ever Been To Washington, DC?					
Age	**Yes**		**No**		
	M	**F**	**M**	**F**	
21-34	86	75	14	25	
35-44	66	71	34	29	
45-54	58	43	42	57	
55+	40	67	60	33	
Totals	63	57	37	43	
percentages	60		40		

Source: *The First Really Important Survey of American Habits,* Mel Poretz and Barry Sinrod

WORLD VIEW

In 1989, the East Japan Railway Co. carried 14,660,000 passengers daily. That year passengers left 377,712 umbrellas, 141,200 articles of clothing, 143,761 books, 89,799 purses, and 4,359 accessories on the train.

Exchange Rates

Here's what $1 was worth in various countries on one day.

Foreign currency	Currency/ U.S. dollar
Australia (dollar)	1.4650
Britain (pound)	0.6768
Canada (dollar)	1.2776
France (franc)	5.7065
Germany (mark)	1.6962
Greece (drachma)	230.90
Israel (shekel)	2.7670
Italy (lira)	1,533.37
Japan (yen)	110.87
Mexico (pesos)	3.1105
Spain (peseta)	129.30
Switzerland (franc)	1.5110

Source: *The Wall Street Journal*

WHAT YOU WILL LEARN

- how to model integers and work with integers
- how to model, write, and solve equations
- how to use technology to explore integers
- how to solve problems by making a table

international dateline

prime meridian

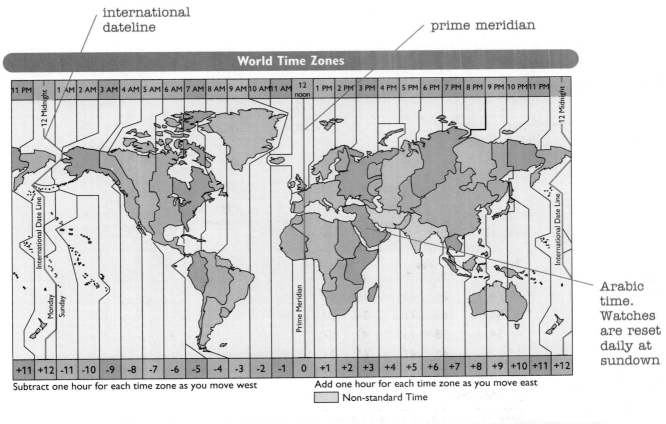

World Time Zones

| 11 PM | | 1 AM | 2 AM | 3 AM | 4 AM | 5 AM | 6 AM | 7 AM | 8 AM | 9 AM | 10 AM | 11 AM | 12 noon | 1 PM | 2 PM | 3 PM | 4 PM | 5 PM | 6 PM | 7 PM | 8 PM | 9 PM | 10 PM | 11 PM | |

12 Midnight

International Date Line

Monday / Sunday

Prime Meridian

International Date Line

12 Midnight

Arabic time. Watches are reset daily at sundown

| +11 | +12 | -11 | -10 | -9 | -8 | -7 | -6 | -5 | -4 | -3 | -2 | -1 | 0 | +1 | +2 | +3 | +4 | +5 | +6 | +7 | +8 | +9 | +10 | +11 | +12 |

Subtract one hour for each time zone as you move west

Add one hour for each time zone as you move east

☐ Non-standard Time

Where United States Travelers Went in a Recent Year

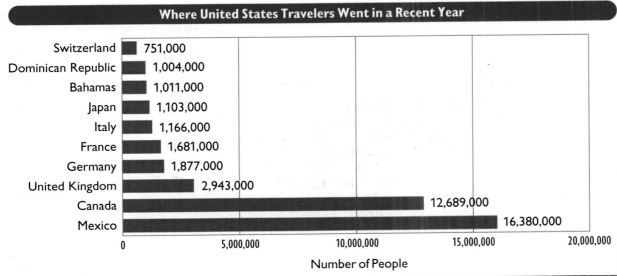

	Number of People
Switzerland	751,000
Dominican Republic	1,004,000
Bahamas	1,011,000
Japan	1,103,000
Italy	1,166,000
France	1,681,000
Germany	1,877,000
United Kingdom	2,943,000
Canada	12,689,000
Mexico	16,380,000

Number of People

Source: AAA World

investigation

Memo

You will need a simple balance scale so that you can weigh pennies. The balance scale shown has the basic features you will need. It balances at its center point on a pencil. The balance point is numbered zero. The ruler is renumbered in both directions from zero to twelve. Test your balance scale by placing a penny at seven on the left side of the scale. Your device should swing back into balance when you place a penny at seven on the right side of the scale. Make other similar tests and practice using your balance scale.

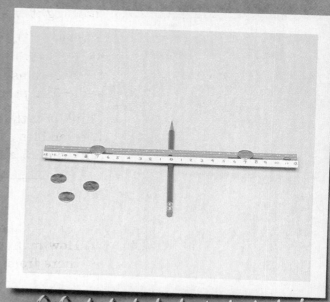

LeADs tO FOLLow

✓ How can you balance one penny on one side of the scale against two, three, or more pennies on the other side?

✓ What must you do on one side of the balance scale to balance pennies at two different positions on the other side?

Mission: Experiment with your balance scale. Place different numbers of pennies at different positions on the scale. Find what you must do to bring the scale back into balance. Describe what you notice about the positions of the pennies when your scale balances.

4-1 Comparing and Ordering Integers

FLASHBACK

A positive number can be written with or without a "+" sign.

$$5 = +5$$

THINK AND DISCUSS

"Wear your heavy winter coat tomorrow, folks, because the high will be about five degrees above zero. When you wake up in the morning it will be about five degrees below zero."

You can write the temperature above zero as +5°C or 5°C. You write the temperature below zero as −5°C. You read the numbers 5 and −5 as *positive* 5 and *negative* 5.

Think of a thermometer turned on its side. It resembles a horizontal number line. You can graph 5 and −5 on this number line.

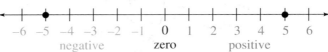

1. How many units are there from 0 to 5? How many units are there from 0 to −5?

Two numbers are **opposites** if they are the same distance from 0 on a number line, but in opposite directions. The numbers 5 and −5 are opposites. **Integers** are the set of whole numbers and their opposites.

2. What two integers are 6 units from 0 on a number line?

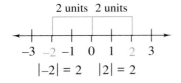

The **absolute value** of an integer is its distance from 0 on a number line. Distance is considered positive. Since −2 is 2 units from 0, |−2| is 2. You read |−2| as "the absolute value of −2."

3. **a.** Write |−4| in words.

   b. Find |−4|.

4. What two numbers have an absolute value of 1?

5. Can the absolute value of a number be −3? Why or why not?

FLASHBACK

The symbol < means *is less than.* The symbol > means *is greater than.*

Numbers increase in value from left to right on a horizontal number line.

Example Which city is colder, St. Paul or Madison?

• Find −7 and 1 on a number line.

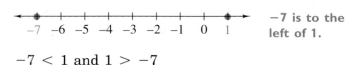

−7 is to the left of 1.

$-7 < 1$ and $1 > -7$

It is colder in St. Paul than it is in Madison.

6. Complete with <, >, or =: 5 ■ −8

7. Order −9, 6, 0, −4, and 1 from least to greatest.

T R Y THESE

Name the integer represented by each point on the number line.

8. *A*   9. *B*

10. *C*   11. *D*

12. On the number line above, which two points represent opposites?

13. Draw a number line and graph the following points: −3, 7, 4, −1, and 0.

Write an integer to represent each situation.

14. a debt of $20   15. a child's fever of 101 degrees

O N YOUR OWN

16. Explain how you would use the number line to determine which is greater, −3 or −9.

17. **a.** Which integer is greater, −43 or 22?

   b. Which integer has the greater absolute value, −43 or 22?

18. Which integer is its own opposite?

The boiling point of water in degrees Fahrenheit is 212°. In degrees Celsius, the boiling point is 100°. **If a child's temperature is 101°, which scale was used?**

Write an integer to represent each situation.

19. Earth Science The city of New Orleans, Louisiana, is 8 ft below sea level.

20. a. Astronomy The surface temperature on the light side of the moon is 210°F, almost hot enough to boil water.

b. Astronomy The surface temperature on the dark side of the moon is about 240°F below zero.

Graph each integer and its opposite on a number line.

21. −5   **22.** 4   **23.** −8   **24.** 3

Compare. Use <, >, or =.

25. 10 ■ −10   **26.** |12| ■ |−12| **27.** −6 ■ −2   **28.** 0 ■ −14

29. a. What is the opposite of the opposite of 8?

b. Enter 8 on your calculator. Press ![+/-], the change-sign key, three times. How are the four numbers related?

c. Writing Write a statement describing the opposite of the opposite of any number. Give examples to show your statement is correct.

30. Write integers that represent the temperatures on Mars which are mentioned in the article at the right.

31. Research Find the high and low surface temperatures of two other planets.

Complete with an integer that makes the statement true.

32. −7 < ■   **33.** ■ > −9   **34.** |12| < ■   **35.** −15 > ■

36. a. Critical Thinking Write three numbers that are between −3 and −4.

b. Are the numbers you wrote integers? Why or why not?

37. Writing Suppose a friend does not know how to order integers. Write an explanation for how to order the following numbers from least to greatest:

$$-32 \quad 12 \quad 0 \quad -4 \quad 22$$

Mixed REVIEW

Round to the digit underlined.

1. 6.86<u>7</u>7   2. 0.4<u>8</u>32

Evaluate for $h = 8.2$.

3. $2h - 5.5$

4. $418.2 \div 3h$

5. In 20 y, Nelson will be three times as old as he is now. How old is Nelson?

The Red Planet

In 1971, the unmanned spacecraft Mariner 9 transmitted pictures and other data as it passed near Mars. Scientists learned that the temperature of Earth's nearest planetary neighbor ranged from 68°F below zero during the day to 176°F below zero at night. The planet has a red, stony, desert landscape, much like what scientists and science fiction writers had imagined for years.

Modeling Integers

■ **WHAT YOU'LL NEED**

✓ **Algebra tiles**

✓ **Number cubes**

TH**I**N**K** **A**N**D** **D**I**S**C**U**S**S**

Colored tiles, like the algebra tiles below, can help you understand integers.

□ 1   ■ −1
positive   negative

1. Write the integer represented by each set of tiles.

   a. □□   **b.** ■■■

   c. ■   **d.** □□□□□□

2. Draw a set of tiles to represent each integer and its opposite.

   a. −2   **b.** 4   **c.** −7   **d.** 3

A combination of an equal number of positive and negative tiles represents zero.

□■ represents zero, *or* □ + ■ = 0.

3. Suppose you have 8 positive tiles. How many negative tiles will you need to represent zero?

4. Suppose you have 5 negative tiles. How many positive tiles will you need to represent zero?

5. Combine tiles to make zero pairs. Write the integer that represents the remaining tiles.

   a. ■□■■   **b.** □■■■
        □□□■   ■■

6. Can you combine an odd number of tiles to make zero? Why or why not?

7. What integer can you represent with 7 negative tiles and 3 positive tiles using all of the tiles?

8. What integer can you represent with 2 negative tiles and 5 positive tiles using all of the tiles?

Jaime Escalante proved to the students at Garfield High School in Los Angeles that with dedication and hard work, "There are no limits. You can become whatever you want to be." In the first year of his calculus class, all 18 students passed the Advanced Placement exam in college calculus, seven with top scores.

Source: *Readers Digest*

Work with a partner. You will need a bag of algebra tiles and two number cubes. Take turns rolling the number cubes.

Player 1	Player 2	
−5	3	−5 < 3

• The number you roll is the number of tiles you draw from the bag without looking. For example, if you roll a 7, you draw 7 tiles from the bag.

• Find the integer represented by the tiles. Record it in a chart like the one at the right. Use <, >, or = to compare the integers. The person with the lesser value scores 1 point.

• Repeat the activity until one of you has 10 points.

ON YOUR OWN

Name the integer represented by each set of tiles.

9. 10. 11.

12. 13. 14.

15. a. Choose three integers. Sketch the tiles that represent each integer and its opposite.

b. What number do all of the tiles for an integer and its opposite represent?

Use tiles to represent each number in more than one way.

16. 7   17. −1   18. −6   19. 2

20. **Writing** Explain how to find the integer represented by 6 positive and 9 negative tiles.

21. What integer can you represent using 24 positive and 32 negative tiles?

22. A set of tiles represents the integer 7. The set contains 4 negative tiles. How many positive tiles does it contain?

23. **Critical Thinking** Describe how you can represent |−8| using 12 tiles.

Adding Integers

WHAT YOU'LL NEED

✓ **Algebra tiles**

✓ **Calculator**

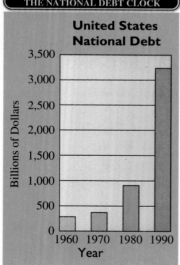

OUR NATIONAL DEBT:

$?????????????

YOUR *Family Share* $??????

THE NATIONAL DEBT CLOCK

United States National Debt

Billions of Dollars

3,500
3,000
2,500
2,000
1,500
1,000
500
0

1960 1970 1980 1990

Year

Estimate the amount of the national debt for each year shown in the graph.

THINK AND DISCUSS

Suppose a friend borrows $5 from you and then borrows $3 more. You can use tiles to find how much your friend is in debt. Let the red tiles represent the amounts your friend borrowed.

$$-5 \ + \ (-3) \ = \ \blacksquare$$

1. What number belongs in the gray box?

2. Use tiles to find the following sums.

   a. $-4 + (-6)$ **b.** $-1 + (-8)$ **c.** $-5 + (-2)$

3. What is the sign of the sum of two negative integers?

4. **a.** Write a number sentence for the sum below.

   b. What is the sign of the sum of two positive integers?

5. Complete the statement below with the correct word: To find the sum of two integers with the same sign, add their absolute values. The sum has the ■ sign as the addends.

Now suppose your friend who borrowed $8 pays back $3. Let the red tiles represent the amount that your friend borrowed and the yellow tiles represent the amount he repaid.

$$-8 \ + \ 3 \ = \ \blacksquare$$ The 3 positive tiles and 3 of the negative tiles make zero pairs.

6. **a.** What number belongs in the gray box?

   b. How much does your friend owe you now?

You can also use a number line to model addition of integers.

Example
1

Use a number line to find $-6 + 4$.

Step 1 Begin at 0. To represent -6, move *left* 6 units to *negative* 6.

Step 2 To represent adding positive 4, move *right* 4 units to *negative* 2.

$-6 + 4 = -2$

7. Write a numerical expression for each model.

a.

b.

Problem Solving Hint

The first arrow above the number line represents the first integer in a sum.

c. What is the sign of the integer with the greater absolute value in each expression?

d. Use the models to find each sum.

e. What is the sign of each sum?

f. Which addend has the same sign as the sum?

8. Write an expression for the sum represented by each model.

a.

b.

c. What is the sign of the integer with the greater absolute value in each expression?

d. Use the models to find each sum.

e. What is the sign of the sum of each expression?

f. Which addend has the same sign as the sum?

9. Choose the correct word to complete the statement below:

To add two integers with different signs, first find their absolute values. Then subtract the lesser absolute value from the greater absolute value. The sum of the integers has the same sign as the addend with the *(lesser, greater)* absolute value.

When it is not convenient to use a model to add integers, you can use the summary statement in Question 9 to find sums.

Example 2

During the day, the temperature in Barrow, Alaska, rose 17°F. The low temperature for the day was −45°F. What was the high temperature for the day?

• You want to find (−45) + 17.

$$|17| = 17 \quad |-45| = 45 \quad \text{Find the absolute values.}$$

$$45 - 17 = 28 \quad \text{Subtract.}$$

$$(-45) + 17 = -28 \quad \text{−45 has the greater absolute value, so the sum is negative.}$$

The high temperature for the day was −28°F.

Is the state capital of Alaska or North Dakota colder in January? You may be surprised that the average temperature in Juneau is 10°C warmer than in Bismarck. Bismarck's average temperature is −16°C. **What is the average January temperature in Juneau?**

You can also use a calculator to add integers.

Example 3

Use a calculator to find the sum of −127 and 48.

• 127 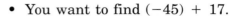 48 **= −79**   The change-sign key changes 127 to −127.

WORK TOGETHER

Work with a partner. Use models to represent each sum. Then find the sum.

10. −5 + (−4)   **11.** 2 + (−8)   **12.** −6 + 7   **13.** 12 + (−7)

TRY THESE

Write a numerical expression for each model. Then find the sum.

14.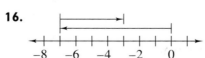

15.

16.

$$\begin{array}{c} \longleftarrow \\ +\!\!-\!\!+\!\!-\!\!+\!\!-\!\!+\!\!-\!\!+\!\!-\!\!+\!\!-\!\!+\!\!-\!\!+\!\!-\!\!+ \\ -8 \quad -6 \quad -4 \quad -2 \quad 0 \end{array}$$

17.

$$\begin{array}{c} \longrightarrow \\ +\!\!-\!\!+\!\!-\!\!+\!\!-\!\!+\!\!-\!\!+\!\!-\!\!+\!\!-\!\!+\!\!-\!\!+\!\!-\!\!+\!\!-\!\!+\!\!-\!\!+ \\ 0 \quad 2 \quad 4 \quad 6 \quad 8 \quad 10 \end{array}$$

Find each sum.

18. −8 + (−4)   **19.** 7 + (−2)   **20.** 3 + (−12)   **21.** −14 + 16

ON YOUR OWN

Write a numerical expression and find each sum.

22. two plus six

23. two plus negative six

24. negative two plus six

25. negative two plus negative six

Choose Use a calculator, paper and pencil, or mental math. Write a number sentence for each situation.

26. Money On Friday Sherry borrowed $10 from her sister. The next day she paid back $5. Then on Monday she borrowed $4 more. How much does Sherry owe her sister?

27. Weather At midnight, the temperature was $-12°F$. By 6 A.M. the next morning the temperature had risen $19°$. What was the temperature at 6 A.M.?

28. Writing Explain how you would find the sum of two integers that have different signs.

Write a number sentence to match these calculator keys.

29. 16 $\boxed{+/-}$ $\boxed{+}$ 24 $\boxed{=}$ 8

30. 112 $\boxed{+}$ 158 $\boxed{+/-}$ $\boxed{=}$ -46

Use a calculator to find each sum.

31. $126 + (-92)$ **32.** $-68 + (-72)$ **33.** $-99 + 137$ **34.** $67 + 48$

35. a. Lauren uses the expression $t + 3$ to find the time in New York, where her grandmother lives. The variable t stands for the time in Los Angeles where Lauren lives. Use Lauren's expression to find the time in New York when it is 5 P.M. in Los Angeles.

   b. Data File 4 (p. 142–143) Using the variable t for the time in your time zone, write an expression for finding the time in London.

   c. When it is 6 A.M. in London what time is it where you live?

Mental Math Simplify each expression.

36. $4 + 7 + (-2)$ **37.** $|-3| + 5 + (-3)$ **38.** $28 + (-12) + (-26)$

39. Entertainment How far below ground level will the roller coaster at the right go?

Mixed REVIEW

Estimate using front-end estimation.

1. $8.033 + 9.23 + 6.82$

2. $5.77 + 10.09 + 4.15$

Draw a set of tiles to represent each integer and its opposite.

3. 8   **4.** -5

5. Mrs. Gonzales has two children. The sum of their ages is 22 and the product is 117. How old are the children?

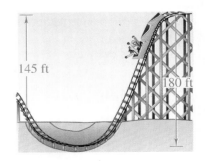

145 ft

180 ft

Problem Solving Practice

READ
PLAN
LOOK
BACK
SOLVE

PROBLEM SOLVING STRATEGIES

Make a Table
Use Logical Reasoning
Solve a Simpler Problem
Too Much or Too Little
Information
Look for a Pattern
Make a Model
Work Backward
Draw a Diagram
Guess and Test
Simulate a Problem
Use Multiple Strategies
Write an Equation

Use any strategy to solve each problem. Show all your work.

1. Karla wants to buy a used car. She can pay $3,600 cash for the car, or she can pay $1,000 down and $120 a month for two years. Karla has $4,500 in savings. She earns $250 a month at her part-time job.

   a. If Karla chooses to make a down payment and pay $120 monthly, how much will she pay for the car?

   b. Why do you think anyone in Karla's situation would choose to make payments on a car?

   c. What is an advantage of paying cash for the car?

   d. Which payment method would you use in similar circumstances? Why?

2. Suppose you are the set designer for a play. In one scene you need a sofa and a chair. In the storeroom there are three sofas you can choose from, a solid blue, a floral print, and a striped one. There are four chairs to choose from, a rocking chair, an arm chair, a recliner, and a swivel chair. How many different combinations of one sofa and one chair are there?

3. Langston plans to make a 4 × 4 mosaic using 16 square tiles. The tiles he is using are red, yellow, blue, and green. Langston does not want any row, column, or diagonal containing four tiles to have the same color more than once. Show two possible arrangements he could use.

4. Suppose express trains leave New York for Washington, D.C., every 40 min. The first train leaves at 5:20 A.M. What is the departure time closest to 12:55 P.M.?

5. Suppose you have a container that holds eight gallons of apple cider. You also have two empty containers that can hold five gallons and three gallons. How can you divide the cider into two equal portions using only the three containers?

Amtrak carries about 58,000 people between cities in the United States every day.

Source: *Amtrak*

What's Ahead

4-4 Subtracting Integers

• Subtracting integers

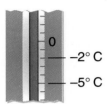

┌─ **THINK AND DISCUSS**

The coldest recorded temperature for Sacramento is −5°C. The coldest recorded temperature for San Diego is −2°C. To find the difference in the two temperatures, you subtract.

1. Which expression describes subtracting −2 from −5:
−2 − (−5) or −5 − (−2)?

Algebra tiles can help you understand how to subtract integers.

Example 1 Use algebra tiles to find −5 − (−2).

  Start with 5 negative tiles.

  Take away 2 negative tiles. There are 3 negative tiles left.

−5 − (−2) = −3

2. Use algebra tiles to find each difference.

   a. −7 − (−2)   **b.** 5 − 3   **c.** −5 − (−4)

Example 2 Find 4 − 6.

   • ▪▪▪ Start with 4 positive tiles.

   ▪▪▪ ▪▪ There are not enough positive tiles to take 6 away. Add 2 zero pairs.

  Take away 6 positive tiles. There are 2 negative tiles left.

4 − 6 = −2

3. Use algebra tiles to find each difference.

   a. 4 − 7   **b.** 3 − 9   **c.** 1 − 5

   d. 7 − (−5)   **e.** 2 − (−4)   **f.** 6 − 10

WHERE? Temperatures in Verkhoyansk, Russia, have measured from a low of −90°F to a high of 98°F.
What is the temperature range for Verkhoyansk?

Source: *The Guinness Book of Records*

You can develop a method for subtracting integers by looking for a pattern in related addition and subtraction problems.

4. Use tiles to find each difference and sum.

   a. $5 - 3$ **b.** $-9 - (-6)$ **c.** $4 - (-5)$

   $5 + (-3)$ $-9 + 6$ $4 + 5$

   d. What do you notice about the sums and differences?

   e. Complete the statement below:
   To subtract an integer, ■ its opposite.

To calculate $-7 - (-13)$ mentally, you could think "In order to remove 13 tiles, I will need to add 6 zero pairs. That will leave 6 positive tiles." Another way you could solve the same problem is to think, "I can add the opposite of *negative* 13, which is *positive* 13. So, $-7 + 13$ is 6."

5. **Mental Math** Find each difference.

   a. $3 - 7$ **b.** $-2 - (-8)$ **c.** $6 - 2$ **d.** $-4 - 7$

Example
3
A scientist measured the temperature at the surface of a 7 in. deep snow. The temperature was $-27°F$. At ground level the temperature was $24°F$. How much warmer was the temperature at ground level?

• $24 - (-27) = 24 + 27$ **To subtract -27, add its opposite, 27.**

$= 51$

The temperature at ground level was $51°F$ warmer.

*Meteorologists use satellites, airplanes, radar, and super computers to record and predict the path of hurricanes. They can use the barometric pressure of a hurricane to measure its strength. Hugo's central pressure was only 934 millibars, which is about 80 millibars below normal. **What is normal barometric pressure?***

WORK TOGETHER

Work with a partner.

• Begin with 3 yellow tiles each.

• Take turns rolling a number cube. Consider an odd number as positive and an even number as negative. The number you roll is the number of tiles you must subtract. You will use the tiles you have at the end of each turn for the beginning of the next turn.

• Record what you do by writing a subtraction sentence. Then write the related addition sentence.

• Continue the activity until you each have had 5 turns.

TRY THESE

Use models to find each difference.

6. $-4 - (-2)$ **7.** $-4 - (-8)$ **8.** $3 - 9$

9. Choose A, B, C, or D. At 8 P.M. the wind speed was 10 mi/h. The windchill temperature was $-9°F$. One hour later, the wind speed had increased to 25 mi/h. The windchill temperature had fallen to $-29°F$. Which number sentence below shows the change in the windchill temperature?

A. $29 + (-9) = 20$ **B.** $-29 - (-9) = -20$

C. $-9 - (-29) = 20$ **D.** $-29 - 9 = -38$

10. Work with a partner. Tell if each of the subtraction sentences would *always, sometimes,* or *never* be true. Support your answer with examples.

a. $(+) - (+) = (+)$ **b.** $(-) - (+) = (-)$ **c.** $(-) - (-) = (+)$

d. $(+) - (-) = (-)$ **e.** $(-) - (+) = (+)$ **f.** $(+) - (+) = (-)$

Write the related addition sentence for each subtraction sentence. Find each difference.

11. $-9 - (-6) = \blacksquare$ **12.** $6 - 11 = \blacksquare$ **13.** $5 - (-3) = \blacksquare$

ON YOUR OWN

Without calculating, determine whether each difference is positive or negative.

14. $-7 - (-13)$ **15.** $-18 - 25$ **16.** $9 - (-2)$ **17.** $46 - (-65)$

Choose Use a calculator, paper and pencil, or mental math to find each difference.

18. $4 - 15$ **19.** $-3 - 9$ **20.** $17 - (-8)$

21. $-10 - (-18)$ **22.** $58 - 35$ **23.** $-121 - 98$

24. $0 - (-22)$ **25.** $-54 - 82$ **26.** $-8 - (-12)$

Mental Math Simplify each numerical expression.

27. $-4 + 5 - (-4)$ **28.** $-3 - (-3) + (-6)$ **29.** $-7 + (-7) + 5$

30. $2 + 8 - (-2)$ **31.** $-8 + 4 - (-8)$ **32.** $2 + (-3) - (-5)$

33. **Weather** The highest and lowest temperatures ever recorded in the United States are 134°F and −80°F. The highest temperature was measured at Death Valley, California. The coldest temperature was recorded at Prospect Creek, Alaska. What is the difference in these temperature extremes?

34. **Data File II (pp. 456–457)**

   a. Find the difference between the highest and lowest average temperatures in degrees Fahrenheit.

   b. Find the difference between the lowest average temperature in the north latitudes and the lowest average temperature in the south latitudes in degrees Fahrenheit.

   c. Find the difference between the average recorded temperature at 70° north latitude and 70° south latitude in degrees Fahrenheit.

   d. Are the northern or southern latitudes colder?

GREAT EXPECTATIONS

Bicycle Designer

The career that interests me is bicycle designer. I feel it would be exciting finding out what kind of bikes kids like and trying to meet their needs. Bikes have always intrigued me.

The construction and design of a bicycle play a big part in whether it sells or not. I would like to be a part of finding out how it is done. It would be fun to see if the designing takes place on a drafting table, a computer, or in some other way.

Drawing has been a hobby of mine. Biking is very important to me. I spend a lot of time riding my bike, taking apart bikes, and reading BMX and other magazines.

Jason Rodgers

Use the diagram at the right to answer each of the following questions.

35. **a.** Does the temperature rise or fall in the troposphere?

   b. About how much does the temperature change in the troposphere?

36. About how much does the temperature change in the stratosphere? the mesosphere?

37. Estimate the range of the temperatures that a space ship would travel through as it flew from ground level to 150,000 ft above Earth.

38. **Writing** In your own words, explain how you add and subtract integers. Use examples.

Estimation **Round each number. Then estimate the sum or difference.**

39. $-38 + 17$

40. $124 - 238$

41. $-53 + (-110)$

42. $122 - 16$

43. $-74 - 52$

44. $65 + 92$

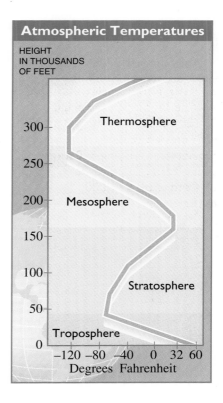

Atmospheric Temperatures

HEIGHT IN THOUSANDS OF FEET

Thermosphere

Mesosphere

Stratosphere

Troposphere

Degrees Fahrenheit

Dear Jason,

Today, bicycles are designed and drawn on a computer. The designer's computer tells the milling machines on the factory floor where to cut the metal tubes. You need metal working skills, good math and engineering skills, and a love of bicycles. Today you need great computer skills too.

   I am always using the math I studied when I was a teenager. I regularly use algebra and conduct surveys. I use a skill you're practicing too, Jason: I used to take my bike apart too! Learn to be a good mechanic and learn to take a machine apart and study how it works. It works together with math, physics, and engineering to make you a good designer.

   John Schubert
   Bicycle Designer

What's Ahead

- Using integers with bank accounts

- Using spreadsheets to explore positive and negative changes

✓ Computer

✓ Spreadsheet software

4-5 **W**orking with Integers

T H I N K A N D D I S C U S S

When people write checks, they must have money in the bank to cover the checks. Suppose Sydney Cash has $100 in a checking account. Then he writes a check for $100.

1. What is Sydney's bank balance?

Some bank accounts allow you to borrow money automatically if you write a check for more than is in your account.

2. Suppose Sydney has $100 in such an account. Then he writes a check for $150. What is his balance?

You can use a computer spreadsheet to keep track of a checking account. A deposit is a positive entry. A check is a negative entry.

	A	B	C	D
1	**Date**	**Deposit**	**Checks**	**Balance**
2				$200
3	4/29	$100		$300
4	4/30		$400	−$100

3. How was the amount in cell D3 calculated? cell D4?

4. a. What will the entries for row 5 be after Sydney makes the deposit shown below?

b. What will the entries for row 6 be after Sydney writes check #147 shown below?

Computer Work with a partner. The Eagle Record company wants to keep track of its income, expenses, and balance. The data at the right shows the income and expenses for a year.

- Make a spreadsheet like the one below to find the balance at the end of each month.

Month	Income	Expenses
Jan	$12,385	$10,760
Feb	10,426	10,825
Mar	11,680	10,476
Apr	11,720	10,344
May	11,457	10,256
Jun	12,870	10,280
Jul	12,408	10,255
Aug	12,539	10,349
Sep	9,906	10,265
Oct	10,124	10,368
Nov	10,569	10,398
Dec	13,165	11,458

	A	B	C	D	E
1	Month	Balance—Beginning of Month	Income	Expenses	Balance—End of Month
2	Jan		12,385	10,760	1,625
3	Feb	1,625	10,426	10,825	1,226

- Make a line graph of the values in the Balance column.
- Make a bar graph of the values in the Balance column.

5. a. How can you tell when there is a positive change in the balance for each graph? a negative change?

   b. Critical Thinking How does the steepness and direction of the lines on the line graph relate to the length and position of the bars on the bar graph?

   c. Which graph is best for showing the change over time? Which is best to use for comparing the balances?

6. a. Computer The check register at the right shows the monthly activity for Valerie Carpenter's account. Enter the data into a spreadsheet or make a table and use a calculator to find the balance. Valerie had $250 in her account at the beginning of the month.

   b. At the end of the month, Valerie received a statement from her bank. The bank charged her $10 each time her balance went below zero and $.25 for each check. The bank also charged her $5.50 for maintaining her account. Since these charges are taking money from her account, will you put them in the Check or Deposit column?

   c. Find Valerie's balance at the end of the month.

	Check	Deposit
1	$25.98	
2	$239.40	
Dep		$122.00
3	$54.65	
Dep		$350.00
4	$85.48	
5	$163.80	

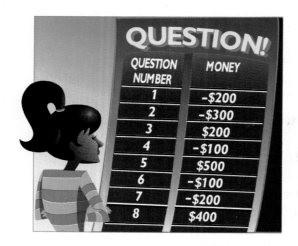

7. Entertainment The chart at the left shows how one contestant did on the first eight questions that she answered on a TV quiz show. The negative amounts indicate that the contestant missed an answer. Find how much she won or lost on the eight questions.

8. a. Data File 3 (pp. 90–91) Make a spreadsheet using the year, the number sold, and the dollars received in sales for basketballs. Use the data to estimate the mean price of a basketball.

b. In which year was the mean price of a basketball the greatest? the least?

9. Business The Royal Rappers want to make a CD. The variable and fixed costs are at the left. The fixed costs are those costs that do not change no matter how many CDs are sold. Use the spreadsheet to answer the questions below.

Costs for Making a CD

Variable Costs

Blank CD: $1.83 each

Fixed Costs

Studio Costs:	$5,120
Studio Musicians:	3,000
Photographer:	500
Graphic Artist	500
Promoter	2,000

	A	B	C	D	E
1	Units	1,000	2,000	3,000	4,000
2	Variable Costs				
3	Fixed Costs				
4	Sales Income				
5	Profit or Loss				

a. How do you find the variable costs for 1,000 units? What formula will you use for B2?

b. Writing Complete row 2. Then explain why the term "variable costs" is appropriate.

c. What value will go into all cells in row 3?

d. The rappers expect a return of $6 for each CD sold. How will you find the sales income for 1,000 units? What formula will you use for cell B4?

e. Put the data into a spreadsheet or copy the table. Find the profit or loss for the units shown.

f. Suppose the Rappers' CD "goes gold" by selling 500,000 units. How much profit will they make?

g. What would be the profit or loss if the Rappers made 10,000 CDs but sold only 5,000?

 **REVIEW**

Draw the following.

1. a rhombus

2. a trapezoid

Find each difference.

3. $8 - 1$ 4. $3 - (-6)$

5. $-4 - (-9)$

6. What are the next two numbers in the following pattern?

2, 3, 5, 6, 8, 9, . . .

4-6

Multiplying and Dividing Integers

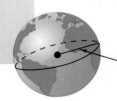

Earth's radius ≈ 6,380 km

The deepest cave yet discovered is the Pierre St. Martin in France, which is 1,332 m deep. **About how many times deeper would it need to be to reach the center of the Earth?**

THINK AND DISCUSS

The entrance to Lechuguilla Cave in New Mexico was discovered in 1986. So far, it is the deepest cave discovered in the United States. Cave explorers, called *spelunkers,* move very slowly as they go down into a cave so that they do not disturb any of the cave formations. Suppose a spelunker descends 4 ft/min for 3 min. You can picture the descent on a vertical number line.

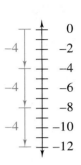

1. **a.** How far does the spelunker descend in 3 min?

   b. What integer represents the spelunker's descent?

You can also use repeated addition or multiplication to show the spelunker's movements.

Repeated Addition	Multiplication
$(-4) + (-4) + (-4) = -12$	$3(-4) = -12$

2. Find each of the following products using repeated addition.

   a. $2(-5)$ **b.** $4(-2)$

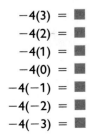

FLASHBACK

Commutative Property

$ab = ba$

3. Using the commutative property, you can write $3(-4)$ as $-4 \cdot 3$. What is the product of $-4 \cdot 3$? of $-5 \cdot 2$? of $-2 \cdot 4$?

4. Complete the following statement:

   The sign of the product of two integers with different signs is ■.

Patterns can help you find the product of two negative integers.

$-4(3) = ■$
$-4(2) = ■$
$-4(1) = ■$
$-4(0) = ■$
$-4(-1) = ■$
$-4(-2) = ■$
$-4(-3) = ■$

5. **a.** Copy and complete the pattern at the left.

   b. Describe the pattern you see in the products as you go from $-4(3)$ to $-4(-3)$.

   c. Write a pattern to find $-2(-5)$. Start with $-2(3)$.

   d. Complete the following statement:

   The sign of the product of two negative integers is ■.

You have developed the two rules for multiplying integers.

Rules for Multiplying Integers
When you multiply two integers with the same sign, the product is positive.
When you multiply two integers with different signs, the product is negative.

Multiplication and division are *inverse operations* because one undoes the other. You can use the relationship between multiplication and division to develop rules for the division of integers.

6. Use what you know about inverse operations to find each quotient.

 a. $3 \cdot 4 = 12$ **b.** $3(-4) = -12$ **c.** $(-3)(-4) = 12$

    $12 \div 4 = \blacksquare$ $-12 \div (-4) = \blacksquare$ $12 \div (-4) = \blacksquare$

    $12 \div 3 = \blacksquare$ $-12 \div 3 = \blacksquare$ $12 \div (-3) = \blacksquare$

 d. When two integers have the same sign, what is the sign of the quotient?

 e. When two integers have different signs, what is the sign of the quotient?

 f. Rewrite the Rules for Multiplying Integers to include dividing integers.

Some problems may require you to use more than one operation with integers to solve.

Example   In one week the Dow Jones Industrial Average rose 1 point on Monday, fell 3 points on Tuesday, rose 4 points on Wednesday, fell 4 points on Thursday, and fell 3 points on Friday. What was the average daily change?

$$\frac{1 + (-3) + 4 + (-4) + (-3)}{5} = \frac{-5}{5}$$ **Find the sum of the changes and divide by 5.**

The average daily change was -1 point, or down 1 point.

7. Find the average of the following low temperatures:

     $-12°$ $-8°$ $-6°$ $-3°$ $0°$ $3°$ $5°$

 The Dow Jones Industrial Average is an average of the common stock prices of 30 industrial firms. Investors use the average to track market trends. The Dow Jones & Company, a financial publishing firm, computes the average each trading hour while the stock market is open. The firm started publishing an industrial average in 1896 using the stocks of 12 companies to compute the average.

Work with a partner to complete each of the following. Then write two examples to illustrate each relationship.

8. $+ \cdot + = $ ▪

9. $+ \cdot - = $ ▪

10. $- \cdot + = $ ▪

11. $- \cdot - = $ ▪

12. $+ \div + = $ ▪

13. $+ \div - = $ ▪

14. $- \div + = $ ▪

15. $- \div - = $ ▪

TRY THESE

Tell whether each product or quotient will be *positive* or *negative*.

16. $7(-4)$

17. $-25 \div (-5)$

18. $-48 \div 6$

19. $-81 \div 9$

20. $(-4)^3$

21. $(-4)(9)(2)$

Mental Math **Find each answer.**

22. $36 \div (-12)$

23. $72 \div 9$

24. $39 \div (-3)$

25. $0 \div (-2)$

26. $(-4 \cdot 6) \div (-3)$

27. $(2)^4$

28. Write two related division sentences for $7(-3) = -21$.

ON YOUR OWN

Choose **Use a calculator, paper and pencil, or mental math.**

29. Hobbies Suppose a scuba diver is 180 ft below sea level and rises to the surface at a rate of 30 ft/min. How long will it take the diver to reach the surface?

30. Business The price of a stock fell $2 each day for 8 days.

a. What was the total change in the price of the stock?

b. Before the price of the stock started falling, its value was $38. What was the price of the stock after the drop?

31. Critical Thinking Write the calculator steps you would use to find the product of -23 and -45. Then find the product.

Evaluate for $m = 1.8$ and $n = 4.6$.

1. $4m - n$

2. $4(n + 2) + m^2$

Find each answer.

3. $120 + 43 - 95 + 11$

4. $28 - 9 + 35 + 14$

5. In how many ways can you order the letters, A, B, C, and D? Do not repeat a letter in any arrangement.

*Atmospheric pressure at sea level is 1 atmosphere, which is 14.7 lb/in². At 33 ft below sea level the pressure is 2 atmospheres. The pressure is 3 atmospheres 66 ft below sea level. **What is the pressure in atmospheres 198 ft below sea level? in pounds per square inch?***

Estimation **Estimate each product or quotient.**

32. $-24 \cdot 35$

33. $428 \div (-58)$

34. $-108(-55)$

35. $-265 \div (-129)$

36. $-72 \cdot 68$

37. $64 \cdot 93$

Find the point on the number line that shows each product or quotient.

38. $-2 \cdot 0$ **39.** $-16 \div (-2)$ **40.** $(-1)^4$ **41.** $4(-2)^0$ **42.** -1^4

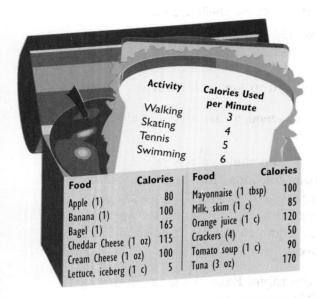

43. Nutrition Suppose you swam for 25 min and then had lunch. For lunch you had 1 c of tomato soup, 3 oz of cheddar cheese, and 8 crackers.

   a. Find the number of calories used while swimming and the number of calories consumed in the lunch.

   b. Find the net gain or loss of calories.

44. Critical Thinking Use the table at the left. Select foods for a lunch and one of the activities for 40 min of exercise. Find the total number of calories consumed in the lunch and the number of calories burned during exercise. Find the net gain or loss of calories.

45. Writing Explain how to find the sign of the product or quotient of any two integers.

CHECK POINT

Write an integer for each situation.

1. The Dead Sea is 1,300 ft below sea level.

2. Miami's average July temperature is 83°F.

Choose **Use a calculator, pencil and paper, or mental math to evaluate.**

3. $153 + (-67)$

4. $86 - (-17)$

5. $37 + (-89)$

6. $-54 \div (-9)$

7. $12 \cdot (-15)$

8. $(-5)^2 + 6(2 - 4)$

What's Ahead

- Solving problems by making a table

PROBLEM SOLVING

4-7 Make a Table

READ PLAN SOLVE LOOK BACK

When a problem requires you to look at a lot of possibilities, you can organize the information in a table.

> Sheila works at a variety store after school. Three children bought the same item, and each time she made 45¢ in change using a different combination of coins. Sheila wondered how many ways she could make 45¢ in change without using pennies.

READ

Read and understand the given information. Summarize the problem.

1. Restate what you are to find in your own words.
2. What information will you need to use to solve the problem?

PLAN

Decide on a strategy to solve the problem.

Making a table of the coins and their values will help you find all the possible coin combinations that have a total value of 45¢. A table will also help you avoid using the same combination more than once. Develop a systematic way of entering the coin choices so that you do not have the same combination more than once.

SOLVE

Try out the strategy.

3. a. Copy and complete the table. Extend the table until you have found all possible combinations.

Coin	Number of Coins (Value)			
Quarter	1 (25¢)	1 (25¢)	1 (25¢)	0 (0¢)
Dime	0 (0¢)	1 (10¢)	2 (20¢)	■
Nickel	4 (20¢)	2 (10¢)	0 (0¢)	■
Total value	45¢	45¢	45¢	■

b. How many different ways can Sheila make 45¢ in change without using pennies?

LOOK BACK

You can use a table to solve other kinds of coin problems.

4. Suppose you have a penny, a nickel, a dime, and a quarter. How many different amounts of money are possible using one or more of these coins?

Use the strategy Make a Table to solve each problem.

5. Each day Jamal selects a pair of jeans and a sweatshirt from his wardrobe.

  a. How many different combinations of jeans and sweatshirts can Jamal make with his clothes?

  b. Discussion Describe any patterns or shortcuts you found that helped you solve the problem.

6. Joe remembered that the three digits in his locker combination were 3, 5, and 7, but he forgot the order of the numbers. What is the maximum number of combinations he must check in order to open his lock?

ON YOUR OWN

Use any strategy to solve each problem. If there is not enough information, state what information you need. Show all your work.

7. Hanon and Oliver collected $39 for tickets to the science museum. Adult's tickets cost $7, and children's tickets cost $5. How many adults and how many children plan to visit the museum?

8. The local library sponsored a used book sale to raise money. The books were priced at $.59 for paperback books and $.99 for hardcover books. Kim spent $17.19. How many of each kind of book did she buy?

9. a. The town of Dornville is 15 mi south of Chester. Topson is 12 mi north of Dornville. Ludberg is 4.5 mi north of Topson. What is the order of the towns from north to south?

  b. What is the distance between Dornville and Ludberg?

10. Without looking, Gordon drew marbles from a bowl containing red, green, blue, and white marbles. When he had one marble of each color, he was told to stop. What is the least number of marbles he could have selected? the greatest number?

The Library of Congress, established by the U.S. Congress in 1800, now has over 84 million items in its collections, including books, musical compositions, photographs, and recordings. The Library of Congress is one of the largest research libraries in the world. The Library of Congress also provides books in Braille for people who are visually impaired.

Source: *World Book*

11. A science teacher discovered that students had used, and misplaced, several of his weights. He can find the 9 mg, 7 mg, 2 mg, and 5 mg weights. How can he use these weights to find out if a piece of copper wire weighs 1 mg?

12. During a 10-minute period in a busy office building, an elevator started at the ground floor, rose 8 floors, rose 7 floors, descended 3 floors, rose 5 floors, descended 1 floor, rose 2 floors, rose 8 floors, and descended 11 floors. On which floor was the elevator at the end of the 10-minute period?

13. After a stormy voyage, Sam Skar landed on the desert island where he had buried a treasure chest many years before. To his dismay, a hungry animal had gnawed around the edges of the map he had left in a hollow palm tree. Luckily, Sam remembered that he had walked away from the old palm tree in one of the four compass directions (north, south, east, or west) and that he then made a 90° turn. The fragment of map told him he had first walked 12 paces from the palm tree. Then he had walked 5 paces before burying his treasure. What is the greatest number of places Sam will have to dig to find his treasure?

14. The measure of the first of three angles of a triangle is three times the measure of the second angle. The measure of the third angle is twice the measure of the second angle. What is the measure of each of the angles?

15. List the ways you can add two or more consecutive positive integers to get a sum of 90.

16. **Physical Science** A ball is dropped from a 16-ft height. Each time it hits the ground it bounces one-half its previous height. The ball is caught when the height of its bounce is 2 ft. What is the total vertical distance the ball traveled?

17. **Physical Science** The diagram at the right shows how a ray of light strikes a mirror and then bounces off. The angle formed by the incoming ray and the mirror is congruent to the angle formed by the reflected ray and the mirror. Suppose the angle between the incoming and reflected rays of light is 124°. At what angle is the light reflected from the mirror?

FLASHBACK

Two integers are consecutive if the second integer is one greater than the first integer.

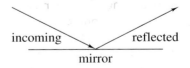

incoming   reflected

mirror

WHAT YOU'LL NEED

✓ **Algebra tiles**

4-8 Addition and Subtraction Equations

THINK AND DISCUSS

An equation is like a scale. The weights on both sides of a scale must be the same for the scale to balance. For an equation to be true, the values on both sides of the equation must be equal.

You can represent a quantity that is unknown with a **variable.** In equations, you use a letter like x to represent the variable. The green rectangular tile in the model below represents the variable. The value of the variable that makes the equation true is the **solution.**

1. **Discussion** How would you remove weights to get the variable alone but keep the scale balanced?

Some problems are easy to solve by inspection. However, developing a method to solve easy problems will help you solve more difficult ones. To find the value of a variable, you need to get it alone on one side of the equal sign. The models below show the steps in solving the equation $x + 3 = 7$.

2. Complete the equation that each model represents.

$x + 3 = 7$

$x + 3 - \blacksquare = 7 - \blacksquare$

$x = \blacksquare$

3. Model and solve each equation. Show all the steps.

   a. $x + 3 = 5$ **b.** $y + 5 = 8$ **c.** $7 + a = 12$

The most precise scale ever made is produced in Gottingen, Germany, and is called the Sartorius 4108. It is accurate to the nearest 350 trillionth of an ounce which is less than $\frac{1}{16}$ of the ink used to print the period at the end of this sentence.

Source: *Guinness Book of Records*

A model can be especially helpful when you solve equations with negative integers.

Example 1   Model the equation $n - 4 = -1$ and solve.

$n - 4 = -1$ Subtracting is the
$n + (-4) = -1$ same as adding the opposite.

 $= \blacksquare$ Represent the equation.

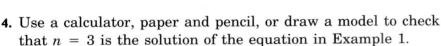   Add zero pairs so that 4 negative tiles can be removed from both sides.

$= \square\square\square$

$n = 3$

4. Use a calculator, paper and pencil, or draw a model to check that $n = 3$ is the solution of the equation in Example 1.

5. Model each equation. Then solve and check.

   a. $x - 4 = 5$ **b.** $y - 2 = 8$ **c.** $a - (-5) = -3$

You can solve equations using *inverse operations*. Addition is the inverse operation of subtraction.

Example 2   Solve $-4 = x - 3$. Check your answer.

$$-4 = x - 3$$
$$-4 + 3 = x - 3 + 3 \quad \text{Add 3 to both sides of}$$
$$-1 = x \quad\quad\quad\quad\quad \text{the equation.}$$

Check $-4 = x - 3$
$\quad\quad\quad -4 = -1 - 3$ Replace x with -1.
$\quad\quad\quad -4 = -4$

6. Stephen solved $x - 5 = -3$. His solution was $x = -8$. How can checking his solution help Stephen? Find his mistake.

7. Latonia solved $a - 9 = 4$ mentally by thinking "I must get the variable a alone. So I must add 9 to both sides of the equation." What solution should Latonia get? Check the solution.

Mixed REVIEW

Use the data: 8, 12, 12, 11, 7, 12, 10, 8, 10, 9

1. Draw a line plot.

2. Make a frequency table.

Find each answer.

3. $54 \div (-9)$

4. $8(-3 + 4)$

5. $-24 \div 3$

6. $4(5)(-3)$

7. The 16 teams in the summer softball league held a tournament. A team was eliminated after a single loss. How many games were played to determine the league championship?

When you add or subtract the same number from each side of an equation, the result is an **equivalent equation.** Equivalent equations have the same solution. The following properties summarize how you can add and subtract from both sides of an equation to form equivalent equations.

Addition Property of Equality

You can add the same value to both sides of an equation.

Arithmetic	Algebra
$5 = 5$	If $a = b$, then
$5 + 3 = 5 + 3$	$a + c = b + c$.

Subtraction Property of Equality

You can subtract the same value from both sides of an equation.

Arithmetic	Algebra
$5 = 5$	If $a = b$, then
$5 - 2 = 5 - 2$	$a - c = b - c$.

8. State whether you would use the Addition Property of Equality or the Subtraction Property of Equality to solve each equation. Then state what you would add or subtract.

   a. $x + 19 = 36$ b. $x - 54 = -28$ c. $x - (-15) = -42$

TRY THESE

Write the equation represented by each model. Then solve the equation.

9.   10.   11.

Use a model to solve each equation.

12. $x + 4 = 5$ 13. $x - 3 = -2$ 14. $x + 1 = -4$

Solve.

15. $y + 1 = 9$ 16. $3 = a - 5$ 17. $2 + n = -3$

18. $8 = p + 7$ 19. $x - (-5) = 3$ 20. $-8 = (-7) + b$

ON YOUR OWN

Mental Math **Solve each equation.**

21. $x + 6 = -6$ **22.** $x - 6 = -6$ **23.** $x + 6 = 6$ **24.** $x - 6 = 6$

25. $x - 3 = 0$ **26.** $-5 = p + 8$ **27.** $q - 6 = 4$ **28.** $7 = 9 + y$

Choose **Use a calculator, paper and pencil, or mental math. Solve each equation and check the solution.**

29. $n - 35 = 84$ **30.** $166 = m + 97$ **31.** $x + 25 = 16$

32. $-17 = x + 6$ **33.** $r - 54 = 74$ **34.** $8 = 19 + d$

35. **Choose A, B, C, or D.** Kira had $58.25 after buying a calculator. Which equation could you use to find how much money Kira had to start with if the calculator cost $13.45?

A. $m - \$13.45 = \$58.25$ **B.** $m + \$13.45 = \$58.25$

C. $m + \$58.25 = \$13.45$ **D.** $\$58.25 - \$13.45 = m$

36. **Writing** Explain the meaning of inverse operations.

37. Are $5 + x = 4$ and $3 + x = 2$ equivalent equations? Explain.

38. **Business** The bar graph at the right shows the projected changes in the number of jobs for the given occupational groups.

   a. Which group expects the greatest increase in jobs from 1988 to 2000? Which expects a decrease?

   b. Which equation could you use to find the group that expects 1.7 million more jobs than the clerical group, $n - 2.5 = 1.7$ or $n + 1.7 = 2.5$?

   c. Which group will have 1.7 million more jobs than the clerical group?

39. **Critical Thinking** Explain how you could solve $x + 15 = 34$ using the Addition Property of Equality.

 40. **Investigation (p. 144)** Use your balance scale to solve $x + 3 = 8$. Place a penny at 3 on the left side and another penny at 8 on the right side of the scale. Where should you place a third penny on the left side to balance the scale?

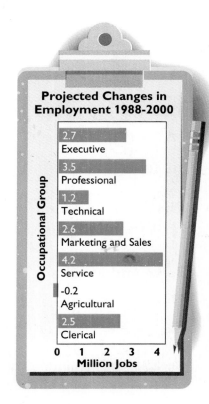

Projected Changes in Employment 1988-2000

Occupational Group	Million Jobs
Executive	2.7
Professional	3.5
Technical	1.2
Marketing and Sales	2.6
Service	4.2
Agricultural	-0.2
Clerical	2.5

Graph each integer and its opposite on a number line.

1. -3 **2.** 5   **3.** -6 **4.** 2   **5.** 4   **6.** -5

Compare. Use <, >, or =.

7. $|-11| \; ■ \; |5|$ **8.** $|-1| \; ■ \; |-2|$ **9.** $|7| \; ■ \; |-7|$ **10.** $|9| \; ■ \; |13|$

Name the integer represented by each set of tiles.

11.   **12.**   **13.**   **14.**

Mental Math Find each sum.

15. $-6 + 2$ **16.** $-5 + 7$ **17.** $13 + (-17)$ **18.** $-9 + (-18)$

Choose Use a calculator, paper and pencil, or mental math to find each difference.

19. $5 - 15$ **20.** $-9 - 13$ **21.** $18 - (-1)$ **22.** $-44 - 72$

23. $-17 - (-8)$ **24.** $-198 - (-105)$ **25.** $265 - (-123)$ **26.** $66 - 0$

Find the product or quotient.

27. $8 \cdot (-3)$ **28.** $-24 \div (-4)$ **29.** $-9(-7)$ **30.** $-54 \div 6$

31. $10 \cdot 7$ **32.** $(7)(-3)(4)$ **33.** $81 \div (-3)$ **34.** $(-13)(-8)(4)$

Find each answer.

35. $2(3 - 8) \div 5$ **36.** $(-7)^3$ **37.** $(-1)^{12}$ **38.** -1^{12} **39.** $6(-3) + 5(-2)$

Solve and check.

40. $a + 2 = 8$ **41.** $6 = p - 4$ **42.** $q + 3 = -5$ **43.** $y - 2 = -7$

44. $7 + r = -147$ **45.** $23 = n - 4$ **46.** $-2 + n = -56$ **47.** $q - 12 = 5$

48. Elizabeth had 16 coins in her pocket totaling $1.50. What are two combinations of coins she could have?

4-9 Multiplication and Division Equations

T H I N K A N D D I S C U S S

You and a friend agree to wash windows for an elderly neighbor. You are paid $10, which you share equally. Let m represent the money each of you gets. Then the equation $2m = 10$ represents the situation. You can solve the equation using a model.

$2m = 10$ Represent the equation.

$\dfrac{2m}{2} = \dfrac{10}{2}$ Divide the tiles on each side of the equal sign into two groups of equal size.

$m = 5$

1. How much money do you each get?

Since multiplication and division are *inverse operations,* you can use division to undo multiplication in an equation.

Example 1   Solve $4b = 48$.

$$4b = 48$$

$$\frac{4b}{4} = \frac{48}{4} \qquad \text{Divide both sides of the equation by 4.}$$

$$b = 12$$

Check $4b = 48$

$4 \cdot 12 = 48$ Replace b with 12.

$48 = 48$ ✓

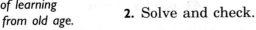

The excitement of learning separates youth from old age. As long as you're learning you're not old.

—Rosalyn S. Yalow (1921–)

2. Solve and check.

   a. $2g = 14$ **b.** $2g = -14$ **c.** $-2g = -14$ **d.** $-2g = 14$

3. Discussion How can you predict the sign of a solution before you solve an equation? (*Hint:* Use the equations and your solutions in Question 2 to look for a pattern.)

You can use multiplication to solve division equations.

Example 2 Solve $\frac{s}{-4} = -5$.

$$\frac{s}{-4} = -5$$

$$(-4)\frac{s}{-4} = -5(-4) \quad \text{Multiply both sides of the equation by } -4.$$

$$s = 20$$

Check $\frac{s}{-4} = -5$

$$\frac{20}{-4} = -5 \quad \text{Replace } s \text{ with 20.}$$

$$-5 = -5 \checkmark$$

4. Solve and check.

    a. $\frac{x}{8} = 9$ **b.** $\frac{x}{6} = -15$ **c.** $\frac{x}{-5} = -23$

The following properties summarize how you can use division and multiplication to write equivalent equations.

Multiplication Property of Equality

You can multiply both sides of an equation by the same value.

Arithmetic	**Algebra**
$6 = 6$	If $a = b$, then
$6 \cdot 2 = 6 \cdot 2$	$a \cdot c = b \cdot c$.

Division Property of Equality

You can divide both sides of an equation by the same nonzero value.

Arithmetic	**Algebra**
$6 = 6$	If $a = b$, then
$6 \div 2 = 6 \div 2$	$a \div c = b \div c, c \neq 0$.

5. State whether you would use the Division Property of Equality or the Multiplication Property of Equality to solve.

    a. $5x = 95$ **b.** $\frac{x}{-12} = -24$ **c.** $-3x = 42$

6. Frank used the equation $12x = -36$ to estimate the solution for the equation $12x = -38$. Do you think his equation will result in a good estimate? Why or why not?

TRY THESE

Write the equation represented by each model. Then solve and check the equation.

7. ▮▮▮ = ▪▪▪▪ / ▪▪▪▪ / ▪▪▪▪
8. ▮▮ = ▪▪▪▪

Mental Math **Solve each equation.**

9. $2x = 4$

10. $3x = -27$

11. $\frac{y}{-4} = -12$

12. $\frac{n}{-5} = 11$

13. $-7y = -28$

14. $t \div 6 = -10$

ON YOUR OWN

Choose **Use a calculator, paper and pencil, or mental math to solve.**

15. $8n = 112$
16. $\frac{n}{3} = -42$
17. $-4 = -2r$
18. $\frac{q}{-5} = 30$

19. $\frac{t}{8} = 120$
20. $-9x = 189$
21. $\frac{r}{-4} = -104$
22. $7 = \frac{n}{9}$

Estimate the solution.

23. $\frac{x}{18} = -40$
24. $-2x = -61$
25. $\frac{x}{-78} = -63$
26. $19x = -117$

27. Writing Susan's solution for the equation $\frac{n}{-6} = 12$ is $n = -2$. Explain how Susan may have found this solution and how you would help her correct her mistake.

28. Critical Thinking For what values of x is the equation $5|x| = 10$ true?

29. **Choose A, B, or C.** Which equation would you use to represent the following situation: An actively growing tree absorbs about 26 lb of carbon dioxide a year. How many years, y, would it take a growing tree to absorb 390 lb of carbon dioxide?

   A. $26 + y = 390$
   B. $\frac{y}{26} = 390$
   C. $26y = 390$

30. Investigation (p. 144) Use your scale to solve $4x = 8$. Place a penny at 8 on the right side. Find where you must place 4 pennies on the left side to balance the scale.

Mixed REVIEW

Name the property shown.

1. $3(4 + 8) = 12 + 24$
2. $21 \cdot 1 = 21$
3. $0(17.56) = 0$
4. $3 + 4 = 4 + 3$

Solve.

5. $4 + x = -6$
6. $x - 8 = 5$

7. A clock gains 4 min every hour. One day it is set to the correct time at 9:00 A.M. What is the correct time when the clock shows 1:00 P.M.?

On average, miners dig up *about 625 acres of land every day. They also replant about 337 acres a day.*

Source: In One Day

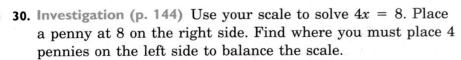

THINK AND DISCUSS

You can solve many types of problems by writing an equation. First you must identify the variable, then translate the words into two equal expressions joined by an equal sign.

Example 1

Write an equation for "One-fourth of a number is ten."

Let n = the unknown number.   Identify the variable.

$\frac{n}{4} = 10$ Write an equation.

1. What word in the sentence translates as an equal sign?

When problems have phrases like *less than* or *more than*, you must pay careful attention to the two parts of the sentence joined by the word *equals* or *is*.

2. Fifteen equals three more than a number.

   a. What number is to the left of the word *equals*?

   b. Let n = the unknown number. Write an expression for the phrase on the right side of the word *equals*.

   c. Write an equation joining the two parts you identified.

In some word problems, you must change the order of the numbers from how they occur in the English sentence.

3. **Choose A, B, or C.** Which equation is correct for "Fifteen is three less than a number"?

   A. $15 = 3 - n$ **B.** $15 = n - 3$ **C.** $15 - 3 = n$

4. Write an equation for each sentence.

   a. Three times a number is twelve.

   b. Three less than a number is twelve.

   c. A number increased by three equals twelve.

   d. A number divided by three equals twelve.

Most problems are not stated in a way that allows you to easily translate the words into an equation. You can simplify such problems by rewording the key information into one sentence that uses *is* or *equals*.

Example 2

Write an equation for the following situation.

On Tuesday, 80 students were absent from school. There were 478 students present. How many students attend the school?

- Think: 478 students is 80 less than the number of students that attend the school.

- Let s = the number of students who attend the school. *Identify the variable.*

$478 = s - 80$ *Write an equation.*

5. Read the following problem: The CN Tower in Toronto and the Sears Tower in Chicago are the two tallest buildings in the world. The CN Tower is 553 m tall. It is 110 m taller than the Sears Tower. How tall is the Sears Tower?

   a. Reword the problem using *is* or *equals*.

   b. Write an equation and find the height of the Sears Tower.

   c. Solve the equation you wrote.

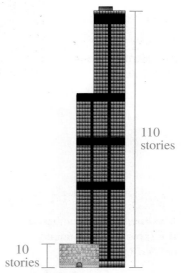

110 stories

10 stories

Originally called cloudscrapers, *the first true skyscraper was built in Chicago in 1884 for the Home Insurance Corporation. It had 10 stories. The Sears Tower has 110 stories.*

TRY THESE

Match the word sentence with the equation.

6. Four less than a number equals seven.

7. Ten times a number is negative fifty.

8. A number minus twelve is three.

9. Twenty-five is three more than a number.

10. Eight equals a number divided by negative two.

11. The product of a number and nine is negative thirty-six.

12. Six plus a number is two.

A. $25 = 3 + n$

B. $8 = \dfrac{n}{-2}$

C. $m - 12 = 3$

D. $9n = -36$

E. $p - 4 = 7$

F. $25 + 3 = n$

G. $10n = -50$

H. $6 + a = 2$

I. $4 - q = 7$

FLASHBACK

Equivalent equations have the same solution.

Ride on Steam

For a great ride up a beautiful mountain, take the Cog Railway up Mt. Washington in New Hampshire. Built in 1869, the Cog Railway takes about one hour to make the three-mile journey.

The train stops about $\frac{1}{4}$ of the way up for water. Each locomotive uses a ton of coal and a thousand gallons of water for each passenger car. The water cools the hot coals to produce the steam needed to run the engine.

What a leisurely way to visit the ''top'' of the world!

⌐O N YOUR OWN

13. **Writing** *Eucalyptus deglupta,* a gum tree, grows quickly. One such tree reached 150 ft in 15 years. Cathy and Darla wrote different equations to find the yearly average growth of the tree, *g*. Cathy wrote $15g = 150$. Darla wrote $150 \div 15 = g$. Are these equivalent equations? Explain.

Write an equation. Then solve.

14. The sum of 52 and some number is 75.

15. A number divided by 6 equals 8.

16. Five times some number is 45.

17. Fifty-six is fourteen less than a number.

18. **Biology** A honeybee hive contains 35,000 cells. How many cells are there in 50 hives?

19. You are putting glasses on display shelves. You have 120 glasses. You know that each shelf holds 30 glasses. How many shelves will you need?

20. Hillary spends 3 h a week at soccer practice. This is one-third the time she spends on her homework. How much time does she spend on her homework?

21. **Astronomy** Ptolemy, an astronomer from the ancient world, named 48 constellations. Today, there are 88 constellations named in all. How many constellations were not named by Ptolemy?

22. **Travel** It is 604 mi from Albuquerque to Salt Lake City. Suppose you drive 50 mi/h.

   a. About how many hours will it take you to drive from Salt Lake City to Albuquerque?

   b. If you stop after driving 238 mi, how much farther must you drive?

Use the article at the left for Exercises 23–24. Write and solve an equation to find each of the following.

23. the amount of water used per passenger for one passenger car carrying 40 people

24. the age of the Cog Railway

4-11 Exploring Two-Step Equations

WHAT? The earliest mathematical records that archaeologists have found come from Babylon, now central Iraq. About 300 clay tablets, dating about 2100 B.C. to A.D. 300, include many equations and their solutions.

WORK TOGETHER

Take turns with a partner.

• Without showing your partner, write an equation that uses both multiplication and addition, for example $2(3) + 5 = 11$. Rewrite the equation using a variable for one of the factors of the product. For instance x is substituted for 3 in $2x + 5 = 11$.

• Show the equation with the variable to your partner. Have your partner find the solution.

• After three turns each, discuss the strategies you used to find the solution to each equation your partner wrote.

THINK AND DISCUSS

One way to solve equations like those you have written is to use the problem solving strategy Guess and Test. Another way, which is more efficient, is to have a system for solving two-step equations.

1. **a.** To solve the equation below, which do you think you should do first, subtract 1 tile from each side or divide each side into two equal groups? Explain your choice.

b. Use tiles to solve the equation. Then check your solution.

c. Describe the steps you used to solve the equation.

2. Write the equation that is represented by each model. Use algebra tiles to solve. Write an equation for each step you use in solving the equation. Then check your solution.

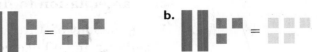

You can solve two-step equations without using models by thinking of inverse operations. Because the equation involves two operations, you must undo two operations.

3. Solve $5n + 7 = -18$.

  a. How can you undo adding 7?

  b. Do the same thing to both sides of the equation. Write the resulting equation.

  c. How can you undo multiplying n by 5?

  d. What is the value of n?

  e. Check your solution.

The way you solved the equation in Question 3 leads to the following method for solving two-step equations.

Solving a Simple Two-Step Equation

1. Undo addition or subtraction.

2. Undo multiplication or division.

4. Are the two steps above the same as the ones you used to solve the equations using models on page 181? Explain.

5. Solve and check $\frac{n}{3} + 2 = 6$.

ON YOUR OWN

Write the equation represented by each model. Then solve and check.

6. **7.**

Use a model to solve each equation. Then check your solution.

8. $2n + 6 = -8$ **9.** $3x + 6 = 12$ **10.** $2y - 10 = -2$

Solve each equation.

11. $8r - 8 = -32$ **12.** $5t + 12 = 67$ **13.** $\frac{m}{-11} + 1 = -10$

14. $\frac{n}{8} + 4 = 13$ **15.** $7r - 6 = -104$ **16.** $\frac{x}{3} + 9 = 9$

17. Calculator Write the calculator steps you would use to solve $5x + 12 = 67$. Then use your calculator to solve.

Mental Math Solve each equation.

18. $5c + 5 = 0$ **19.** $\frac{n}{4} + 2 = 4$ **20.** $10t - 10 = 90$

21. Choose A, B, C, or D. Jeremy bought some pencils for $.32 each and a pad of graph paper for $1.58. The total cost for the supplies was $3.82. Which equation would you use to determine how many pencils Jeremy bought?

   A. $382p + 158 = 32$ **B.** $32p + 158 = 382$

   C. $158p + 32 = 382$ **D.** $32p + 382 = 158$

Write a situation for each equation.

22. $4g + 7 = 35$ **23.** $\frac{n}{3} + 5 = 10$

24. Writing Suppose a friend was absent from today's class. Write a note to your friend explaining how to solve the equation $5x - 23 = -13$.

25. Investigation (p. 144) Use your scale to solve $2x + 4 = 10$. Explain where you placed your pennies to find the solution.

CHECKPOINT

1. You have three 29-cent stamps and two 23-cent stamps. How many different amounts of postage do you have?

Solve.

2. $-7n = -91$ **3.** $\frac{n}{-4} + 6 = -3$ **4.** $y - (-3) = 4$

5. $\frac{n}{13} = -3$ **6.** $-5 = x + 16$ **7.** $\frac{x}{5} - 8 = 7$

8. Choose A, B, C, or D. Kendra uses 14 calories/min while running. If she burned 154 calories, which equation will help you find how many minutes (m) she has run?

   A. $m + 14 = 154$ **B.** $m - 14 = 154$

   C. $m \cdot 14 = 154$ **D.** $\frac{m}{14} = 154$

Wrap Up

Integers, Opposites, and Absolute Value 4-1, 4-2

Opposites are two numbers that are the same distance from 0 on the number line, but in opposite directions. The set of **integers** is the set of whole numbers and their opposites.

The **absolute value** of an integer is its distance, a nonnegative number, from 0 on a number line.

1. What integer represents 9°F below zero?

2. Draw a model for zero using 6 tiles.

3. Write the absolute value of each integer.
   a. -5 **b.** 2 **c.** -17

4. Order from least to greatest:
   7 -6 0 -3 1

Compare. Use <, >, or =.

5. -7 ■ 7 6. $|-3|$ ■ $|3|$ 7. -12 ■ 0 8. $|-9|$ ■ -4 9. 8 ■ -15

10. **Choose A, B, C, or D.** Which number of tiles could model -5?

   A. 4 tiles **B.** 9 tiles **C.** 10 tiles **D.** 12 tiles

Adding and Subtracting Integers 4-3, 4-4, 4-5

To add integers with the *same* sign, *add* the absolute values of the integers. The sum has the same sign as the addends.

To add integers with *different* signs, *subtract* the absolute values of the integers. The sum has the same sign as the integer with the greater absolute value.

To subtract an integer, add its opposite.

Write a numerical expression for each model. Find the sum or difference.

11.

12.

13.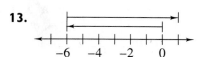

Find each sum or difference.

14. $-4 + 7$ 15. $-14 + (-8)$ 16. $3 - 8$ 17. $17 - (-12)$ 18. $15 + (-18)$

Multiplying and Dividing Integers   4-6

The product or quotient of two integers with the *same* sign is *positive*.

The product or quotient of two integers with *different* signs is *negative*.

Find each product or quotient.

19. $-5 \cdot 6$ **20.** $-14 \cdot -6$ **21.** $125 \div -5$ **22.** $-98 \div -49$

23. Writing Explain how to determine the signs of each of the following: the sum of -5 and 8 and the product of -5 and 8.

Writing and Solving Equations with Integers   4-3, 4-9, 4-10, 4-11

To solve an addition or subtraction equation, subtract or add the same value from both sides of the equation.

To solve a multiplication or division equation, divide or multiply both sides of the equation by the same nonzero value.

Use models, a calculator, or paper and pencil to solve and check.

24. $x - (-2) = -4$ **25.** $2y = 8$ **26.** $\frac{q}{5} = 7$ **27.** $3m + 4 = -2$

Write an equation. Then solve and check.

28. The sum of a number and 17 is -24. **29.** The quotient of a number divided by -9 is -6.

Strategies and Applications   4-7

You can use the strategy Make a Table to solve problems.

30. Scott sold school banners for a band money raiser. Small banners cost $1.25. The large ones cost $1.75. He sold $20 worth on Monday. How many of each size could he have sold? Write all the possible solutions you can find.

GETTING READY FOR CHAPTER 5

Estimate the area of each figure.

1.  **2.**  **3.**   **4.**

PUTTING IT ALL TOGETHER

Follow Up

Balancing Act

Two children are playing on a see-saw like the one shown below.

You solved equations using a balance model in the problems preceded by a magnifying glass (p. 173, # 40; p. 177, # 30; and p. 183, # 25). Use what you have learned to recommend where the children should sit for the see-saw to balance.

1. Suppose Child A sits 2 ft from the center. Where should Child B sit?
   a. Child A, 80 lb, Child B, 40 lb
   b. Child A, 100 lb, Child B, 75 lb
2. For a 12 ft long see-saw, where else could the children sit for the see-saw to be balanced?

Excursion: The word *balance* is used in many situations. Explain the following expressions. What does each expression have in common with a balance scale?
   a. Balance the budget.
   b. the balance of nature
   c. Balance the car's tires.
   d. Balance your checkbook.
   e. Our government is based on a system of checks and balances.

Where to Look:
- an encyclopedia

SKY HIGH

The modern Olympic Games started in 1896. That year Ellery Clark, representing the United States, won the high jump with a jump of 5' 11". As the years went by, the height jumped by the winner generally was greater than that of the previous champion. Research and graph the heights of all the high jumps during the modern Olympics. Do you think that there will be an Olympic champion who will double Clark's record? If you do, in approximately what year do you think this will happen?

Women began competing in track and field events in 1928 when Ethel Catherwood of Canada jumped 5' 2 1/2". Research and then graph the heights jumped by women in this event. What conclusions can you draw when comparing the two graphs?

HAPPY BIRTHDAY!

What is your birthday? Write your birthday as a number. For example, January 1 would be 1/1. Then write a word problem using the numbers of your birthday. Give your problem to someone else in the class to solve.

What do you think?

Cartographers make contour maps, which show the shape of the land. Their maps show the tips of the tallest mountains as well as the depths of the deepest valleys. Which continent do you think has the greatest difference between the height above sea level of the tallest mountain and the depth below sea level of the lowest valley? Find the data needed to answer this question.

SOLID TO GAS

Water is a compound that naturally exists in three states on Earth:

    solid—ice
    liquid—water
    gas—water vapor

At 32°F, water changes from liquid to solid or solid to liquid. This is called the freezing or melting point. At 212°F, water changes from liquid to gas or gas to liquid. This is called the boiling or condensation point. There is a range of 180° between the freezing and boiling points of water. Find the freezing and boiling points of some common materials such as gold, oxygen, salt, mercury, and one or two others that interest you. Chart their freezing and boiling points. What is the difference in degrees between these two points for each material?

187

1. Complete with an integer that makes each statement true.

   a. $-1 < \blacksquare$ **b.** $\blacksquare > -7$

   c. $|-13| > \blacksquare$ **d.** $-17 < \blacksquare$

2. Use models to represent each number in two different ways.

   a. 8 **b.** -1 **c.** -5

3. Write the following integers in order from least to greatest: $-2, 5, 0, -7, -3$.

4. Use models to represent each sum. Then find the sum.

   a. $7 + (-1)$ **b.** $-3 + 2$

   c. $-4 + (-2)$ **d.** $-11 + (-5)$

   e. $-8 + (-5)$ **f.** $5 + (-7)$

5. **Mental Math** Evaluate.

   a. $-3 + 5$ **b.** $-2 + (-2)$

   c. $-4 - 9$ **d.** $-11 + 15$

   e. $8 + (-8) + 4$ **f.** $7 - 13 + (-7)$

6. Evaluate.

   a. $6(-11)$ **b.** $-63 \div (-7)$

   c. $48 \div (-3)$ **d.** $-8(-9)$

   e. $22(4) \div -8$ **f.** $(-2 \cdot 8) \div 4$

7. A weight lifter can lift 90 kg plus the weight of the bar. At the gym, there are 5 kg, 10 kg, and 25 kg weights. The bar will hold up to 7 weights on each side. Each side must have the same weights. How many different combinations of weights can be placed on the bar for a total of 90 kg?

8. Solve.

   a. $x + 3 = 9$ **b.** $a - 4 = -1$

   c. $c - 2 = 5$ **d.** $y + 1 = -12$

   e. $n + (-4) = -10$ **f.** $z - (-2) = -8$

9. Write an equation for each sentence. Then solve.

   a. A number divided by 7 equals 3.

   b. Six less than a number is 52.

   c. A number times 6 equals -48.

   d. Five more than a number is -14.

10. Solve.

    a. $6n = -42$ **b.** $m \div 8 = 8$

    c. $\frac{q}{2} = -11$ **d.** $-9x = -180$

    e. $-12c = -132$ **f.** $\frac{m}{7} = -14$

11. A submarine was at a depth of 250 m below sea level. It rose 75 m. Then it dove 20 m. Use an integer to describe the new depth of the submarine.

12. **Writing** Explain the steps you use to solve the equation $5y + 2 = 17$.

13. Solve.

    a. $4d - 3 = 9$ **b.** $7z + 2 = -19$

    c. $9g + 1 = 82$ **d.** $\frac{x}{5} - 8 = -1$

14. **Choose A, B, C, or D.** Which equation is equivalent to $5a - 1 = 9$?

    A. $2a - 1 = 3$ **B.** $6a + 4 = 8$

    C. $13a + 1 = 14$ **D.** $10a - 15 = -4$

Choose A, B, C, or D.

1. Zoom Video charges $3.75/day for overdue videos. Carli had a video that was due on Sunday. She returned it the following Friday. How much did she owe?

   A. $3.75
   B. $22.50
   C. $18.75
   D. $15

2. Estimate to determine which sum is between 21 and 22.

   A. 13.71 + 1.5 + 8.2
   B. 6.75 + 9.02 + 5.838
   C. 5.99 + 2.69 + 15.49
   D. 3.772 + 12.04 + 4.009

3. Name a semicircle in the diagram.

   A. $\overset{\frown}{DCB}$
   B. $\overset{\frown}{DAB}$
   C. $\overline{AB}$
   D. $\overset{\frown}{ABC}$

4. Which set of tiles does *not* represent the integer −2?

   A. ▪▪▪▪
   B. ▪▪▪▪ / ▪▪▪▪
   C. ▪▪
   D. ▪▪▪▪

5. An obtuse triangle has one angle whose measure is 30°. What is the measure of the other acute angle?

   A. Any measure between 0° and 60°.
   B. Any measure less than 90°.
   C. Any measure between 30° and 60°.
   D. Any measure between 60° and 90°.

6. What is the solution to the equation $-15 = m - 9$?

   A. −24
   B. −6
   C. 24
   D. 6

7. Suppose s represents the amount of sugar (in cups) needed in a recipe. The amount of flour needed is always one-half cup more than twice the amount of sugar. Which variable expression represents the amount of flour?

   A. $\frac{1}{2} + s$
   B. $\frac{1}{2} + \frac{s}{2}$
   C. $\frac{1}{2} + 2s$
   D. $2(s + \frac{1}{2})$

8. Round 3.8962 to the nearest hundredth.

   A. 3.89
   B. 3.90
   C. 3.896
   D. 3.9

9. What can you conclude about $\triangle ABC$ and $\triangle DEF$?

   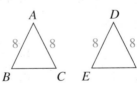

   A. $\triangle ABC \cong \triangle DEF$
   B. $\angle A \cong \angle D$
   C. $\overline{BC} \cong \overline{EF}$
   D. $\overline{AB} \cong \overline{DF}$

10. How many different combinations of one sandwich and one drink can Eric order if he has at most $3 to spend?

Tuna	$2.50
Hot dog	$1.75
Roast Beef	$2.95
Milk	$.60
Lemonade	$.50

    A. 3
    B. 4
    C. 5
    D. 6

Data **F**ile 5

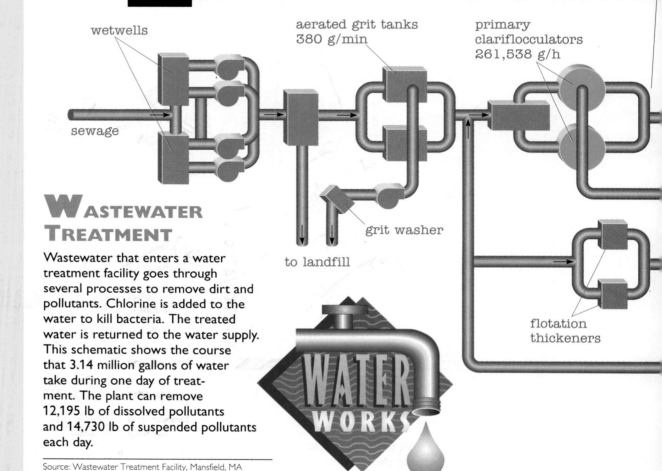

wetwells

aerated grit tanks
380 g/min

primary
clariflocculators
261,538 g/h

sewage

grit washer

to landfill

flotation
thickeners

WASTEWATER **T**REATMENT

Wastewater that enters a water treatment facility goes through several processes to remove dirt and pollutants. Chlorine is added to the water to kill bacteria. The treated water is returned to the water supply. This schematic shows the course that 3.14 million gallons of water take during one day of treatment. The plant can remove 12,195 lb of dissolved pollutants and 14,730 lb of suspended pollutants each day.

Source: Wastewater Treatment Facility, Mansfield, MA

Water Saved with Water-saving Products			
Conventional Fixture	**Gallons Used***	**Water-saver Fixture**	**Gallons Used***
Toilet	4–6 gal	Air-assisted toilet	0.5 gal
Shower	4–6 gal	Low-flow shower	2.1 gal
Faucets		Faucet-flow control aerators	
Bathroom	4–6 gal	*Bathroom*	0.5 gal
Kitchen	4–6 gal	*Kitchen*	1.5 gal
Top-load clothes washer	40–55 gal	Front-load clothes washer	22–33 gal

*toilet: gal/flush; shower, faucet: gal/min; clothes washer: gal/use

Source: EPA Journal

WHAT YOU WILL LEARN

- how to use measurement formulas
- how to model the surface area of prisms and cylinders
- how to use technology to apply the Pythagorean theorem
- how to solve problems by using guess and test

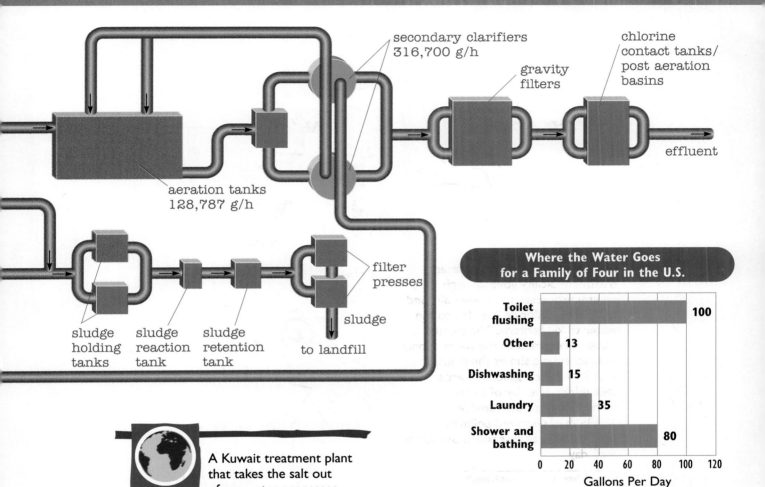

secondary clarifiers
316,700 g/h

gravity filters

chlorine contact tanks/ post aeration basins

effluent

aeration tanks
128,787 g/h

sludge holding tanks

sludge reaction tank

sludge retention tank

filter presses

sludge

to landfill

Where the Water Goes for a Family of Four in the U.S.

	Gallons Per Day
Toilet flushing	100
Other	13
Dishwashing	15
Laundry	35
Shower and bathing	80

Source: *Information Please Environmental Almanac*

WORLD VIEW

A Kuwait treatment plant that takes the salt out of sea water processes 5,000,000 gal of water each day.

A Look at the Great Lakes

	Lake Erie	Lake Huron	Lake Michigan	Lake Ontario	Lake Superior
Length	241 mi	206 mi	307 mi	193 mi	350 mi
Breadth	57 mi	183 mi	118 mi	53 mi	160 mi
Greatest depth	210 ft	750 ft	923 ft	802 ft	1,330 ft
Volume of water	116 mi^3	850 mi^3	1,180 mi^3	393 mi^3	2,900 mi^3
Area of water's surface	9,910 mi^2	23,000 mi^2	22,300 mi^2	7,550 mi^2	31,700 mi^2

Source: *World Almanac*

investigation

Memo

Companies manufacture thousands of new products every year. Nearly all of these products are sold in some kind of package. Many large companies employ packaging engineers to design packages for their products. The packaging engineers must come up with the best possible package design for a product. But what exactly does best mean?

Mission: Choose a common product. With the members of your group, design and construct several different packages for the product. Your packages may differ in shape, size, and packaging material. Then decide which package would be best for a manufacturer who intends to produce millions of the product. Explain why you think the package design you chose is best.

LeADs tOFoLLoW

✓ What factors must a manufacturer take into consideration when designing a package?

✓ Think of things you like to buy. What do you like about the packages?

5-1 Estimating Length and Area

Measures of length, area, and weight have interesting histories. For example, an acre was the amount of land that a farmer and two oxen could plow in one day. This varied from place to place. Finally, King Henry VIII of England standardized the area of an acre as 40 poles long by 4 poles wide. A pole equals 16.5 ft.

Source: *Why Do Clocks Run Clockwise?*

FLASHBACK

Perimeter is the distance around an object or figure.

WORK TOGETHER

Work with a group.

• Have each member of your group walk the length of your classroom heel-to-toe. Count the number of steps.

• Measure your foot and determine the length of the room.

• Average the lengths found by the members of your group.

• Compare your result with other groups' results.

THINK AND DISCUSS

1. How close were the lengths your group found in the Work Together activity?

2. What accounts for the differences in the measures the members of your group found and for the differences in the averages of the groups?

3. Which estimate do you think is the more accurate, the individual measurements or the average of the individual measurements? Explain.

Like other measurements, estimates of measure must include a unit in order to make sense. For example, knowing that a building has a height of 12 doesn't give you enough information. However, if you know that the building is 12 in. tall, then you know that the building is a miniature instead of a building that people could enter.

4. What unit of measure would you use to estimate each of the following?

   a. the width of a lake

   b. the wing span of a butterfly

   c. the perimeter of a picture frame

   d. the perimeter of an amusement park

5. a. How could you use a piece of string to estimate the perimeter of the puzzle piece at the right?

b. Estimate the perimeter.

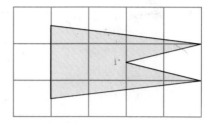

When you find the number of square units inside a figure, you are finding the **area** of the figure.

6. Each square at the right is 1 cm by 1 cm.

a. What is the area of each square?

b. Estimate the area of the pennant. How did you find the area?

c. There are 10 mm in 1 cm. How many 1 mm by 1 mm squares do you think are in a 1 cm by 1 cm square?

d. Estimate the area of the pennant using square millimeters.

7. Each square below is 1 cm by 1 cm.

a. How could you estimate the area of the figure?

b. Estimate the area of the figure.

c. Suppose the figure is a map of a lake. Each square represents 25 km². Estimate the area of the lake.

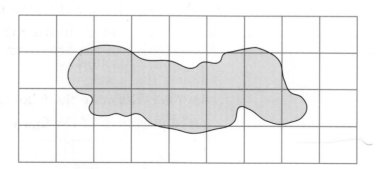

8. What square unit of measure would you use to estimate the area of a playground? the area of your kitchen? the area of a fingernail?

9. Critical Thinking You use units to express perimeter, but you use square units to express area. Why?

Romans set the measure of an inch as the width of a man's thumb. This remains a fairly accurate estimate of an inch. The dollar above is half the size of a real bill. Find the perimeter of this bill in "thumb widths." **Estimate the perimeter of a real dollar bill in inches.**

Source: *Why Do Clocks Run Clockwise?*

ON YOUR OWN

Estimate each length in inches. <u>1 in.</u>

10. _____

11. _____

Estimate each length in centimeters. <u>1 cm</u>

12. _____

13. _____

Choose the unit of measure listed that you would use to measure the given length or area.

14. the height of a telephone pole: mm, cm, m, km

15. the perimeter of a picture frame: ft, yd, in., mi

16. the area of a swimming pool: ft^2, yd^2, in.^2, mi^2

17. the length of a paper clip: mm, cm, m, km

18. the area of a soccer field: cm^2, m^2, km^2

A soccer field is large enough for more than 51,000 people to stand on.

Source: *Comparisons*

19. a. Measure the length of your *pace* (the distance you cover when you take a normal walking step).

   b. Use your pace to estimate the length and width of a room in your home. Then estimate the perimeter of the room.

   c. **Writing** Which would be more accurate, measuring the length of your room using your pace or the heel-to-toe method you used in the Work Together. Why?

20. Each square below is 1 cm by 1 cm. Estimate the following.

   a. the area of the figure   **b.** the perimeter of the figure

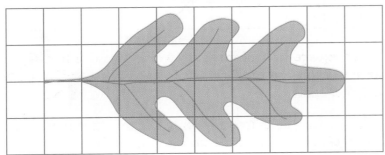

Oldest Park Celebrates 150th Year

Tivoli Gardens in Copenhagen, Denmark, the oldest amusement park in the world, turned 150 in 1993. The park covers 20 acres, and has 29 restaurants, but only 25 attractions.

The park's roller coaster was built in 1914. The driver still operates manual brakes. The park also features animated scenes from the Hans Christian Andersen's fairy tales.

Each year, gardeners plant over 400,000 flowers in the park. Also 110,718 lights of different colors light up the park each night.

After his visit to the Tivoli Gardens in the 1950s, Walt Disney started his plans for a theme park.

21. **a.** An acre has 43,560 ft². Does this mean that an acre must be square in shape? Explain.

   b. Estimate the number of square feet in the world's oldest amusement park.

22. Disneyland, Walt Disney's first theme park, has 180 acres. About how many times larger than Tivoli Gardens is Disneyland?

23. **a.** A football field measures 57,600 ft². Does a football field have more area or less area than an acre?

   b. About how many football fields of area does Tivoli Gardens have?

24. **Data File 5 (pp. 190–191)** The area of one of the Great Lakes is about four times the area of another. Which lakes are they?

Each square represents 25 mi². Estimate the area of each region below.

25.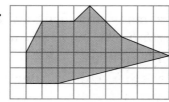

26.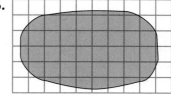

What's Ahead

- Finding areas and perimeters of rectangles, squares, and parallelograms

5-2 Area of Rectangles and Parallelograms

WHAT YOU'LL NEED

✓ Calculator

Rectangle
$A = lw$
$P = 2(l + w)$

Square
$A = s^2$
$P = 4s$

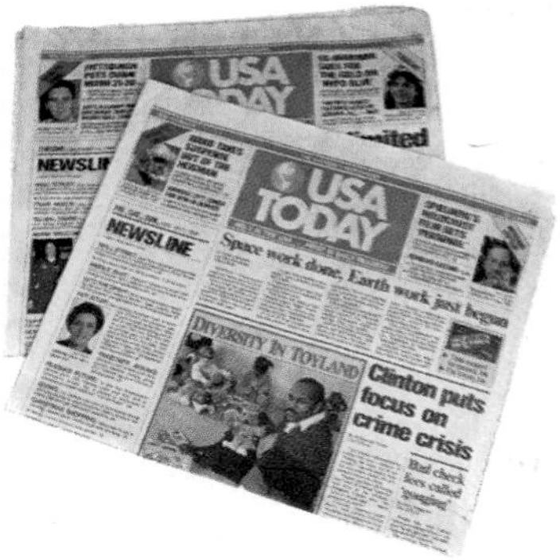

WHAT? The dimensions of a sheet of paper that is used to print four pages of the *USA Today* are 22 in. × 27.5 in. **What is the area of the sheet of paper? Find the area of a sheet of paper used to print four pages in your local newspaper.**

THINK AND DISCUSS

Some familiar formulas for the area and perimeter of rectangles and squares are shown at the left.

1. What do l and w represent? What does s represent?

2. How is the formula for the area of a square related to the formula for the area of a rectangle?

3. a. **Mental Math** Find the area of the rectangle.

b. Find the perimeter.

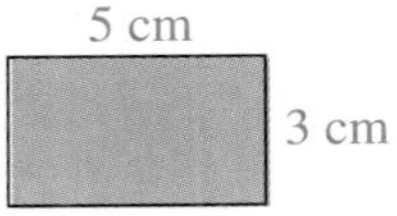

4. a. **Mental Math** Find the area of the square.

b. Find the perimeter.

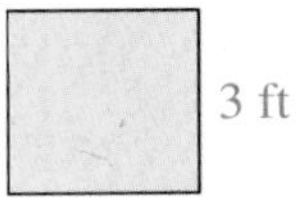

Suppose you want to find the area of this parallelogram that is not a rectangle.

5. If you draw the perpendicular segment from one vertex to the opposite side, what figures are formed?

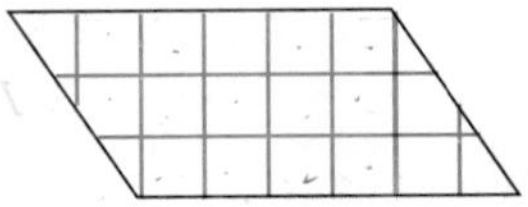

6. a. If you cut along the perpendicular segment and rearrange the two figures as shown, what new figure is formed?

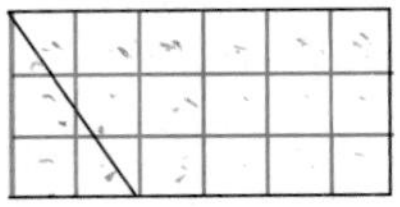

b. What is the area of this new figure?

c. What was the area of the original parallelogram? Why?

7. a. How many units long are the *base length* b and the *height* h of the original parallelogram?

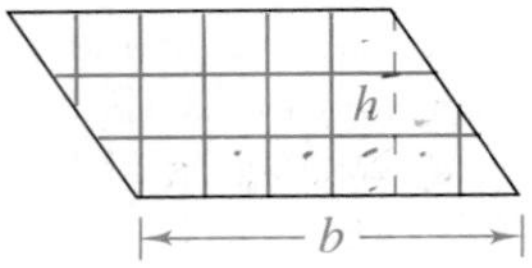

b. How are b and h related to the length and width of the rectangle that was formed?

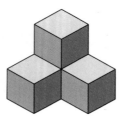

You can use parallelograms to make a design that gives the illusion of being three-dimensional. **Do all of the parallelograms in the design above have the same area? Why or why not?**

The formula for the area of a parallelogram follows from the formula for the area of a rectangle.

Area of Parallelograms
$A = bh$

Example 1

Estimate the area of the parallelogram. Then use a calculator to find the area.

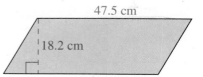

• $A = bh$.

Estimate: $50 \times 20 = 1{,}000 \text{ cm}^2$

47.5 ⊠ 18.2 ▤ *864.5*

The area is 864.5 cm².

8. Suppose you want to find the perimeter of the parallelogram in Example 1. What information do you need?

9. a. Calculator Find the perimeter of the parallelogram.

b. Find the area of the parallelogram.

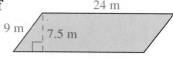

If you know the area and one dimension of a rectangle or parallelogram, you can find the other dimension.

Example 2

The area of a rectangle is 225 m². The length is 18 m. What is the perimeter of the rectangle?

• Use $A = lw$ to find the width.

$225 = 18w$ **Substitute 225 for A and 18 for l.**

$\dfrac{225}{18} = \dfrac{18w}{18}$ **Divide both sides by 18.**

225 ⊡ 18 ▤ *12.5*

The width is 12.5 m.

• $P = 2(l + w)$

$P = 2(18 + 12.5) = 2(30.5) = 61$

The perimeter is 61 m.

WORK TOGETHER

What do you think happens to the area and perimeter of a rectangle if you double the dimensions? if you triple the dimensions?

7 in.
4 in.

10. Find the area and perimeter of the rectangle shown.

11. Copy and complete the table at the right to find the area and perimeter of rectangles with the dimensions shown.

l	w	P	A
7 in.	4 in.	■	■
14 in.	8 in.	■	■
21 in.	12 in.	■	■
28 in.	16 in.	■	■

12. What happens to the area of a rectangle when you double, triple, or quadruple the dimensions?

13. What happens to the perimeter of a rectangle when you double, triple, or quadruple the dimensions?

TRY THESE

Find the area of each quadrilateral.

14. rectangle: $l = 8$ cm, $w = 6$ cm

15. parallelogram: $b = 12$ in., $h = 7$ in.

16. square: $s = 14$ m

Ben Nicholson painted this abstract work in 1937. The canvas measures 62.75 in. by 72.25 in. **What is the perimeter of the painting? What is the area of the painting?**

ON YOUR OWN

Choose Use a calculator, pencil and paper, or mental math to find the area and perimeter of each figure.

17. square

5 in.

18. rectangle

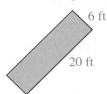
6 ft
20 ft

19. parallelogram

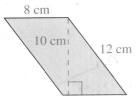
8 cm
10 cm
12 cm

20. parallelogram

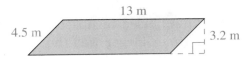
13 m
4.5 m
3.2 m

21. parallelogram

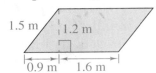
1.5 m
1.2 m
0.9 m
1.6 m

Which unit is best for measuring each of the following?

1. the perimeter of your desk: ft, yd, in., mi

2. the area of the gym floor: cm², m², km²

Find each product

3. −8(−7) 4. 6(−4)(3)

5. If the area of one shaded square is 3.4 in.², what is the area of the unshaded portion of the figure?

FLASHBACK

1 m = 100 cm

4 m
2 m

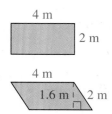
4 m
1.6 m 2 m

22. The perimeter of a square is 28 in. What is the area?

23. The area of a rectangle is 120 cm². The width of the rectangle is 8 cm. What is the perimeter of the rectangle?

24. **a. Critical Thinking** What happens to the area of the rectangle in the Work Together activity if you multiply the dimensions by n?

    b. What happens to the perimeter of the rectangle if you multiply the dimensions by n?

25. If you have 30 m of fencing, what are the areas of the different rectangles you could enclose with the fencing? Consider only whole-number dimensions.

26. **a. Data File 1 (pp. 2–3)** What was the area of the Chinese one kwan note?

    b. Calculator To the nearest tenth of a square inch, what was the area of a bani note?

    c. Critical Thinking What *might* be the dimensions of a bani note?

27. Find the area and perimeter of a rectangle with length 3 m and width 50 cm.

28. The area of a certain rectangle is 20 in.². The perimeter is 21 in. If you double the length and width, what will be the area and perimeter of the new rectangle?

29. **Writing** Why is the area of the rectangle at the left greater than the area of the parallelogram even though they have equal side lengths?

30. Find the area and perimeter of the figure at the right.

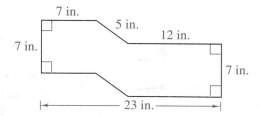
7 in.
5 in.
12 in.
7 in.
7 in.
23 in.

31. **History** The largest page size ever used for a newspaper was 51 in. by 35 in., used for *The Constellation* in 1859. The smallest page size was 3 in. by 3.75 in., used in Roseberg, Oregon, in 1876. About how many times larger was the largest page than the smallest page?

Use any strategy to solve each problem. Show all your work.

1. There are fewer than 50 chips in a game. The chips can be divided among 2, 3, or 7 teams so that each team gets the same number of chips. How many chips are in the game?

2. How many rectangles are in this figure?

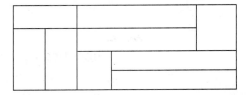

3. John, Lynn, and Rayquon are in charge of decorating for the spring dance. They decide to use streamers and balloons. Streamers will connect each of six points to each other. How many streamers will they need?

4. Tyler's family went on a vacation. At their first stop, Tyler spent $3 more than half his money to buy a souvenir T-shirt and a book. Later, he spent $3 more than half of the money that was left to buy some postcards and souvenirs. After he bought the postcards and souvenirs, he had $3 left. How much money did Tyler have before his purchases?

5. **a.** Use the six digits 4, 5, 6, 7, 8, and 9 to write a division expression that results in the greatest quotient when a four-digit number is divided by a two-digit number.

   b. Estimate the quotient.

6. Sari can walk 3 km in the same amount of time that Kim can ride 10 km on her bicycle. How far will Sari have walked when Kim has ridden 30 km?

7. What two integers have a sum of -7 and a product of 12?

8. A rectangle is 8 ft longer than it is wide. The area of the rectangle is 240 ft^2. What are the dimensions of the rectangle?

T-shirts became popular during World War II. By 1978 around 500 million T-shirts were sold. In 1990, the number sold had jumped to over one billion.

Source: *Comparisons*

5-3 **A**rea of Triangles and Trapezoids

WHAT YOU'LL NEED

✓ **Centimeter graph paper**

✓ **Scissors**

✓ **Calculator**

 The trapeze, high above the center ring of a circus, gets its name from trapezoids. Originally a trapeze was the name for a gymnastic device where a bar was hung from a large post with ropes. The bar and the post were the two parallel sides with the longer one always higher up.

Source: *Word Mysteries and Histories*

WORK TOGETHER

• Use centimeter graph paper to draw two congruent triangles. An example is shown.

• Cut out both triangles. Put them together to form a parallelogram.

  1. What is the area of the parallelogram?

  2. What is the area of each triangle? Explain your answer.

Use centimeter graph paper to draw two congruent trapezoids. An example is shown.

• Cut out both trapezoids. Put them together to form a parallelogram.

  3. What is the area of the parallelogram?

  4. What is the area of each trapezoid? Explain your answer.

THINK AND DISCUSS

Any side of a triangle can be considered the *base* of the triangle, with length b. The *height* h is the length of the perpendicular segment from the opposite vertex to the line containing the base.

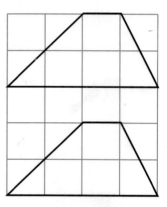

The two parallel sides of a trapezoid are the *bases* of the trapezoid, with lengths b_1 and b_2. The *height* h is the length of a perpendicular segment connecting the bases.

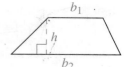

5. a. If you put two congruent copies of this trapezoid together to form a parallelogram, what will be the length of the base of the parallelogram?

b. What will be the height of the parallelogram?

c. What is an expression for the area of the parallelogram?

d. What is an expression for the area of the trapezoid?

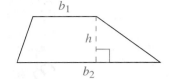

As you discovered in the Work Together activity, the formulas for the areas of triangles and trapezoids follow from the formula for the area of a parallelogram.

Area of Triangles and Trapezoids

Triangle: $A = \frac{1}{2}bh$

Trapezoid: $A = \frac{1}{2}h(b_1 + b_2)$

Example 1   Find the area and perimeter of the triangle.

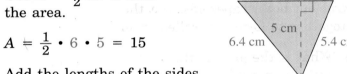

- Use $A = \frac{1}{2}bh$ to find the area.

   $A = \frac{1}{2} \cdot 6 \cdot 5 = 15$

- Add the lengths of the sides to find the perimeter.

   $P = 6.4 + 6 + 5.4 = 17.8$

The area is 15 cm². The perimeter is 17.8 cm.

6. Why did we not include 5 cm when we found the perimeter in Example 1?

7. Mental Math Find the area and the perimeter of the triangle.

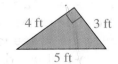

8. The area of a triangle is 16 in.². The height of the triangle is 2 in.

a. Critical Thinking How would you find the length of the base of the triangle?

b. Find the length of the base.

> In seeking knowledge,
> the first step is silence,
> the second listening,
> the third remembering,
> the fourth practicing,
> and the fifth—teaching others.
> —Solomon Ibn Gabirol
> (c. 1020–1057)

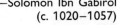

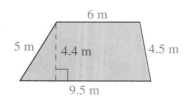

6 m
5 m · 4.4 m · 4.5 m
9.5 m

Example 2 Find the area and perimeter of the trapezoid.

- Use $A = \frac{1}{2}h(b_1 + b_2)$ to find the area.

$$A = \frac{1}{2} \times 4.4(6 + 9.5) \quad \text{Substitute.}$$

1 ÷ 2 ✕ 4.4 ✕ (6 + 9.5) ▤   *34.1*

- To find the perimeter, add the lengths of the sides.

9.5 + 4.5 + 6 + 5 ▤   *25*

The area is 34.1 m². The perimeter is 25 m.

9. a. What are the lengths of the bases of this trapezoid? What is the height?

b. Find the area.

c. Find the perimeter.

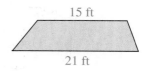

15.8 cm
8.5 cm · 13.5 cm
15 cm

10. The area of the trapezoid is 90 ft². What is the height? Check your answer.

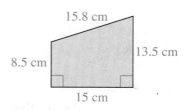

15 ft
21 ft

Mi𝓍ed REVIEW

1. Write an integer for 600 ft above sea level.

2. Find the perimeter and area of the rectangle below.

0.83 cm
1.4 cm

Complete.

3. A ■ is a segment that has both endpoints on a circle.

4. The vertex of a(n) ■ angle is at the center of a circle.

5. Four test scores are 87, 80, 77, and 83. A fifth score makes the mean 82. Find the mode.

TRY THESE

Find the area of each triangle or trapezoid.

11.
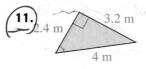
2.4 m · 3.2 m
4 m

12.
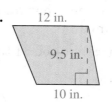
12 in.
9.5 in.
10 in.

13.
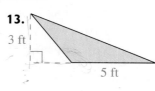
3 ft
5 ft

ON YOUR OWN

Choose Use a calculator, paper and pencil, or mental math to find the area and perimeter of each figure.

14.
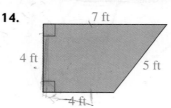
7 ft
4 ft · 5 ft
4 ft

15.
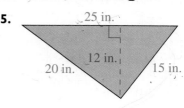
25 in.
20 in. · 12 in. · 15 in.

Choose Use a calculator, paper and pencil, or mental math to find the area and perimeter of each figure.

16.

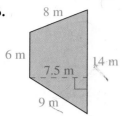

8 m
6 m
7.5 m
14 m
9 m

17.

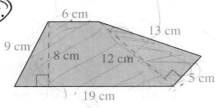

6 cm
13 cm
9 cm
8 cm
12 cm
5 cm
19 cm

18. Choose A, B, C, or D. What is the area of the shaded region?

A. 24 cm^2 **B.** 64 cm^2 **C.** 16 cm^2 **D.** 40 cm^2

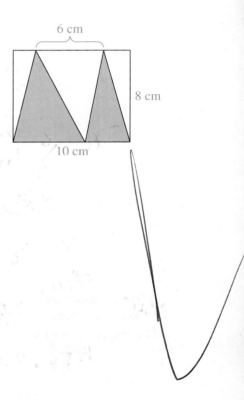

6 cm
8 cm
10 cm

19. a. Use graph paper to draw a triangle that has an area of 8 square units.

b. Suppose you know that the area of a triangle is 8 square units and that both the height and the length of the base are whole numbers. What are the possible base lengths and heights?

c. The area of a triangle is 8 square units. Give one possibility for the base length and height so that at least one of these is *not* a whole number.

20. a. Use graph paper to draw a trapezoid that has an area of 3 square units and a height of 1 unit.

b. What are the whole-number possibilities for the lengths of the bases if a trapezoid has an area of 3 square units and a height of 1 unit?

c. Writing Explain how you found the different lengths in part (b).

21. Critical Thinking How do you think that the areas of the two shaded regions compare? Explain.

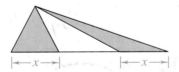

x x

Problem Solving Hint

Use a centimeter ruler.

22. a. Estimate the area of the garden in square centimeters.

b. Estimate the area in square meters if a square centimeter equals 2.5 m^2.

5-4 Circumference and Area of Circles

WORK TOGETHER

Circumference is the distance around a circle, just as perimeter is the distance around a polygon.

• Use string to measure the circumference C and the diameter d of the bases of three cans that have bases that are different sizes.

• Use a calculator to find the quotient $\frac{C}{d}$ for each can. Round each quotient to the nearest tenth.

• Record your results in a table.

What seems to be true about each quotient $\frac{C}{d}$?

THINK AND DISCUSS

No matter what size a circle is, the *ratio* of its circumference to its diameter is always the same, a number that is close to 3.14. Mathematicians have given this ratio the name π, read as "pi."

$$\pi = \frac{C}{d}$$

1. For each circle below, do the following:

• Find the radius r.

• Estimate the area A.

• Use a calculator to find the ratio $\frac{A}{r^2}$.

 In wrestling, the contest area is a ring with a diameter of 29.5 ft. The circumference is about 92 ft. **Estimate the ratio of the circumference to the diameter to the nearest whole number.**

a.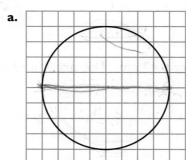

b.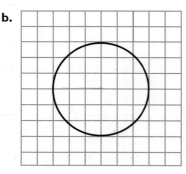

Did you find that in each case the quotient was a little more than 3? In fact, the quotient is equal to π!

$$\frac{A}{r^2} = \pi$$

If you multiply both sides of $\pi = \frac{C}{d}$ by d and both sides of $\frac{A}{r^2} = \pi$ by r^2, you get the following formulas.

Circumference and Area of a Circle

$$C = \pi d = 2\pi r$$
$$A = \pi r^2$$

---

2. **a.** How can you estimate the circumference and area of a circle if you know the radius of the circle?

5 in.

   b. Estimate the circumference of this circle.

   c. Estimate the area.

Many calculators have a $\boxed{\pi}$ key.

3. Press the $\boxed{\pi}$ key on your calculator. What is the result?

Example 1   The diameter of a circle is 15 cm. Find the circumference and area of the circle to the nearest unit. Use the calculator key for π.

* Use $C = \pi d$ to find the circumference.

   $\boxed{\pi}$ $\boxed{\times}$ 15 $\boxed{=}$ 47.123890

* Use $A = \pi r^2$ to find the area.

   $r = 15 \div 2 = 7.5$ **First find r.**

   $\boxed{\pi}$ $\boxed{\times}$ 7.5 $\boxed{x^2}$ $\boxed{=}$ 176.71459

The circumference is about 47 cm. The area is about 177 cm².

Tipis of the Sioux and Cheyenne tribes were often over 12 ft tall. The circular base had a diameter of about 15 ft. **What was the area of a base?**

Source: *Native American Architecture*

4. **a.** The diameter of the inner rim of a basketball hoop is 18 in. Find the circumference of the hoop's inner rim.

   b. What is the area enclosed by a basketball hoop?

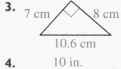 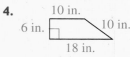
If you know the circumference of a circle, you can solve for the radius or diameter.

Example 2   The circumference of a circle is about 35 in. What is the radius to the nearest half inch?

$$C = 2\pi r$$
$$35 = 2\pi r \quad \text{Substitute.}$$
$$\frac{35}{2\pi} = \frac{2\pi r}{2\pi} \quad \text{Divide each side by } 2\pi.$$
$$\frac{35}{2\pi} = r$$

35 ÷ 2 ÷ π = 5.570423

The radius is about 5.5 in. (to the nearest half inch).

5. **Calculator** The circumference of a circle is about 50 cm. What is the diameter to the nearest unit?

TRY THESE

Calculator Find the circumference and area of each circle to the nearest unit.

6.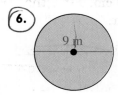
   9 m

7.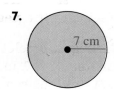
   7 cm

8.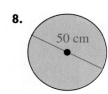
   50 cm

ON YOUR OWN

Calculator Find the circumference and area of each circle to the nearest unit.

9.
   1.9 cm

10.
    3.2 cm

11.
    1.2 m

Mental Math Estimate the circumference and area of each circle with the diameter d or radius r.

12. $d = 2$ cm

13. $r = 10$ ft

14. $r = 6$ in.

15. a. Calculator Use the π key to find the area of this circle to the nearest hundredth.

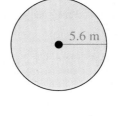

5.6 m

b. Calculator Find the area of the circle to the nearest hundredth, using 3.14 for π.

c. Writing Kenny said that the area of the circle is about 99 m². Lynn said that the area is about 98 m². Who is right? What answer would you give for the area? Explain.

16. a. Estimate the area of the circle at the right. Each square represents 1 cm².

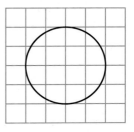

b. Use the area formula to find the area of the circle.

17. Choose A, B, C, or D. If you double the radius of a circle, what happens to the area?

   A. It remains the same.   **B.** It is doubled.

   C. It is tripled.   **D.** It is quadrupled.

Given the circumference of a circle, find the radius to the nearest half unit.

18. $C \approx 58$ m   **19.** $C \approx 41$ ft

20. The radius of the large circle shown at the right is 3.6 cm. The radius of each of the small circles is 0.9 cm. Find the area of the shaded region to the nearest unit.

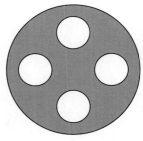

21. Cooking The world's largest omelet was cooked in Belgium in a skillet with diameter 41 ft 1 in. The largest omelet ever made in the United States was cooked in a skillet with diameter 30 ft. About how much larger was the omelet made in Belgium?

22. Sports Each lane of the track shown is 1 m wide.

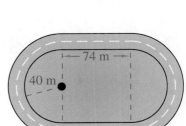

$\leftarrow$ 74 m $\rightarrow$

40 m

   a. What is the difference between the inside perimeter and the outside perimeter of the first lane, which is the innermost lane? How does that compare to the difference between the perimeters of the second lane?

   b. The runner in the first lane is to run once around the track. Where should the runner in the second lane start if both runners are to run equal distances? Explain.

23. Investigation (p. 192) Collect several boxes that are not identical. Take them apart. How are they alike? How are they different?

What's Ahead

• Finding perfect
squares and square
roots of perfect
squares

5-5

Exploring Square Roots

WORK TOGETHER

If you form a square with 3 tiles on each side, you will use 9 tiles. This shows that $3^2 = 9$.

• Use square tiles to form squares with 1, 2, . . . , 12 tiles on each side.

• Make a table that shows the number of tiles needed for each square. Label the columns of the table n and n^2.

THINK AND DISCUSS

A number like 9 that is the square of a whole number is a **perfect square.** The opposite of squaring a number is finding its **square root.** Because $3^2 = 9$, the square root of 9 is 3.

1. If the area of a square garden is 16 ft², what is the length of each side of the garden?

The symbol $\sqrt{}$ is used to indicate nonnegative square roots.

2. What is $\sqrt{4}$?

3. a. What is 7^2?   b. What is $\sqrt{49}$?

   c. What other number, besides 7, can you square to get 49?

4. a. Expand the table you made in the Work Together activity by including the squares of 13, 14, and 15.

   b. Name 15 perfect squares.

You can use your table as needed to find certain squares and square roots. However, try to use mental math as much as possible.

5. **Mental Math** What is $\sqrt{121}$?

 Chess players have enjoyed the game from as early as A.D. 500. **If the area of one square on a chessboard is 2.25 cm², what is the area of the chessboard?**

Source: *Colliers Encyclopedia*

Pythagoras was a Greek mathematician born about 500 B.C. He is most famous for discovering the following relationship involving the lengths of the sides of a right triangle.

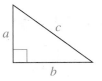

The Pythagorean Theorem

In any right triangle the square of the length c of the hypotenuse is equal to the sum of the squares of the lengths a and b of the legs.

$$c^2 = a^2 + b^2$$

In the Work Together activity you explored two examples of the Pythagorean Theorem.

4. a. For the first triangle in the Work Together activity, what numbers correspond to a, b, and c in the Pythagorean Theorem?

b. For the second triangle, what numbers correspond to a, b, and c?

If you know the lengths of two sides of a right triangle, you can use the Pythagorean Theorem to find the length of the third side.

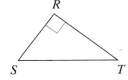

5. a. Which sides of $\triangle RST$ are the legs?

b. Which side is the hypotenuse?

6. Suppose you know that the length of $\overline{RS}$ is 6 m and the length of $\overline{RT}$ is 8 m.

a. What is x^2? Why?

b. What is the length of $\overline{ST}$? Why?

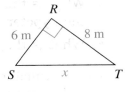

7. Suppose you know that $\overline{RT}$ is 12 m long and $\overline{ST}$ is 15 m long.

a. Complete: $y^2 + \blacksquare^2 = \blacksquare^2$

$y^2 + \blacksquare = \blacksquare$

$y^2 = \blacksquare - \blacksquare = \blacksquare$

b. What is the length of $\overline{RS}$?

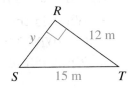

The followers of Pythagoras associated numbers with every aspect of their lives. The mind was 1; opinion, 2; justice, 3; and 10 was the number of perfection. **Do you have a number you consider your favorite?**

Source: *Americana Encyclopedia*

FLASHBACK

You can use the x^2 key on your calculator to square numbers.

8. Describe how you can use the Pythagorean Theorem to find the length of a side of a right triangle if you know the lengths of the other two sides.

9. One leg of a right triangle is 40 in. long. The hypotenuse is 41 in. long. What is the length of the other leg?

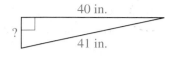

10. **Critical Thinking** Suppose you know that the sides of a right triangle are 30 in., 50 in., and 40 in. long. What is the length of the hypotenuse? Why?

If you know the lengths of three sides of a triangle, you can use the following to determine whether the triangle is a right triangle.

> **Converse of the Pythagorean Theorem**
>
> If $a^2 + b^2 = c^2$, then a triangle with sides of length a, b, and c is a right triangle.

11. Is a triangle with sides of length 7 cm, 25 cm, and 24 cm a right triangle? Why or why not?

12. Is a triangle with sides of length 3 ft, 5 ft, and 6 ft a right triangle? Why or why not?

Mi$x$ed REVIEW

Find each sum.
1. $-11 + (-8)$
2. $9 + (-14)$

Find the length of a side of a square with the following area.
3. 169 mm²   4. 81 in.²

5. Find the area of the frame.

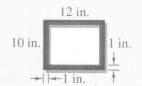

ON YOUR OWN

Find the missing side length.

13.
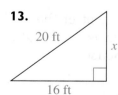

14.
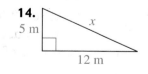

15.
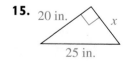

16. The hypotenuse of a right triangle is 37 ft long. One leg is 35 ft long. What is the length of the other leg?

17. The two longest sides of a right triangle are 60 m and 61 m long. What is the length of the third side?

18. A large tent has an adjustable center pole. A 26-ft long rope connects the top of the pole to a post 24 ft from the bottom of the pole. What is the height of the pole?

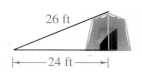

Determine whether each triangle is a right triangle. Explain your answer.

19.
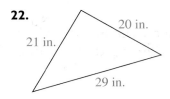
15 ft   36 ft   39 ft

20.
4 m   7 m   8 m

21.
12 yd   8 yd   9 yd

22.
20 in.   21 in.   29 in.

23. The sides of a triangle are 28 mm, 53 mm, and 45 mm long. Is the triangle a right triangle? Explain your answer.

24. **History** It is thought that the ancient Egyptians used a knotted rope to help them relocate property lines after the annual flooding of the Nile River. They divided a rope into 12 equal parts by tying knots. Then they used the rope to form a right triangle. The right angle helped them re-establish the square corners of boundary lines.

   a. How many knots would be needed to divide a rope into 12 equal parts?

   b. **Writing** Explain why the Egyptians were able to use the knotted rope to form a right triangle.

25. An extension ladder is stretched to 13 ft. The foot of the ladder is 5 ft from the side of the house. What is the height at which the ladder touches the side of the house?

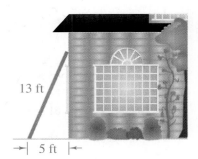
13 ft   5 ft

26. A rectangular section of wood fencing is reinforced with a piece of wood nailed across the diagonal of the rectangle. The height of the fence section is 6 ft. The length of the diagonal is 10 ft. What is the length of the fence section?

5-7

TECHNOLOGY

Applying the Pythagorean Theorem

THINK AND DISCUSS

The water splashes around you as you rocket down the longest slide at the water park. As soon as you reach the bottom, you're up and set to go again.

1. What mathematics do you think you would need to know in order to design water slides?

2. What kind of triangle is shown in the drawing of the slide's basic components?

Suppose you want to find x.

3. **a.** Use the Pythagorean Theorem. Write an equation using the sides of the triangle.

   b. Solve the equation for x^2.

   c. Is x^2 a perfect square? Explain.

   d. Find two consecutive perfect squares that x^2 lies between.

   e. Find two consecutive whole numbers that x lies between.

9 m (height)

x (slide length)

7 m (horizontal length)

Problem Solving Hint

If $81 < c^2 < 100$, then $9 < c < 10$.

You can use the square root key $\boxed{\sqrt{x}}$ on your calculator to find the square root of any nonnegative number.

4. Use your calculator to find x. Round the result to the nearest tenth of a meter.

5. **a.** Suppose you wish to slow the speed at which someone will go down the slide. What would you change?

   b. Draw a sketch of a "slower" slide. Write the dimensions you would use for the height and the horizontal length. Find the length of your slide.

6. a. Critical Thinking How could you use your calculator to determine whether a number is a perfect square?

b. Is 18,769 a perfect square? Why or why not?

c. Is 7,925 a perfect square? Why or why not?

Example   A jet airplane takes off in a straight path. When it has traveled 1 km, it has covered a horizontal distance of 900 m. To the nearest meter, what is the height of the jet at that point?

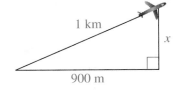

- Use the Pythagorean Theorem.

$$1,000^2 = 900^2 + x^2 \quad \text{1 km = 1,000 m}$$

$$1,000^2 - 900^2 = x^2$$

1000 $\boxed{x^2}$ $\boxed{-}$ 900 $\boxed{x^2}$ $\boxed{=}$ $\boxed{\sqrt{x}}$ *435.88989*

The jet is about 436 m high.

T R Y THESE

Estimation Find two consecutive whole numbers that each square root is between. (Do not use a calculator!)

7. $\sqrt{95}$ **8.** $\sqrt{61}$ **9.** $\sqrt{42}$ **10.** $\sqrt{125}$

Calculator Find the length of a side of a square with the given area.

11. 841 in.^{2} **12.** 20.25 ft^2 **13.** 1,225 mm^2

The lengths of two sides of a right triangle are given. Find the length of the third side to the nearest tenth of a unit.

14. legs: 8 m and 11 m   **15.** leg: 25 cm; hypotenuse: 35 cm

O N YOUR OWN

Find the missing side length to the nearest tenth.

16.
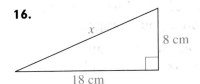

17.
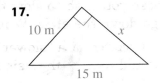

Mixed REVIEW

1. Estimate the area of the trapezoid.

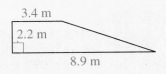

2. Find the missing length.

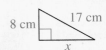

Estimate.

3. $-23 \cdot 41$

4. $-84 \div -8$

5. What is the area of the largest circle that can be cut from a square that is 36 in.^{2}?

Find the missing side length to the nearest tenth.

18.

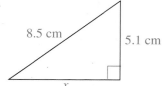

8.5 cm   5.1 cm

x

19.

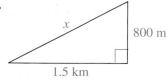

x   800 m

1.5 km

20. A park is 600 m long and 300 m wide. Carla walked diagonally across the park from corner to corner. How far did Carla walk, to the nearest meter?

21. A support wire is attached to the top of a 60-m tower. It meets the ground 25 m from the base of the tower. How long is the support wire?

22. A ladder is 6 m long. How much farther up a wall does it reach when the foot of the ladder is 2 m from the wall than when it is 3 m from the wall? Give the answer to the nearest tenth of a meter.

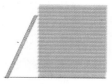

Suppose a baseball game were played on the moon! It is estimated that a home run hit by a major league player would travel 4,200 ft.

Source: *Harper's Index*

23. Sports A softball diamond is a square 60 ft by 60 ft. A baseball diamond is a square 90 ft by 90 ft.

  a. How far is it from home plate to second base on a softball diamond?

  b. How far is it from home plate to second base on a baseball diamond?

  c. A baseball right fielder catches a fly ball on the first base line, 30 ft beyond first base. If he throws it to second base, how far does he throw the ball?

  d. A baseball right fielder catches a fly ball on the first base line, 30 ft beyond first base. If he throws it to third base, how far does he throw the ball?

24. a. Find the perimeter and area of this quadrilateral.

  b. Writing Which of the following is the best name for this quadrilateral: square, parallelogram, rhombus, trapezoid? Explain your choice.

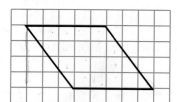

25. a. $\overline{AC}$ is the diameter of circle O.
What is the length of $\overline{AC}$?

b. Find the circumference and area of the circle.

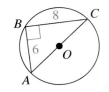

26. The area of $\triangle RSW$ is 216 cm^2.
The area of $\triangle TSW$ is 540 cm^2.

a. Find the lengths of $\overline{RW}$ and $\overline{WT}$.

b. Find the lengths of $\overline{RS}$ and $\overline{ST}$.

c. Find the perimeter of $\triangle RST$.

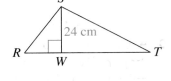

27. a. Which is the longest
segment shown in the
rectangular prism at
the right?

b. What measurements do
you need to use to find x?
to find y?

c. Find x and then find y.

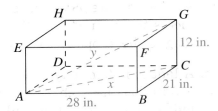

Pisa Leans Too Far!

Since its construction in 1173, the Leaning Tower of Pisa has sunk over 2.5 m into the sandy ground below its foundation. During the 199 years it took to construct the tower, builders noticed that the tower was beginning to lean. They tried to remedy the problem by weighting the stable side with heavier blocks of marble. Also, they built the bell chamber slightly off center.

Over the past 800 years, the 14,000-ton tower has continued to tilt further.

In 1930 the foundation was strengthened with concrete. Unfortunately this only made the problem worse.

The 54-meter leaning tower draws tourists from all over the world. To reduce stress on the structure, tourists are no longer allowed to climb the 294 steps to the top.

28. Suppose someone dropped a weight from the top of the
tower. It would fall 53.75 m. When the weight hit the
ground, how far would it be from the base of the tower?

5-8 **S**urface Area

10 cm
4 cm 3 cm

THINK AND DISCUSS

When manufacturers make boxes for products, the patterns are cut from cardboard and then folded into boxes.

1. **Choose A, B, or C.** Which pattern could you fold to form the box shown at the left?

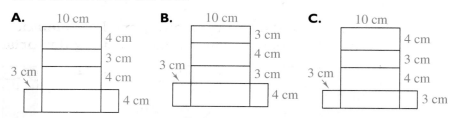

A.
10 cm
4 cm
3 cm
4 cm
3 cm

B.
10 cm
3 cm
4 cm
3 cm
4 cm
3 cm

C.
10 cm
4 cm
3 cm
4 cm
3 cm
3 cm

2. How did you decide which pattern could be folded to form the box?

The **surface area** of a prism is the sum of the areas of the faces.

3. What is the surface area of the box shown above?

4. How many *faces* does a rectangular prism, like the box below, have? Are any of them congruent? Explain.

5. **a.** Describe the polygons that make the faces of this rectangular prism.

   b. Find the surface area.

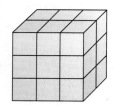

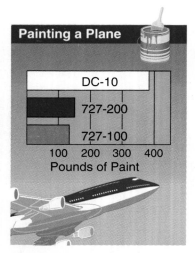

Painting a Plane

DC-10

727-200

727-100

100   200   300   400
Pounds of Paint

The graph shows the number of pounds that are added to the weight of a plane when the surface of the plane is painted. Each pound of paint adds $30 a year to fuel costs. **Estimate the increased yearly costs for each type of plane.**

Source: *American Airlines*

6. A rectangular prism is 8 in. by 6 in. by 2 in.

   a. What dimensions does each face of the prism have?

   b. Find the surface area.

7. Each edge of a cube is 4 in. long.

   a. What dimensions does each face of the cube have?

   b. Find the surface area.

8. a. Describe the polygons that make the faces of this prism.

  b. Do you know all the dimensions you need? If not, can you find them?

9. Find the surface area of the prism.

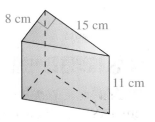

ON YOUR OWN

Choose Use a calculator, paper and pencil, or mental math to find the surface area of each rectangular prism.

10.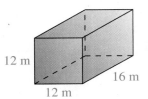

11.

12.

13. 10 cm by 20 cm by 8 cm   **14.** 5 ft by 4 ft by 5 ft

15. 2 m by 1.5 m by 6 m   **16.** 8 m by 2 m by 50 cm

17. a. Use graph paper to draw a pattern that you could fold to form a rectangular prism 3 units by 4 units by 7 units.

  b. Draw a different pattern that you could fold to form the same prism.

  c. Critical Thinking Why are both patterns correct?

18. a. Each edge of a cube is 8 cm long. Find the surface area.

  b. Critical Thinking What happens to the surface area if you double the length of each edge?

19. The surface area of a cube is 294 ft². What is the length of each edge?

20. Choose A, B, C, or D. The surface area of this rectangular prism is 52,800 in.². What is the value of x?

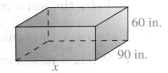

  A. 120 in.   **B.** 130 in.

  C. 140 in.   **D.** 150 in.

21. **a. Investigation** (p. 192) Take an empty box and open it out flat. What is the surface area?

   b. Design a different box that would have the same surface area. Draw and label a pattern for that box.

   c. Critical Thinking Why do you think that the manufacturer might have chosen the original dimensions?

22. Suppose you have a package that you want to send through the mail. The package is a box 24 in. by 14 in. by 10 in.

   a. What is the surface area of the package?

   b. Can you wrap the package with a piece of paper 24 in. by 48 in.? Why or why not?

23. The North Central High School's swimming pool needs resurfacing. The pool is 35 ft by 70 ft by 7 ft.

   a. Which parts of the pool need to be resurfaced?

   b. What is the total number of square feet to be resurfaced?

   c. The materials for resurfacing the pool cost $2.15/ft². What is the cost of resurfacing the pool?

24. A cylinder used for a juice can and its pattern are shown.

5.5 cm

8.8 cm

8.8 cm

M*x*ed REVIEW

What two consecutive whole numbers is each square root between?

1. $\sqrt{40}$ 2. $\sqrt{69}$

3. The support bars of the kite are perpendicular. Find the perimeter of the kite.

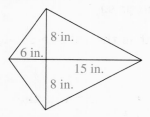

8 in.

6 in.

15 in.

8 in.

4. A group of four businessmen shook hands at a meeting. How many handshakes were there?

   a. Choose A, B, C, or D. One dimension of the rectangle in the pattern is 8.8 cm. What is the other dimension?

   A. 5.5 cm   **B.** $(\pi \cdot 5.5)$cm

   C. 8.8 cm   **D.** $(\pi \cdot 2.75^2)$cm

   b. Writing Explain your choice in part (a).

   c. Find the surface area of the cylinder to the nearest square centimeter.

Volume

• Finding the volume
of a rectangular
prism or cylinder

WHAT YOU'LL NEED

✓ Calculator

THINK AND DISCUSS

The **volume** of a three-dimensional figure is the number of cubic units needed to fill the space inside the figure.

1. What are some objects in our everyday world that have volume?

2. Why might you want or need to know the volume of a three-dimensional figure?

The rectangular prism below is 10 cm long, 4 cm wide, and 3 cm high. Suppose you want to find its volume by filling it with cubes that are 1 cm on each edge.

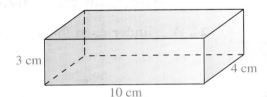

3. How many cubes would it take to make one layer in the bottom of the prism?

4. How many layers of cubes do you need to fill the prism?

5. How many cubes do you need to fill the prism?

6. Each cube has a volume of 1 cm³. What is the volume of the prism?

You can express the volume V of a rectangular prism as the product of the length l, width w, and height h.

 In one second approximately 212,000 ft³ of water flows over Niagara Falls. If all of this water were actually put in a cube, the edges of the cube would be about 59.6 ft long.

Volume of a Rectangular Prism
$V = lwh$

7. If e is the length of each edge of a cube, what is a formula for the volume of the cube?

8. a. What is an expression for the area B of a base of a rectangular prism with length l, width w, and height h?

   b. If B represents the area of a base of a rectangular prism, what is the formula for the volume in terms of B?

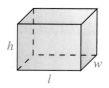

9. Critical Thinking In what ways are a rectangular prism and a cylinder alike? In what ways are they different?

10. a. The area of a base of a cylinder is 3 cm². The height of the cylinder is 5 cm. What do you think is the volume of the cylinder? Why?

   b. The radius of a base of a cylinder is 1 cm. The height is 5 cm. What do you think is the volume of the cylinder? Why?

You find the volume V of a cylinder by multiplying the area of a base by the height.

Volume of a Cylinder
$V = \pi r^2 h$

Example 1   A cylinder is 8.2 m high and has a base radius of 2.1 m. Estimate the volume. Then use a calculator to find the volume.

• Use $V = \pi r^2 h$. Use 3 to estimate π.

Estimate: $V \approx 3 \cdot 2 \cdot 2 \cdot 8 = 96 \text{ m}^3$

$\boxed{\pi}$ $\boxed{\times}$ 2.1 $\boxed{x^2}$ $\boxed{\times}$ 8.2 $\boxed{=}$ *113.60627*

The volume is about 113.6 m³.

8.2 m

2.1 m

11. The base radius of a cylinder is 4.8 cm. The height is 15 cm. Estimate the volume. Then use a calculator to find the volume.

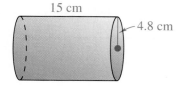

15 cm

4.8 cm

Covered wagons, also known as prairie schooners, carried pioneers west of the Mississippi. These wagons were about 4 ft wide, 10 ft long, and 8 ft high. In this small space, pioneer families carried their possessions and the supplies they needed to survive the long trips to their new homes.

You can solve for one of the dimensions if you know the volume and the other dimension.

Example 2
The volume of a cylinder is about 628 in.³. The radius of the base is 4 in. Find the height.

- $V = \pi r^2 h$

  $628 \approx \pi(4^2)h$ **Substitute.**

  628 ÷ π ÷ 4 x² = *12.493663*

  The height is about 12.5 in.

12. How can you check the solution in Example 2?

A cube that has a volume of 1 cm³ has a *capacity* of 1 mL. You can find the capacity of a container by first finding the number of cubic centimeters in the container.

Example 3
Find the number of liters that the container at the right will hold.

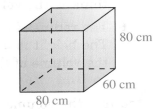
80 cm
60 cm
80 cm

- $V = lwh$

  $V = 60 \cdot 80 \cdot 80$

  $V = 384{,}000 \text{ cm}^3$

  $384{,}000 \text{ cm}^3 = 384{,}000 \text{ mL}$ **Change to milliliters.**

- Divide milliliters by 1,000 to change to liters.
  $384{,}000 \div 1{,}000 = 384$

  The container holds 384 L.

13. What is the advantage of expressing the capacity of the container in Example 3 in liters rather than milliliters?

> The progress of the human race in understanding the universe has established a small corner of order in an increasingly disordered universe.
>
> —Stephen Hawking,
> Professor of Physics,
> Cambridge University

⚡ FLASHBACK
1L = 1,000 mL

⌐**T R Y** THESE

Use mental math to estimate each volume.

14.
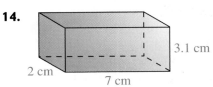
3.1 cm
2 cm
7 cm

15.

4 in.
10 in.

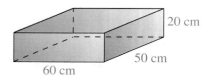

16. a. Find the capacity of the rectangular prism at the left in milliliters.

b. Find the capacity of the rectangular prism in liters.

ON YOUR OWN

Choose Use a calculator, paper and pencil, or mental math to find each volume.

17.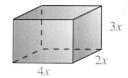

18.

19. 13 m 7 m

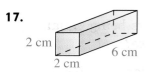

20. Choose A, B, C, or D. Which expression represents the volume of the rectangular prism at the left?

A. $9x$ **B.** $24x$ **C.** $24x^2$ **D.** $24x^3$

Choose Use a calculator, pencil and paper, or mental math to find the unknown dimension.

21. rectangular prism: $V = 56\ \text{m}^3$, $l = 7$ m, $h = 2$ m, $w = $ ■

22. cylinder: $V \approx 712\ \text{cm}^3$, $r = 4.5$ cm, $h \approx$ ■

23. cylinder: $V \approx 339\ \text{m}^3$, $h = 3$ m, $r \approx$ ■

24. a. The volume of a rectangular prism is $60\ \text{m}^3$. Find all possible whole number triples that could be the dimensions of the prism. For example, 2 m, 3 m, 10 m is a possible triple.

b. Writing Explain how you solved the problem in part (a).

25. Find the volume of a rectangular prism with length 11 ft, width 5 ft, and height 2 yd.

26. Find the capacity of a cylinder with a base radius of 2 cm and a height of 4 cm to the nearest milliliter.

27. A gallon of milk occupies 231 in.^{3} of space. Can a container 15 in. by 6 in. by 8 in. hold 3 gallons? Why or why not?

The world's largest sound stage was built in Great Britain in 1976 for the James Bond movie *The Spy Who Loved Me*. It is 336 ft by 160 ft by 40.5 ft.

Source: *The Guinness Book of Records* and Eon Productions, Ltd.

28. a. Data File 5 (pp. 190–191) Use the length, breadth, and volume to find the *average* depth in miles and then in feet of Lake Michigan and Lake Ontario. Which lake has the greater average depth?

  b. Writing Explain the difference between greatest average depth and greatest depth.

29. a. Investigation (p. 192) Choose a box that you would like to redesign. Find the volume. Design a different box that would have the same volume.

  b. Compare the surface areas. Other things being equal, which would be cheapest to manufacture?

30. a. A cylinder has a base diameter and height of 5.5 cm. A cube has edges 5.5 cm long. Compare the volumes.

  b. Critical Thinking What accounts for the difference in the volumes?

31. a. Find the surface area of the triangular prism.

  b. Writing Using what you know about the volume of a rectangular prism, explain how you could find the volume of this triangular prism. Then find the volume.

32. Data File 1 (pp. 2–3) About how many dollar bills will have a total volume of 1 ft³?

FLASHBACK

1 mi = 5,280 ft

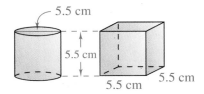

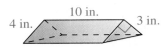

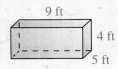

Mixed REVIEW

Solve.

1. $n + 8 = -10$

2. $n - 5 = 19$

3. $3n - 12 = 6$

4. Find the surface area of the prism.

5. Adam can mow Mrs. Jones' lawn twice as fast as Peter. Jody can mow the same lawn in 45 min. How long does it take Adam to mow the lawn? What do you need to know to solve the problem?

CHECKPOINT

The lengths of two sides of a right triangle are given. Find the length of the third side to the nearest tenth.

1. leg: 5 cm; hypotenuse: 25 cm   2. legs: both 6 in.

Draw and label a figure for each description. Find the surface area and the volume of each. Use 3.14 for π.

3. a rectangular prism with dimensions 6 ft, 10 ft, and 5 ft

4. a cylinder with radius 8 m and height 20 m

5. **Choose A, B, C, or D.** A cylinder has a radius of 1 ft and a height of 3 ft. If you double the radius, the volume is ■.

  A. doubled   **B.** tripled   **C.** quadrupled   **D.** unchanged

What's Ahead

- Solving problems by using *Guess and Test*

5-10

Guess and Test

WHAT YOU'LL NEED

✓ Calculator

How would you solve the following problem?

> The volume of a cube is 10,648 cm³. What is the length of each edge of the cube?

Sometimes the best way to solve a problem is to make a guess and then test your guess. Using what you learn from testing your guess, you make another guess and test it. You repeat this process until you are able to solve the problem.

READ

Read and understand the given information. Summarize the problem.

1. Think about the information you are given and what you are asked to find.

   a. What type of three-dimensional figure is involved?

   b. What dimensions are important in the figure?

   c. Summarize the goal of this problem.

PLAN

Decide on a strategy to solve the problem.

Guess and Test is a good strategy to use here. You can guess the length of each edge of the cube and then test your guess by using a calculator to multiply the dimensions. If the test reveals that you guessed too high or too low, you can make a better guess and try again. A table can help you organize your guesses and the results.

SOLVE

Try out the strategy.

2. Suppose you start with a guess of 30 cm.

   a. Find the volume of the cube.

   b. Is the volume too high or too low?

3. **a.** What number would you use for your next guess for the length of each edge? Why?

   b. What will be the volume of the cube with this edge length? Use a table like the one below.

Length of Each Edge	Volume	Too High or Too Low?
30 cm	■	■

Continue your guesses if necessary.

4. What length of each edge of the cube will give a volume of 10,648 cm^3?

5. How did the *Guess and Test* strategy help you solve the problem?

LOOK BACK

Think about how you solved the problem.

TRY THESE

Solve using the Guess and Test strategy.

6. What are two whole numbers whose product is 147 and whose quotient is 3?

7. What whole number is a solution of $x^2 + x = 56$?

ON YOUR OWN

Solve if possible. If not, tell what information is needed. Show all your work.

8. Find the next two numbers in the pattern below.

    100, 25, 50, 12.5, 25, ■, ■

9. After selling food during a soccer game, the cashier at the concession stand has some $1 bills, $5 bills, and $10 bills. She has 13 bills worth a total of $69. How many $1 bills, $5 bills, and $10 bills does she have?

10. Beka has a bag of 16 blocks. Each block has a 1, 2, 3, or 4 on it. When Beka pulls four blocks out of the bag, the sum of the numbers on the blocks is 12. What numbers are on the four blocks she pulls from the bag?

11. Adam and Eric each made a purchase at the bookstore. Adam bought 1 pencil and 2 pens for 86¢. Eric bought 2 pencils and 1 pen for 67¢. How much does 1 pencil cost?

12. The volume of a rectangular prism is 2,058 cm^3. The length of the prism is three times the width. The height is twice the width. Find the width, length, and height of the prism.

13. The sum of the digits of a certain two-digit number equals the square root of the number. What is the number?

Mixed REVIEW

1. What is the measure of a right angle?

2. What range of degrees can an acute angle measure?

Find the volume.

3. 4 in.   4 in.   4 in.

4. 30 cm   15 cm

5. Elicia, Michelle, and Cary are an engineer, a teacher, and a salesperson. Elicia and the engineer drove Cary to work on Saturday. Who is the teacher?

14. Jamaal, Kim, Lea, and Mark each have a pet. Kim is in the same class with the dog owner and the parrot owner. Jamaal and Mark sometimes help the dog owner walk her dog. Mark's pet is older than the cat and the gerbil, and his pet is younger than Lea's pet. Who owns which pet?

15. Erin has just moved to Pedalboro. The garage and basement of her new house are crammed with bicycles and tricycles. The Wheelers, the former owners of the house, left behind their cycle collection when they moved. As she prepared for a yard sale, Erin calculated that the collection contained a total of 100 vehicles and 239 wheels. How many of each type of vehicle did the Wheelers leave behind?

16. The width of a rectangle is 4 cm less than the length of the rectangle. The area of the rectangle is 96 cm². Find the length and width of the rectangle.

17. Mr. Franklin has cartons that measure 3 ft × 2 ft × 6 in. He wishes to store them in a 15 ft × 9 ft × 24 ft space. He can only stack the cartons on top of each other, not inside one another. How many boxes can he store?

18. Suppose you have 12 square tiles that measure 1 in. on each side. What are the dimensions of the rectangle you can make with the tiles that has the greatest perimeter? the least perimeter?

19. **Science** The *mass* of 1 cm³ of water is 1 gram.
    a. A cube with edges 4 cm long is filled with water. What is the mass of the water?
    b. A cube is filled with water that has a mass of 343 g. What is the length of each edge of the cube?

20. a. Use a calculator to find the following products.

    15 • 15   25 • 25   35 • 35   45 • 45

    b. **Writing** Look for patterns in part (a). Describe any patterns that you find.

    c. Use the patterns you found to write each of the following products without multiplying the given numbers.

    55 • 55   65 • 65   75 • 75   85 • 85

21. **Gardening** A rose bush is planted about every three feet on the edge of a circular opening in the city park. If the circle has a diameter of 12 ft, how many bushes are needed?

WHAT? The mass of 8 cm³ of aluminum is 22 g. The mass of the same volume of gold is 154.4 g. Name two sets of dimensions that could give an 8 cm³ rectangular prism.

Practice

Find the area and perimeter of each figure.

1.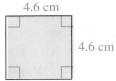
4.6 cm
4.6 cm

2.
15 in.
8 in.

3.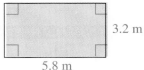
3.2 m
5.8 m

4.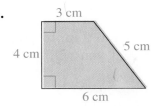
3 cm
4 cm
5 cm
6 cm

5.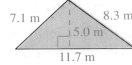
7.1 m
8.3 m
5.0 m
11.7 m

6.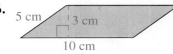
5 cm
3 cm
10 cm

Find the circumference and area of each circle to the nearest tenth of a unit. Use 3.14 for π.

7. $r = 12.5$ cm   **8.** $d = 35$ in.   **9.** $d = 0.75$ mi   **10.** $d = 8.6$ m

Use a calculator to find each to the nearest tenth of a unit.

11. $\sqrt{552.25}$ **12.** $\sqrt{3}$ **13.** $\sqrt{2}$ **14.** $\sqrt{50}$

Find the length of a side of a square with the given area.

15. 400 ft^2 **16.** 289 cm^2 **17.** $2{,}500$ mi^2 **18.** 2.25 in.^{2}

The lengths of two sides of a right triangle are given. Find the third side to the nearest tenth of a unit.

19. hypotenuse: 60 in.; leg: 35 in.   **20.** leg: 10 cm; leg: 14 cm

Determine whether each triangle is a right triangle.

21. 9 m, 40 m, 41 m   **22.** 12 mi, 15 mi, 25 mi   **23.** 2.4 cm, 3.2 cm, 4.0 cm

24. Find the surface area of a cube with an edge of 9 cm.

25. Find the volume of a rectangular prism with dimensions 5 ft, 6 ft, and 8 ft.

26. Find the volume of a cylinder with a diameter of 9 in. and a height of 15 in.

What's Ahead

• Solving perimeter, area, and surface area problems

5-11 Perimeter, Area, and Volume

WHAT YOU'LL NEED

✓ Calculator

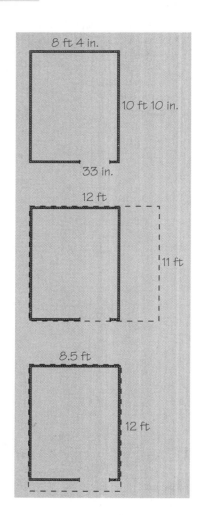

WORK TOGETHER

You have been hired to do some remodeling in an office building. You will begin with the room shown at the left. The room needs carpet installed on the floor and baseboard installed around the perimeter of the room.

To determine how much carpet is needed, you measure the maximum length and width of the room and add 2 in. to each dimension to allow for cutting. The carpet that you will use for this room is 12 ft wide.

1. a. If you add 2 in. to each dimension, what are the new dimensions you will consider when deciding on the amount of carpet needed? Express the dimensions in terms of feet only.

b. Calculator One way to lay the carpet is so that the nap runs in the direction of the larger dimension, as in the second drawing. If you do this, you will need a piece of carpet 12 ft by 11 ft. How many square feet is this?

c. Calculator Another way to lay the carpet is so that the nap runs in the direction of the smaller dimension, as in the third drawing. If you do this, you will need a piece of carpet 12 ft by 8.5 ft. How many square feet is this?

d. Which placement of the carpet is more efficient? How many square feet of carpet does that placement save?

e. Calculator The carpet costs $15.95 per square yard. There are nine square feet in a square yard. How much money will you save by using the more efficient placement?

2. a. What is the perimeter of the room? Use the original dimensions of the room.

b. You will use 4-ft sections of baseboard. You will not need baseboard for the doorway, which is 33 in. wide. How many pieces of baseboard will you need?

THINK AND DISCUSS

Problems that occur in everyday life, like the carpet and baseboard problems, often involve perimeter, area, and volume. Decide if perimeter, surface area, or volume is involved if you want to determine each of the following.

3. the amount of paint needed for a room

4. the amount of wood baseboard needed for a room

5. the amount of trim needed around a window

6. the amount of water a swimming pool can contain

7. the amount of wallpaper needed for a room

8. the amount of paint needed for a toy chest

9. The room in the Work Together activity could be carpeted with only one piece of carpet. A room that has both dimensions larger than 11 ft 10 in. will need more than one piece of carpet. Why?

ON YOUR OWN

10. The floor of Sabrina's room measures 12 ft 5 in. by 14 ft 4 in. There is one door that is 33 in. wide. How many 4-ft sections of baseboard will Sabrina need to replace what she has?

11. **Data File 5 (pp. 190–191)** The Osbornes have decided to replace some of their home's conventional fixtures with water-saving devices.

  a. If the Osbornes flush their toilet an average of 15 times a day, how much water will they save each day with an air-assisted toilet?

  b. The Osbornes spend a total of 45 minutes in the shower each day. How much water will they save in a week if they install a low-flow shower head?

  c. The Osbornes will save 125–225 gallons of water per day with an aerating kitchen faucet. About how many minutes per day do they run their kitchen faucet?

Source: *Popular Science*

Write the next three numbers in each pattern.

1. 2, 5, 8, 11, . . .

2. 3, 5, 9, 15, . . .

Write an equation. Then solve.

3. The sum of a number and 6 is 112.

4. Two less than 4 times a number is 13.

5. How many 3 in. × 2 in. rectangles can you cut from a 6 in. × 5 in. rectangle?

The washer/dryer on space station *Freedom* uses just 1.1 gal of water to wash 1 lb of clothes. Conventional washers use 7 gal/lb.

In 1739, Plunket Fleeson of Philadelphia manufactured the first wallpaper in the colonies of North America. Wood blocks were used to print designs on small sheets of paper. The paper was then hand painted. **If a sheet of the wall paper was 6 in. × 6 in., how many would be needed for a 10 ft × 12 ft wall?**

Source: *Famous First Facts*

12. Sheila bought an old chest for her bedroom. She needs to know how much stain and varnish to buy in order to refinish all of the sides. The chest is 5 ft long, 2 ft 6 in. wide, and 3 ft high.

a. What is the surface area of the chest?

b. Each can of stain or varnish will cover 45 ft^2. How many cans of each will Sheila need to refinish the chest?

c. Each can of stain costs $6.95. Each can of varnish costs $7.95. How much will the stain and varnish cost?

d. After Sheila refinishes the chest, she will put a 2 in. metal strip around the perimeter of the base of the chest to protect against scratches. What length of metal strip should Sheila buy? Allow 1 in. for overlap and error.

e. Sheila plans to use the chest to store cloth that she uses in sewing. What volume of cloth could she store?

GREAT EXPECTATIONS

Detective

I would like to become a police detective. Should I go through a Police Academy to become a detective?

I think that there are many ways I might use problem solving and math in this job. If I had to find out who committed a crime, I would gather information. I would interview suspects and witnesses. I would look at the scene and try to figure out what happened.

What is it really like to be a detective? I know it must not be like it is in the movies. What do you do during a typical day? How do you get your cases? What is the longest and most involved case you have ever worked on? How did you solve it?

Evon Burroughs

13. Theo wants to replace the baseboards in a room that is 20 ft by 16 ft.

   a. If Theo buys three 8-ft boards, how many 12-ft boards should he buy?

   b. If Theo buys two 12-ft boards, how many 8-ft boards should he buy?

   c. Do the boards in part (a) or part (b) cost less? How much less?

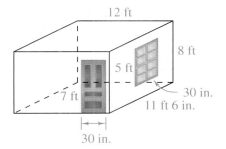

Baseboard

8-ft boards $1.10/ ft
12-ft boards $1.20/ ft

14. La Dena has decided to paint the walls and ceiling of this room.

   a. La Dena will not paint the door (or window!). What is the surface area she will paint?

   b. A gallon of the paint La Dena will use covers about 250 ft². How many gallons will she need for one coat? for two coats?

   c. **Writing** The paint costs $16.95 per gallon. Can La Dena apply one coat for $25? two coats for $50? Explain.

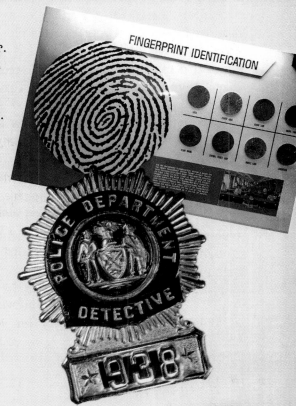

Dear Evon,

   You attend a training academy to become a police officer. After you spend a certain amount of time as an officer, you may take a test to become a detective.

   Problem solving is a very important part of my job. I often work backwards and look for patterns to solve crimes. A typical day for me includes interviewing witnesses and suspects, making arrests, testifying in court, and using a computer to find information. Cases are usually assigned to me by my supervisor or from 911 calls.

   One of the most involved cases I worked on dealt with arresting drug dealers. When I was asked how far away from the suspects my partners and I were, I used the Pythagorean theorem to calculate the distance between each of us. When I had to explain the theorem on the witness stand, I was reminded of my math classes!

   Ernesto (Tito) Whittington
   Detective, Boston Police Department

Wrap Up

Area and Perimeter 5-1, 5-2, 5-3

Perimeter is the distance around an object or figure. Perimeter is measured in units of length such as inches, meters, and feet.

Area is the number of square units inside a figure. Area is measured in square units such as square inches, square meters, and square feet.

Find the perimeter and area of each figure.

1.

4 cm
7 cm

2.

3 cm
3.8 cm
3.5 cm
4.9 cm
7.9 cm

3.
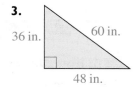
36 in.
60 in.
48 in.

4.
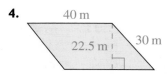
40 m
22.5 m
30 m

Circumference and Area of Circles 5-4

Circumference is the distance around a circle. The **ratio** of the circumference to the diameter of any circle is always the same. This ratio, represented by π, is close to 3.14.

Find the circumference and area of each circle. Round your answers to the nearest tenth.

5.
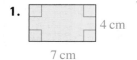
12 cm

6.

8 in.

7.

40 ft

8.

9 mm

Squares and Square Roots 5-5, 5-6, 5-7

A **perfect square** is a square of a whole number. The opposite of squaring a number is finding its **square root.** The symbol used for square root is $\sqrt{\ }$.

9. Estimation The value of $\sqrt{87}$ is between what two consecutive whole numbers?

Mental Math Find each of the following.

10. 11^2 **11.** 7^2 **12.** $\sqrt{16}$ **13.** $\sqrt{64}$ **14.** $\sqrt{144}$ **15.** $\sqrt{4}$

The Pythagorean Theorem 5-6, 5-7

The **Pythagorean Theorem** states if a and b are legs of a right triangle and c is the hypotenuse, then $a^2 + b^2 = c^2$. You can use the **Converse of the Pythagorean Theorem** to determine whether a triangle is a right triangle.

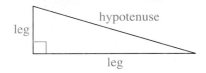

16. **Choose A, B, C, or D.** Which lengths would *not* make the sides of a right triangle?

    A. 3 m, 4 m, 5 m   **B.** 2 cm, 2 cm, 4 cm   **C.** 51 in., 85 in., 68 in.   **D.** 16 ft, 20 ft, 12 ft

The lengths of two sides of a right triangle are given. Find the length of the third side to the nearest tenth of a unit.

17. leg: 12 mm; hypotenuse: 15 mm   18. legs: both 1 m   19. leg: 8 m; hypotenuse: 14 m

Surface Area and Volume 5-8, 5-9, 5-11

The **surface area** of a prism is the sum of the areas of the faces.

The **volume** of a three-dimensional figure is the number of cubic units needed to fill the space inside the figure.

20. Find the volume and surface area of a rectangular prism with length 7 ft, width 5 ft, and height 2.5 ft.

21. A cylinder is 14 cm high and has a base radius of 8 cm. Find the volume of the cylinder.

Applications and Strategies 5-10

You can use the problem solving strategy Guess and Test to solve many problems.

22. The volume of a rectangular prism is 24 m³. The surface area is 52 m². Find the dimensions of the prism.

GETTING READY FOR CHAPTER 6

Find the missing number that makes each statement true.

1. $5,000 = 5 \times$ ■   2. $4,500,000 = 4.5 \times$ ■   3. $325,000 = 3.25 \times$ ■

4. Mary and Simon are playing the game "Guess My Rule." When Mary applies her rule to 3, the result is 14. When she applies her rule to 5, the result is 22. Simon guesses that the rule is "Multiply a number by 3 and add 5." Is he correct? Explain.

PUTTING IT ALL TOGETHER

follow Up

Designing a Package

At the beginning of the chapter, you chose a "best" package design for a product. Look back at your decision. Revise it, if necessary, or design an entirely new package for the product based on your study of the chapter. When you are satisfied that your package is the best one possible, write a letter to the manufacturer of the product. Enclose a sample of your package design and explain why you believe the manufacturer should switch from the present package to yours. The following are suggestions to help you support your proposal.

✓ Use a spreadsheet.
✓ Conduct a survey.
✓ Design an ad featuring the new package.

The problems preceded by the magnifying glass (p. 209, # 23; p. 222, # 21; and p. 227, # 29) will help you write your letter.

Excursion: A box has a volume of 24 in.³. Make a list of possible dimensions (length, width, and height) the box might have. Find the surface area of the box for each set of dimensions. If two boxes have the same volume, do they have the same surface area? Explain your answer.

BUT OFFICER, I WAS ONLY DOING...

0 10 20 30 40 50 60 70 80

The accuracy of the speedometer of an automobile is not always accurate. Different variables, such as tires that are larger than the original ones, can change the actual speed of a vehicle. How would you check the accuracy of the speedometer of an automobile? Make a plan and write it up. If possible, carry out your plan.

DIGITAL TIME

There are four possible digits which read-out the time on a digital clock at any minute. For example: 12:30 contains four digits. Which digit is used most frequently during a 24-h period? Why? Which is the second most frequently used digit?

A Hair Raising Experience

Hair grows at what seems to us a very slow rate. It also stops growing at different lengths for different people. Use your resources to find out the following facts.

- How fast does hair grow? Is that a steady rate?
- How long is the longest hair ever grown?

Using this information and assuming that your hair would grow continually, answer the following.

- How long would it take your hair to touch the floor?
- Suppose you lived to 100 and never cut your hair. How long would it be?
- Suppose you lived to 100 and never cut your hair. How much would it weigh?

MEASURING HEADS & FEET

When people first began to measure, they used body parts as standard measures. Today we still use a foot for length and the hand when measuring horses. These are now standard units of measure. You will use nonstandard units with this investigation.

- Cut a piece of paper the length of your foot and measure your height with it. How many of "Your Feet" tall are you?
- With a string, measure the circumference of your head. Use this as your measure to find out how many "Heads" tall you are.
- Measure a number of people of different ages with their own foot lengths and head circumferences. Make a chart for heads and a chart for feet to keep track of your data as you collect it. Have you found anything interesting happening? If so, what is it?

BOXING YOURSELF IN

What are the dimensions of the smallest box that you could squeeze yourself into? Use the dimensions to find the volume. Is there another shaped box with the same volume that would be more comfortable? How many square feet of cardboard would you need to make your own personal box?

1. **Choose A, B, C, or D.** Which unit is the best to use when you want to measure the length of an automobile?

   A. mm **B.** cm **C.** m **D.** km

2. Find the area and perimeter of each figure described below.

   a. square: $s = 2.1$ ft

   b. rectangle: $l = 19$ km, $w = 15$ km

3. Find the area of each figure described below.

   a. triangle: $b = 12$ cm, $h = 10$ cm

   b. parallelogram: $b = 14$ m, $h = 9$ m

4. The area of a rectangular-shaped piece of land is 114 yd². One dimension is 19 yd. Find the perimeter.

5. Find the area and perimeter of the trapezoid.

   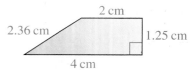

6. The diameter of a circle is 21 cm. Find the circumference and area of the circle to the nearest unit.

7. **Mental Math** Find each of the following.

   a. 8^2 **b.** 10^2 **c.** $\sqrt{25}$ **d.** $\sqrt{81}$

8. **Calculator** Find the length, to the nearest unit, of a side of a square with the given area.

   a. 576 mm²   **b.** 269 cm²

   c. 325 in.²   **d.** 121 ft²

9. **Writing** Explain how you can use the Converse of the Pythagorean Theorem to find if a triangle is a right triangle.

10. Find x.

11. A rectangular garden is 40 m long and 30 m wide. Find the length of a diagonal walkway across the garden.

12. **Choose A, B, C, or D.** The surface area of a cube is 150 cm². Find the volume.

    A. 15 cm³   **B.** 30 cm³

    C. 125 cm³   **D.** 150 cm³

13. Rectangular prism A has dimensions 10 cm, 2 cm, and 3 cm. Rectangular prism B has dimensions 5 cm, 2 cm, and 6 cm. Use $<$, $>$, or $=$ to compare the volumes of A and B.

14. **Estimation** The base radius of a cylinder is 9.7 cm. The height is 20 cm. To make a quick mental estimate of the volume, what would you use for a value of π? What is your estimate?

15. A cylinder-shaped tank is 12 ft long. It has a base diameter of 18 ft. Find the volume of the tank to the nearest unit.

16. **Choose A, B, C, or D.** Suppose you want to estimate the number of bricks you could store in a shed. Which must you know about the shed?

    A. perimeter   **B.** area

    C. surface area   **D.** volume

Choose A, B, C, or D.

1. Which number has the greatest value?

A. 2^5 **B.** 3^3

C. 5^2 **D.** 20^1

2. Rectangle *ABCD* is 3 ft × 4 ft. What is the area and the perimeter of *ABCD*?

A. $A = 12 \text{ ft}^2$, $P = 12$ ft

B. $A = 12 \text{ ft}^2$, $P = 14$ ft

C. $A = 6 \text{ ft}^2$, $P = 12$ ft

D. $A = 12 \text{ ft}^2$, $P = 7$ ft

3. Which expression has a value *closest* to the value of $3(10 - 2.5)$?

A. $3(10)$

B. $2.5(10 - 3)$

C. $3(5 + 2)$

D. $2(10 + 1)$

4. Which of the following could *not* be the sides of a right triangle?

A. 8, 15, 17   **B.** 10, 24, 26

C. 15, 35, 40   **D.** 12, 16, 20

5. Which expression equals 8.23?

A. $6.584 \div 0.8$ **B.** $74.34 \div 9$

C. $1{,}152.2 \div 14$ **D.** $57.61 \div 7.1$

6. Which expression could you use to find the area of the cylinder's base?

A. $(2 \cdot \pi \cdot 5)$

B. $(\pi \cdot 2.5 \cdot 2.5)$

C. $(\pi \cdot 5 \cdot 5)$

D. $(2 \cdot \pi \cdot 2.5 \cdot 6)$

7. Which expression equals -12?

A. $-3 \cdot (-4)$ **B.** $-10 + 2$

C. $-48 \div 3$ **D.** $-16 - (-4)$

8. Which container has the greatest volume?

A. 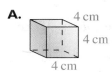   **B.**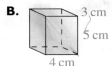

C. 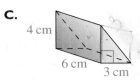   **D.**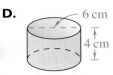

9. Which equation could you use to represent the following problem: Five more than half of the people (*p*) on the bus were students (*s*)?

A. $\dfrac{p}{2} + 5 = s$ **B.** $(p - 5) \div 2 = s$

C. $\dfrac{p}{2} - 5 = s$ **D.** $(p - 5) \div 2 = s$

10. Which expression does *not* have the same value as the other expressions?

A. $\sqrt{144}$

B. $\sqrt{36} + \sqrt{36}$

C. $\sqrt{4} + \sqrt{64}$

D. $\sqrt{81} + \sqrt{9}$

11. What is the value of x to the nearest tenth?

A. 17.0   **B.** 12.7

C. 7.0   **D.** 8.5

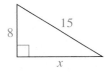

MOVIE **M**AKER

A movie camera records a sequence of still images on a strip of film. A movie camera normally takes 24 pictures or frames per second. A movie projector also shows 24 frames/s. However, it projects each frame three times so that our eyes are seeing 72 separate pictures of the same image. This reduces flicker and fools the eye into seeing a continuous moving picture.

soundtrack
sprocket holes

Movie Film Widths	
35 mm	cinema
16 mm	television
8 mm	home movies
super–8	home movies

image area
single frame of film

Data File 6

Sales in Different Music Categories

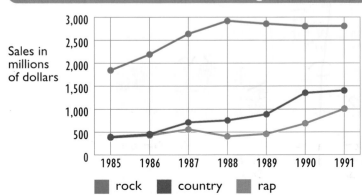

Sales in millions of dollars

rock   country   rap

WHAT YOU WILL LEARN

- how to find and use patterns to solve problems
- how to graph functions
- how to use technology to explore exponents
- how to solve problems by looking for a pattern

WORLD VIEW

In 1979, filmmakers in India produced 714 films. That same year, Japan produced 335 films, France made 234 films, United States produced 167 films, and England made 38 films.

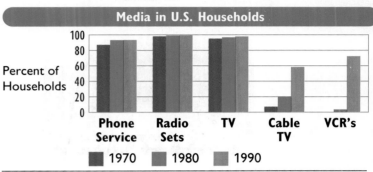

Media in U.S. Households

Percent of Households

Phone Service, Radio Sets, TV, Cable TV, VCR's

■ 1970 ■ 1980 ■ 1990

Source: *Statistical Abstract of the United States*

Oprah Winfrey was the top money making entertainer in 1992. She earned an estimated $46,000,000.

Source: *Forbes*

Activity Survey

Teenagers were asked "Have you participated in this activity during the last seven days?" The table shows who answered "Yes."

Activity	Percent Male	Female
Read magazines for pleasure	66.4	75.7
Read books for pleasure	57.2	72.8
Watched TV	95.7	97.8
Watched videos	70.8	66.5
Listened to records, tapes, or CDs	83.3	87.2
Played a musical instrument	34.7	43.2

Source: *Teenage Research Unlimited*

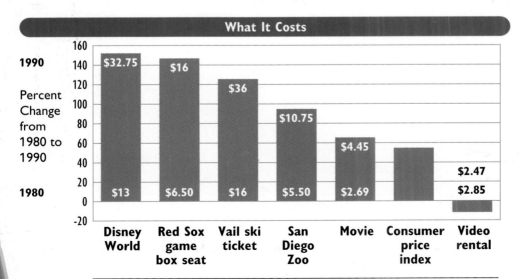

What It Costs

1990

Percent Change from 1980 to 1990

1980

Disney World: 1990 $32.75, 1980 $13
Red Sox game box seat: 1990 $16, 1980 $6.50
Vail ski ticket: 1990 $36, 1980 $16
San Diego Zoo: 1990 $10.75, 1980 $5.50
Movie: 1990 $4.45, 1980 $2.69
Consumer price index
Video rental: 1990 $2.47, 1980 $2.85

Source: *Money*

WHAT IT COSTS

During the 1980s, the price of a day at Disney World rose faster than the cost of most other family pastimes.

243

inVestigation

Memo

During the Renaissance, some artists tried to find mathematical relationships among the measurements of the human body. In one of his drawings, Leonardo da Vinci showed a man fitting neatly inside a circle. Today we know that the human body is not quite as mathematical as the artists believed. Nevertheless, it exhibits some very interesting numerical relationships.

Mission: Take the following measurements of each member of your group: height; distance from (1) fingertip to fingertip (arms spread), (2) wrist to elbow, and (3) ankle to kneecap. Find relationships among the following pairs of measurements: height/fingertip to fingertip; height/wrist to elbow; height/ankle to kneecap.

LeADs tO FoLLoW

✓ How can you record your data so that you can easily recognize mathematical relationships?

✓ What kinds of mathematical relationships can you expect to find?

✓ Which pairs of measurements seem most closely related?

Number Patterns

WHAT YOU'LL NEED

✓ **Pattern blocks**

Figure 1   Figure 2   Figure 3

Figure 1   Figure 2   Figure 3

FLASHBACK

The three dots, . . . , indicate that the pattern continues without end.

WORK TOGETHER

1. **a.** Use pattern blocks to make the next two figures in the pattern shown at the left.

   b. How many blocks do you add to each figure to make the next figure in the pattern?

   c. Copy and complete this table.

Figure	1	2	3	4	5	6	7	8
Total Blocks in Figure	■	■	■	■	■	■	■	■

   d. How many blocks would be in the twelfth figure?

2. **a.** Make a table like the one above for the pattern at the left.

   b. How many blocks would be in the twelfth figure?

THINK AND DISCUSS

The set of numbers you found in the Work Together is a *sequence*. A **sequence** is a set of numbers arranged according to some pattern. Each number is called a **term** of the sequence. You find each term of an **arithmetic sequence** by adding the same number to the preceding term.

Example 1 Write a rule to describe the sequence 6, 13, 20, 27, ... Then find the next three terms in the sequence.

• 6   13   20   27

+7   +7   +7

The rule for the sequence is: *Start with 6 and add 7 repeatedly.*

• 27 + 7 = 34 → 34 + 7 = 41 → 41 + 7 = 48

The next three terms are 34, 41, and 48.

3. Write a rule for the sequence 35, 24, 13, 2, . . . Then find the next three terms.

For a **geometric sequence,** you find each term by multiplying the preceding term by the same number.

Example 2

Write a rule to describe the sequence 1, 3, 9, 27, . . . Then find the next three terms in the sequence.

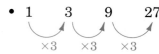

The rule for the sequence is: *Start with 1 and multiply by 3 repeatedly.*

• $27 \times 3 = 81 \rightarrow 81 \times 3 = 243 \rightarrow 243 \times 3 = 729$

The next three terms are 81, 243, and 729.

4. **a.** Why is −2, 4, −8, 16, . . . a geometric sequence?

   b. Write a rule to describe the sequence.

   c. Find the next three terms of the sequence.

Some sequences are neither arithmetic nor geometric.

Example 3

Write a rule to describe the sequence 1, 3, 6, 10, . . . and find the next three terms.

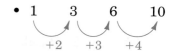

The rule for the sequence is: *Start with 1 and add 2, then add 3, then add 4, and so on.*

• To find the next three terms, continue the pattern.

   $10 + 5 = 15 \rightarrow 15 + 6 = 21 \rightarrow 21 + 7 = 28$

The next three terms are 15, 21, and 28.

5. Explain why the sequence in Example 3 is not arithmetic.

6. **Discussion** How can you tell if a sequence is arithmetic, geometric, or neither?

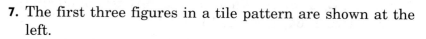

T R Y THESE

7. The first three figures in a tile pattern are shown at the left.

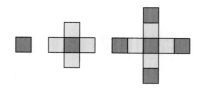

   a. How many red tiles would be in the ninth figure?

   b. How many yellow tiles would be in the ninth figure?

Identify each sequence as arithmetic, geometric, or neither. Then find the next three terms.

8. 5, 10, 15, 20, . . .

9. 2, 6, 18, 54, . . .

10. 600, 300, 150, 75, . . .

11. 63, 54, 45, 36, . . .

12. 2, 5, 10, 17, 26, . . .

13. 1, −3, 9, −27, 81, . . .

14. Many people draw a dollar sign as an S-shape with one line through it. The line divides the S into four parts, as shown at the right. Other people draw two lines, dividing the S into seven parts. Suppose you drew the S with 15 vertical lines through it. Into how many parts would the S be divided?

 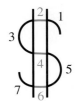

ON YOUR OWN

Identify each sequence as arithmetic, geometric, or neither. Write a rule to describe each arithmetic and geometric sequence.

15. 1, 2, 4, 8, . . .

16. −15, −11, −7, −3, . . .

17. 1, 2, 4, 7, 11, . . .

18. 1, −1, 1, −1, . . .

19. 300, 60, 12, 2.4, . . .

20. 1, 4, 9, 16, 25, . . .

21. Suppose that January 1 is a Monday. What are the dates of the other Mondays in January?

22. A pattern of numbers is shown at the right.

    a. List the numbers in rows, 4, 5, 6, and 7.

    b. Find the sum of the numbers in each of the first 7 rows.

    c. Predict the sum of the numbers in the twentieth row.

    d. Write a rule that describes the sums of the numbers in each row of the triangular pattern.

row 1					1			
row 2				1	2	1		
row 3			1	2	3	2	1	

23. **Writing** Do you think the sequence 1, 1, 1, . . . is arithmetic, geometric, both, or neither? Explain.

24. **Choose A, B, C, or D.** What are the next two numbers in the sequence 1, 64, 2, 32, 4, 16, . . . ?

    A. 16, 8   **B.** 8, 16   **C.** 8, 8   **D.** 32, 64

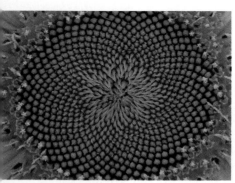

The sunflower is an example of the Fibonacci sequence appearing in nature. The number of seed pods in each ring equals the sum of the pods in the two preceding rings.

25. The *Fibonacci sequence* is 1, 1, 2, 3, 5, 8, . . .

   a. Write the next three terms of the sequence.

   b. Is the sequence arithmetic, geometric, or neither?

26. Critical Thinking The figure at the right shows the first four arrows in a sequence of arrows.

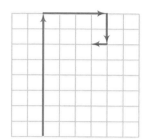

   a. Do you think the next arrow points left, right, up, or down?

   b. How long is the next arrow?

   c. What will be the direction of the eighth arrow in the sequence?

27. Biology A female bee has two biological parents, a female and a male. A male bee has one biological parent, a female.

   a. Make a "family tree" that shows the first seven generations of ancestors for a female bee. Find the number of ancestors in each of the seven generations.

   b. The numbers of ancestors form a number sequence. Is the sequence arithmetic, geometric, or neither?

28. a. On graph paper draw a 16 × 16 square like the one shown in Figure 1 below. Find its area.

  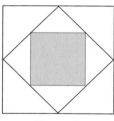

Figure 1   Figure 2   Figure 3

   b. Join the midpoints of the sides of the square, as shown in Figure 2. Find the area of the inner square.

   c. Join the midpoints of the sides of the inner square, as shown in Figure 3. Find the area of the innermost square.

   d. What would be the area of the innermost square in the sixth figure in this sequence?

29. Business Suppose an employer starts new employees at $4/h and raises the salary $.50/h every six months. What kind of sequence is this? Write a rule to describe the sequence.

What's Ahead

• Writing numbers greater than 10 using scientific notation

6-2

Scientific Notation

FLASHBACK

A power of 10 is a number like 10^5. The exponent 5 indicates that the base 10 is used as a factor 5 times.

$10^5 = 10 \cdot 10 \cdot 10 \cdot 10 \cdot 10$
$\quad = 100,000$

THINK AND DISCUSS

1. a. Copy and complete each statement.

$3 \times 10^1 = 3 \times 10 = \blacksquare$ $\qquad$ $3 \times 10^4 = 3 \times \blacksquare = \blacksquare$

$3 \times 10^2 = 3 \times 100 = \blacksquare$ $\qquad$ $3 \times 10^5 = 3 \times \blacksquare = \blacksquare$

$3 \times 10^3 = 3 \times 1,000 = \blacksquare$ $\qquad$ $3 \times 10^6 = 3 \times \blacksquare = \blacksquare$

b. What patterns do you see in your answers to part (a)?

Solar flares are bursts of high-energy particles that can travel through space at 3,000,000 km/h. Scientists write large numbers like this in a special form called **scientific notation,** which consists of two factors. The first factor is a number greater than or equal to 1 and less than 10. The second factor is a power of 10. Written in scientific notation, the speed of the particles is 3×10^6 km/h.

Example 1

Write 51,900,000 in scientific notation.

5.1900000 $\qquad$ Write as a number between 1 and 10.

$5.19 \times 10,000,000$ $\qquad$ To keep the value the same, multiply by a power of 10.

5.19×10^7 $\qquad$ Write the power of 10 using an exponent.

2. a. Explain why the scientific notation for 51,900,000 is *not* 519×10^5.

b. Write 396,000,000 in scientific notation.

You can change a number from scientific notation to **standard form** by multiplying.

Example 2

The mean distance from Earth to the Sun is about 1.5×10^8 km. Write this number in standard form.

• $1.5 \times 10^8 = 1.5 \times 100,000,000$
$\qquad\qquad\qquad = 150,000,000$

The mean distance is about 150,000,000 km.

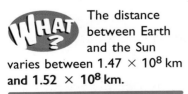

The distance between Earth and the Sun varies between 1.47×10^8 km and 1.52×10^8 km.

Source: *Atlas of the Solar System*

You can enter a number in scientific notation into a scientific calculator using the *exponent* key. For example, this is how you enter 7.36×10^{11}.

key sequence: 7.36 **EXP** 11 → display: *7.36   11*

T R Y THESE

Explain why each number is *not* in scientific notation.

3. 35.4×10^6 **4.** 8×2^{10} **5.** 0.387×10^7

Write each number in scientific notation.

6. 490,000,000,000   **7.** 75 million   **8.** 125

Write each number in standard form.

9. 8.6×10^7 **10.** 5×10^{11} **11.** 7.02×10^1

12. **Mental Math** The first balloon to carry passengers in flight weighed 1.6×10^3 lb. Write this number in standard form.

WHEN? The first manned flight of a hot-air balloon took place in France on November 21, 1783. The balloon rose to a height of 3,000 ft and landed 23 min later, having traveled $5\frac{1}{2}$ mi.

Source: *Encyclopedia Britannica*

GREAT EXPECTATIONS

Airline Pilot

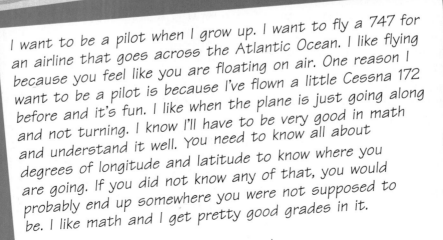

I want to be a pilot when I grow up. I want to fly a 747 for an airline that goes across the Atlantic Ocean. I like flying because you feel like you are floating on air. One reason I want to be a pilot is because I've flown a little Cessna 172 before and it's fun. I like when the plane is just going along and not turning. I know I'll have to be very good in math and understand it well. You need to know all about degrees of longitude and latitude to know where you are going. If you did not know any of that, you would probably end up somewhere you were not supposed to be. I like math and I get pretty good grades in it.

Joshua Gitersonke

Write each number in scientific notation. Then enter it into a scientific calculator, and write what appears in the display.

13. There are about 350,000 different kinds of plants on Earth.

14. A light year is the distance light can travel in a vacuum in one year. This distance is 5,880 trillion miles.

15. Dinosaurs first appeared about 190 million years ago.

Write each number in standard form.

16. At the beginning of the next century the world population will be about 6.127×10^9.

17. The mean distance from Mars to the Sun is 2.277×10^8 km.

18. Writing Explain how you find the power of 10 to write 725,000,000 in scientific notation.

M*x*ed REVIEW

Find the mean, mode, and median.

1. 2, 17, 18, 9, 13, 15, 17

2. 71, 75, 75, 78, 79, 75

Find the next three terms.

3. 5, 7, 9, 11, . . .

4. 1, 3, 9, 27, . . .

5. The six members of the Estrella family walked a total of 60 mi in 5 days. What is the average number of miles each family member walked each day?

Dear Joshua,

I'm excited to tell you more about how to become an airline pilot. You are right about the importance of math and the use of numbers. Flying airplanes will require you to work with numbers quickly and accurately. Just as you stated in your letter, it's very important to know where you are at all times. I have used the multiplication facts I learned in school more times while flying than you can imagine. Numbers tell me where I am, where I am going, what the weather is like at my destination, and even the condition of my airplane. I couldn't fly without understanding and using math. So, study hard—especially your math. Someday, maybe we will meet in the skies!

Louis Smith
Pilot and President of Future American Pilots

What's Ahead

• Solving problems by looking for a pattern

6-3 **L**ook for a Pattern

Sometimes you can solve a problem that appears complicated by solving a series of simpler problems and looking for a pattern.

> What is the units digit of 2^{50} when you write the number in standard notation?

READ

Read and understand the given information. Summarize the problem.

1. Think about the information you are given.
   a. What is the meaning of the expression 2^{50}?
   b. Why is it not practical to evaluate 2^{50} with paper and pencil?
   c. What happens when you try to evaluate 2^{50} with a calculator?

PLAN

Decide on a strategy to solve the problem.

Neither paper and pencil nor a calculator is a very efficient method for solving this problem. Instead, think about the types of calculations that you can do with these methods.

2. What is the meaning of 2^1?

3. How do you evaluate 2^2, 2^3, 2^4, and so on?

SOLVE

Try out the strategy.

You need to solve a number of simpler problems, so it is a good idea to organize your answers in a table.

4. Copy and complete the table at the right.
   a. Circle the units digit of each number in the Value column. What pattern do you see?
   b. What would be the fiftieth number in the pattern?
   c. What is the units digit of 2^{50}?

Power of 2	Value
2^1	■
2^2	■
2^3	■
2^4	■
2^5	■
2^6	■
2^7	■
2^8	■
2^9	■
2^{10}	■

5. How did looking for a pattern help in solving this problem?

6. Explain how you can find the units digit of any positive integer power of 2.

◀ **LOOK BACK**

Think about how you solved the problem.

T R Y THESE

Look for a pattern to solve each problem. Show all your work.

7. a. Find a pattern for the units digits of the powers of 3. Describe the pattern you find.

  b. What is the units digit of 3^{21}?

8. Discussion Do the units digits follow a pattern of four different repeating digits for the powers of any whole number? Explain.

9. Find the sum of the first one hundred odd whole numbers. That is, find the sum $1 + 3 + 5 + 7 + \cdots + 199$.

10. What is the value of $(-1)^{427}$?

11. a. The figures at the right show the first three *pentagonal numbers*. How many dots will be on each side of the fourth figure? Include the endpoints.

  b. What is the sixth pentagonal number?

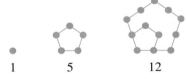

1   5   12

O N YOUR OWN

Use any strategy to solve each problem. Show all your work.

12. It takes two minutes to make one cut through a log. How long will it take to cut a ten-foot log into four equal pieces?

13. Cars A new car is available in five different exterior colors and three different interior colors. How many different color combinations are available?

14. Nita, a six-year old, can stretch her legs to take two steps at one time. How many different ways can she climb the six steps on her porch using any combination of one or two steps?

Compare using <, >, or =.

1. 4.5 ■ 4.493

2. 72.013 ■ 72.13

Write each number in scientific notation.

3. 57,000,000,000

4. 14,500,000,000,000

Write in standard form.

5. 3×10^5 6. 4.7×10^8

7. Suppose it takes 18 min to cut a board into 6 pieces. How long would it take to cut the board into 8 pieces?

15. Show how to cut a round pizza into eleven pieces with exactly four straight cuts.

16. Six building blocks are shaped like cubes with edges of 1 cm, 2 cm, 3 cm, 4 cm, 5 cm, and 6 cm. Can you use all the blocks to make two towers of the same height? Justify your answer.

17. **Data File 1 (pp. 2–3)** Suppose that a family's chief form of entertainment is watching movies. Do you think they spent more on movie tickets in 1980 or in 1990? Explain.

18. **Choose A, B, C, or D.** How long is one side of the seventh square in this pattern?

| 225 square units | 196 square units | 169 square units | 144 square units |

A. 121 **B.** 81 **C.** 40.5 **D.** 9

19. In a class of 30 students, 18 students study Spanish, 15 study French, and 5 study neither Spanish nor French. How many students study both Spanish and French?

20. Five pears weigh the same as three apples and two strawberries. An apple weighs the same as 21 strawberries. How many strawberries weigh the same as a pear?

CHECKPOINT

Identify each sequence as arithmetic, geometric, or neither. Write a rule to describe each arithmetic or geometric sequence. Then find the next three terms.

1. 0.2, 0.4, 0.8, 1.6, . . .

2. 0.2, 0.4, 0.6, 0.8, . . .

3. 13, 5, −3, −11, . . .

4. 2, 8, 10, 18, 28, . . .

Write each number in scientific notation.

5. 66.1×10^2

6. 738,000,000

7. 88.8×10^6

row 1				1	1			
row 2			1	2	1			
row 3		1	3	3	1			
row 4	1	4	6	4	1			

8. **a.** Write the numbers in row 6 of the pattern at the left.

   b. Which row will have a sum of 1,024?

6-4 Using Exponents

What's Ahead

• Using spreadsheets and calculators to explore savings

WHAT YOU'LL NEED

✓ Computer

✓ Spreadsheet software

✓ Calculator

An uncirculated $20 Gold Double Eagle coin minted in 1865 now has a value of $32,000. Its value has increased at a rate between $.05 and $.06 for every dollar each year.

THINK AND DISCUSS

Money may not grow on trees, but it can grow in a bank! If you deposit $1,000 in a bank account now, next year you will have more than $1,000 in the account. The bank pays you *interest* on your deposit, because they use your money to earn more money.

Imagine that, on the day you were born, someone deposited $1,000 in a bank account for you. The bank pays interest at a *rate* of $.05 for every dollar in the account each year. To find how much money will be in the account on your eighteenth birthday, you can use a spreadsheet like the one below.

	A	B	C	D	E
1	Year	Start of Year	Rate	Interest	End of Year
2	1st	$1,000.00	0.05	$50.00	$1,050.00
3	2nd	$1,050.00	0.05	$52.50	■

1. **a.** How was the amount in cell D2 calculated?

   b. How was the amount in cell E2 calculated?

   c. Why is the amount in cell B3 the same as that in cell E2?

   d. Why is the number in cell C3 the same as that in cell C2?

   e. How was the amount in cell D3 calculated?

   f. Calculate the amount that should appear in cell E3.

2. **Computer** Make a spreadsheet like the one above.

   a. How much money will be in the account at the end of 18 y?

   b. In which year does the original $1,000 double in value?

3. **a.** Suppose the bank pays interest at a rate of $.06 for every dollar in the account each year. How much money will be in the account at the end of 18 y?

   b. Use your answers to Questions 2(a) and 3(a) to find how much more interest is earned in 18 y when the rate increases from $.05 for every dollar in the account to $.06 for every dollar in the account.

Another way to find the amount in an account is to use the following formula.

$$A = p(1 + r)^n$$

In this formula, A is the final amount, p is the starting amount (called the *principal*), and r is the rate. When r is the rate the bank pays you each year, the exponent n is the number of years.

4. Suppose you deposit $1,000 in a bank account that pays interest at a rate of $.05 for every dollar in the account each year. You will use the formula to find the amount in your account at the end of 18 y.

   a. What values will you use for p, r, and n?

   b. Write the calculator key sequence you will use to find the amount in your account at the end of 18 y.

   c. **Calculator** Calculate the final amount after 18 y.

   d. Compare the amount found using the formula to the amount found using the spreadsheet in Question 3.

5. **Calculator** Find the final amount in a bank account under each of the following sets of conditions.

   a. You deposit $1,000 for 21 y. The bank pays interest at a rate of $.05 for every dollar in the account each year.

   b. You deposit $1,500 for 18 y at a rate of $.06 for every dollar in the account each year.

In 1992 teenagers in the United States had an income of $70 billion from jobs, allowances, handouts from parents, and gifts. About $9 billion went to savings.

Source: *Rand Youth Poll*

⌐WORK TOGETHER

6. Work in groups. Consider the original problem again. That is, you deposit $1,000 for 18 y in a bank that pays interest at a rate of $.05 for every dollar in the account each year.

   a. Without calculating, predict which of these changes would increase the final amount the most.

   • doubling the starting amount from $1,000 to $2,000

   • doubling the rate the bank pays to $.10 for every dollar in the account each year.

   • doubling the time from 18 y to 36 y

   b. **Computer/Calculator** Use either a spreadsheet or the formula to check your predictions. Which change increases the final amount most?

Banking **Use a calculator or a computer.**

7. You deposit $500 in an account that pays interest at a rate of $.04 for every dollar in the account each year. How much money is in the account at the end of three years?

8. You invest $100 in a stock whose value doubles in value each year.

   a. Find the value of your investment at the end of each of the first four years.

   b. At this rate, how long will it take for your investment to be worth $1,000,000?

9. Some accounts pay interest monthly. To find the final amount, you use the formula $A = p(1 + r)^n$. This time r is the rate paid on each dollar in the account every month, and n is the number of months.

   a. You deposit $1,000 in an account that pays $.01 for every dollar in the account each month. What is the final amount after one year?

   b. **Writing** The Must-Trust Bank offers the two savings plans shown below. Which would you choose? Explain.

YEARLY PLAN	MONTHLY PLAN
Interest rate = $.12 for every dollar in an account each year	Interest rate = $.01 for every dollar in an account each month

Use the article at the right to answer each question.

10. When Lisa was born, her parents deposited $1,000 in an account that pays $.06 for every dollar in the account each year. Her parents add $1,000 to the account each birthday.

    a. Copy and complete the table below to find how much money Lisa's parents will have saved by the time she is 18. Include their deposit on her 18th birthday.

Age	Start of Year	Rate	Interest	End of Year
0	$1,000.00	0.06	$60.00	$1,060.00
1	$2,060.00	0.06	$123.60	■

    b. How much more will Lisa need than is in her savings if she goes to a public college? a private college?

Make a stem-and-leaf plot.

1. 34 46 50 48 53 32 33
   20 44 48 45 34 56 41

2. 9.6 9.2 7.3 8.1 7.4
   8.1 7.8 7.5 8.5 9.6

Simplify each expression.

3. $|-3| + 9 + (-1)$

4. $-17 + (-3) + (-1)$

5. Find two whole numbers whose sum is 23 and whose product is 132.

College Costs Soar

In 1975 the cost of a college education ranged from an average of $7,000* for four years at public universities to $16,000 at private universities. By the year 2000—when many of the 3.6 million Americans born in 1982 will be ready to attend college—financial analysts predict this range may extend from $40,000 to $100,000. Parents who hope to send a child to college are advised to begin a savings program almost from the moment of a child's birth.

*All costs cited include tuition, room, and board.

Representing Functions

What's Ahead

• Introducing function ideas including function machines, tables, rules, and graphs.

WHAT YOU'LL NEED

✓ **Graph paper**

✓ **Stopwatch or clock with second hand**

THINK AND DISCUSS

Suppose your family is planning a sightseeing vacation by car. You expect to drive at an average speed of 50 mi/h. To decide where to stay each night, you want to know the distances you will drive in different amounts of time.

1. How many miles will you drive in 1 h? in 2 h?

2. How many hours will it take to drive 200 mi?

You know that there is a relationship between the amount of time you drive and the distance you drive. One way to represent this relationship is to think of a *machine* like the one at the right. The number of hours you drive is the *input* for the machine. The number of miles you drive is the machine's *output*.

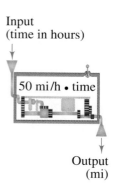

Input
(time in hours)

50 mi/h • time

Output
(mi)

3. When the input is 3, what is the output?

4. If the output is 300, what is the input?

Another way to represent the relationship between the time and the distance you drive is to use a *table*.

5. a. Copy and complete the table at the left.

   b. What kind of sequences are the number patterns that you see in each column?

You also can use the following *rule* to describe the relationship between the time and distance you drive.

$$\text{distance} = 50 \cdot \text{time}$$
$$d = 50t \qquad \leftarrow \textbf{Variables represent the input and output.}$$

6. Use the rule to find the number of miles you drive in 3.5 h.

Input t (hours)	Output d (miles)
1	■
2	■
3	■
4	■
5	■
6	■
7	■
8	■

One other way to represent the relationship between distance and time is to make a *graph*. On the graph at the right each dot represents a time and the related distance. If you draw a vertical line through 4 h and a horizontal line through 200 mi, they will intersect at a point. You place a dot where these two lines intersect to represent that the time 4 h is related to the distance 200 mi.

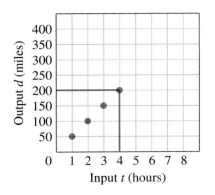

7. Copy the graph on graph paper. Add dots to represent the remaining rows of the table you made in Question 5.

8. Would it make sense to add a dot at the "zero point" of your graph? Explain.

9. **a.** Connect the dots on your graph with a line.

   b. Which is a better graph of the relationship between distance and time, a graph with only dots or a line? Explain.

   c. Use your graph to estimate the number of miles traveled in 6.5 h.

   d. Use your graph to estimate the number of hours it takes to travel 225 mi.

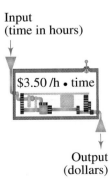

At full speed, a downhill skier travels at 31 m/s. **At this speed how far has the skier traveled after 2 s? 3 s? 5 s?**

Source: *Science World*

It is clear that the distance you drive depends upon the time you drive at a certain speed. You say that the distance is a *function* of the time. Many everyday situations are examples of functions.

10. **Jobs** The function machine at the right shows that Tim's wages are a function of the number of hours he works.

   a. Suppose Tim works six hours (input). What are his wages (output)?

   b. Make a table of ten inputs and the related outputs for this machine.

   c. Make a graph of the function using the data in your table.

   d. Write a rule for the function.

Input
(time in hours)

$3.50/h • time

Output
(dollars)

 Most people can hold their breath for about 1 min. Experienced skin divers can hold their breath for about $2\frac{1}{2}$ min. A beaver can stay under water for about 15 min.

Source: *Encyclopedia Britannica*

Input p (Amount of Purchase)	Output c (Change from $5.00)
$ .50	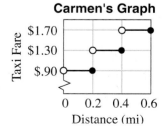
$1.00	
$1.50	
:	:
$5.00	

WORK TOGETHER

- Work in pairs. Count the number of times your partner breathes in one minute. Record the result.
- Repeat the experiment four times.
- Find the average of the five results.

11. a. Use your average number of breaths per minute. Copy and complete this table.

Input t (minutes)	1	2	3	4	5	6	7	8
Output b (no. of breaths)								

b. Make a graph of the data in your table.

c. Write a rule for the function.

ON YOUR OWN

12. a. Copy and complete the function table at the left.

b. Use the data from your table to make a graph.

c. Write a rule for the function.

d. List three more input/output pairs for the function.

13. Business A taxi meter is a type of function machine. It finds fares according to rules like those shown at the right.

a. Make a table of fares for distances starting at zero and increasing by 0.2 mi up to 2 mi.

b. Carmen and Brian started graphs for the taxi data. Which graph could you use to find the cost of a 0.5 mi trip? Why?

Sunshine Taxi
FARES
First 0.2 mile: $.90
Each additional 0.2 mile (or less): $.40

Carmen's Graph

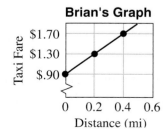

Brian's Graph

14. Cars The graph at the right shows the relationship between distance and time for a car driven at a constant speed.

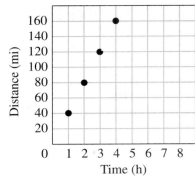

Distance (mi) vs Time (h)

a. What is the speed?

b. Write a rule to represent the function.

c. Make a table for the function, listing at least eight input/output pairs.

15. Writing Write a paragraph explaining to a friend three ways you can show or describe the function machine at the right.

Input
(time in hours)

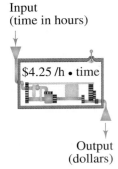

$4.25 /h • time

Output
(dollars)

16. Data File 6 (pp. 242–243) Make a function table that represents the relationship between the volume of sales of rock music and the year of the sales.

17. The formula $A = s^2$ is an example of a function rule. It represents the area of a square as a function of the length of a side.

a. Using the rule, copy and complete the table at the right.

b. Use the data from the table to make a graph of the function.

c. Describe what your graph looks like.

Input *s* (units)	Output *A* (square units)
1	■
2	■
3	■
4	■

18. Refer to the function machine at the right.

a. Make an input/output table for input values from −5 to 5.

b. What two inputs result in an output of 22?

c. Use the data from the table to make a graph of the function.

Input

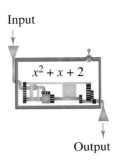

$x^2 + x + 2$

Output

19. Investigation (p. 244) Find the quotient for each pair of measurements you found for each member of your team. Describe any patterns that you see.

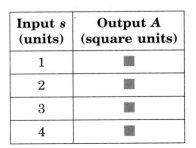

PROBLEM SOLVING STRATEGIES

Make a Table
Use Logical Reasoning
Solve a Simpler Problem
Too Much or Too Little Information
Look for a Pattern
Make a Model
Work Backward
Draw a Diagram
Guess and Test
Simulate a Problem
Use Multiple Strategies
Write an Equation

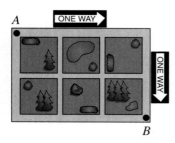

A   ONE WAY ►

◄ ONE WAY

B

Walking is the fastest growing participant sport in the United States. Nearly 30 million people walk to stay in shape.

Source: *Mayo Clinic Family Health Book*

Solve. The list at the left shows some possible strategies you might use.

1. **Business** A clerk at a mail-order company must pack items that weigh 2, 5, 10, 11, 13, 16, 19, and 23 lb for shipment to one customer. How can the clerk pack the items in two boxes that each hold a maximum of 50 lb?

2. A square piece of paper is folded in half. The perimeter of the resulting rectangle is 24 in. Find the area of the original square.

3. Find values of a and b so that $ab + b = ba$.

4. **Money** Adult tickets to a band concert cost $8, and student tickets cost $3. Charlie sold 20 tickets and collected $100. How many adult tickets did he sell?

5. In this section of the city of Gridville, all the streets are either one-way going east or one-way going south. A six-block section of the city is shown at the left. How many possible routes are there from point A to point B?

6. The last Friday of a particular month is the 30th. What is the date of the first Friday of that month?

7. Lupe and two friends start a computer club. They each recruit two new members each month. Each new member must agree to do the same. At the end of the first month, there were three old members and six new members. How many members will the club have after four months?

8. **Business** A fruit seller has three weights that can be used to weigh any whole number of pounds from 1 lb to 13 lb in a balance scale. What are the weights?

9. **Health** Suppose a 125-lb person burns 110 calories walking 2 mi/h, 180 calories walking 3 mi/h, and 260 calories walking 4 mi/h. How many calories do you think a 125-lb person would burn walking 5 mi/h?

6-6 **F**unctions

At the right is a function table. Consider these three rules.

    I. Output = 2 × Input
    II. Output = Input + 1
    III. Output = 2 × Input − 1

Input	Output
1	2
2	3
3	4
4	5

1. Which rule(s) describes the relationship between the first input and output?

2. Which rule(s) describes the relationship between the input and output when the input is 2?

3. Which rule(s) describes the relationship between the input and output in all of the rows?

4. Which is an appropriate rule for this function?

5. Use the variable n to represent any input. Write a variable expression that represents the related output.

THINK AND DISCUSS

Input	Output
1	4
2	5
3	6
4	7

The table at the left represents a function. To give a rule for this function, you might say: *Each output is three greater than the input.* To make the rule shorter, you might write:

$$\text{OUTPUT} = \text{INPUT} + 3$$

Mathematicians give the rule for this function in an even shorter form called *function notation*.

    You write: $f(n) = n + 3$
    You say: f of n equals n plus 3

In $f(n) = n + 3$, the variable n represents any input. The variable expression $n + 3$ represents the related output.

You also use function notation to name specific input/output pairs. For the above function, you would write the following:

    $f(1) = 4$ $f(2) = 5$ $f(3) = 6$ $f(4) = 7$

Fractals, like the one pictured above, are created using a feedback process. This means that an output is used for the next input. For example, suppose you used $n = 0.8$ as the first value for n in $f(n) = n^2$. The output is 0.64. You would use the output 0.64 as the second input value for n. **What would you use for the third input value for n?**

Source: The Beauty of Fractals

Example 1

The rule for a function is $f(n) = -3n + 5$. Find $f(1)$, $f(2)$, $f(3)$, and $f(4)$. Then make a table for the function.

- Use the expression $-3n + 5$.
  Replace n with 1, 2, 3, and 4.

$f(1) = -3(1) + 5 = -3 + 5 = 2$
$f(2) = -3(2) + 5 = -6 + 5 = -1$
$f(3) = -3(3) + 5 = -9 + 5 = -4$
$f(4) = -3(4) + 5 = -12 + 5 = -7$

The function table is at the right.

n	$f(n)$
1	2
2	-1
3	-4
4	-7

6. Use the function rule in Example 1. Find $f(5)$.

When you are given a function table, you can find a function rule by looking for patterns.

Example 2

Write a rule for the function represented by the table at the right.

- Each number in the second column is the product of the number in the first column multiplied by -4.

$1 \times (-4) = -4$ $2 \times (-4) = -8$
$3 \times (-4) = -12$ $4 \times (-4) = -16$

n	$f(n)$
1	-4
2	-8
3	-12
4	-16

So, the function rule is $f(n) = n \times (-4)$, or $f(n) = -4n$.

Sometimes looking for a pattern involves two steps.

Example 3

Write a rule for the function represented by the table at the right.

- If 1, 2, 3, and 4 are multiplied by 3, the results would be 3, 6, 9, and 12.

  Each number in the second column is one less than one of these multiples of 3.

n	$f(n)$
1	2
2	5
3	8
4	11

$(3 \times 1) - 1 = 2$ $(3 \times 2) - 1 = 5$
$(3 \times 3) - 1 = 8$ $(3 \times 4) - 1 = 11$

So the function rule is $f(n) = 3n - 1$.

7. a. What are the results when 1, 2, 3, and 4 are multiplied by 4?

b. Write a rule for the function represented by the table at the left.

n	$f(n)$
1	5
2	9
3	13
4	17

Use the function rule $f(n) = 2n + 7$. Find the following.

8. $f(3)$ **9.** $f(0)$ **10.** $f(-1)$ **11.** $f(-4)$ **12.** $f(0.5)$

13. The rule for a function is $f(n) = 12 - n$. Find $f(1)$, $f(2)$, $f(3)$, and $f(4)$.

Write a rule for the function represented by each table.

14.

n	$f(n)$
1	−5
2	−6
3	−7
4	−8

15.

n	$f(n)$
1	8
2	15
3	22
4	29

16.

n	$f(n)$
1	1
2	4
3	9
4	16

17. At the library you pay $.05 for each day a book is overdue. Use n to represent the number of days a book is overdue. Write a function rule to represent the overdue charge.

ON YOUR OWN

Make a table for the function represented by each rule. Find $f(1)$, $f(2)$, $f(3)$, and $f(4)$.

18. $f(n) = n + 2$ **19.** $f(n) = 12 - 2n$ **20.** $f(n) = n^2 + 1$

21. a. Make a table of input/output pairs for the graph at the right.

  b. Use your table to write a rule for the function.

22. The rule for a function is $f(n) = n + 5$. Find $f(1)$, $f(2)$, $f(3)$, and $f(4)$. Then make a graph of the function.

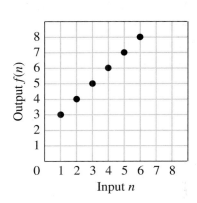

Write a rule for the function represented by each table.

23.

n	$f(n)$
1	−2
2	−1
3	0
4	1

24.

n	$f(n)$
1	−8
2	−16
3	−24
4	−32

25.

n	$f(n)$
1	5
2	8
3	11
4	14

26. Writing Summarize the methods that you can use to represent a function. Give an example of each.

27. Money Suppose you put $.50 in your piggy bank on January 1, $1.00 on January 2, $1.50 on January 3, $2.00 on January 4, and so on. Use n to represent the date in January. Write a function rule that represents the amount you put in the piggy bank on any date in January.

28. Investigation (p. 244) Use photographs of adults in magazines. Measure the height of a person and the height of the person's head. Find the quotient of the two measurements. Describe any patterns you find.

29. a. For the rectangular dot patterns at the left, suppose you know the number of dots on the shorter side. How can you find the number of dots on the longer side?

   b. Choose A, B, or C. Which function rule describes the total number of dots in the dot pattern at the left when n represents the number of dots on a shorter side?

   A. $f(n) = n^2$ **B.** $f(n) = n(n + 1)$ **C.** $f(n) = n(n - 1)$

CHECK POINT

1. The cost of cheese is $4/lb.

   a. Copy and complete the function table at the left.

   b. Use the data from the table to make a graph of the function.

2. You deposit $600 in an account that pays $.04 for every dollar in the account each year. What is the amount in the account at the end of two years?

Number of Pounds	Total Cost (dollars)
1	▪
2	▪
3	▪
4	▪

Write a rule for the function represented by each table.

3.

n	$f(n)$
1	−12
2	−24
3	−36
4	−48

4.

n	$f(n)$
1	−4
2	−3
3	−2
4	−1

5.

n	$f(n)$
1	1
2	4
3	7
4	10

Identify each sequence as arithmetic, geometric, or neither. Then find the next three terms in the sequence.

1. 23, 19, 15, 11, . . .

2. 1, 4, 16, 64, . . .

3. 0.4, 0.45, 0.5, 0.55, . . .

4. 400, 200, 100, 50, . . .

5. 5, 7, 11, 17, . . .

6. 0, 2, 8, 18, . . .

Write each number in scientific notation.

7. 57,000

8. 90,000,000

9. 112,000

10. 603,000,000

11. 72

Write each number in standard form.

12. 4×10^5

13. 1.49×10^2

14. 5.7×10^6

15. 1.07×10^{11}

16. 8×10^1

17. What is the units digit of 8^{41}?

18. The figures at the right show the first three *triangular numbers*. What is the eighth triangular number?

1   3   6

19. You deposit $400 in an account that pays $.03 for every dollar in the account each year. How much is in your bank account at the end of 5 y? Use the formula $A = p(1 + r)^n$.

20. a. You earn $5.50 per hour mowing lawns. Make a function table showing the amount you would earn as you work 1 h, 2 h, 3 h, and 4 h.

b. Write a rule for the function.

Find $f(-1)$ for the function represented by each rule.

21. $f(n) = n + 6$

22. $f(n) = -3n$

23. $f(n) = n^2$

24. $f(n) = 7n - 4$

Write a rule for the function represented by each table.

25.

n	f(n)
1	−9
2	−18
3	−27
4	−36

26.

n	f(n)
1	−5
2	−4
3	−3
4	−2

27.

n	f(n)
1	5
2	9
3	13
4	17

28.

n	f(n)
1	0
2	2
3	4
4	6

6-7 **I**nterpreting Graphs

WORK TOGETHER

In this experiment, you will explore the relationship between the volume and the height of a substance in a container. Begin with a transparent vase or pitcher shaped like a cylinder. Work in pairs.

• Pour one measuring cup of water, sand, rice, or a similar substance into the container.

• Measure the height of the substance in the container.

• Pour several additional cups into the container. Measure the height after each addition.

• Record the data in a table.

• Make a graph of the data in the table. (The figure at the right should help you get started.)

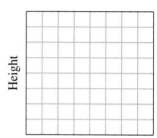

1. What would happen to your graph if you use a cup that holds

   a. exactly half as much?   **b.** exactly twice as much?

2. **Discussion** Do you think you can "connect the dots" on your graph? Explain.

3. Suppose you fill the vase at the left with sand. Which graph below better shows the relationship between the height and the number of measures of sand? Why?

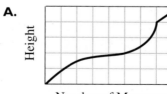

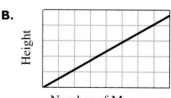

• Choose a pitcher or vase that is not shaped like a cylinder. Predict what its graph would look like when you fill it. Then repeat the experiment above. How accurate was your prediction?

⬛T⬛H⬛I⬛N⬛K⬛ ⬛A⬛N⬛D⬛ ⬛D⬛I⬛S⬛C⬛U⬛S⬛S

4. Lee, Paulo, and Mary each walked six blocks from school to the library. The graphs below represent the time and distance for each person's walk.

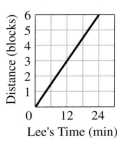
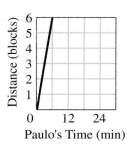
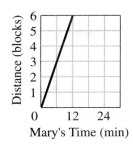

a. Who walked fastest? slowest? Explain how you know.

b. How is the steepness of the line related to the speed?

5. Tonnjo lives six blocks from school. Graphs I and II represent his walk home on a sunny day and a rainy day.

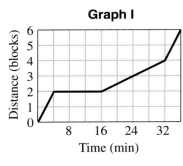

a. What does the "flat" segment of Graph I represent?

b. Which graph do you think represents the sunny day? the rainy day? Explain the reasons for your choices.

6. a. One day Tonnjo's sister Anique drove him part of the way to school. After he got out of the car, Tonnjo waited for his friend Minos. Then they walked the rest of the way to school. Make a graph to represent Tonnjo's trip to school that day.

b. Discussion Compare your graph with others in class. How are they alike? How are they different?

7. Make a graph that represents your trip home from school yesterday.

Mixed REVIEW

ON YOUR OWN

Graphs I, II, III, and IV each represent one of the four situations described below. Match each graph with the appropriate situation. Explain your choices.

I.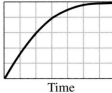
Time

II.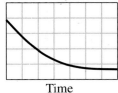
Time

III.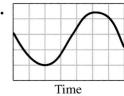
Time

IV.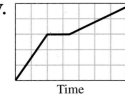
Time

8. distance in a hurdles race, falling over a hurdle

9. air temperature in the 24-h period starting from midnight

10. height of a person from birth to age 20

11. weight of a person on a diet

12. **Sports** The graph at the right shows the results of a 50-m race. In this race Edwin had a 15-m head start over Carl.

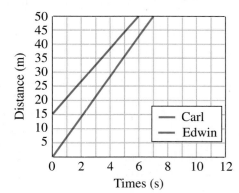

a. Who won the race?

b. By how many seconds did he win?

c. Predict what might happen in another race between Edwin and Carl if Edwin does not have a head start.

13. Make a graph that represents the height above the ground of one car on a Ferris wheel during three turns of the wheel. You can use a coin to simulate the Ferris wheel as it turns.

Ferris Wheel

14. Writing Describe a situation that the graph at the right might represent.

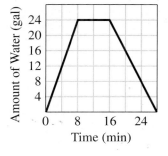

 15. Investigation (p. 244) Use the data you collected for your group. Draw a graph for each of the pairs of measurements that you made. Use the horizontal axis for one measurement and the vertical axis for the other. Which pairs of measurements appear to be functions? Why?

16. Janette ran the first 3 blocks from the library to her house, then walked the remaining 5 blocks. Draw a graph that represents her trip home.

17. Estimation The graph at the right shows what happens when a ball is thrown into the air.

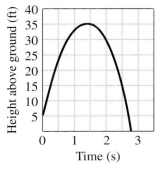

   a. What is the greatest height that the ball reaches?

   b. How long does it take for the ball to hit the ground?

   c. What is the height of the ball 1 s after it was thrown?

   d. Why are there two times when the height of the ball is 20 ft? What are the times?

   e. When the time is 0, why is the height of the ball *not* 0?

The Population Explosion

From A.D. 1 to A.D. 1650, the world population grew by 300 million. This translates to an average of just 180,000 people per year. This is about 21 people per hour. In contrast, today nine babies are born every two seconds, but only three people die. This means that the population is growing by about 10,800 people per hour, 259,200 per day, 1.8 million per week, 7.2 million per month, and 86.4 million per year. By the year 2000, the population will increase 94 million per year, and by 2020 that number will be 98 million per year.

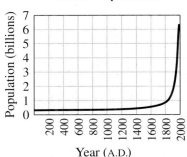

18. a. Explain how the graph at the right illustrates the point of the article.

   b. At what time in history would you say that the rate of population growth began a dramatic increase?

Wrap Up

Number Patterns 6-1

A *sequence* is a set of numbers arranged according to some pattern.

You find each term of an *arithmetic sequence* by adding the same number to the preceding term.

For a *geometric sequence,* you find each term by multiplying the preceding term by the same number.

Identify each sequence as arithmetic, geometric, or neither. Then find the next three terms of each sequence.

1. 7, 11, 15, 19, . . .   **2.** 48, 24, 12, 6, . . .   **3.** 3, −9, 27, −81, . . .   **4.** 20, 16, 11, 5, . . .

5. Write a rule for the sequences in Exercises 2 and 3.

6. Choose A, B, C, or D. What is the seventh term of the sequence 1, 3, 7, 15, . . . ?

    A. 127   **B.** 99   **C.** 64   **D.** 101

Exponents and Scientific Notation 6-2, 6-4

A number in *scientific notation* consists of two factors. One is a number greater than or equal to 1 and less than 10. The other factor is a power of 10.

You can use *exponents* to calculate the total amount in an account that earns interest. You use the formula $A = p(1 + r)^n$.

Write the following numbers using scientific notation.

7. 1,524,000,000   **8.** 250,000   **9.** 383 million   **10.** 87,600

11. You deposit $1,500 in an account that pays $.05 for every dollar in the account each year. How much is in the account at the end of 5 years? Use the formula $A = p(1 + r)^n$.

12. Writing Would you earn more or less if the account in Exercise 11 paid $.005 for every dollar each month? Explain.

13. The population of the United States in 1990 was about 2.49×10^8. Write this number in standard notation.

Functions

You can represent a *function* using a table, a rule, or a graph.

14. Write a rule for the function represented by the table at the right.

n	f(n)
1	4
2	6
3	8
4	10

15. Make an input/output table for the graph at the right. Then write a rule for the function.

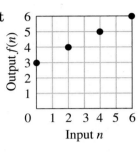

16. A rule for a function is $f(n) = 2n + 5$. Find $f(-1)$, $f(0)$, $f(1)$, and $f(2)$.

Interpreting Graphs

You can use graphs to represent real-world situations.

17. Describe a situation that the graph below might represent.

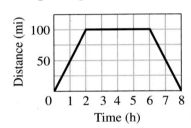

18. Tani walks at a rate of about 3 mi/h. She leaves home and walks for 3 h. She stops and spends 1 h eating lunch. Then she walks one more hour. Make a graph that represents the distance she has walked over the 5-h period.

Strategies and Applications

Sometimes you can solve a problem by looking for a pattern.

19. **Writing** Find a pattern for the units digit of the powers of 7 and describe it.

GETTING READY FOR CHAPTER 7

Use the divisors 2, 3, 5, 9, 10 to divide each number below. State which divisors leave no remainder.

1. 34   **2.** 216   **3.** 45   **4.** 648   **5.** 1,080   **6.** 70

follow Up

The Human Figure

Some art critics do not agree with Leonardo that there are mathematical relationships among the measurements of the human body. The Friends of da Vinci Society has come to Leonardo's defense. The society is seeking testimonials supporting Leonardo's position. Write a letter to the society summarizing your findings concerning mathematical relationships among measurements of the human body. The following are suggestions to help you show the relationships.

✓ Use number patterns.
✓ Use graphs.
✓ Use functions.

The problems preceded by the magnifying glass (p. 261, # 19; p. 266, # 28; and p. 271, # 15) may help you write your testimonial.

Excursion: Use the average of your measurements to write a formula to find each of the following:

  a. height in terms of length from fingertip to fingertip
  b. height in terms of length from wrist to elbow
  c. height in terms of length from ankle to kneecap

Measure the length from fingertip to fingertip, from wrist to elbow, and from ankle to kneecap of a student not in your group. Use your formulas to find the student's height. Then measure the student's height to determine which formula best predicted the height.

$$$ YOU'RE RICH!! $$$

Most people dream of getting a million dollars. Suppose you have a million dollars, and that you spend $1 each minute. How old would you be when you run out of money? If you had to spend a million dollars in a year, how much would you need to spend each minute? What would you do with the money?

Most calculators have an 8-digit readout. How many perfect squares can be displayed on your 8-digit calculator? What are the smallest and largest perfect squares you can calculate?

How many perfect cubes can be displayed? What are the smallest and largest perfect cubes you can calculate?

CROSS COUNTRY

Fundraisers sometimes organize walks and races to raise money for their causes. Sponsors fund participants with a contribution for the distance walked or run. Plan a fundraising walk for your community. Determine a goal— how much do you want to raise? Obtain a map and show your route. How long will it take participants to walk the entire route? If sponsors pay 10¢ per mile, how much will each participant raise? How many participants will you need to meet your goal?

1. Identify each sequence as arithmetic, geometric, or neither. Then find the next three terms.

    a. 1, 3, 9, 27, . . .   b. 4, 9, 14, 19, . . .

    c. 3, 4, 6, 9, . . .   d. 10, 8, 6, 4, . . .

    e. −1, 3, 7, 11, . . .   f. 1.5, 3, 6, 12, . . .

2. Write rules for the arithmetic and geometric sequences in Exercise 1.

3. Write each number in scientific notation.

    a. 175,000,000   b. 600

    c. 9,600,000,000   d. 22 million

4. Suppose you deposit $1,000 in an account that pays $.06 for every dollar in the account each year. How much is in the account at the end of three years? Use the formula $A = p(1 + r)^n$.

5. Write each number in standard form.

    a. 4×10^2 b. 6.72×10^7

6. Make a table of the input/output pairs for each of the following.

    a. the cost of 1 to 5 books at $2.95 each

    b. the perimeter of a square with sides 5 in., 6 in., 7 in., 8 in., and 9 in. long

7. Find $f(-2)$, $f(0)$, and $f(5)$ for the function represented by each rule below.

    a. $f(n) = n - 5$ b. $f(n) = 9 + n$

    c. $f(n) = 2n + 1$ d. $f(n) = n^2 - 1$

8. **Choose A, B, C, or D.** Which is *not* an output for $f(n) = 2n^2 - 5$?

    A. −3   **B.** 45   **C.** 27   **D.** −8

9. **Writing** Tori earns $4.50/h. How can she use a function to find out her earnings for any number of hours she works?

10. Write a rule for the function represented by each table.

    a.

n	$f(n)$
1	3
2	6
3	9
4	12

    b.

n	$f(n)$
1	3
2	5
3	7
4	9

11. Use the graph for the questions below.

    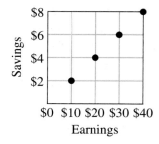

    a. Use the graph to make a table of input/output pairs.

    b. Write a rule for the function.

    c. Find how much money is saved when $100 is earned.

12. An amusement park costs $12/person. The park offers special rates for groups. Admission charges are $40 for four people, $49 for five, $57 for six, $64 for seven, and so on. How much does each member of a group of twelve save by getting a group rate?

Choose A, B, C, or D.

1. Which number is written in scientific notation?

A. 0.2×10^9 **B.** 9.14×2^5

C. 10×10^8 **D.** 7.12×10^{11}

2. Which equation is represented by the model shown?

A. $x + 3 = 2$ **B.** $-3x = -2$

C. $x - 3 = -2$ **D.** $x + 3 = -2$

3. The A-One Hotel charges $88/da for two people in a room, plus $7 for each additional person. Which equation could you use to find the cost for more than two people to stay in a room one day.

A. $C = 88 + n(7)$

B. $C = 2(88) + n(7)$

C. $C = (n + 2)(88 + 7)$

D. $C = 2(88) + (n + 2)(7)$

4. What could the graph below represent?

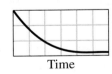

Time

A. the height of a ball t seconds after it is thrown upward

B. the temperature of an oven t minutes after it is turned on

C. the value of a new car after t years

D. the distance a car has traveled at 45 mi/h after t hours

5. Gabe earns $16/week. Which equation can you use to find how many weeks it took him to earn $400?

A. $16 + w = 400$ **B.** $16w = 400$

C. $\dfrac{16}{w} = 400$ **D.** $\dfrac{16}{400} = w$

6. Find the median of the data in the stem-and-leaf plot.

7	0 0 5 8
8	1 5 6 9 9
9	4

9|4 means 94

A. 81.7   **B.** 89

C. 85   **D.** 83

7. Which expression has the greatest value?

A. $32 - (-12)$ **B.** $32 - |-12|$

C. $-32 - (-12)$ **D.** $|-32 - (-12)|$

8. Find two numbers whose sum is 10 and whose product is -24.

A. -6 and 4   **B.** 12 and -2

C. -8 and -3 **D.** 6 and -4

9. Which type of graph would best display the following data on the number of viewers (in millions) watching television during prime time?

Mon., 91.9   Tue., 89.8   Wed., 93.9
Thu., 93.9   Fri., 78.0   Sat., 77.1
Sun., 87.7

A. line   **B.** double line

C. bar   **D.** double bar

10. Which expression has the same value as $(-1)^{57} \cdot x^4$?

A. $(-x)^4$ **B.** $-x^4$ **C.** x^{57} **D.** $-x^{57}$

Number Theory

PICTURE PERFECT

WORLD VIEW

The Lumiere brothers from France invented the first practical color film developing process in 1903.

Data File 7

focus ring

aperture ring
(the size of the aperture is measured in units called f-stops)

$$\frac{\text{focal length}}{\text{f-stop}} = \text{diameter of the aperture}$$

shutter speed ring

WHAT YOU WILL LEARN

- how to understand fraction concepts
- how to model and write fractions and decimals
- how to use technology to explore fraction patterns
- how to solve problems by solving simpler problems

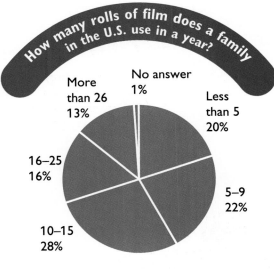

How many rolls of film does a family in the U.S. use in a year?

More than 26
13%

No answer
1%

Less than 5
20%

16–25
16%

5–9
22%

10–15
28%

The mean number of rolls was 15.

Source: Wolfman Report

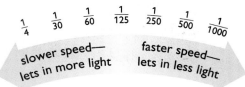

$\frac{1}{4}$ $\frac{1}{30}$ $\frac{1}{60}$ $\frac{1}{125}$ $\frac{1}{250}$ $\frac{1}{500}$ $\frac{1}{1000}$

slower speed—
lets in more light

faster speed—
lets in less light

Many cameras include a dial for setting the shutter speed. Numbers on the dial represent fractions of a second. The fraction tells how long light will enter the eye of the camera and expose the film. For example, a 4 means the shutter will be open for $\frac{1}{4}$ s.

Source: *Scholastic Math*

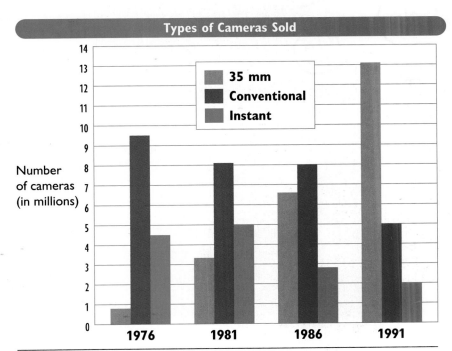

Types of Cameras Sold

- 35 mm
- Conventional
- Instant

Number of cameras (in millions)

14 13 12 11 10 9 8 7 6 5 4 3 2 1 0

1976   1981   1986   1991

Source: Wolfman Report

Shutter Speeds

The table shows suggested shutter speeds for action shots when using 100 speed film.

Person walking	$\frac{1}{125}$
Person running	$\frac{1}{500}$
Cyclist	$\frac{1}{250} - \frac{1}{1000}$
Galloping horse	$\frac{1}{250} - \frac{1}{1000}$
Sports activity	$\frac{1}{500}$
Moving vehicle	$\frac{1}{250} - \frac{1}{1000}$

Source: *Usborne Guide to Photography*

i**n**vestigation

Memo

Truly Tabletop Company produces do-it-yourself table kits. Each kit comes with congruent square tiles that exactly cover the rectangular tabletops. Their table designers have discovered that every tabletop can be covered by several different-sized squares. An 18-by-27 in. tabletop can be covered with 1-in. squares, 3-in. squares, or 9-in. squares. (All squares must have whole-number dimensions.) The company always chooses the largest possible squares for its kits.

For its 18-by-27 in. tabletops the company supplies customers with 9-in. square tiles.

Mission: Cut rectangles from grid paper to represent tables. Model all possible ways the rectangles can be covered with squares. Find the size of the square tiles the company would choose for each tabletop. Keep accurate records of all your trials and results.

LeADs tO FoLLoW

✓ Which size rectangles are better to concentrate on, small ones or large ones?

✓ What patterns in rectangle dimensions and square dimensions can you find?

What's Ahead

• Relating fractions and models

7-1 **T**he Meaning of Fractions

MATH AND CRAFTS

WHAT YOU'LL NEED

✓ **Pattern blocks**

THINK AND DISCUSS

You can use fractions to describe many kinds of situations. Fractions are used in measurement, when describing parts of a whole, and when describing members of a group.

1. Describe each situation that is modeled below.

   a.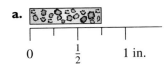

   b.

   c.

2. **a.** Measure the figures at the left. What can you conclude about the areas of the yellow rectangles.

   b. What fraction of each figure is the yellow rectangle?

   c. Why are different fractions used to describe the yellow rectangles?

WORK TOGETHER

You can use pattern blocks to explore fractions that are part of a whole.

3. Use 4 green triangles to make a large equilateral triangle. Suppose this large triangle represents one whole.

   a. What part of a whole does a red trapezoid represent?

   b. What part of a whole does a blue rhombus represent?

You can also use pattern blocks to explore fractions that are greater than a whole.

4. What mixed number does the large triangle you formed for Question 3 represent if a red trapezoid is a whole?

5. Use 3 green triangles and a yellow hexagon to form a large equilateral triangle. What mixed number does the large triangle represent if a blue rhombus is a whole?

Square A

Square B

Square C

Square D

By using a variety of fabrics and colors, you can create beautiful patterns to form the pieces of a quilt. These pieces are usually put together to form squares. Then the squares are put together to form the quilt.

6. **a.** What fraction of each quilt square at the left is blue?

   b. Design a quilt square in which $\frac{1}{3}$ of the square is red.

   c. Design a quilt square in which $\frac{3}{8}$ of the square is green.

ON YOUR OWN

Write a fraction for each model.

7.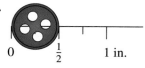

8.

9.

10. **Writing** Cora's younger brother described the shaded region at the right as $\frac{1}{3}$ of a pie. Is he correct? Why or why not?

GREAT EXPECTATIONS

Cartoonist

The career that I would pick is to become a cartoonist. This interests me very much because I love to draw funny animals and people. I have had personal experience as a cartoonist. I draw cartoons in my art class and for my own reference. I keep a pad of paper that I doodle on. It helps me to get started. One day I hope I can get into a good art college and maybe be accepted as a professional cartoonist. Then I'll be working with something I love to do—drawing!

Amanda Johnson

Write a mixed number for each model. A blue rhombus is a whole.

11.

12.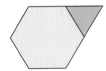

Write the fraction or a mixed number represented by the fraction bars.

13.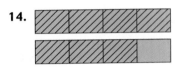

14.

15. **a.** Draw a rectangle. Be sure the length and the width are not equal. Draw the two diagonals of your rectangle.

   b. Is each of the triangles formed by the two diagonals $\frac{1}{4}$ of the area of the rectangle? Explain.

16. **a.** Create your own design for a quilt square using at least four different colors. Make three copies of your design. Put the squares together to form a paper quilt.

   b. What fraction of your paper quilt is each color?

Dear Amanda,

Sounds to me like you're off to a good start! Many of today's top cartoonists began their careers just like you. Keeping a sketch pad close by and drawing every chance you get will keep your ideas flowing and improve your drawing skills. I teach cartooning to people your age. I tell them there are three main rules to remember in cartooning. They are PRACTICE . . . PRACTICE . . . PRACTICE . . . !

One sure way to practice and get the experience you need as a cartoonist is to join the staff of your school newspaper or yearbook. It is extremely gratifying to participate in a school activity and to see your work in print.

Good luck to you and your career.

Joe Duffy
Chairman of the National Cartoonist Society

7-2 Equivalent Fractions

WORK TOGETHER

Work with a partner.

1. On graph paper, draw all of the rectangles you can that have an area of 24 square units.

2. On graph paper, draw all of the rectangles you can that have an area of 7 square units.

THINK AND DISCUSS

One number is a **factor** of another if it divides that number with no remainder.

3. Use the rectangles that you made in the Work Together.
   a. List the dimensions of the rectangles you found that have an area of 24 square units.
   b. How do the dimensions you found relate to the factors of the number 24?
   c. List all of the factors of 24 in order from least to greatest.
   d. List the factors of 7.

4. Are both 9 and 5 factors of 40? Why or why not?

A **multiple** of a number is the product of that number and any nonzero whole number.

5. a. List four factors of 6.
   b. List four multiples of 6.

6. Describe the relationship between 15, 5, and 3 using the words factor and multiple.

7. What number is a factor of all other numbers?

8. A number n is a multiple of 2. Is $n + 1$ a multiple of 2? Explain using examples.

Fractions that are equal to each other are **equivalent fractions.** You can use models to find equivalent fractions.

9. Do the models at the right show that $\frac{2}{3} = \frac{4}{6}$? Explain.

10. Draw a model of the fraction $\frac{1}{4}$. Use the model to find a fraction that is equivalent to $\frac{1}{4}$.

⚡**FLASHBACK**

In the fraction $\frac{2}{3}$, the numerator is 2, and the denominator is 3.

You can also find equivalent fractions by multiplying the numerator and denominator of a fraction by the same number.

$$\frac{2 \cdot 2}{3 \cdot 2} = \frac{4}{6}$$

To find several fractions equivalent to a given fraction, you can make a table of multiples, much like the multiplication tables you used when learning how to multiply.

Example 1   Use a table of multiples to find three fractions equivalent to $\frac{3}{4}$.

• List multiples of 3 and 4.

	×2	×3	×4
3	6	9	12
4	8	12	16

Multiples in the same column will form fractions equivalent to $\frac{3}{4}$.

Three fractions equivalent to $\frac{3}{4}$ are $\frac{6}{8}$, $\frac{9}{12}$, and $\frac{12}{16}$.

11. Find two more fractions that are equivalent to $\frac{3}{4}$.

Another way to find equivalent fractions is to divide the numerator and denominator by the same nonzero number. To find a number to use as the divisor, find the common factors.

Example 2   Find three fractions equivalent to $\frac{24}{30}$.

Factors of 24: 1, 2, 3, 4, 6, 8, 12, 24

Factors of 30: 1, 2, 3, 5, 6, 10, 15, 30

Common factors other than 1 include 2, 3, and 6. So divide to get equivalent fractions.

$$\frac{24 \div 2}{30 \div 2} = \frac{12}{15} \qquad \frac{24 \div 3}{30 \div 3} = \frac{8}{10} \qquad \frac{24 \div 6}{30 \div 6} = \frac{4}{5}$$

Three fractions equivalent to $\frac{24}{30}$ are $\frac{12}{15}$, $\frac{8}{10}$, and $\frac{4}{5}$.

12. Find two fractions equivalent to $\frac{30}{36}$ using division.

TRY THESE

Mental Math **List all of the factors of each number.**

13. 17   **14.** 18   **15.** 32   **16.** 42

17. What two equivalent fractions are modeled below?

18. a. Write the first five multiples of 8 and 12.

    b. Write three fractions equivalent to $\frac{8}{12}$.

19. a. Write the factors of 8 and 12.

    b. What factors do 8 and 12 have in common?

    c. Write two fractions equivalent to $\frac{8}{12}$ that you can find using common factors.

ON YOUR OWN

20. a. Write the first five multiples of 9 and 15.

    b. What is the least multiple 9 and 15 have in common?

21. a. Write the factors of 9 and 15.

    b. What factors do 9 and 15 have in common?

22. Mr. Quaid's class has 24 students, and Mrs. Carlson's class has 30 students. Each class is divided into several teams. What is the greatest number of people on a team if both classes have teams that are equal in size?

23. Choose A, B, C, or D. Which square does *not* have $\frac{1}{4}$ of the area shaded?

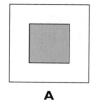 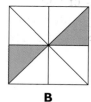 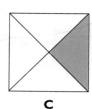 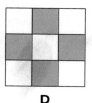

    A   **B**   **C**   **D**

 Fraction relationships are part of stringed instruments, like a guitar. If a string makes a middle C when strummed, then a string $\frac{1}{2}$ as long makes the C one octave higher. A guitarist shortens a string by pressing it against a ridge called a *fret*.

Source: *Mathematics*

Choose A, B, C, or D. Which fraction is *not* equivalent to the first fraction.

24. $\frac{21}{24}$ A. $\frac{14}{16}$ B. $\frac{7}{8}$ C. $\frac{42}{48}$ D. $\frac{5}{6}$

25. $\frac{2}{7}$ A. $\frac{6}{20}$ B. $\frac{4}{14}$ C. $\frac{10}{35}$ D. $\frac{8}{28}$

26. $\frac{5}{9}$ A. $\frac{20}{36}$ B. $\frac{15}{27}$ C. $\frac{15}{45}$ D. $\frac{10}{18}$

27. $\frac{1}{2}$ A. $\frac{9}{18}$ B. $\frac{19}{40}$ C. $\frac{4}{8}$ D. $\frac{12}{24}$

28. $\frac{28}{48}$ A. $\frac{1}{2}$ B. $\frac{7}{12}$ C. $\frac{14}{24}$ D. $\frac{35}{60}$

29. $\frac{27}{30}$ A. $\frac{18}{20}$ B. $\frac{9}{10}$ C. $\frac{54}{60}$ D. $\frac{7}{10}$

30. Name two fractions that are modeled below.

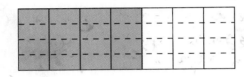

31. **Data File 7 (pp. 278–279)** For each year shown, estimate what fraction of the cameras sold were 35 mm cameras.

Use the multiplication table below. Find the number that makes a true statement.

	1	2	3	4	5	6	7	8	9
5	5	10	15	20	25	30	35	40	45
6	6	12	18	24	30	36	42	48	54
7	7	14	21	28	35	42	49	56	63
8	8	16	24	32	40	48	56	64	72

32. $\frac{5}{6} = \frac{20}{\blacksquare}$ 33. $\frac{25}{40} = \frac{\blacksquare}{8}$ 34. $\frac{7}{8} = \frac{35}{\blacksquare}$ 35. $\frac{\blacksquare}{72} = \frac{30}{48}$

36. Simone's father ate four pieces of the pie she baked. Her brother ate two pieces. Simone and her mother each ate one piece. If there were no pie left, what fraction of the pie did each family member eat?

37. **Writing** Beth ate $\frac{2}{8}$ of a peanut butter sandwich. Jane ate $\frac{1}{4}$ of another peanut butter sandwich. Yet Jane ate more than Beth. Explain how this could happen since $\frac{2}{8}$ equals $\frac{1}{4}$.

Mixed REVIEW

1. Draw a diagram to model the fraction $\frac{7}{8}$.

2. Draw a diagram to model the fraction $1\frac{1}{3}$.

Find $f(-1)$ and $f(2)$.

3. $f(n) = 2n + 5$

4. $f(n) = n^2 - 3$

5. Write 4,560,000 in scientific notation.

6. **Calculator** Find the square root of 1,225.

7. Find the length of the hypotenuse of a right triangle with legs 5 cm and 12 cm long.

Simplifying Fractions

WHAT YOU'LL NEED

✓ Calculator

World Leader Survey

Leader	Frequency
François Mitterrand	16
Carlos Salinas	20
Yitzhak Rabin	15
King Hussein	12
Bill Clinton	24
Nelson Mandela	18
Jean Crétien	21

THINK AND DISCUSS

Jeremy conducted a survey for his social studies class. He asked 24 people to identify the country each of the people in the table at the left are from. The frequency table shows the number of correct responses.

1. Jeremy wrote the fraction $\frac{12}{24}$ to report the fraction of people who identified that King Hussein is from Jordan. Jeremy's brother thinks he should use the fraction $\frac{1}{2}$. Which fraction do you think Jeremy should use? Why?

To simplify a fraction, you can divide both the numerator and the denominator by the same nonzero number. A fraction is in **simplest form** when the only factor common to both the numerator and the denominator is 1.

Example 1   Simplify $\frac{12}{24}$.

$$\frac{12 \div 2}{24 \div 2} = \frac{6}{12}$$ Divide the numerator and denominator by a common factor.

$$\frac{6 \div 6}{12 \div 6} = \frac{1}{2}$$ If necessary, divide again by another common factor.

In simplest form, $\frac{12}{24}$ is $\frac{1}{2}$.

2. What fraction of the people that Jeremy surveyed recognized the countries that Carlos Salinas and Nelson Mandela were from? Write each fraction in simplest form.

You can use divisibility tests to simplify fractions. A number is *divisible* by another if the remainder is zero. You can combine divisibility tests to develop tests for other numbers.

3. **a.** Use the divisibility tests to explain why 54 is divisible by 2; by 3.

   b. Complete: Since 54 is divisible by 2 and 3, it must also be divisible by ■.

4. Write a divisibility test for 15.

FLASHBACK

Number	Divisibility Test
2	ones' digit is 0, 2, 4, 6, or 8
3	sum of digits is divisible by 3
5	ones' digit is 0 or 5
9	sum of digits is divisible by 9
10	ones' digit is 0

You can use patterns to find divisibility tests for 4 and 8.

5. a. **Calculator** Which of the following numbers are divisible by 4?

   6   16   26   36   106   116   126   136

   b. Complete: If the last ■ digits form a number divisible by 4, then the number is divisible by 4.

6. a. **Calculator** Which of the following numbers are divisible by 8?

   16   36   56   116   136   156   1,016   1,036   1,056

   b. Complete: If the last ■ digits form a number divisible by 8, then the number is divisible by 8.

7. **Critical Thinking** Write a divisibility test for 12.

You can use divisibility tests to help you find common factors.

Example 2 Simplify $\frac{24}{39}$.

- Find a common factor of 24 and 39.

   $2 + 4 = 6; 3 + 9 = 12$

   Since 6 and 12 are divisible by 3, so are 24 and 39.

- $\frac{24 \div 3}{39 \div 3} = \frac{8}{13}$

8. Is $\frac{8}{13}$ the simplest form of $\frac{24}{39}$? How do you know?

An adult has 206 bones. The feet, ankles, wrists, and hands account for 106 of those bones. **What fraction of the bones are in the feet, ankles, wrists, and hands? Which divisibility test can help you reduce the fraction you wrote?**

The **greatest common factor,** or **GCF,** of two or more numbers is the greatest number that is a factor of all the numbers. If you divide the numerator and denominator of a fraction by their GCF, the result will be a fraction in simplest form.

Example 3 Write $\frac{28}{42}$ in simplest form.

- List the factors of 28 and 42 to find the GCF.

   Factors of 28: 1, 2, 4, 7, ⑭, 28

   Factors of 42: 1, 2, 3, 6, 7, ⑭, 21, 42

- Divide the numerator and denominator by the GCF, 14.

   $\frac{28 \div 14}{42 \div 14} = \frac{2}{3}$

9. Write $\frac{15}{45}$ in simplest form by using the GCF of 15 and 45.

Mixed REVIEW

Use mental math to evaluate.

1. (48)(6) **2.** (103)(−7)

3. Write three fractions equivalent to $\frac{4}{5}$.

4. Write three fractions equivalent to $\frac{16}{24}$.

Solve.

5. −12 + n = 3

6. 10 + 7t = −18

7. Find the area of a rectangle that has a perimeter of 84 cm and one side 15 cm long.

Itzhak Perlman, a world-known violinist, gave his first solo recital at age 10. He has toured extensively in the United States, playing with all the major symphony orchestras.

TRY THESE

10. Is 2,268 divisible by 2? 3? 4? 5? 6? 8? 9? 10?

11. Which of the following fractions is in simplest form: $\frac{9}{16}$, $\frac{10}{24}$, $\frac{14}{35}$? Explain how you know.

Use the divisibility tests to write each fraction in simplest form. Tell which divisibility tests you used.

12. $\frac{38}{40}$ **13.** $\frac{35}{100}$ **14.** $\frac{28}{48}$ **15.** $\frac{42}{87}$

Find the GCF of the numerator and denominator. Then write the fraction in simplest form.

16. $\frac{16}{36}$ **17.** $\frac{21}{28}$ **18.** $\frac{36}{49}$ **19.** $\frac{12}{75}$

ON YOUR OWN

Make lists of factors for each set of numbers. Then find the GCF.

20. 54, 80   **21.** 22, 121   **22.** 16, 80   **23.** 10, 85

Write each fraction in simplest form.

24. $\frac{22}{24}$ **25.** $\frac{30}{48}$ **26.** $\frac{35}{95}$ **27.** $\frac{42}{72}$

28. $\frac{18}{30}$ **29.** $\frac{17}{51}$ **30.** $\frac{21}{105}$ **31.** $\frac{36}{90}$

32. Entertainment Larry surveyed the 30 students in his class to find their music preferences. He found that 18 students preferred rock music, 8 preferred country/western music, and 4 preferred classical music. In order to write a news article for the school paper, Larry wanted to write the results in fraction form. What fractions should Larry use?

Estimation Tell if the fraction is closest to 0, $\frac{1}{2}$, or 1.

33. $\frac{275}{312}$ **34.** $\frac{153}{302}$ **35.** $\frac{518}{634}$ **36.** $\frac{141}{1,500}$

37. Writing In her math notes, Violet wrote "14 can be divided by 4, but 14 is not divisible by 4." Is she correct? Explain.

38. Critical Thinking Alan has lumber 63 in. long, 84 in. long, and 105 in. long. He plans to cut all the lumber into pieces of equal length. What is the longest length he can cut?

 39. Investigation (p. 280) For each table top that you designed, find the GCF of the dimensions. Then consider the largest square tile that could be used to cover the table. What do you notice?

The Global Village

Think of the Earth as a global village of only a thousand people. Then 584 of those people would be from Asia, 124 from Africa, 95 from Europe, 84 from Latin America, 52 from North America, 6 from Australia and New Zealand, and 55 from the former Soviet Union.

Only 60 people in the village would be over 65, but 330 would be children.

40. What fraction of the people in the global village are from each area? Write the fractions in simplest form.

41. What fraction of the people are children? adults under 65? adults over 65?

CHECKPOINT

What part of each figure is green?

1.

2.

3.

Write each fraction in simplest form.

4. $\frac{36}{48}$ 5. $\frac{42}{63}$ 6. $\frac{30}{45}$ 7. $\frac{18}{20}$

8. **Choose A, B, C, or D.** Which fraction equals $\frac{1}{5}$?

A. $\frac{1+3}{5+3}$ B. $\frac{15}{55}$ C. $\frac{1 \cdot 3}{5 \cdot 3}$ D. $\frac{17}{95}$

- Identifying a number as prime or composite and finding its prime factorization

- Using prime factorization to write fractions in simplest form

WHAT YOU'LL NEED

✓ Graph paper

✓ Calculator

7-4 Prime Factorization

Work with a partner.

1. Let each number below represent the area of a rectangle. Draw a rectangle on graph paper for each area.

   a. 11   **b.** 12   **c.** 13   **d.** 14   **e.** 15

2. If possible, draw a second rectangle for each number given in Question 1. (A 3 × 4 rectangle is considered the same as a 4 × 3 rectangle.)

3. **a.** Which numbers can be used for the area of more than one rectangle?

   b. Which numbers can be used for the area of only one rectangle?

THINK AND DISCUSS

A **prime** number has exactly two factors, 1 and the number itself. A **composite** number has more than two factors. For some of the numbers in the Work Together you could draw only one rectangle. Those numbers are prime.

4. Tell whether each of the following numbers is prime or composite.

   a. 11   **b.** 12   **c.** 13   **d.** 14   **e.** 15

5. **Calculator** Use divisibility rules and a calculator to write the factors of each number. Then identify the number as prime or composite.

   a. 123   **b.** 125   **c.** 127   **d.** 129

6. Are all even numbers composite? Explain.

7. What are two whole numbers that are neither prime nor composite?

 In 1742, C. Goldbach observed that every even integer greater than two could be represented as the sum of two prime numbers. **The sum of what two prime numbers equals 8, 10, 12?**

To write the prime factorization of a composite number, you write the number as the product of its **prime factors.** A *factor tree* can help you find the prime factors of a number.

Example 1   Write 171 as the product of its prime factors.

- Write the composite number as the product of two factors.
- Continue the first step with any remaining composite factors.
- Stop when all factors are prime.

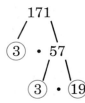

$171 = 3 \cdot 3 \cdot 19$, or $3^2 \cdot 19$

WHAT? Modern codes rely on huge composite numbers. The codes are virtually unbreakable because you must find the prime factors to figure out the code, and the largest known prime numbers have over 100 digits.

Source: *Think of a Number*

8. a. Use a factor tree to find the prime factors of 28.

   b. Write the prime factorization of 28 using exponents.

9. Calculator Find the number whose prime factorization is $2 \cdot 3^2 \cdot 5^2$.

To find the GCF of two numbers, you can use their prime factorizations.

Example 2   Find the GCF of 90 and 72.

- Write the prime factorization of each number
  $90 = 2 \cdot 3^2 \cdot 5$ $72 = 2^3 \cdot 3^2$
- Identify the common factors.
  2 and 3^2 are factors of both numbers.
- The GCF is the product of the common factors.
  $2 \cdot 3^2 = 18$

The GCF of 90 and 72 is 18.

10. a. Write the prime factorizations of 28 and 42.

   b. Find the GCF of 28 and 42.

11. a. What is the GCF of two prime numbers?

   b. Write two composite numbers with a GCF of 1.

   c. Will a prime number and a composite number always have a GCF of 1? Explain.

Another way to write a fraction in simplest form is to first write the prime factorizations of the numerator and the denominator. Then you can divide by common factors.

Example 3 Write $\frac{42}{105}$ in simplest form.

$$\frac{42}{105} = \frac{2 \cdot 3 \cdot 7}{3 \cdot 5 \cdot 7}$$ Write the prime factorization of both the numerator and the denominator.

$$= \frac{2 \cdot \overset{1}{\cancel{3}} \cdot \overset{1}{\cancel{7}}}{5 \cdot \underset{1}{\cancel{3}} \cdot \underset{1}{\cancel{7}}}$$ Divide numerator and denominator by the common factors.

$$= \frac{2}{5}$$ Write the fraction in simplest form.

12. Below is the method Alex used to write $\frac{54}{64}$ in simplest form.

$$\frac{54}{64} = \frac{\overset{1}{\cancel{54}}}{\underset{1}{\cancel{64}}} = \frac{5}{6}$$

Is he correct? Explain.

13. Use prime factorization to write $\frac{18}{48}$ in simplest form.

T R Y THESE

14. Use graph paper to draw as many rectangles as possible with the area 9 and the area 11. Explain how your rectangles show that 9 is composite and 11 is prime.

Mental Math Is the number prime or composite?

15. 104   **16.** 141   **17.** 165   **18.** 47

Sal   Marla

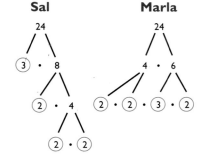

19. Sal and Marla made the two factor trees at the left to find the prime factors of 24. Are both trees correct? Explain.

20. Write the numerator and denominator of $\frac{60}{96}$ using the prime factorizations of 60 and 96. Then write the fraction in simplest form.

Use a factor tree to write the prime factorization of each number.

21. 45   **22.** 64   **23.** 84   **24.** 111

25. Is 1,971 prime or composite? How do you know?

26. List all the prime numbers less than 50.

Write a prime factorization using a factor tree. Use exponents where possible.

27. 100   **28.** 52   **29.** 65   **30.** 132

Calculator Find the number with the given prime factorization.

31. $5^2 \cdot 7^2$ **32.** $2^4 \cdot 3$ **33.** $2 \cdot 5^3 \cdot 13$

Find the GCF of each set of numbers using their prime factorizations.

34. 75, 90   **35.** 38, 76   **36.** 98, 105

Write each fraction in simplest form.

37. $\frac{75}{125}$ **38.** $\frac{108}{120}$ **39.** $\frac{63}{81}$ **40.** $\frac{125}{200}$

41. a. Writing Would you prefer to list factors or use prime factorization to simplify the fraction $\frac{375}{1,000}$? Why?

     b. Use your choice to simplify $\frac{375}{1,000}$.

Tell whether each statement is true or false. Explain your answers and give examples to support your conclusions.

42. The product of any three consecutive integers is divisible by 3.

43. The GCF of any two consecutive integers is 1.

44. If the product of two numbers is divisible by 6, then one of the numbers must be divisible by 6.

45. Data File 3 (pp. 90–91) What fraction of the titles won by major NBA teams were won by the Lakers? the Bulls?

46. Investigation (p. 280) For each table that you designed, write the prime factorization of the lengths and the widths. Use the prime factorizations to name all the sizes of square tiles other than a 1 × 1 square, that can be used to cover the table top.

What's Ahead

- Solving problems by using a simpler problem

7-5 **S**olve a Simpler Problem

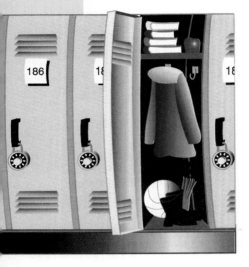

A school has 1,000 students and 1,000 lockers. The lockers are numbered from 1 to 1,000. The students enter the building one at a time. The first student opens all the lockers. The second student begins with the second locker and closes all the lockers with even numbers. The third student begins with the third locker and changes—either by opening closed doors or closing open doors—all lockers with numbers that are multiples of 3. The fourth student begins with the fourth locker and changes all lockers with numbers that are multiples of 4. This pattern continues until all the students walk past all the lockers. After the last student has gone by the lockers, which lockers are open?

READ

Read and understand the given information.

1. Think about the information you are given.

   a. Which lockers are open after the second student closes all the lockers with even numbers?

   b. Is the door to locker 3 open or closed after the second student passes it?

   c. Will any other students change the door to locker 3 after the third student makes changes?

   d. Is the door to locker 4 open or closed before the fourth student passes it? after the fourth student passes it?

   e. Will any other students change the door to locker 4 after the fourth student makes changes?

2. Make a prediction. Do you think the twelfth door will be open or closed after the twelfth student has passed it?

PLAN

Decide on a strategy to solve the problem.

When a problem seems to involve an overwhelming number of steps, it helps to solve a similar but simpler problem. In this case, solve the problem using twenty lockers and twenty students. Then look for a pattern to help you solve the original problem.

3. Copy and complete the table below.

Student Number	Locker Number 1	2	3	4	5	6	7	8	9	Key
1	O	O	O	O	O	O	O	O	O	O Open
2	O	C	O	C	O	C	O	C	O	C Closed
3	O	C	C	C	O	O	O	C	C	
4	■	■	■	■	■	■	■	■	■	
5	■	■	■	■	■	■	■	■	■	
6	■	■	■	■	■	■	■	■	■	

4. a. Which lockers did student number 3 change?

   b. These numbers are multiples of what number?

5. a. Which students open or close the door to locker 6?

   b. These numbers are factors of what number?

6. Extend your table to include 20 students and 20 lockers.

   a. Which of the first 20 lockers are left open after 20 students pass through?

   b. What pattern do you find in the numbers of the lockers that are left open?

7. Tell whether each of the following lockers is open or closed after the last student passes through the building.

   a. Locker 24 **b.** Locker 25

   c. Locker 49 **d.** Locker 1,000

8. a. Choose three closed doors and three open doors. How many factors do the numbers of the closed doors have? the open doors?

   b. Now look at your table. How does the number of factors relate to the number of times a door was opened or closed?

LOOK BACK

Look for more relationships between the numbers.

TRY THESE

Solve by using a simpler problem.

9. The houses on Main Street are numbered from 1 to 140. How many house numbers contain the digit 6 at least once?

 The retail value of flowers sold in the United States in a year is about $12.9 billion. **If the average cost of a flower is $1.50, about how many flowers would $12.9 billion buy?**

Source: *Society of American Florists*

10. You are in charge of scheduling the games for your community basketball league's tournament. If a team loses a game, then it is eliminated. There are 32 teams. How many games do you need to schedule to determine the league champion?

ON YOUR OWN

Use any strategy to solve each problem.

11. Each of the 15 members of the Math Club shakes hands with each of the 12 members of the Science Club. How many handshakes are there?

12. Two neon signs turn on at the same time. One blinks on every 10 s; the other blinks on every 6 s. How many times per minute do they blink on together?

13. Jeff produces 22 items in 15 min. Jose produces 18 items in 12 min. Which worker is more productive? Explain your answer.

14. Ramona had to number 248 class play tickets by hand. How many digits did she have to write?

15. Amrita has her book open. The product of the page numbers on two facing pages is 930. What are the two page numbers?

16. Trevor has $8 in his savings account and adds $1 each week. Aretha has $12 in her savings account and adds $3 each week. After how many weeks will Aretha's account have twice as much money as Trevor's?

17. Select any three-digit number. Make it a six-digit number by repeating the digits. For instance, if you choose 123, then your new number will be 123,123. Find if the following numbers are factors of the number you wrote: 7, 11, 13, 77, 91, 143, and 1,001. Try this again with another number. What can you conclude?

18. A florist can create an arrangement in 14 min. He receives an order for 124 arrangements for a large banquet. To the nearest hour, how long will it take him to make the arrangements?

Practice

Write a fraction for each part that is shaded.

1.
2.
3.
4.

Draw a model for each fraction or mixed number.

5. $\frac{1}{2}$ **6.** $\frac{4}{9}$ **7.** $\frac{2}{3}$ **8.** $\frac{4}{12}$ **9.** $1\frac{1}{3}$ **10.** $2\frac{3}{5}$

Write the first five multiples of each number.

11. 5 **12.** 8 **13.** 18 **14.** 4 **15.** 24 **16.** 7

Write two fractions equivalent to the given fraction.

17. $\frac{12}{30}$ **18.** $\frac{20}{45}$ **19.** $\frac{48}{72}$ **20.** $\frac{21}{84}$ **21.** $\frac{16}{56}$ **22.** $\frac{92}{100}$

Tell whether each number is prime or composite.

23. 2 **24.** 25 **25.** 17 **26.** 63 **27.** 111 **28.** 59

For each number, state whether it is divisible by 4, 8, or 9.

29. 192 **30.** 190 **31.** 120 **32.** 315 **33.** 221 **34.** 216

Find the GCF of each pair of numbers.

35. 30, 54 **36.** 25, 30 **37.** 48, 72 **38.** 36, 51 **39.** 27, 33 **40.** 16, 120

41. 15, 28 **42.** 32, 56 **43.** 10, 95 **44.** 81, 90 **45.** 36, 100 **46.** 24, 300

Use a factor tree to write the prime factorization of each number.

47. 36 **48.** 56 **49.** 45 **50.** 128 **51.** 84 **52.** 75

Write each fraction in simplest form.

53. $\frac{12}{15}$ **54.** $\frac{10}{25}$ **55.** $\frac{48}{84}$ **56.** $\frac{21}{36}$ **57.** $\frac{14}{50}$ **58.** $\frac{36}{96}$

59. $\frac{36}{40}$ **60.** $\frac{32}{40}$ **61.** $\frac{81}{108}$ **62.** $\frac{70}{100}$ **63.** $\frac{54}{90}$ **64.** $\frac{30}{500}$

7-6

Mixed Numbers and Improper Fractions

WHAT YOU'LL NEED

✓ Scissors

FLASHBACK
$2\frac{5}{8} = 2 + \frac{5}{8}$

FLASHBACK
The numerator of an *improper fraction* is greater than or equal to the denominator.

WORK TOGETHER

Work with a partner.

Draw circles the same size. Cut out and divide each circle into eight equal sections like the circle at the right.

1. Use the circles to model the following mixed numbers.

   a. $2\frac{5}{8}$ **b.** $1\frac{3}{8}$ **c.** $1\frac{7}{8}$ **d.** $3\frac{1}{8}$

2. Tell how many $\frac{1}{8}$ sections are in each model.

THINK AND DISCUSS

In the Work Together, you found the number of eighths in each mixed number. There are 21 eighths, or $\frac{21}{8}$ in $2\frac{5}{8}$. You can change a mixed number to an improper fraction by drawing models or by using equivalent fractions.

Example 1   Write $2\frac{5}{8}$ as an improper fraction.

$2\frac{5}{8} = 2 + \frac{5}{8}$ **Write the mixed number as a sum.**

$= \frac{2}{1} + \frac{5}{8}$ **Express the whole number as a fraction.**

$= \frac{16}{8} + \frac{5}{8}$ **Write an equivalent fraction. Then add the numerators.**

$2\frac{5}{8} = \frac{21}{8}$

3. Why was $\frac{16}{8}$ a good choice as the equivalent fraction for $\frac{2}{1}$?

4. Explain how you would change $1\frac{3}{4}$ to an improper fraction.

5. Write each mixed number as an improper fraction.

   a. $1\frac{3}{4}$ **b.** $2\frac{3}{4}$ **c.** $3\frac{3}{4}$ **d.** $4\frac{3}{4}$

6. Describe the pattern you see in the improper fractions you wrote for Question 5.

7. Janet developed the following shortcut for writing a mixed number as an improper fraction. She used her shortcut to write $2\frac{3}{4}$ as an improper fraction.

- Multiply the whole number by the denominator.

  $2 \cdot 4 = 8$

- Add the product to the numerator.

  $8 + 3 = 11$

- Write the sum as the numerator of the improper fraction.

  $\frac{11}{4}$

a. Use Janet's method to write $3\frac{4}{5}$ as an improper fraction.

b. Do you think Janet's shortcut will always work? Explain.

To change an improper fraction to a mixed number, you divide the denominator into the numerator. The remainder becomes the fractional part of the mixed number.

Example 2 Write $\frac{30}{8}$ as a mixed number in simplest form.

- $3 \leftarrow$ whole number   Divide.

  $8\overline{)30}$
  $\underline{24}$
  $6 \leftarrow$ numerator

- $3\frac{6}{8} = 3\frac{3}{4}$ Write the fraction in simplest form.

So, $\frac{30}{8} = 3\frac{3}{4}$.

8. Write $\frac{12}{5}$ as a mixed number.

TRY THESE

9. How can you tell if a fraction is an improper fraction?

10. Write a mixed number and an improper fraction for the model below.

11. a. Draw a model for $2\frac{1}{4}$.

b. Use your model to change $2\frac{1}{4}$ into an improper fraction.

12.

a. Let each triangle represent $\frac{1}{4}$ unit. What improper fraction is shown?

b. What mixed number is shown?

13.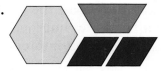

a. Let each hexagon represent 1 unit. What improper fraction is shown?

b. What mixed number is shown?

14. a. At a class party, $\frac{205}{4}$ gallons of punch were served. Write this fraction as a mixed number.

b. Each pizza delivered to the class party was divided into 8 equal pieces. After the party, there were 2 pieces from one pizza, 3 pieces from each of two other pizzas, and 5 pieces from another pizza left on the table. Write the amount of leftover pizza as a mixed number.

Write each number as an improper fraction.

15. $2\frac{5}{8}$ **16.** $5\frac{3}{4}$ **17.** $1\frac{1}{12}$ **18.** $4\frac{3}{5}$

19. $1\frac{3}{7}$ **20.** $4\frac{5}{8}$ **21.** $3\frac{2}{5}$ **22.** $2\frac{7}{12}$

Write each improper fraction as whole number or a mixed number in simplest form.

23. $\frac{17}{3}$ **24.** $\frac{21}{3}$ **25.** $\frac{42}{4}$ **26.** $\frac{31}{12}$

27. $\frac{37}{8}$ **28.** $\frac{49}{6}$ **29.** $\frac{84}{7}$ **30.** $\frac{45}{10}$

31. a. Let each trapezoid represent 1 unit. What improper fraction is shown?

b. What mixed number is shown?

32. Use the digits 2, 5, and 9 to write a fraction with the greatest possible value. Then write the fraction as a mixed number.

---

33. Cooking A cooking class served $25\frac{1}{4}$ loaves of banana bread at a faculty breakfast. Each loaf was sliced into eight equal slices. How many slices of banana bread did they serve?

34. Write the length of the line segment below as an improper fraction and as a mixed number.

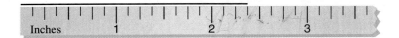

35. Choose A, B, C, or D. A length of material measures between 3 and $3\frac{1}{4}$ feet. Choose the fraction that would fit this description, and write it as a mixed number.

A. $\frac{26}{7}$ **B.** $\frac{11}{3}$ **C.** $\frac{25}{8}$ **D.** $\frac{18}{5}$

Write each improper fraction as a whole number or a mixed number in simplest form.

36. $\frac{18}{4}$ **37.** $\frac{21}{9}$ **38.** $\frac{33}{12}$ **39.** $\frac{48}{8}$

40. Critical Thinking A recipe calls for $1\frac{3}{4}$ c of flour. Darrell and Tanisha only have a quarter cup measure. How many times will they fill the quarter cup for the recipe?

41. Carpentry Daniel and Alisha each measured a board. Daniel said the board was $5\frac{1}{4}$ ft long. Alisha said the board was $5\frac{6}{12}$ ft long. Can they both be correct? Explain.

42. Writing Write an explanation for changing $4\frac{5}{9}$ into an improper fraction.

43. Travel It took the Brook family 3 h 45 min to travel from their home to their cousins' home for Thanksgiving. Write the time as a mixed number. Then write the fraction in simplest form.

44. Carpentry Pearl kept track of the time she worked on her carpentry project. She worked a total of 345 min. Using mixed numbers, write the hours Pearl worked.

45. Investigation (p. 280) Make a list of commercially produced items that, like the tile tabletops, consist of collections of adjacent squares or rectangles.

A piece of lumber is measured in the "rough." This means that it is measured before its surface is evened. A board that is called a 2-by-4 has a rough measurement of 2 in. by 4 in. A surfaced board is likely to measure about $1\frac{1}{2}$ in. by $3\frac{1}{2}$ in.

Source: *Reading the Numbers*

What's Ahead

• Using spreadsheets to graph fraction patterns

7-7 Exploring Fraction Patterns

THINK AND DISCUSS

The next time you listen to your favorite group, notice the pattern in the rhythm. Patterns are the basis of music. Even the notes themselves follow a mathematical pattern.

As the chart shows, musical notes are based on fractions of a whole note.

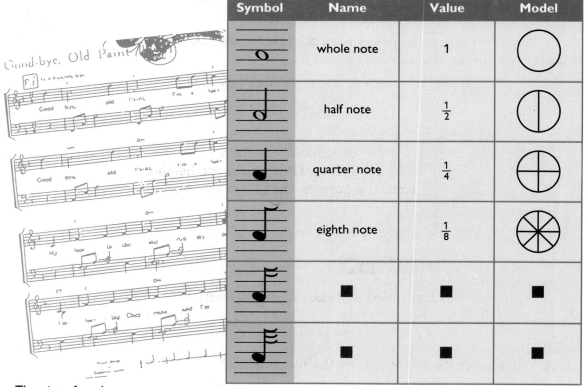

Symbol	Name	Value	Model
	whole note	1	
	half note	$\frac{1}{2}$	
	quarter note	$\frac{1}{4}$	
	eighth note	$\frac{1}{8}$	
	■	■	■
	■	■	■

 The sixty-fourth note is sometimes found in passages that are played very fast. **What do you think the symbol for a sixty-fourth note looks like?**

1. **a.** List the denominators of the fractions in the table. Describe the pattern you see.

b. Based on this pattern, what do you think are the names of the last two notes in the table?

c. Copy and complete the last two rows of the table. You may either draw or describe the models.

2. a. Computer Copy and extend the spreadsheet for the first ten numbers in the pattern.

FLASHBACK

Remember, $\frac{1}{2}$ is the same as $1 \div 2$, which is equal to 0.5. So $\frac{1}{2} = 0.500$.

	A	B	C
1	**Numerator**	**Denominator**	**Decimal Value**
2	1	2	0.500
3	1	4	0.250
4	1	8	▪

b. What formula would you use to find the value in cell C2?

c. Examine the bar graph at the right. It is a graph of Columns B and C in the spreadsheet above. Copy and complete the bar graph to include all the data in Columns B and C of your spreadsheet.

d. How do the heights of the bars change as the value of the denominators increase?

e. Can the height of a bar ever be zero? Explain.

3. a. The first five unit fractions are $\frac{1}{2}, \frac{1}{3}, \frac{1}{4}, \frac{1}{5}, \frac{1}{6}$. What are the next three unit fractions?

b. Suppose you graphed the denominators of the unit fractions to their decimal values. How would the heights of the bars differ from the bars on the graph you made in Question 2?

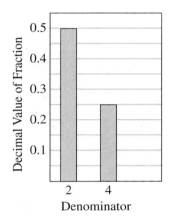

Denominator

WORK TOGETHER

4. Answer the questions below for each group of fractions.

I. $\frac{1}{2}$ $\frac{2}{4}$ $\frac{3}{8}$ $\frac{4}{16}$ II. $\frac{1}{1}$ $\frac{2}{4}$ $\frac{3}{9}$ $\frac{4}{16}$

a. What patterns do you see in the numerators?

b. What patterns do you see in the denominators?

c. List the next three fractions for each group.

d. Calculator Find the decimal values of the fractions in each group. What similarities do you see? What differences do you see?

5. Write a fraction pattern of your own. Have another group find the next three fractions in your pattern.

Mixed REVIEW

Write each improper fraction as a mixed number in simplest form.

1. $\frac{15}{10}$ **2.** $\frac{40}{12}$

3. Draw a model for $\frac{5}{8}$.

4. To the nearest meter, what is the circumference of a circle that has an area of 379.94 m²?

5. The hypotenuse of a right triangle is 10 cm long. One leg is 6 cm long. Find the area of the triangle.

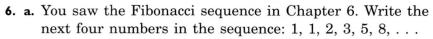
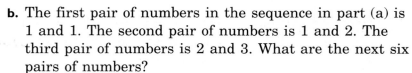

ON YOUR OWN

6. **a.** You saw the Fibonacci sequence in Chapter 6. Write the next four numbers in the sequence: 1, 1, 2, 3, 5, 8, . . .

   b. The first pair of numbers in the sequence in part (a) is 1 and 1. The second pair of numbers is 1 and 2. The third pair of numbers is 2 and 3. What are the next six pairs of numbers?

   c. To make fractions of the pair of numbers, use the first number in a pair as the denominator and the second number as the numerator. The first three fractions are $\frac{1}{1}$, $\frac{2}{1}$, and $\frac{3}{2}$. What are the next six fractions?

   d. **Calculator** Find the decimal values of the fraction pairs. Write all the decimal places you see in your calculator window. What do you notice?

   e. If you had found the 20th and 21st values in the pattern, what do you think their decimal equivalent would be when rounded to the nearest hundredth?

7. **a.** **Writing** Explain how you would find the numerator and denominator for the next fraction in the pattern below.

$$\frac{2}{2}, \frac{6}{4}, \frac{10}{8}, \frac{14}{16}, \cdot \cdot \cdot$$

   b. What kind of sequence do the numbers in the numerators form? the numbers in the denominators?

The fractions formed by pairs of consecutive numbers in the Fibonacci sequence approach the value known as the Golden Ratio. You have your own personal Golden Ratio. Fold your hand as shown in the diagram. Measure lengths *x* and *y*. **Find the decimal value of $\frac{y}{x}$.**

CHECKPOINT

Tell whether each number is prime or composite.

1. 159   **2.** 2,018   **3.** 181   **4.** 51

5. Find the GCF of 81 and 45.

6. Use prime factorization to write $\frac{12}{54}$ in simplest form.

Write as a whole number or mixed number in simplest form.

7. $\frac{29}{6}$ **8.** $\frac{82}{5}$ **9.** $\frac{24}{8}$ **10.** $\frac{45}{6}$

Write as an improper fraction.

11. $2\frac{5}{6}$ **12.** $4\frac{1}{9}$ **13.** $3\frac{1}{8}$ **14.** $1\frac{9}{10}$

PROBLEM SOLVING STRATEGIES

Make a Table
Use Logical Reasoning
Solve a Simpler Problem
Too Much or Too Little Information
Look for a Pattern
Make a Model
Work Backward
Draw a Diagram
Guess and Test
Simulate a Problem
Use Multiple Strategies
Write an Equation

Three-quarters of the adults in the United States give money to charity. Also, a fifth of adults volunteer their time.

Source: *Statistical Abstract*

Solve if possible. If not, tell what information is needed. The list at the left shows some possible strategies that you can use.

1. In a science class the number of bacteria in a jar doubles each day. If the jar is full on the 28th day, on what day was it half full?

2. All the digits of a three digit number are multiples of 3. Find the largest such number that does not repeat any digit.

3. Three out of every five students in a class of 35 volunteer to help at the Bake Sale. How many volunteers are there?

4. There are 32 delegates from one school, 40 from another, and 48 from yet another attending a student-government convention. The convention leaders wish to divide each delegation into groups of equal size. What is the greatest possible number of people in a group?

5. In a swim meet, Susan finishes in 1 min 35 s. Tamara finishes 8 s before Susan, Janine finishes 15 s after Tamara, and Mavis finishes 4 s before Janine. Find each swimmer's time.

6. The sum of four consecutive whole numbers is 78. What are the numbers?

7. At the school car wash, BJ washed twice as many cars as Jayda. Jayda washed three fewer than Tony. Tony washed one more than Kim. How many cars did Kim wash?

8. Suppose three students can fill four holiday food baskets for the needy in eight minutes. How many baskets can four students fill in 12 minutes?

9. Clovis has four ways to walk to school and two ways to walk to the library after school. He does not like to take the same path every day. How many school days elapse before Clovis must repeat a path if he goes to the library after school every day?

Wrap Up

The Meaning of Fractions 7-1

Fractions are used to describe many situations such as measurements, parts of a whole, and members of a group.

1. The hexagon represents one whole. What fraction does the triangle represent? the rhombus?

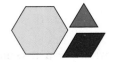

2. Draw a model to represent visually each of the following fractions.

   a. $\frac{3}{4}$ **b.** $\frac{3}{5}$ **c.** $\frac{2}{3}$

Equivalent Fractions and Simplifying Fractions 7-2, 7-3

Fractions that are equal to each other are **equivalent fractions.** To form equivalent fractions, multiply or divide the numerator and denominator by the same nonzero number.

A fraction is in **simplest form** when the only factor common to both the numerator and the denominator is 1.

3. Write all the factors of each number.

   a. 16   **b.** 28   **c.** 57

4. **Writing** Explain how to find a fraction in simplest form that is equivalent to $\frac{12}{18}$.

5. Write each fraction in simplest form.

   a. $\frac{24}{48}$ **b.** $\frac{33}{132}$ **c.** $\frac{54}{72}$

6. **Choose A, B, or C.** Which fraction is *not* equivalent to $\frac{4}{7}$?

   A. $\frac{24}{42}$ **B.** $\frac{48}{74}$ **C.** $\frac{16}{28}$

Prime Factorization 7-4

A **prime** number has exactly two factors, 1 and the number itself. If a number has more than two factors, then it is called **composite.**

To write the **prime factorization** of a composite number, you write the number as the product of its prime factors.

7. Identify each number as prime or composite.

   a. 73   **b.** 87   **c.** 121

8. Write the prime factorization of each number.

   a. 68   **b.** 72   **c.** 110

Mixed Numbers and Improper Fractions 7-6

The numerator of an *improper fraction* is greater than or equal to the denominator.

You can write an improper fraction as a mixed number or a whole number. You can also write a mixed number as an improper fraction.

9. Write each mixed number as an improper fraction.

a. $4\frac{5}{8}$ b. $2\frac{3}{5}$ c. $5\frac{7}{9}$ d. $3\frac{2}{3}$ e. $5\frac{1}{4}$ f. $1\frac{5}{6}$

10. Write each improper fraction as a whole number or a mixed number in simplest form.

a. $\frac{15}{8}$ b. $\frac{23}{5}$ c. $\frac{32}{4}$ d. $\frac{28}{6}$ e. $\frac{16}{3}$ f. $\frac{39}{6}$

Fraction Patterns 7-7

You can investigate number patterns in fractions.

11. Write the next three fractions in the pattern.

$$\frac{3}{4}, \frac{5}{8}, \frac{7}{16}, \frac{9}{32} \cdots$$

Strategies and Applications 7-5

By solving simpler problems, you often see patterns that help you solve the more complex problem that you started with.

12. A grocer plans to stack boxes of cereal as part of a display. Each row of the stack has one less than the row beneath it. The top row will have one box. How many boxes are needed for 20 rows?

GETTING READY FOR CHAPTER 8

Compare. Use <, >, or =.

1. $\frac{5}{8} \blacksquare \frac{7}{8}$ 2. $2\frac{7}{12} \blacksquare 2\frac{5}{12}$ 3. $\frac{8}{16} \blacksquare \frac{5}{10}$ 4. $\frac{9}{14} \blacksquare \frac{9}{20}$

Write the fractions using the same denominator.

5. $\frac{3}{4}, \frac{1}{2}$ 6. $\frac{2}{3}, \frac{5}{6}$ 7. $\frac{3}{8}, \frac{1}{4}$ 8. $\frac{5}{8}, \frac{7}{12}$

Follow Up

Tiles and Tabletops

The chief designer for the Truly Tabletop Company has asked you to write a set of guidelines for the table designers. The guidelines will help designers choose the right size tiles for table kits. Write the guidelines based on your study of the chapter. You may wish to include the following suggestions.

✔ grid-paper table models
✔ a chart of tabletop and tile dimensions
✔ instructions for calculating tile dimensions

The problems preceded by the magnifying glass (p. 291, # 39; p. 295, # 46; and p. 303, # 45) will help you complete the investigation.

Excursion: Each step in a manufacturing process requires decisions and compromises. The Truly Tabletop Company chooses tile sizes that will minimize counting errors. List other factors a company might take into consideration when making a decision.

Who to Talk To:
- the owner of a business

Mathamagic

Ask a friend to pick a number and write it on paper. You should not see the number. Then, ask your friend to:

☞ add 3

☞ then, multiply by 4

☞ then, subtract 12.

☞ then, tell you the results.

When you hear the number, divide it mentally by 4. Announce the answer to your friend. Since this will be the original number, your friend will be flabbergasted!

How does this work? Once you've learned the secret, try to create your own mathematically magic sequence of operations.

Most people watch television for both information and entertainment. Television networks charge a fee to the sponsors of their programs. This fee helps to cover the cost of the show's production and the transmission of the show to viewers.

The sponsors make commercials to attract customers to their products or services.

What fraction of the time that you spend watching television is devoted to commercial advertisements? Make an estimate, then watch your favorite show and time the commercials. How close was your estimate?

Do you think there is a relationship between the amount of time spent on commercials and the type of program shown? Design an experiment to investigate this question.

Chalk It Up!

Chalk comes in a rectangular box; yet a piece of chalk is a cylinder. What fraction of a new box of chalk is filled with air? Show your work to support your findings.

TIME FLIES!

How well do you estimate time? Ask a friend to watch a clock with a second hand. When your friend says to begin, estimate $\frac{1}{2}$ of a minute. Signal with your hand when you think $\frac{1}{2}$ minute has passed. How well can you estimate $\frac{1}{3}$ or $\frac{1}{4}$ of a minute? Take turns checking each other's estimates. Try estimating one or two minutes' time.

Homework

1. What fraction does the shaded part of the model represent?

2. Draw a model to represent each fraction or mixed number.

   a. $\frac{3}{4}$ **b.** $2\frac{3}{5}$

3. Write two fractions equivalent to each fraction.

   a. $\frac{1}{3}$ **b.** $\frac{15}{24}$ **c.** $\frac{4}{5}$ **d.** $\frac{16}{28}$

4. List all the factors of 27.

5. Write the first four multiples of 27.

6. Write a missing digit so that the resulting number is divisible by 3.

   $$3,12\blacksquare,451$$

7. **Writing** Explain how divisibility tests can help you write $\frac{57}{69}$ in simplest form.

8. Find the GCF of 32 and 40.

9. What is a divisibility test for 6? for 4?

10. **Estimation** Tell whether each fraction is closest to 0, $\frac{1}{2}$, or 1.

    a. $\frac{24}{26}$ **b.** $\frac{16}{30}$ **c.** $\frac{5}{21}$ **d.** $\frac{59}{64}$

11. Tell whether each number is prime or composite.

    a. 17   **b.** 75   **c.** 49   **d.** 83

12. Use a factor tree to write the prime factorization of 42.

13. Use prime factorization to write $\frac{36}{96}$ in simplest form.

14. The Fair-Share Salvage crew found a sunken pirate ship that had a chest containing 168 gold and 200 silver coins. All crew members received an equal share of each kind of coin. There were no coins left over. What is the greatest number of crew members that could receive an even share of coins? How many of each type of coin does each crew member get?

15. **Choose A, B, C, or D.** Which statement is *always* true?

    A. Two is a composite number.

    B. Square numbers have an odd number of factors.

    C. A number is divisible by 8 if its last two digits are divisible by 8.

    D. Any factor of a whole number is greater than any multiple of a whole number.

16. Write each mixed number as an improper fraction.

    a. $5\frac{2}{3}$ **b.** $4\frac{5}{6}$ **c.** $8\frac{7}{10}$

17. Write each improper fraction as a whole number or a mixed number.

    a. $\frac{12}{5}$ **b.** $\frac{30}{9}$ **c.** $\frac{48}{12}$

18. Write the next two numbers in the pattern.

    $$\frac{1}{3}, \frac{2}{3}, 1\frac{1}{3}, 2\frac{2}{3}, 5\frac{1}{3}, \ldots$$

Choose A, B, C, or D.

1. Which fraction is *not* equivalent to $\frac{9}{12}$?

A. $\frac{24}{32}$ **B.** $\frac{6}{8}$ **C.** $\frac{15}{20}$ **D.** $\frac{16}{24}$

2. What is the area of the figure at the right?

A. 14 m^2 **B.** 16 m^2

C. 21 m^2 **D.** 44 m^2

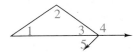

3. Which angle measure could you *not* find if you know that $m\angle 1 = m\angle 3$ and $m\angle 1 = 30°$.

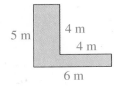

A. $m\angle 2$ **B.** $m\angle 3$ **C.** $m\angle 4$ **D.** $m\angle 5$

4. What is the next fraction in the pattern $\frac{1}{2}, \frac{3}{4}, \frac{9}{8}, \frac{27}{16}, \ldots$?

A. $\frac{36}{24}$ **B.** $\frac{81}{32}$ **C.** $\frac{54}{48}$ **D.** $\frac{40}{25}$

5. Which triangle has the same area as the trapezoid?

A.
B.

C.
D.

6. Which pair of angles is neither complementary nor supplementary?

A. $75°$ and $15°$ **B.** $90°$ and $90°$

C. $80°$ and $120°$ **D.** $144°$ and $36°$

7. Which statement is *false*?

A. The GCF of two prime numbers is 1.

B. Any fraction with composite numbers in the numerator and denominator is *not* in simplest form.

C. More than half of the numbers between 1 and 100 are composite.

D. The GCF of a number and twice that number is the number itself.

8. You want to buy two tickets that regularly cost $354 each. From which airline should you buy your tickets?

Airline	Price Offer
A	"Buy 1 ticket, get the 2nd at $\frac{1}{2}$ off"
B	"$\frac{1}{4}$ off the regular price of all tickets"
C	"Get $\frac{1}{2}$ off any ticket over $400"
D	"$89 off any ticket"

9. A trapezoid represents one whole. Which improper fraction is shown?

A. $\frac{11}{3}$ **B.** $\frac{3}{2}$ **C.** $\frac{7}{3}$ **D.** $\frac{8}{3}$

10. The perimeter of a rectangle is 18 cm. The length of the sides are whole numbers. Which area is possible?

A. 10 cm^2 **B.** 20 cm^2

C. 30 cm^2 **D.** 40 cm^2

Fraction Applications

Manuel Mendes is the cook general at the United States Military Academy in West Point, New York. He and his staff prepare three meals per day for 4,500 students. Each student needs an average of 3,200 calories/da. Manny's kitchen is open 24 h/da, 7 da/wk. This is his favorite recipe for Sloppy Joes.

West Point Sloppy Joes
Serves 100 people

41 lb ground beef	2 lb onions
$7\frac{1}{2}$ lb mushrooms	$4\frac{3}{4}$ oz chili powder
$2\frac{1}{2}$ lb green peppers	$1\frac{2}{3}$ oz garlic powder
$11\frac{1}{2}$ lb tomato puree	$3\frac{1}{4}$ oz sugar
$3\frac{1}{4}$ fl oz cider vinegar	$7\frac{1}{2}$ lb ketchup
$1\frac{1}{2}$ lb red peppers	

WORLD VIEW

In 1978 a citizen in Taiwan ate an average of 86 lb of meat each year. By 1988 that same citizen ate 132 lb of meat.

In the Fall of 1991, Teenage Research Unlimited asked 12-15 year olds if they had spent time in the following activities during the last seven days. These are the percents of teens responding yes.

Teenage Chefs		
Activity	**Male**	**Female**
Cooking/preparing meals for my family	35.0%	53.5%
Cooking/preparing meals for myself	62.6%	71.1%
Baking	25.5%	44.9%
Using a microwave	83.7%	87.8%
Eating at "fast food" restaurants	79.1%	77.6%

Source: Teenage Research Unlimited

WHAT YOU WILL LEARN

- how to model operations with fractions
- how to solve equations with fractions
- how to use technology to explore fraction relationships
- how to solve problems by working backward

THE FOOD GUIDE PYRAMID
A Guide to Daily Food Choices

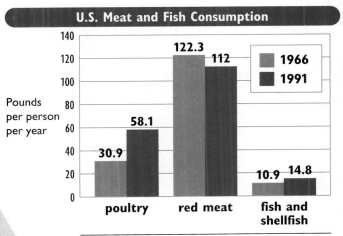

U.S. Meat and Fish Consumption

Pounds per person per year

- 1966
- 1991

poultry: 30.9 (1966), 58.1 (1991)
red meat: 122.3 (1966), 112 (1991)
fish and shellfish: 10.9 (1966), 14.8 (1991)

Source: U.S. Department of Agriculture

Key
- Fat (naturally occurring and added)
- Sugars (added)

fats, oils, & sweets
use sparingly

milk, yogurt, & cheese group
2-3 servings

meat, poultry, fish, dry beans, eggs, & nuts group
2-3 servings

vegetable group
3-5 servings

fruit group
2-4 servings

bread, cereal, rice, & pasta group
6-11 servings

investigation

Memo

You and the rest of the Young Investors Club have raised $500 from bake sales. You hope to increase your earnings by investing in stocks. There are many things to learn before investing money in the stock market. The goal of all stock investors is to buy low and sell high. For example, if you buy a stock for $33 a share and later sell it for $43 a share you will make a profit of $10 a share. You can also lose money by buying high and selling low. Even experts can lose money investing in stocks.

Mission: Research stocks for the Young Investors Club to consider buying. Many newspapers give daily stock market quotes that tell the high, low, and closing price of one share of stock. Newspapers that have stock information are available in libraries and at newsstands.

LeADS tO FoLLow

✓ What do you want to know about a stock before you buy it?

✓ How can you get information about a company whose stock you are thinking about buying?

✓ What information about a company would persuade you that its stock is going to rise in price?

Comparing and Ordering Fractions

• Comparing and
ordering fractions

✓ **Fraction bars**

 People
remember:

• three fourths
of what they say

• one tenth of what they hear

• nine tenths of what they do

THINK AND DISCUSS

1. Name the fractions represented by the fraction bars at the right.

2. For which fraction is the greatest part of the bar shaded? the least?

3. Write the four fractions in order from least to greatest.

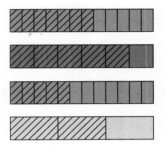

To compare fractions that have the same denominator, you only need to compare their numerators.

Example 1   Use the information at the left. Do people remember more of what they hear or do?

• Compare $\frac{1}{10}$ and $\frac{9}{10}$.

Since $1 < 9$, $\frac{1}{10} < \frac{9}{10}$, or $\frac{9}{10} > \frac{1}{10}$.

People remember more of what they do than hear.

FLASHBACK

The least common multiple (LCM) of two numbers is the least number that is a common multiple of both.

multiples of 4:

4, 8, 12, 16, ⟨20⟩, 24, . . .

multiples of 10:

10, ⟨20⟩, 30, 40, 50, . . .

LCM of 4 and 10 is 20.

To compare two fractions with different denominators, use their *least common denominator*. The **least common denominator (LCD)** of two fractions is the least common multiple of their denominators.

Example 2   Do people remember more of what they say or do?

• Compare $\frac{3}{4}$ and $\frac{9}{10}$.

• The LCM of 4 and 10 is 20, so the LCD is 20.

• Find equivalent fractions.

$$\frac{3}{4} = \frac{3 \cdot 5}{4 \cdot 5} = \frac{15}{20} \qquad \frac{9}{10} = \frac{9 \cdot 2}{10 \cdot 2} = \frac{18}{20}$$

Since $15 < 18$, $\frac{15}{20} < \frac{18}{20}$, and $\frac{3}{4} < \frac{9}{10}$.

People remember more of what they do than say.

4. Use fraction bars to compare the fractions in Example 2.

You can also use the LCD to order three or more fractions.

Example 3   Order $\frac{3}{4}$, $\frac{3}{8}$, and $\frac{5}{6}$ from least to greatest.

- 4, 8, 12, 16, 20, ⑳24   Find the **LCD** by listing multiples of the denominators.

  8, 16, ㉔

  6, 12, 18, ㉔

- $\frac{3}{4} = \frac{3 \cdot 6}{4 \cdot 6} = \frac{18}{24}$ Use the denominator 24 to find equivalent fractions.

  $\frac{3}{8} = \frac{3 \cdot 3}{8 \cdot 3} = \frac{9}{24}$

  $\frac{5}{6} = \frac{5 \cdot 4}{6 \cdot 4} = \frac{20}{24}$

- $\frac{9}{24} < \frac{18}{24} < \frac{20}{24}$ Order the equivalent fractions by their numerators.

So, from least to greatest the fractions are $\frac{3}{8}, \frac{3}{4}, \frac{5}{6}$

5. Each share of Wow! Jeans, Inc. stock cost $7\frac{1}{4}$ on Monday, $7\frac{5}{8}$ on Tuesday, and $7\frac{1}{2}$ on Wednesday.

a. Order the values of the stock from least to greatest.

b. On what day was the value of the stock the greatest?

TRY THESE

Write the two fractions modeled and compare them.

6.    **7.**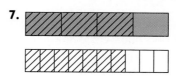

Find the LCD. Then rewrite the fractions with the same denominator.

8. $\frac{3}{4}$ and $\frac{1}{5}$ **9.** $\frac{2}{3}$ and $\frac{7}{9}$ **10.** $\frac{5}{8}$ and $\frac{1}{6}$

Compare. Use <, >, or =.

11. $\frac{3}{8}$ ▇ $\frac{5}{8}$ **12.** $\frac{2}{3}$ ▇ $\frac{3}{5}$ **13.** $11\frac{1}{2}$ ▇ $11\frac{3}{8}$

Order from least to greatest.

14. $\frac{3}{4}, \frac{2}{3}, \frac{5}{6}$ **15.** $\frac{3}{8}, \frac{1}{4}, \frac{2}{3}$ **16.** $\frac{8}{9}, \frac{4}{5}, \frac{7}{12}, \frac{3}{4}$

HOW? In order to raise money, many companies offer stock to investors. Each share of stock represents ownership of a small portion of the company, and investors often trade them. Prices of shares change due to their popularity and availability. The largest stock offering ever was 55 million shares, made on May 12, 1992, by General Motors Corp.

Source: *Guinness Book of Records*

Compare. Use <, >, or =.

17. $\frac{1}{8}$ ▦ $\frac{3}{16}$ **18.** $\frac{3}{4}$ ▦ $\frac{3}{10}$ **19.** $\frac{4}{5}$ ▦ $\frac{2}{3}$ **20.** $\frac{1}{6}$ ▦ $\frac{2}{9}$

21. You want to nail a board that is $\frac{1}{2}$ in. thick onto a wall. You can choose from nails that are $\frac{3}{8}$ in. long and $\frac{3}{4}$ in. long. Which size nail is the best choice? Explain.

22. For their class party, the seventh grade ordered the same number each of cheese pizzas, vegetable pizzas, and meatball pizzas. After the party, the leftovers were $\frac{5}{8}$ of a cheese pizza, $\frac{2}{3}$ of a vegetable pizza, and $\frac{3}{4}$ of a meatball pizza. Which type of pizza was the most popular? Explain.

23. Writing Describe an easy way to compare two fractions that have the same *numerator*, like $\frac{4}{5}$ and $\frac{4}{7}$.

24. Data File 8 (pp. 314–315) Which amount of red peppers is less than the amount needed to make West Point Sloppy Joes for 100 people?

A. $1\frac{1}{5}$ lb   **B.** $1\frac{3}{4}$ lb   **C.** $1\frac{4}{5}$ lb   **D.** $1\frac{1}{2}$ lb

People in the United States eat 75 acres, or 60 football fields, worth of pizza every day. **Write the number of acres in a football field as a mixed number.**

Source: *In One Day*

Estimation Match each fraction with a point on the number line.

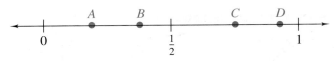

25. $\frac{3}{8}$ **26.** $\frac{11}{12}$ **27.** $\frac{3}{4}$ **28.** $\frac{3}{16}$

Which fractional part would you prefer? Explain.

29. $\frac{2}{3}$ or $\frac{2}{5}$ of an apple to eat   **30.** $2\frac{1}{2}$ or $2\frac{3}{4}$ h of homework

31. $\frac{9}{10}$ or $\frac{3}{4}$ of a dollar in debt   **32.** $\frac{1}{6}$ or $\frac{1}{12}$ year for vacation

33. Investigation (p. 316) Use the financial pages of your newspaper. Choose two stocks to keep a record of for the next two weeks. Start a table that will show the closing value of each stock each day.

M̶i̶x̶e̶d̶ REVIEW

Solve.

1. $6n = 72$

2. $\frac{n}{2} = -13$

Find the sum.

3. $-3 + 7$ **4.** $5 + (-2)$

5. The wheels of a bicycle have a diameter of 60 cm. Estimate the number of revolutions a wheel makes in an 8,000 m race.

What's Ahead

8-2

Fractions and Decimals

- Using calculators to explore fractions and decimals

- Ordering fractions by using decimal equivalents

✓ Calculator

THINK AND DISCUSS

The white blur of the softball speeds toward you. Your body leans, your arms and wrist snap the bat around. Pow! The ball rockets into center field for a hit.

It doesn't happen every time at bat. In fact, few players get a hit more than $\frac{1}{3}$ of the time.

Player	Hits	Times at Bat	Fraction of Times Player Got a Hit
Lisa Fernandez	71	177	$\frac{71}{177}$
Kathi Evans	69	190	$\frac{69}{190}$
Yvonne Gutierrez	69	170	$\frac{69}{170}$
Jo Alchin	51	158	$\frac{51}{158}$
Jenny Brewster	28	92	$\frac{28}{92}$

The women of UCLA's softball team have won 7 championships in 11 years. The team was runner-up in two of the years in which they did not win the championship. **What fraction of the 11 years was UCLA in either of the top two positions?**

Source: *Sports Illustrated Sports Almanac*

1. In what order are the five players listed?

2. Who had more times at bat, Yvonne Gutierrez or Kathi Evans?

3. Do you think Yvonne Gutierrez or Kathi Evans had hits a greater fraction of her times at bat? Why?

4. Was Yvonne Gutierrez or Kathi Evans more likely to get a hit when she came to bat? Explain.

5. Order the fractions in the table above. Then use the order to rank the players.

Batting averages are usually expressed in decimals. To find a player's batting average, change the fraction $\frac{hits}{times\ at\ bat}$ into a decimal.

6. a. Calculator Change the fraction for each player's batting average to a decimal. Round each batting average to the thousandths place.

b. Now list the five players in order from highest to lowest batting average.

c. Was it easier to compare batting averages in fraction form, as you did in Question 5, or in decimal form? Why?

Sometimes when you change fractions to decimals, you get repeating decimals.

7. a. Calculator Change each fraction in the table below to a decimal. Use a bar to show repeating decimals.

Player	Hits	Times at Bat	Fraction
A	32	96	$\frac{32}{96}$
B	75	270	$\frac{75}{270}$
C	57	190	$\frac{57}{190}$
D	52	250	$\frac{52}{250}$

b. List the fractions in order from greatest to least.

You can change decimals to fractions by writing the decimal as a number over some power of 10. Suppose Billy Crane, the best hitter on the baseball team, has a .325 batting average. To write his average as a fraction, you think "Billy's average is three hundred twenty-five *thousandths*. The number in the denominator is *1,000*." So you write $\frac{325}{1,000}$.

$$\frac{325}{1,000} = \frac{325 \div 25}{1,000 \div 25} = \frac{13}{40}$$ Use the GCF, which is 25, to write the fraction in simplest form.

Billy gets about 13 hits out of 40 times at bat.

8. Slugger Sly has a batting average of .285. Find his batting average as a fraction in simplest form.

FLASHBACK

To change a fraction to a decimal, divide the numerator by the denominator.

Example: $\frac{3}{5} = 3 \div 5 = 0.6$

FLASHBACK

To show that a decimal keeps repeating, you can use a bar over the digits that repeat. Examples:

$\frac{1}{3} = 0.33333\ldots = 0.\overline{3}$

$4\frac{2}{11} = 4.181818\ldots = 4.\overline{18}$

Mixed REVIEW

1. Find the mean, the median, and the mode of the following scores: 93, 80, 77, 93, 69, 90, 85, 88.

2. One acute angle of a right triangle measures 60°. What is the measure of the other acute angle?

Compare. Use >, <, or =.

3. $\frac{3}{4}$ ■ $\frac{5}{16}$ **4.** $\frac{3}{5}$ ■ $\frac{2}{3}$

5. The sum of the width and height of a soccer goal is 32 ft. The difference is 24 ft. Find the dimensions of a soccer goal.

Seed Type	Number Sprouted	Number Planted
A	15	48
B	5	20
C	22	44
D	17	35
E	18	52
F	21	63
G	14	55
H	18	35
I	8	15

9. In an experiment with seeds from wild plants, a botanist gathered the data at the left on the number of seeds planted and the number that sprouted for each variety collected.

   a. **Calculator** Write a fraction showing $\frac{\text{number sprouted}}{\text{number planted}}$, then change the fraction to a decimal. Round to the nearest hundredth.

   b. Place the seed types into 3 groups: those that sprout about $\frac{1}{2}$ of the time, those that sprout about $\frac{1}{3}$ of the time, and those that sprout about $\frac{1}{4}$ of the time.

   c. For the fractions in each group, find about how many times greater the denominator is than the numerator.

ON YOUR OWN

Choose Use a calculator, paper and pencil, or mental math to write each fraction as a decimal. Use a bar to indicate any repeating digits.

10. $\frac{2}{5}$ 11. $\frac{5}{6}$ 12. $\frac{3}{20}$ 13. $\frac{3}{8}$ 14. $\frac{11}{12}$ 15. $\frac{3}{2}$

16. **Data File II (pp. 456–457)** What fraction of the icebergs that break away from Greenland each year float into the Atlantic Ocean? Write the fraction in simplest form and as a decimal.

17. **Writing** Describe some everyday situations in which you need to change fractions to decimals.

Write each decimal as a fraction in simplest form.

18. 0.6   19. 0.125   20. 0.66   21. 2.5   22. 3.75

23. The table at the left shows the population of ten states and the number of people under the age of 18 in those states.

   a. In which state is the population a little over $\frac{1}{3}$ children?

   b. For most of the states, would $\frac{1}{2}$, $\frac{1}{3}$, or $\frac{1}{4}$ best describe the fraction of the population that is children?

   c. **Calculator** Write the states in order based on the fraction of the population that is children. List from least to greatest.

State	Total Population (thousands)	Number of Children (thousands)
ME	1,235	310
NY	18,055	4,366
OH	10,939	2,819
CA	30,380	8,163
MD	4,860	1,201
KY	3,713	959
OK	3,175	875
WY	460	154
AK	570	180
FL	13,277	2,998

Source: *Statistical Abstract of the United States*

What's Ahead

• Estimating sums, differences, products, and quotients of fractions and mixed numbers

FLASHBACK

A fraction is close to:

• 0 when the numerator is very small compared to the denominator.

• $\frac{1}{2}$ when the denominator is about twice the numerator.

• 1 when the numerator and the denominator are nearly equal.

Estimating with Fractions

THINK AND DISCUSS

You can estimate sums or differences involving fractions by determining whether each fraction is closest to 0, $\frac{1}{2}$ or 1.

Example 1   Estimate the sum $\frac{7}{8} + \frac{4}{9}$.

$$\frac{7}{8} + \frac{4}{9}$$
$$\downarrow \quad \downarrow$$
$$1 + \frac{1}{2} = 1\frac{1}{2}$$

1. Do you think that the actual sum in Example 1 is *greater than* $1\frac{1}{2}$ or *less than* $1\frac{1}{2}$? Explain.

2. **Critical Thinking** Name two fractions that are each less than 1 and whose sum is just a little greater than 1.

When a sum or difference involves mixed numbers, you get a reasonable estimate by rounding to the nearest whole number.

Example 2   Estimate the difference $8\frac{1}{6} - 4\frac{1}{2}$.

$$8\frac{1}{6} - 4\frac{1}{2}$$

If the fractional part is greater than or equal to $\frac{1}{2}$, round up.

$$\downarrow \quad \downarrow$$
$$8 - 5 = 3$$

You also round to the nearest whole number when finding a product of mixed numbers.

Example 3   Estimate the product: $2\frac{2}{5} \cdot 6\frac{1}{9}$

$$2\frac{2}{5} \cdot 6\frac{1}{9}$$
$$\downarrow \quad \downarrow$$
$$2 \cdot 6 = 12$$

3. Is the actual product in Example 3 *greater than* 12 or *less than* 12? Explain.

4. Estimate the product of $5\frac{1}{3}$ and $3\frac{3}{4}$.

FLASHBACK

Compatible numbers are two numbers that are easy to divide mentally.

FLASHBACK

Using the commutative property, $\frac{1}{8} \cdot 72 = 72 \cdot \frac{1}{8}$.

$72 \cdot \frac{1}{8} = 72 \div 8$

It rains 350 days a year on Mt. Waialeale on the island of Kauai in Hawaii. The average yearly rainfall is 410 inches. **Write the average daily rainfall as a fraction.**

Source: *The Dorling Kindersley Science Encyclopedia*

To estimate a quotient of mixed numbers, you usually use compatible numbers.

Example 4   Estimate the quotient $43\frac{1}{4} \div 5\frac{7}{8}$.

$$43\frac{1}{4} \div 5\frac{7}{8} \qquad \text{$5\frac{7}{8}$ rounds to 6.}$$

$$\downarrow \qquad \downarrow \qquad \text{42 and 6 are}$$

$$42 \div 6 = 7 \qquad \text{compatible numbers.}$$

Sometimes you use compatible numbers to estimate products that involve fractions.

Example 5   Estimate $\frac{1}{8}$ of 74.

$$\frac{1}{8} \text{ of 74 means } \frac{1}{8} \cdot 74.$$

$$\frac{1}{8} \cdot 74 \rightarrow \frac{1}{8} \cdot 72 = 9$$

5. Explain why 74 was rounded to 72 in Example 5.

6. In Example 5, is the actual answer greater than 9 or less than 9? Explain.

TRY THESE

Estimate each sum or difference.

7. $\frac{1}{7} + \frac{3}{8}$ 8. $\frac{2}{3} + \frac{9}{10}$ 9. $9\frac{1}{11} - 3\frac{7}{9}$ 10. $5\frac{3}{5} + 3\frac{2}{3}$

Estimate each product or quotient.

11. $\frac{1}{4}$ of 55   12. $13\frac{1}{2} \cdot \frac{1}{3}$ 13. $10\frac{7}{8} \div 3\frac{1}{9}$ 14. $7\frac{3}{5} \div 1\frac{1}{2}$

15. **Weather** The average annual rainfall in Nashville, Tennessee, is about $48\frac{1}{2}$ in. Estimate the average monthly rainfall.

16. **a.** Estimate the sum $\frac{1}{8} + \frac{1}{3}$ by determining whether each of the addends is closest to 0, $\frac{1}{2}$ or 1.

   b. Estimate by rounding to the nearest whole number.

   c. Discussion Why is the estimation method used in part (a) more appropriate than the method used in part (b)?

ON YOUR OWN

17. Writing Write a paragraph explaining why it is useful to estimate when you perform operations with fractions.

18. Cooking Your recipe for a loaf of bread calls for $2\frac{3}{4}$ c of flour. You want to triple the recipe. The label on a two-pound bag of flour says that it contains about 7 c. Will that be enough flour to make three loaves of bread? Explain.

19. Cooking You want to make three pasta salads. One salad requires $2\frac{1}{3}$ c of pasta. Another requires $\frac{3}{4}$ c. The third requires $1\frac{2}{3}$ c. You have 4 c of pasta. Do you have enough? Explain.

Estimate each answer.

20. $5\frac{1}{8} - 2\frac{6}{7}$ **21.** $\frac{1}{9} \cdot 33\frac{1}{2}$ **22.** $\frac{5}{6} + \frac{7}{9}$

23. $16\frac{1}{7} \div 3\frac{3}{5}$ **24.** $4\frac{2}{3} \cdot 5\frac{1}{3}$ **25.** $7\frac{1}{6} + \frac{8}{10}$

26. $\frac{8}{9} \cdot \frac{19}{20}$ **27.** $6\frac{2}{9} - 5\frac{9}{10}$ **28.** $29\frac{5}{6} \cdot \frac{13}{25}$

29. $20\frac{7}{8} \div 1\frac{1}{12}$ **30.** $\frac{49}{50} - \frac{1}{2}$ **31.** $9\frac{3}{5} + \frac{1}{2}$

32. a. Critical Thinking Estimate $\frac{1}{5}$ of 248.

    b. Use your answer to part (a) to estimate $\frac{3}{5}$ of 248.

    c. Explain how to estimate $\frac{5}{8}$ of 55.

33. Suppose you jog $16\frac{1}{4}$ times around a track that is 125 yd long. Have you jogged more than a mile? Explain.

34. Sian and Alex are making place mats to sell at a school fair. Each mat requires $14\frac{3}{4}$ in. of fabric. They are cutting the mats from a piece of fabric that is $89\frac{3}{4}$ in. long. About how many place mats can they make?

35. Choose A, B, C, or D. Which is between 6 and 7?

    A. $\frac{1}{2}$ of $14\frac{1}{2}$ **B.** $2 \cdot 3\frac{15}{16}$ **C.** $5\frac{11}{12} + \frac{24}{25}$ **D.** $7\frac{8}{9} - \frac{1}{2}$

 36. Investigation (p. 316) Use the closing values from your stock table (Investigation, Exercise 33, p. 319) to create a double-line graph. Continue the graph using the data you collect each day.

Find the next three terms.

1. 1, 4, 7, 10, . . .

2. −2, 8, −32, 128, . . .

Write each decimal as a fraction in simplest form.

3. 0.33   **4.** 5.125

Find two equivalent fractions.

5. $\frac{3}{12}$ **6.** $\frac{2}{9}$

7. At the school store notebooks cost $1.75, pencils $.05, pens $1, and folders $.75. How much would 2 notebooks and 4 pencils cost?

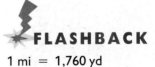

FLASHBACK

1 mi = 1,760 yd

Addition and Subtraction of Fractions

THINK AND DISCUSS

You can use fraction bars to model addition and subtraction.

A. 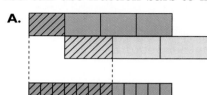   **B.**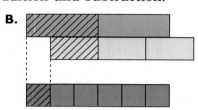

1. Which model shows addition? subtraction?

2. Write a number sentence for each model.

To find the sum of two fractions with different denominators, you first find their LCD.

Example 1   Find the sum $\frac{4}{5} + \frac{2}{3}$.

Estimate: $\frac{4}{5} + \frac{2}{3} \approx 1 + \frac{1}{2} = 1\frac{1}{2}$

$$\frac{4}{5} + \frac{2}{3} = \frac{4 \cdot 3}{5 \cdot 3} + \frac{2 \cdot 5}{3 \cdot 5} \quad \text{The LCD is 15.}$$

$$= \frac{12}{15} + \frac{10}{15} \quad \text{Add the numerators.}$$

$$= \frac{22}{15}$$

$$= 1\frac{7}{15} \quad \text{Write the answer as a mixed number.}$$

In adding mixed numbers, you may need to rename the sum.

Example 2   Find the sum $2\frac{7}{8} + 7\frac{1}{4}$.

Estimate: $2\frac{7}{8} + 7\frac{1}{4} \approx 3 + 7 = 10$

$$2\frac{7}{8} + 7\frac{1}{4} = 2\frac{7}{8} + 7\frac{2}{8} \quad \text{The LCD is 8.}$$

$$= 9\frac{9}{8}$$

$$= 9 + 1\frac{1}{8}$$

$$= 10\frac{1}{8}$$

 The ancient Egyptians represented all fractions, except $\frac{2}{3}$, as a *unit fraction* or the sum of unit fractions. A unit fraction is a fraction with a numerator of 1, such as $\frac{1}{2}$. The Egyptians would write $\frac{3}{4}$ as $\frac{1}{2} + \frac{1}{4}$. **Write $\frac{3}{5}$ as the sum of two unit fractions.**

You also use the LCD to subtract fractions with different denominators.

Example 3

Find the difference $\frac{2}{3} - \frac{7}{12}$.

Estimate: $\frac{2}{3} - \frac{7}{12} = \frac{1}{2} - \frac{1}{2} = 0$

$$\frac{2}{3} - \frac{7}{12} = \frac{2 \cdot 4}{3 \cdot 4} - \frac{7}{12} \qquad \text{The LCD is 12.}$$

$$= \frac{8}{12} - \frac{7}{12} \qquad \text{Subtract the numerators.}$$

$$= \frac{1}{12}$$

3. Find the difference in Example 3 using fraction bars.

When you subtract mixed numbers, you may need to rename before subtracting.

Example 4

Find the difference $6\frac{1}{8} - 2\frac{3}{4}$.

Estimate: $6\frac{1}{8} - 2\frac{3}{4} \approx 6 - 3 = 3$

$$6\frac{1}{8} - 2\frac{3}{4} = 6\frac{1}{8} - 2\frac{6}{8} \qquad \text{The LCD is 8.}$$

$$= 5\frac{9}{8} - 2\frac{6}{8} \qquad 6\frac{1}{8} = 5 + 1\frac{1}{8} = 5\frac{9}{8}.$$

$$= 3\frac{3}{8}$$

WORK TOGETHER

Work in pairs. In the addition at the right, replace each ▩ with one of the digits 1, 3, 4, 6, 7, and 8. You may use each digit only once. Find the two fractions that meet each set of conditions.

4. They have the greatest possible sum.

5. Each fraction is less than 1, and they have the greatest possible sum.

6. They have the greatest possible sum less than 1.

7. They have the least possible sum greater than 0.

8. Critical Thinking The sum is about $\frac{1}{2}$.

Write a number sentence for each model shown.

9.

10.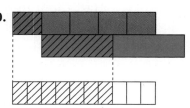

Use a model to find each sum or difference.

11. $\frac{3}{4} - \frac{1}{3}$ 12. $\frac{1}{5} + \frac{3}{10}$ 13. $\frac{2}{3} - \frac{1}{2}$ 14. $\frac{7}{12} + \frac{1}{6}$

15. Casey hiked $1\frac{3}{4}$ mi along a nature trail to a fork in the trail. He then hiked $2\frac{1}{2}$ mi along a path that led to a waterfall.

   a. When Casey reached the waterfall, how far had he hiked altogether?

   b. How much longer is the trail from the fork to the waterfall than the first part of the trail?

Find each sum or difference.

16. $\frac{1}{2} - \frac{1}{8}$ 17. $4\frac{1}{5} + 3$ 18. $\frac{7}{12} + \frac{5}{12}$

19. $9\frac{3}{10} - 4\frac{1}{10}$ 20. $14 - 5\frac{1}{5}$ 21. $\frac{7}{10} + 2\frac{1}{6}$

Lemon Rasberry Fizz

$1\frac{1}{2}$ qt lemonade
$2\frac{1}{4}$ qt ginger ale
$1\frac{2}{3}$ qt lemon sherbet
$\frac{1}{2}$ qt rasberry juice

Sketch or use a model to find each sum or difference.

22. $\frac{3}{10} + \frac{2}{5}$ 23. $\frac{3}{4} - \frac{1}{8}$ 24. $2\frac{1}{3} + \frac{3}{4}$ 25. $1\frac{1}{2} - \frac{5}{6}$

26. The capacity of your punch bowl is 6 qt. Is it large enough to hold the recipe for Lemon Raspberry Fizz at the left? Explain.

27. **Hobbies** Emma is braiding a border to put around a rectangular footstool that is $14\frac{5}{8}$ in. long and $9\frac{3}{4}$ in. wide.

   a. Show how to estimate the total length of braid she needs.

   b. Find the actual length needed.

28. **Writing** Explain the steps you would use to find $3\frac{2}{3} + 4\frac{1}{2}$.

Find each sum or difference.

29. $8\frac{2}{5} - 5\frac{3}{5}$ **30.** $\frac{2}{3} + \frac{3}{4}$ **31.** $4\frac{2}{3} - \frac{5}{6}$

32. $2\frac{1}{8} + 4\frac{7}{8}$ **33.** $10 - \frac{5}{6}$ **34.** $3\frac{5}{8} + 2\frac{1}{4}$

Write each period of time as a fraction in simplest form.

Sample   7:00 A.M. to 8:20 A.M.

           The elapsed time is 1 h 20 min.

           You can write this as $1\frac{20}{60}$ h, or $1\frac{1}{3}$ h.

35. 6:00 A.M. to 6:30 A.M.   **36.** 3:05 P.M. to 3:50 P.M.

37. 1:15 P.M. to 2:25 P.M.   **38.** 7:45 A.M. to 10:00 A.M.

39. Jobs Simon works in a dry-cleaning shop. On Saturday he started work at 8:45 A.M. He finished at 4:15 P.M.

    a. How many hours did Simon work before noon?

    b. How many hours did he work after noon?

    c. Simon spent $\frac{3}{4}$ h at lunch. How many hours did he work altogether on Saturday?

Find each answer.

40. $4\frac{2}{3} + 6 + 3\frac{1}{3}$ **41.** $8\frac{2}{5} - 3\frac{2}{3} + 2$

Critical Thinking **Use what you know about addition of integers to predict whether each sum will be positive, negative, or zero. Explain your reasoning.**

42. $-\frac{2}{3} + \frac{5}{6}$ **43.** $-\frac{4}{5} + \frac{8}{10}$ **44.** $-\frac{7}{8} + \frac{3}{4}$

45. Calculator On your calculator you can use the fraction key and the following key sequence to add $5\frac{1}{2} + 4\frac{3}{4}$.

    5 $\boxed{a^{b/c}}$ 1 $\boxed{a^{b/c}}$ 2 $\boxed{+}$ 4 $\boxed{a^{b/c}}$ 3 $\boxed{a^{b/c}}$ 4 $\boxed{=}$ $10\_1\lrcorner 4$

     The calculator fraction $10\_1\lrcorner 4$ means $10\frac{1}{4}$.

    a. Write the key sequence you could use to subtract $4\frac{1}{8} - 1\frac{3}{4}$.

    b. Use your key sequence to find $4\frac{1}{8} - 1\frac{3}{4}$.

Mixed REVIEW

Subtract.

1. $17 - (-13)$

2. $-15 - 18$

Estimate each answer.

3. $12\frac{1}{2} - 5\frac{2}{3}$

4. $16\frac{1}{2} \div 4\frac{3}{4}$

Solve.

5. $x + 2 = 7$

6. $x - 3 = -12$

7. Mrs. Okimoto has 20 students in her French class, $\frac{3}{5}$ of whom have taken French before. What number have not taken French?

Addition and Subtraction Equations

WHAT YOU'LL NEED

✓ Fraction bars

THINK AND DISCUSS

1. At the right is a model of one of the following equations. Which equation do you think it is?

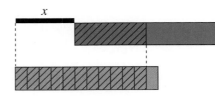

I. $x + \frac{11}{12} = \frac{1}{2}$ II. $x + \frac{1}{2} = \frac{11}{12}$ III. $x - \frac{1}{2} = \frac{11}{12}$

2. What is the solution of the equation modeled above?

3. a. How is the model at the right different from the model above?

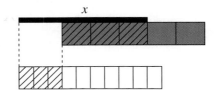

b. Complete: The model represents the equation $x - \blacksquare = \blacksquare$.

c. What is the solution of the equation?

4. Model and solve the equation $x + \frac{1}{4} = \frac{5}{6}$.

FLASHBACK

Addition and subtraction are inverse operations. Subtraction "undoes" addition, and addition "undoes" subtraction.

You can use algebra to solve an equation involving fractions in the same way you solve an equation involving integers. If the equation involves a subtraction, use addition to "undo" it.

Example
1

Solve $n - \frac{1}{2} = 4\frac{3}{4}$.

$$n - \frac{1}{2} = 4\frac{3}{4}$$

$$n - \frac{1}{2} + \frac{1}{2} = 4\frac{3}{4} + \frac{1}{2} \qquad \text{Add } \frac{1}{2} \text{ to each side.}$$

$$n = 4\frac{3}{4} + \frac{2}{4} \qquad \text{Find a common denominator.}$$

$$n = 4\frac{5}{4} = 5\frac{1}{4} \qquad \text{Rewrite } 4\frac{5}{4} \text{ as } 5\frac{1}{4}.$$

5. Why do you add $\frac{1}{2}$ to each side of the equation in Example 1?

6. What would you add to each side of the equation to solve $x - \frac{2}{5} = \frac{5}{6}$?

If an equation involves addition, use subtraction to "undo" it.

Example 2   Solve $s + \frac{1}{3} = 2\frac{1}{6}$.

$$s + \frac{1}{3} = 2\frac{1}{6}$$

$$s + \frac{1}{3} - \frac{1}{3} = 2\frac{1}{6} - \frac{1}{3} \quad \text{Subtract } \frac{1}{3} \text{ from each side.}$$

$$s = 2\frac{1}{6} - \frac{2}{6} \quad \text{Find a common denominator.}$$

$$s = 1\frac{7}{6} - \frac{2}{6} \quad \text{Rewrite } 2\frac{1}{6} \text{ as } 1\frac{7}{6}. \text{ Then subtract.}$$

$$s = 1\frac{5}{6}$$

You can use fractions in equations to solve many every day problems.

Example 3   Derek needs $2\frac{3}{4}$ lb of fish for a stew. The store has $1\frac{1}{4}$ lb of bluefish. Derek decides to fill out the recipe with cod fillets. How many pounds should he buy?

- Use c to represent the number of pounds of cod.

pounds of cod	plus	pounds of bluefish	equals	total pounds
c	$+$	$1\frac{1}{4}$	$=$	$2\frac{3}{4}$

$$c + 1\frac{1}{4} = 2\frac{3}{4} \quad \text{Solve the equation.}$$

$$c + 1\frac{1}{4} - 1\frac{1}{4} = 2\frac{3}{4} - 1\frac{1}{4} \quad \text{Subtract } 1\frac{1}{4} \text{ from each side.}$$

$$c = 1\frac{2}{4} \quad \text{Simplify } 1\frac{2}{4}.$$

$$c = 1\frac{1}{2}$$

Derek should buy $1\frac{1}{2}$ lb of cod.

Cod fishing is an important industry in Alaska. In 1980, about 20 million pounds of cod were caught. In 1990 the amount was 544 million pounds. **About how many times greater was the 1990 catch than the 1980 catch?**

Source: *Statistical Abstract of the United States*

WORK TOGETHER

- Work in groups of three or four. Write a word problem for each equation.

7. $m + \frac{1}{2} = 1\frac{3}{4}$ **8.** $m - 1\frac{3}{4} = \frac{1}{2}$ **9.** $m - \frac{1}{2} = 1\frac{3}{4}$

- Exchange problems with another group. Match the other group's problems with the appropriate equation.

Order from least to greatest.

1. 0.438, 0.4381, 0.4, 0.43

2. 11.2, 11.02, 11.201, 11.1

Find each difference.

3. $\frac{1}{2} - \frac{1}{4}$ 4. $9\frac{2}{3} - 4\frac{5}{9}$

Change to an improper fraction.

5. $3\frac{1}{2}$ 6. $5\frac{2}{3}$

7. What is the largest two-digit number that is prime that has prime numbers for both of its digits?

During the last Ice Age, 18,000 years ago, worldwide sea level was about 400 ft lower than now. Since then 17 million mi^3 of water have been added to the oceans as ice caps melted.

Source: *Ice Ages*

T R Y THESE

Write and solve an equation for each model.

10.

11.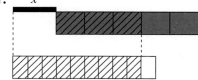

Solve each equation.

12. $q - \frac{1}{4} = 2\frac{1}{8}$ 13. $2\frac{1}{5} + t = 4\frac{3}{10}$ 14. $\frac{1}{4} = b + \frac{1}{3}$

15. Rebecca's height on her last birthday was $51\frac{1}{2}$ in. When she measured her height this year, she was $52\frac{1}{4}$ in. tall.

   a. Write an equation that you can use to find how many inches Rebecca grew this year.

   b. How many inches did Rebecca grow this year?

Mental Math Solve each equation mentally.

16. $y + \frac{1}{2} = 1$ 17. $k - \frac{3}{8} = \frac{5}{8}$ 18. $\frac{3}{4} + a = \frac{3}{4}$

19. In the recent dry spell, the water level of the Baileys' pond decreased $1\frac{3}{4}$ ft. The pond is now only $10\frac{1}{3}$ ft deep. Write and solve an equation to find the depth before the dry spell.

20. **Estimation** Is the solution of $r - \frac{4}{7} = \frac{2}{99}$ closest to 0, $\frac{1}{2}$, or 1? Explain.

O N YOUR OWN

Solve each equation.

21. $j + \frac{3}{4} = \frac{7}{8}$ 22. $p - \frac{4}{5} = 6\frac{1}{5}$ 23. $\frac{1}{2} + d = 7\frac{5}{6}$

24. $z + \frac{7}{9} = 4$ 25. $4\frac{3}{4} = v - 1\frac{1}{2}$ 26. $s - \frac{2}{9} = \frac{1}{3}$

27. a. Write an addition equation and a subtraction equation that each have a solution of $\frac{2}{5}$.

   b. Write a word problem for each equation you wrote for part (a).

28. Choose A, B, or C. For which equation is n less than 1?

A. $\frac{3}{4} + n = 1\frac{4}{5}$　　**B.** $n + 1\frac{2}{7} = 1\frac{4}{9}$　　**C.** $2\frac{3}{4} - n = 1\frac{3}{5}$

Solve each problem by writing and solving an equation.

29. Charley had a board that was $5\frac{1}{4}$ ft long. While making a fence, he cut a piece $3\frac{3}{4}$ ft long from the board. What was the length of the piece of board that remained?

30. Environment The average U.S. household recycles about $\frac{1}{10}$ of its trash. The average Japanese household recycles about $\frac{1}{2}$ of its trash. By how much would a U.S. household have to increase its recycling rate to match a Japanese household?

31. Sports At one baseball stadium, $\frac{1}{10}$ of the seats are box seats, $\frac{2}{3}$ are general admission seats, and another $\frac{1}{10}$ are bleacher seats. The rest of the seats are premium seats. What part of the total seats are premium?

32. Writing How is solving equations that involve fractions and mixed numbers similar to solving equations that involve integers? How is it different?

Fenway Park, shown above, is the home of the Boston Red Sox. It seats 34,182 fans. This is the fewest number of seats of any stadium for a professional baseball team. The Cleveland Stadium, home of the Cleveland Indians, has the greatest seating capacity of any baseball stadium. It has 74,483 seats.

CHECK POINT

Compare. Use <, >, or =.

1. $\frac{8}{9}$ ■ $\frac{2}{9}$　　　　**2.** $\frac{7}{10}$ ■ $\frac{5}{6}$　　　　**3.** $3\frac{1}{4}$ ■ $3\frac{1}{5}$

4. Write $\frac{5}{11}$ as a decimal.　　　　**5.** Write 0.72 as a fraction.

Estimate each answer.

6. $8\frac{1}{3} \cdot 2\frac{4}{5}$　　　　**7.** $\frac{1}{8} + \frac{5}{12}$　　　　**8.** $4\frac{2}{5} - 1\frac{1}{4}$

Find each sum or difference.

9. $\frac{3}{4} + \frac{7}{8}$　　　　**10.** $\frac{4}{5} + 3\frac{2}{3}$　　　　**11.** $7\frac{1}{2} - 3\frac{3}{7}$

Solve each equation.

12. $\frac{3}{8} = t - \frac{3}{4}$　　　　**13.** $n + 2\frac{1}{3} = 3\frac{4}{5}$　　　　**14.** $3\frac{1}{2} + a = 5\frac{3}{10}$

8-6 **M**ultiplication of Fractions

TH**I**N**K** **A**N**D** **D**I**S**C**U**S**S**

1. **a.** Fold a sheet of plain paper vertically into four equal sections. Using a colored pencil, shade $\frac{1}{4}$ of the paper.

   b. Now fold the paper horizontally into three equal sections. Using a pencil of a different color, shade $\frac{1}{3}$ of the paper.

   c. Count the total number of rectangles created by the folds. How many contain both colors? What fraction of all the rectangles is this?

   d. Use your model to complete: $\frac{1}{4} \cdot \frac{1}{3} = $ ■.

To multiply fractions, you multiply their numerators and multiply their denominators.

Example 1 Find the product $\frac{7}{8} \cdot \frac{2}{3}$.

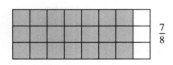 $\frac{7}{8}$

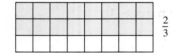 $\frac{2}{3}$

 $\frac{7}{8} \cdot \frac{2}{3}$

$$\frac{7}{8} \cdot \frac{2}{3} = \frac{7 \cdot 2}{8 \cdot 3}$$

$$= \frac{14}{24} \qquad \text{Write } \frac{14}{24} \text{ in simplest form.}$$

$$= \frac{7}{12}$$

2. Why is the figure at the left a model of the product in Example 1?

3. Make a model to find the product $\frac{1}{2} \cdot \frac{1}{3}$.

When a numerator and denominator have a common factor, you can simplify before multiplying.

Example 2 Find the product $\frac{7}{8} \cdot \frac{2}{3}$.

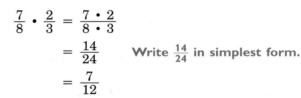

4. Find the product of $\frac{5}{6} \cdot \frac{3}{4}$.

To multiply a fraction and a whole number, write the whole number as a fraction with a denominator of 1.

Example 3   Find the product: $\frac{3}{7} \cdot 28$

$$\text{Estimate: } \frac{3}{7} \cdot 28 \approx \frac{1}{2} \cdot 28 = 14$$

$$\frac{3}{7} \cdot 28 = \frac{3}{7} \cdot \frac{28}{1}$$

$$= \frac{3 \cdot 28}{7 \cdot 1}$$

$$= \frac{84}{7} = 12$$

5. Show how to simplify before multiplying in Example 3.

You can multiply with fractions on your calculator using the fraction key. For instance, use this key sequence to find the product in Example 3.

3 [a^b/c] 7 [×] 28 [=]   *12*

To multiply mixed numbers, first write each mixed number as an improper fraction.

Example 4   Find the product $2\frac{3}{5} \cdot 4\frac{1}{2}$.

$$\text{Estimate: } 2\frac{3}{5} \cdot 4\frac{1}{2} \approx 3 \cdot 5 = 15$$

$$2\frac{3}{5} \cdot 4\frac{1}{2} = \frac{13}{5} \cdot \frac{9}{2}$$

$$= \frac{13 \cdot 9}{5 \cdot 2}$$

$$= \frac{117}{10} = 11\frac{7}{10}$$

You can multiply mixed numbers on your calculator using the fraction key, [a^b/c]. Below is the key sequence to find $2\frac{3}{5} \cdot 4\frac{1}{2}$.

2 [a^b/c] 3 [a^b/c] 5 [×] 4 [a^b/c] 1 [a^b/c] 2 [=]   *11_ 7⌐ 10*

The calculator readout *11_ 7⌐ 10* means $11\frac{7}{10}$.

Of course, if you remember that $\frac{3}{5}$ is equal to 0.6 and $\frac{1}{2}$ is equal to 0.5, you can use the following key sequence.

2.6 [×] 4.5 [=]   *11.7*

6. Use a calculator to find $3\frac{1}{2} \cdot 1\frac{3}{4}$.

> **FLASHBACK**
> To write a mixed number as an improper fraction:
> • Multiply the whole number by the denominator of the fraction.
> • Add the numerator to this product.
> • Write this sum over the denominator.
> $$2\frac{1}{5} = \frac{2 \cdot 5 + 1}{5} = \frac{11}{5}$$

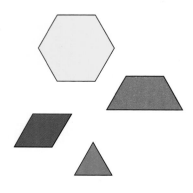

Work in pairs. Use the pattern blocks shown at the left.

Sample: Model $\frac{1}{3} \cdot 1\frac{1}{2} = \frac{1}{2}$.

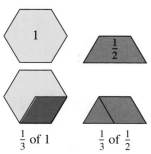

Model $1\frac{1}{2}$. Use a hexagon to represent one whole. Use a trapezoid to represent $\frac{1}{2}$.

$\frac{1}{3}$ of 1 $\frac{1}{3}$ of $\frac{1}{2}$

Find a shape that represents $\frac{1}{3}$ of the hexagon. Find a shape that represents $\frac{1}{3}$ of the trapezoid.

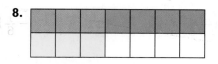

Show how much of the whole (the hexagon) these shapes make.

7. Use pattern blocks to show each product.

   a. $\frac{1}{2} \cdot 1\frac{1}{3} = \frac{2}{3}$ **b.** $\frac{2}{3} \cdot 2 = 1\frac{1}{3}$ **c.** $\frac{1}{3} \cdot 2\frac{1}{2} = \frac{5}{6}$

Write a multiplication sentence for each model.

8.

9.

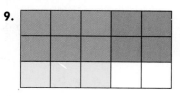

Sketch or use a model to find each product.

10. $\frac{1}{2} \cdot \frac{1}{3}$ **11.** $\frac{1}{4} \cdot \frac{3}{5}$ **12.** $\frac{2}{3} \cdot \frac{3}{4}$ **13.** $\frac{1}{3} \cdot 2\frac{1}{2}$

14. You want to make a design by gluing shells end-to-end along a board. The length of the board is $16\frac{1}{2}$ in. You have five West Indian worm shells that are each $3\frac{3}{8}$ in. long.

   a. Estimate the total length of the five shells. Do you think they might fit along the length of the board? Explain.

   b. Find the total length of the shells. Will they actually fit along the length of the board?

Mental Math Use the distributive property to multiply.

Sample
$$2 \cdot 3\frac{1}{2} = 2 \cdot \left(3 + \frac{1}{2}\right)$$
$$= 2 \cdot 3 + 2 \cdot \frac{1}{2}$$
$$= 6 + 1 = 7$$

15. $4 \cdot 5\frac{1}{4}$ **16.** $1\frac{1}{3} \cdot 12$ **17.** $10 \cdot 1\frac{4}{5}$ **18.** $\frac{1}{2} \cdot 6\frac{1}{2}$

Choose Use a calculator, paper and pencil, or mental math to find each product.

19. $3 \cdot 2\frac{3}{8}$ **20.** $\frac{3}{4} \cdot \frac{1}{5}$ **21.** $6\frac{2}{5} \cdot 3\frac{1}{3}$ **22.** $2 \cdot 3\frac{2}{3}$

23. $\frac{1}{3} \cdot 2\frac{2}{5}$ **24.** $\frac{7}{8} \cdot 32$ **25.** $\frac{1}{2} \cdot \frac{4}{5}$ **26.** $3\frac{1}{6} \cdot 4\frac{3}{4}$

27. Writing Describe how multiplying two fractions is different from adding two fractions.

28. Find the perimeter and the area of the figure at the right.

29. Write two different key sequences to find $1\frac{1}{4} \cdot 3\frac{1}{5}$.

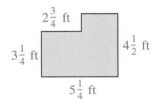

Critical Thinking Predict whether each product will be positive or negative. Then find the product.

30. $-\frac{1}{5} \cdot \frac{5}{7}$ **31.** $-\frac{4}{9} \cdot \left(-\frac{3}{8}\right)$ **32.** $2\frac{1}{4} \cdot \left(-\frac{1}{6}\right)$

What's on Earth?

Earth has nearly 200 million square miles of surface area. What is it *really* like? A little more than seven tenths of that area is water. What remains is land, of course. But nearly one fifth of the land is desert. The largest desert is the Sahara Desert, which is $3\frac{1}{2}$ million square miles. The Sahara is roughly equal to the land area of the United States!

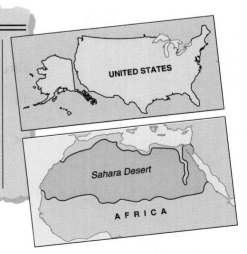

33. a. How many square miles of Earth's surface is land?

b. What fraction of Earth's surface is neither water nor desert?

PROBLEM SOLVING STRATEGIES

Make a Table
Use Logical Reasoning
Solve a Simpler Problem
Too Much or Too Little
Information
Look for a Pattern
Make a Model
Work Backward
Draw a Diagram
Guess and Test
Simulate a Problem
Use Multiple Strategies
Write an Equation

Solve. The list at the left shows some possible strategies you can use.

1. List all the possible orders in which Kim, Chan, Marie, and Helmer can run a relay race.

2. Chloe and LaTanya started work on the same day. Chloe will earn a salary of $28,000 the first year. She will then receive a $4,000 raise each year that follows. LaTanya's salary for the first year is $41,000, followed by a $1,500 yearly raise. In what year will Chloe's salary be more than LaTanya's?

3. There are three more students in Mr. Smith's seventh-grade class than there are in Mr. Lightfoot's class. The product of the numbers of students in the classes is 1,054. How many students are in each class?

4. Ten students are standing in a row. At the first cue, every even-numbered student sits down. At the second cue, all who are standing sit, and all who are sitting stand. At the third cue, students in the third, sixth, and ninth places in line take the opposite positions (sitting or standing) from the one they are in. At the last cue, students in odd-numbered places stand up, regardless of whether they were sitting or standing. How many students are sitting after the last cue?

5. At a fundraiser attended by 150 people, $2,000 was collected for charity. Suppose 25 people gave nothing. How much was the average donation from those who gave?

6. Jerome attached a string to a peg and put the peg in the ground. He walked $4\frac{1}{2}$ ft and put another peg in the ground to hold the string. Then he turned left 90° and walked for 9 ft and put another peg in the ground to hold the string. Then he tied the end of the string to the first peg. How many square feet does the string enclose?

7. Find $\frac{1}{2} + \frac{1}{4} + \frac{1}{8} + \frac{1}{16} + \frac{1}{32} + \frac{1}{64} + \frac{1}{128}$.

8-7 Division of Fractions

THINK AND DISCUSS

"What is $4 \div \frac{1}{3}$?" is the same as asking, "How many thirds are in four wholes?"

1. Complete each statement.

$$4 \div \frac{1}{3} = \blacksquare \qquad 4 \cdot 3 = \blacksquare \qquad 4 \div \frac{1}{3} = 4 \cdot \blacksquare$$

2. a. How many "two thirds" are in four wholes?

b. Complete each statement.

$$4 \div \frac{2}{3} = \blacksquare \qquad 4 \cdot \frac{3}{2} = \blacksquare \qquad 4 \div \frac{2}{3} = 4 \cdot \blacksquare$$

FLASHBACK

Reciprocals are two numbers whose product is 1.

$$\frac{5}{6} \cdot \frac{6}{5} = 1$$

$\frac{5}{6}$ and $\frac{6}{5}$ are reciprocals.

You can find the reciprocal of a fraction by interchanging the numerator and the denominator.

To divide fractions, you multiply by the *reciprocal* of the divisor.

Example 1   Find $\frac{2}{3} \div \frac{5}{6}$.

• $\frac{2}{3} \div \frac{5}{6} = \frac{2}{3} \cdot \frac{6}{5}$ The reciprocal of $\frac{5}{6}$ is $\frac{6}{5}$.

     $= \frac{2 \cdot \overset{2}{6}}{\underset{1}{3} \cdot 5}$ Write the quotient in simplest form.

     $= \frac{4}{5}$

When you divide a fraction by a whole number, begin by writing the whole number as a fraction with a denominator of 1.

Example 2   Find the quotient of $\frac{3}{5} \div 2$.

• $\frac{3}{5} \div 2 = \frac{3}{5} \div \frac{2}{1}$ Write 2 as $\frac{2}{1}$.

     $= \frac{3}{5} \cdot \frac{1}{2}$ The reciprocal of $\frac{2}{1}$ is $\frac{1}{2}$.

     $= \frac{3 \cdot 1}{5 \cdot 2}$

     $= \frac{3}{10}$

When division involves one or more mixed numbers, first rewrite the mixed numbers as improper fractions.

Example 3　Joanne has a coil of rope that is $13\frac{1}{2}$ yd long. How many pieces $2\frac{1}{4}$ yd long can she cut from it?

- You need to find the quotient of $13\frac{1}{2} \div 2\frac{1}{4}$.

Estimate: $13\frac{1}{2} \div 2\frac{1}{4} \approx 14 \div 2 = 7$

$$13\frac{1}{2} \div 2\frac{1}{4} = \frac{27}{2} \div \frac{9}{4}$$　Write the mixed numbers as improper fractions.

$$= \frac{27}{2} \cdot \frac{4}{9}$$　Write the reciprocal of $\frac{9}{4}$.

$$= \frac{27^{3} \cdot 4^{2}}{2_{1} \cdot 9_{1}}$$

$$= 6$$

Joanne can cut six pieces of rope from the coil.

You can divide fractions on your calculator using the fraction key. Use this key sequence to divide $2\frac{1}{2} \div \frac{5}{6}$.

2 **a^b/c** 1 **a^b/c** 2 **÷** 5 **a^b/c** 6 **=** *3*

3. **Calculator** Describe the key sequence that you would use to find the quotient in Example 3.

WORK TOGETHER

Work in pairs. Use the pattern blocks at the left to model each division. What is the quotient?

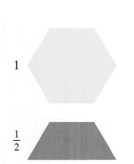

1

$\frac{1}{2}$

$\frac{1}{3}$

$\frac{1}{6}$

4. $4\frac{1}{2} \div \frac{1}{2}$　　**5.** $2 \div \frac{1}{3}$　　**6.** $\frac{1}{2} \div \frac{1}{6}$　　**7.** $2\frac{1}{3} \div \frac{1}{6}$

TRY THESE

Find the reciprocal of each number.

8. $\frac{3}{4}$　　**9.** 5　　**10.** $\frac{1}{7}$　　**11.** $\frac{5}{4}$　　**12.** $4\frac{5}{8}$

13. **a.** One serving of cereal contains $1\frac{1}{2}$ oz. Estimate the number of servings in a $19\frac{1}{2}$-oz box.

b. Find the actual number of servings in the box.

Find each quotient.

14. $\frac{4}{5} \div \frac{1}{4}$　　　15. $6 \div \frac{1}{7}$　　　16. $1\frac{7}{8} \div 3$　　　17. $\frac{2}{9} \div 2\frac{2}{3}$

18. **a. Discussion** Which positive number is its own reciprocal?

　　b. Which number has no reciprocal? Explain.

ON YOUR OWN

Mental Math Find each quotient mentally.

Sample　　$4 \div \frac{1}{5} = 4 \cdot \frac{5}{1} = 4 \cdot 5 = 20$

19. $8 \div \frac{1}{2}$　　　20. $5 \div \frac{1}{3}$　　　21. $2 \div \frac{1}{9}$　　　22. $10 \div \frac{1}{10}$

23. **a. Writing** Explain how you can recognize a "mental math division" like those in Exercises 19–22.

　　b. Make up four other problems involving division of fractions that you can solve mentally. Then solve.

Choose Use a calculator, paper and pencil, or mental math to find each quotient.

24. $2\frac{1}{6} \div \frac{5}{6}$　　25. $\frac{3}{4} \div 3$　　26. $\frac{1}{4} \div \frac{2}{3}$　　27. $4\frac{3}{4} \div 1\frac{1}{4}$

28. $8\frac{2}{5} \div \frac{3}{10}$　　29. $\frac{7}{9} \div \frac{1}{4}$　　30. $11 \div \frac{1}{9}$　　31. $8\frac{1}{3} \div 2\frac{1}{2}$

32. **Life Science** A killer whale can swim 40 mi in $1\frac{1}{4}$ h. At this rate, how far can the whale swim in 1 h?

33. **Map Making** Use the map at the right to answer each question.

　　a. Kim lives the same distance from Bob as she lives from Max. How far does Kim live from each?

　　b. The distance from Bob's house to school is one third the distance from Bob's house to Kim's house. How far does Bob live from school?

　　c. What is the shortest distance from school to the library?

　　d. Bob jogged from his house to Max's, to the soccer field, to the library. Then he jogged home by the shortest route. How far did he jog?

Mixed REVIEW

Is the angle acute, right, obtuse, or straight?

1. $m\angle A = 90°$

2. $m\angle B = 166°$

Find each product.

3. $3 \cdot 4\frac{5}{8}$

4. $2\frac{1}{2} \cdot 3\frac{3}{4}$

5. The sum of Mark and Maria's ages is 55. The difference of their ages is 3. Find their ages.

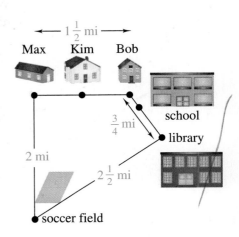

Max　Kim　Bob

$1\frac{1}{2}$ mi

$\frac{3}{4}$ mi

2 mi

$2\frac{1}{2}$ mi

school

library

soccer field

What's Ahead

8-8 **W**ork Backward

• Solving problems by working backward

To solve some problems, you may need to work backward.

> Mrs. Ruiz is taking her son Javier and his friends to dinner, and then to a concert that starts at 8:00 P.M. It will take $\frac{3}{4}$ h to pick up his friends and $1\frac{1}{4}$ h to eat. They want to be at the theater 15 min before the concert starts. When should they leave home?

READ

Read and understand the given information. Summarize the problem.

1. Think about the information you are given.
   a. At what time does the concert start?
   b. What activities are planned between the time Mrs. Ruiz and Javier leave home and the time the concert starts?
   c. What amount of time is planned for each activity?
   d. Summarize the goal of the problem in your own words.

PLAN

Decide on a strategy to solve the problem.

In this problem, you know that a series of events must *end* at 8:00 P.M. It makes sense to work backward to find the time that the events must *begin*. Mentally picture each time on a clock.

SOLVE

Try out the strategy.

2. **a.** Write the time for each event.

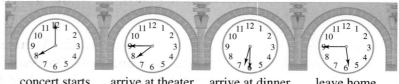

concert starts   arrive at theater   arrive at dinner   leave home

   b. What is the solution to the problem?

LOOK BACK

Think about how you solved this problem.

3. Show how to check your solution by working *forward*.

4. **a.** Think of 15 min as $\frac{1}{4}$ h. Find the sum $\frac{3}{4} + 1\frac{1}{4} + \frac{1}{4}$.
   b. How could you use your answer to part (a) to solve the problem in a different way?

Work backward to solve each problem.

5. Look back at the problem about Javier and the concert.

   a. Suppose that the concert starts at 8:30 P.M. At what time should Mrs. Ruiz and Javier leave home?

   b. Suppose that the concert starts at 8:00 P.M., but it takes only 20 min to pick up Javier's friends. At what time should Mrs. Ruiz and Javier leave home?

6. a. **Entertainment** The new movie that opened yesterday was so boring that $\frac{1}{2}$ of the people in the theater at the start of the movie left after the first 45 min. In the next 15 min, $\frac{1}{2}$ of the remaining people left. In the next $\frac{1}{4}$ h, 18 more people left. Only 36 of the people who were there at the start stayed to see the end of the movie. How many people were in the theater at the start of the movie?

   b. **Discussion** Which parts of the given information were not needed to solve the problem?

7. a. If you start with a number, add 5, then multiply by 7, the result is 133. What was the original number?

   b. Which operations did you use to solve this problem?

   c. What is the relationship between the operations you used and the operations that are mentioned in the problem?

O N YOUR OWN

Use any strategy to solve each problem. Show all your work.

8. Darren spent one third of his money on lunch. At lunch, his friend gave him $2.50 to repay a loan. Then Darren spent $3.25 for a movie ticket and $.75 for a snack. He had $4.90 left. How much money did Darren have before lunch?

9. Mia has ten coins that have a total value of $.65. None of the coins is greater than a quarter. What are the coins?

10. Mrs. Jacobs plans to build a wheelchair ramp for her store entrance. The door is 2 ft above ground level. The ramp will start 30 ft from the foundation of the building. How long will the ramp be to the nearest hundredth of a foot?

For safety reasons, a ramp for a wheelchair should rise no more than 1 ft for every 12 ft of horizontal length.

11. a. Business The manager of a department store plans to make an electronic game shop in a section of the store that is 12 ft wide and 20 ft long. Using the pattern shown at the left, the manager wants to cover the floor with tiles that measure 1 ft on each side. How many black tiles will be needed? How many white tiles?

   b. How can you use the formula for the area of a rectangle to check that you found the correct number of tiles?

12. Gardening Nina wants to plant a triangular garden in the shade of the old apple tree. One side of the garden will run $8\frac{1}{2}$ ft due north from the tree. Another side will run 9 ft due east from the tree. Find the area of the garden.

13. Banking The check register below is only partially completed. It shows the deposit made and the checks written for the period October 3 to October 4. How much money was in the account at the start of this period?

DATE	DESCRIPTION OF TRANSACTION	PAYMENT/DEBIT	DEPOSIT/CREDIT	BALANCE
10 / 3	Bolton Electric	$37.65		
10 / 3	Dr. Freidrich	$65.00		
10 / 4	paycheck		$147.50	
10 / 4	Village Auto Repair	$863.15		$246.11

14. Money Lydia went shopping with $35 in her purse. She found a sweater that she liked, and it was on sale for half price. She also had a coupon that was good for an additional $5 off the sale price. After buying the sweater, Lydia had $10.50 left. How much did she pay for the sweater?

15. The difference of two fractions with unlike denominators is $\frac{1}{6}$. The denominator of the greater fraction is an even number less than 8. Its numerator is 5. The denominator of the other fraction is half the denominator of the greater fraction, and it is an odd number. What are the fractions?

BASEBALL CARD BONANZA!!!

Single cards $9.00
Buy three cards –
get a fourth for $7.00
Buy five cards –
for $44.50

16. Money Rosita saved $60 to spend on baseball cards at the sale advertised on the sign at the left. What is the least expensive way to buy five cards?

17. Sports Meytal practiced gymnastics 28 h in one week. Each day she practiced one hour more than the day before. How many hours did she practice on the fifth day?

8-9 Customary Measurement

WHAT YOU'LL NEED

✓ Calculator

Weight of Frame: $4\frac{1}{4}$ lb
Cost: $179.99

Weight of Frame: 76 oz
Cost: $195.95

THINK AND DISCUSS

Suppose that you want to buy a mountain bike. You know that the lighter the frame of the bike, the easier it is to cycle. Which bike shown in the ads at the left will be easier to cycle?

To make a decision, you need to compare the weights. One way to do this is to change $4\frac{1}{4}$ lb to ounces. To change from a larger unit to a smaller unit, you *multiply*.

Example 1   Change $4\frac{1}{4}$ lb to ounces.

• Think of the relationship between pounds and ounces: 1 lb = 16 oz
  $\times 16$

• To change $4\frac{1}{4}$ lb to ounces, multiply $4\frac{1}{4}$ lb by 16.

$$4\frac{1}{4} \cdot 16 = \frac{17}{\overset{}{\underset{1}{4}}} \cdot \frac{\overset{4}{16}}{1}$$

$$= 68$$

$$4\frac{1}{4} \text{ lb} = 68 \text{ oz}$$

You also could compare the weights by changing 76 oz to pounds. To change from a smaller unit to a larger unit, you *divide*.

Example 2   Change 76 oz to pounds.

• Think of the relationship between ounces and pounds: 16 oz = 1 lb
  $\div 16$

• To change 76 oz to pounds, divide 76 oz by 16.

76 ⚌ 16 ⚌ **4.75**   Use a calculator.

76 oz = 4.75 lb = $4\frac{3}{4}$ lb

1. a. Which is lighter, $4\frac{1}{4}$ lb or 76 oz? How many ounces lighter? How many pounds lighter?

b. Which bike will be easier to cycle?

Customary Units of Measurement

Length

12 inches (in.) = 1 foot (ft)
3 feet = 1 yard (yd)
5,280 feet = 1 mile (mi)

Weight

16 ounces (oz) = 1 pound (lb)
2,000 pounds = 1 ton (T)

Capacity

8 fluid ounces (fl oz) = 1 cup (c)
2 cups = 1 pint (pt)
2 pints = 1 quart (qt)
4 quarts = 1 gallon (gal)

Often it is necessary to add or subtract measures. When a measure involves a mixed unit, it may be helpful to change the mixed unit to a mixed number involving just one unit.

Example 3   Sarah has a board that is 10 ft long. She plans to cut a piece that is 5 ft 3 in. long from the board. What will be the length of the remaining piece?

• You need to subtract 5 ft 3 in. from 10 ft. Write 5 ft 3 in. as a number of feet, then subtract.

$$5 \text{ ft } 3 \text{ in.} = 5\frac{3}{12} \text{ ft} = 5\frac{1}{4} \text{ ft} \qquad \leftarrow \text{12 in.} = 1 \text{ ft}$$

$$10 \text{ ft} - (5 \text{ ft } 3 \text{ in.}) = 10 - 5\frac{1}{4}$$

$$= 9\frac{4}{4} - 5\frac{1}{4} \quad \text{Write 10 as } 9\frac{4}{4}.$$

$$= 4\frac{3}{4}$$

The remaining piece will be $4\frac{3}{4}$ ft long.

2. Suppose Sarah cut 8 ft 5 in. from the 10 ft board. What would be the length of the remaining piece?

3. In the chart at the left, which abbreviation is followed by a period? Why must this abbreviation have a period?

WORK TOGETHER

Cooking Work in pairs. Suppose that you operate a catering service. You have a basic recipe for split pea soup that serves eight. Copy and complete the chart below to adjust the recipe for 16, 24, 32, and 48 servings. Whenever possible, change an amount to a larger unit of measure.

	Ingredient	Number of Servings				
		8	16	24	32	48
4.	dried split peas	$2\frac{1}{4}$ c	■	■	■	■
5.	water	2 qt	■	■	■	■
6.	chopped onion	$\frac{3}{4}$ c	■	■	■	■
7.	chopped celery	1 c	■	■	■	■
8.	ham shanks	2 lb	■	■	■	■
9.	sliced carrots	$\frac{1}{4}$ lb	■	■	■	■

TRY THESE

Tell whether you would *multiply* or *divide* to change from one unit of measure to the other.

10. pounds to tons   **11.** quarts to pints   **12.** yards to feet

Mental Math Complete.

13. 10 qt = ■ gal   **14.** $3\frac{1}{2}$ T = ■ lb   **15.** $2\frac{1}{3}$ yd = ■ ft

16. Yung Mi has three packages of walnuts that weigh 12 oz, 32 oz, and $1\frac{1}{2}$ lb. How many pounds of walnuts does she have altogether?

17. Hobbies Jim has a pattern that requires $1\frac{3}{4}$ yd of 60-in. fabric. At a sale, he finds a remnant of 60-in. fabric that someone has marked "$5\frac{1}{2}$ ft." Will this be enough? Explain.

Choose Use a calculator, paper and pencil, or mental math to change from one unit of measure to the other.

18. $5\frac{1}{4}$ gal = ■ qt   **19.** 5,250 lb = ■ T   **20.** 4 yd = ■ in.

21. Discussion What do you think is the best unit for measuring each of the following quantities? Explain.

   a. the length of the hallway outside your classroom

   b. the weight of a zebra

   c. the capacity of a bathtub

ON YOUR OWN

Choose Use a calculator, paper and pencil, or mental math to change from one unit of measure to the other.

22. 26 in. = ■ ft   **23.** 4 c = ■ fl oz   **24.** 68 oz = ■ lb

25. $3\frac{1}{2}$ mi = ■ ft   **26.** 16 ft = ■ yd   **27.** $4\frac{1}{2}$ qt = ■ c

28. Will 4 gal of milk make 64 one-cup servings? Explain.

29. The length of the Amazon River in South America is about 4,000 mi. How many feet is this?

 The Amazon River Basin contains $\frac{1}{5}$ of the world's fresh river water, $\frac{1}{3}$ of its forests, and may produce up to $\frac{1}{2}$ of the oxygen added to the atmosphere each year.

Source: *Curious Facts*

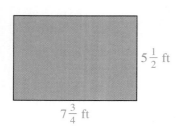

$5\frac{1}{2}$ ft

$7\frac{3}{4}$ ft

30. The figure at the left is a rectangle.

    a. What is its perimeter in feet? in inches?

    b. What is its area in square feet? in square inches?

31. Data File 9 (pp. 362–363) Find the area of the living room and the two bedrooms in the layout of the apartment.

32. a. Calculator In one day, people in the United States discard an average of 200,000 T of food. Suppose that one garbage truck can hold 12,000 lb of this food. How many trucks would be needed to haul all of it?

    b. Suppose that the length of a garbage truck is 25 ft. All the trucks carrying the discarded food are lined up front-to-back. How many miles of highway would they cover?

33. Writing Explain why you multiply to change from a larger unit to a smaller unit and divide to change from a smaller unit to a larger unit. Be sure to give examples.

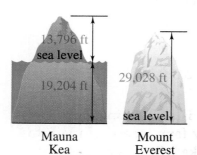

13,796 ft
sea level

19,204 ft

29,028 ft

sea level

Mauna
Kea

Mount
Everest

Climb or Dive?

What is the tallest mountain in the world? You may be surprised to know that the answer is *not* Mount Everest. It is true that Everest, which borders Nepal and Tibet, can claim the title as the world's highest elevation above sea level. As shown at the left, however, Hawaii's Mauna Kea is *truly* the world's tallest mountain, although much of it is hidden in the waters of the Pacific Ocean.

So what is the *lowest* elevation on Earth? For "landlubbers," the lowest point is the Dead Sea. Located between Israel and Jordan, the Dead Sea is 1,312 ft below sea level. For the oceans, the lowest elevation is the Marianas Trench, which plummets 36,198 ft below the surface of the Pacific Ocean. If Mount Everest were placed in the Marianas Trench, its peak would be about $1\frac{1}{3}$ mi below sea level.

34. Earth Science How many miles high is Mauna Kea?

35. Earth Science About how many miles taller than Mount Everest is Mauna Kea?

36. Earth Science About how many miles in elevation separate the highest and lowest elevation on Earth?

• Solving one-step
multiplication and
division equations

Multiplication and Division Equations

In a tour of the United States mint, Rita learned that it costs $.30 to produce one dozen $100 bills. She wondered how much it costs to produce just one of these bills. So, Rita wrote this equation.

one dozen	times	cost of one bill	equals	total cost
12	$\times$	c	$=$	30

FLASHBACK

Multiplication and division are inverse operations. Division "undoes" multiplication, and multiplication "undoes" division.

Example 1

Solve $12c = 30$.

$$12c = 30$$

$$\frac{12c}{12} = \frac{30}{12} \quad \text{Divide each side by 12.}$$

$$c = \frac{30}{12} \quad \text{Write the solution as a mixed number in simplest form.}$$

$$c = \frac{5}{2}$$

$$c = 2\frac{1}{2}$$

1. What is the cost of producing one $100 bill?

Rita also learned that paper money is printed in sheets of 32 bills. Inspectors check one of every four sheets. While Rita was at the mint, 44 sheets were checked. She wondered how many were printed. So, Rita wrote another equation.

one fourth	of	sheets printed	equals	sheets checked
$\frac{1}{4}$	$\times$	s	$=$	44

WHAT? All currency is printed on a special paper that is made only by a company in Massachusetts. The paper is made of a secret blend of cotton, linen, and other fabric scraps. Some very small threads of blue and red are added to the blend to help prevent counterfeiting.

Example 2

Solve $\frac{1}{4}s = 44$.

$$\frac{s}{4} = 44 \quad \text{Write } \frac{1}{4}s \text{ as } \frac{s}{4}.$$

$$4 \cdot \frac{s}{4} = 4 \cdot 44 \quad \text{Multiply each side by 4.}$$

$$s = 176$$

2. How many sheets were printed?

The solution of an equation may be a fraction less than one.

Example
3
Solve $14h = 6$.

• $14h = 6$

$\dfrac{14h}{14} = \dfrac{6}{14}$ Divide each side by 14.

$h = \dfrac{6}{14}$ Write the solution in simplest form.

$h = \dfrac{3}{7}$

3. Explain how you can check the solution of Example 3.

T R Y THESE

Solve each equation.

4. $3w = 14$ 5. $\dfrac{d}{8} = 36$ 6. $\dfrac{1}{5}t = 25$ 7. $36m = 4$

8. **Business** On a recent day, a store manager noted that 65 customers bought at least eight items. This was one fifth of the total number of customers that day. Write and solve an equation to find the total number of customers.

Mental Math Solve each equation mentally.

9. $\dfrac{x}{6} = 2$ 10. $4p = 9$ 11. $12f = 2$ 12. $\dfrac{1}{3}b = 12$

13. **Estimation** Carl and Ed each estimated the solution of $20g = 49$. Carl's estimate was $\dfrac{2}{5}$. Ed's estimate was $2\dfrac{1}{2}$.

   a. Whose estimate is correct? How do you think he made the estimate?

   b. What error do you think the other person made?

O N YOUR OWN

Choose Use a calculator, paper and pencil, or mental math to solve each equation.

14. $\dfrac{k}{5} = 16$ 15. $9a = 20$ 16. $48q = 36$ 17. $28 = \dfrac{1}{4}z$

18. $14n = 60$ 19. $\dfrac{1}{8}s = 128$ 20. $88 = 22c$ 21. $\dfrac{w}{7} = 628$

M̶i̶x̶e̶d̶ REVIEW

Solve.
1. $x - 3 = -24$
2. $y + 13 = -42$

Complete
3. $8c = \blacksquare$ pt
4. $5 \text{ lb} = \blacksquare$ oz

5. Earth is 93 million mi from the sun. It takes light from the Sun 8 min 20 s to reach Earth. What is the speed of light in mi/s?

Estimation **Estimate the solution of each equation. Explain how you made your estimate.**

22. $23q = 4$ **23.** $10a = 121$ **24.** $\frac{n}{21} = 12$ **25.** $82 = \frac{1}{9}t$

26. Writing How is solving the equation $4y = 24$ similar to solving $24y = 4$? How is it different?

Solve each problem by writing and solving an equation.

27. Geography About one eighth of the total area of the New England states is covered by water. This is about 9,000 mi². What is the total area of the New England states?

28. Sports It took Arnetha 3 h to hike the $4\frac{1}{2}$-mi length of the Shady Mountain Trail. What was her average speed?

29. Mount McKinley, the tallest mountain peak in North America, is 20,320 ft tall. The Sears Tower in Chicago, the tallest office building in the world, is 1,454 ft tall. About how many times as tall as the Sears Tower is Mount McKinley?

30. Review the examples on page 349. Write two different equations that have the solution $5\frac{1}{2}$. One should be similar to the equation in Example 1, and one should be similar to the equation in Example 2.

Of the world's tallest skyscrapers $\frac{1}{3}$ are in Chicago (top). About $\frac{1}{6}$ are in New York City (middle), and $\frac{1}{7}$ are in Houston (bottom).

Source: *The World Book Encyclopedia.*

CHECKPOINT

Find each product or quotient.

1. $\frac{4}{5} \cdot \frac{5}{8}$ **2.** $\frac{1}{3} \div \frac{4}{9}$ **3.** $\frac{5}{6} \div 6\frac{2}{3}$ **4.** $7\frac{1}{2} \cdot 3\frac{4}{7}$

5. Alicia has a job interview at 8:30 A.M. She needs 15 min to have breakfast, $\frac{1}{2}$ h to get dressed, and 40 min to drive to the interview. What is the latest time that she should get up?

Complete.

6. 28 in. = ▉ ft **7.** $8\frac{1}{2}$ lb = ▉ oz **8.** 15 qt = ▉ gal

Solve each equation.

9. $\frac{1}{4}t = \frac{7}{8}$ **10.** $12p = 78$ **11.** $\frac{x}{7} = 3$ **12.** $15 = 18d$

Compare. Use <, >, or =.

1. $\dfrac{2}{9}$ ■ $\dfrac{8}{9}$

2. $\dfrac{4}{7}$ ■ $\dfrac{4}{15}$

3. $\dfrac{5}{16}$ ■ $\dfrac{3}{8}$

4. $\dfrac{1}{2}$ ■ $\dfrac{24}{49}$

5. $\dfrac{13}{20}$ ■ $\dfrac{5}{8}$

Write each fraction as a decimal. Write each decimal as a fraction in simplest form.

6. $\dfrac{3}{5}$

7. $\dfrac{3}{11}$

8. 0.92

9. 0.4

10. $\dfrac{7}{10}$

11. 0.875

12. $\dfrac{7}{12}$

Estimate each sum, difference, product, or quotient.

13. $4\dfrac{1}{2} - 1\dfrac{24}{25}$

14. $138 \cdot \dfrac{1}{7}$

15. $22\dfrac{7}{8} \div 3\dfrac{5}{6}$

16. $\dfrac{5}{11} + \dfrac{1}{15}$

17. $8\dfrac{1}{11} \cdot 5\dfrac{11}{12}$

Find each sum, difference, product, or quotient. Write the answer in simplest form.

18. $\dfrac{3}{4} + \dfrac{5}{6}$

19. $4\dfrac{1}{5} \cdot \dfrac{6}{7}$

20. $2\dfrac{1}{3} + 7\dfrac{3}{4}$

21. $\dfrac{3}{8} \div \dfrac{1}{12}$

22. $15 - 5\dfrac{2}{7}$

Solve each equation.

23. $m - \dfrac{3}{10} = \dfrac{4}{5}$

24. $8y = 28$

25. $9\dfrac{1}{3} = k + \dfrac{3}{4}$

26. $\dfrac{d}{4} = 16$

27. $15w = 6$

Complete.

28. $9 \text{ pt} = $ ■ qt

29. $8\dfrac{1}{3} \text{ yd} = $ ■ ft

30. $84 \text{ oz} = $ ■ lb

31. $2\dfrac{3}{4} \text{ c} = $ ■ fl oz

32. The newspaper clipping at the right shows how the price of a certain stock rose and fell during the course of one day. The opening price was ripped off by mistake.

   a. What must the opening price have been?

   b. What would have been the value of 25 shares at 12:00 noon?

8:00 A.M. (Opening price)	
10:00 A.M.	$+\dfrac{1}{4}$
12:00 NOON	$-\dfrac{3}{8}$
2:00 P.M.	$-\dfrac{1}{2}$
4:00 P.M. (Closing price)	$21\dfrac{3}{8}$

33. In March, Keino's puppy weighed $4\dfrac{3}{4}$ lb. In August, it weighed $5\dfrac{7}{8}$ lb. How much weight did the puppy gain?

34. Martha rides her bicycle $4\dfrac{1}{2}$ mi to school. At the end of the day, she stops at a park that is on her way home. The park is $2\dfrac{3}{10}$ mi from school. How far is it from Martha's house?

What's Ahead

• Solving problems using fractions and decimals

8-11 Using Fractions and Decimals

THINK AND DISCUSS

Everyday problems often involve both fractions and decimals. For instance, to find the amount you save on the CD player advertised at the left, you need to find $\frac{1}{4}$ of $329.29.

It is always a good idea to start by making an estimate.

$$\frac{1}{4} \text{ of } \$329.29 \approx \frac{1}{4} \text{ of } \$320 = \$80$$

1. To make the estimate, why do you round $329.29 to $320?

To find the actual amount of savings, use a calculator.

$$\frac{1}{4} \cdot \$329.29 \rightarrow 0.25 \; \boxed{\times} \; 329.29 \; \boxed{=} \quad 82.3225$$

or

$$\$329.29 \div 4 \rightarrow 329.29 \; \boxed{\div} \; 4 \; \boxed{=} \quad 82.3225$$

2. Explain why you can find $\frac{1}{4}$ of $329.29 using 0.25×329.29.

3. Explain why you can find $\frac{1}{4}$ of $329.29 using $329.29 \div 4$.

4. What is the amount of savings, rounded to the nearest cent?

5. What is the sale price of the CD player?

You can find the sale price in a different way if you remember that a savings of *one fourth* means that you pay *three fourths*.

6. If the sale price of an item is two thirds the original price, what fraction is the savings?

7. How can you estimate three fourths of $329.29?

8. Use a calculator to find $\frac{3}{4} \cdot \$329.29$. What is the sale price?

9. a. Describe two methods to find the sale price of the keyboard advertised at the left. Then find the sale price.

b. Discussion Which method do you prefer? Explain.

Solve.

1. $15x = 3$ **2.** $\frac{y}{4} = 34$

3. $6m = 22$ **4.** $\frac{1}{9}b = 81$

Find the missing length.

5.

9 ft x

12 ft

6. The volume of a cube is 1,728 cm³. What is the length of each edge of the cube?

10. Pamela is planning to make a dress. She needs to buy a zipper that costs $1.98 and $2\frac{3}{4}$ yd of a fabric that costs $5.59 per yard. What will be the total cost?

11. At a clearance sale, a stereo that originally cost $229.95 was tagged "$\frac{1}{4}$ off."

  a. What was the sale price of the stereo?

  b. On the final day of the sale, the stereo was offered at $\frac{1}{3}$ off the tagged price. What was the final price?

12. **Writing** Your little cousin says that "$\frac{1}{2}$ off" is the same as "two for the price of one," so "$\frac{1}{3}$ off" is the same as "three for the price of one." Is this true? Explain.

13. **Critical Thinking** A store advertises "Buy 2, get 3rd one free!" Is this the same as one half off? Explain using examples.

GREAT EXPECTATIONS

Attorney

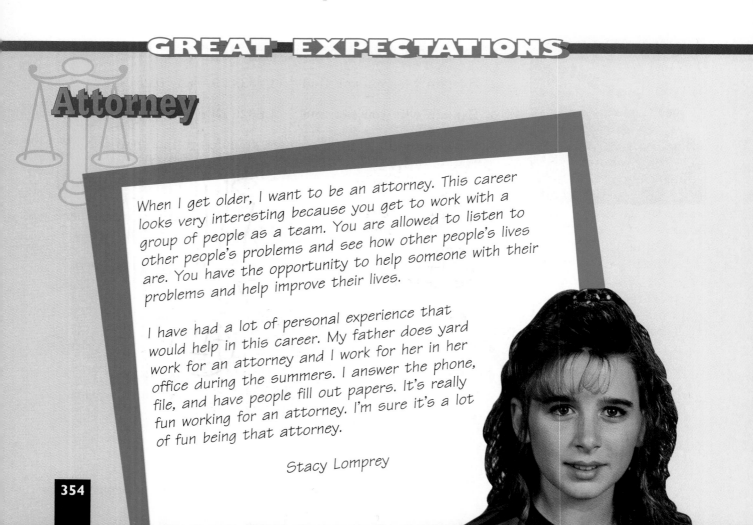

When I get older, I want to be an attorney. This career looks very interesting because you get to work with a group of people as a team. You are allowed to listen to other people's problems and see how other people's lives are. You have the opportunity to help someone with their problems and help improve their lives.

I have had a lot of personal experience that would help in this career. My father does yard work for an attorney and I work for her in her office during the summers. I answer the phone, file, and have people fill out papers. It's really fun working for an attorney. I'm sure it's a lot of fun being that attorney.

Stacy Lomprey

14. **a. Investigation (p. 316)** In the stock market, shares of stock are priced in whole dollars and in halves, fourths, and eighths of a dollar. Elena bought 15 shares of a stock priced at $27\frac{5}{8}$ and 25 shares of a stock priced at $32\frac{1}{2}$. What was the total cost?

   b. Find today's closing price on 15 shares each of the two stocks on which you are collecting data.

15. **a.** At the sale advertised at the right, what is the price of a jacket that originally cost $75?

   b. Is the sale price of the jacket more or less than the sale price of a coat that originally cost $100? How much more or less?

   c. What would be the total cost of two pairs of shoes with original prices of $24.98 and $35?

   d. Critical Thinking Adam paid $171.75 for a coat at this sale. What was the original price of the coat?

The
Clothing Place

$\frac{1}{4}$ off all jackets

$\frac{1}{3}$ off all coats

Shoes — Shoes — Shoes
Buy one pair

Second Pair *$\frac{1}{2}$ off

*of equal or lesser value

Dear Stacy,

It's wonderful that you enjoy working with an attorney! You should like the work that a profession requires—it's one way to know you will be satisfied with your career choice.

   Attorneys must use logical reasoning and creativity in order to help their clients deal with life's situations. Sometimes people's legal problems do not have easy solutions. You might have to sift through a lot of facts and information before the important issues emerge for you.

   Reading, writing, and mathematics are tools you will use each day as an attorney. They will help you perform your duties well. The work you will do can affect many people's lives. Whether you work alone or as part of a team, you must care about the case and the people involved.

   Veronica C. Boda
   President of National Association
      of Women Lawyers

Wrap Up

Comparing, Ordering, and Estimating

8-1, 8-3

To compare fractions, first find a common denominator.

Order from least to greatest.

1. $\frac{3}{8}, \frac{1}{2}, \frac{1}{4}$

2. $\frac{3}{4}, \frac{7}{12}, \frac{1}{6}$

3. $\frac{2}{5}, \frac{1}{3}, \frac{7}{15}$

4. $\frac{6}{10}, \frac{4}{5}, \frac{8}{20}$

Estimate each answer.

5. $\frac{5}{8} + 1\frac{2}{3}$

6. $5\frac{1}{4} - 2\frac{2}{5}$

7. $3\frac{1}{8} \cdot 9\frac{9}{10}$

8. $12\frac{2}{5} \div 3\frac{8}{9}$

Fractions and Decimals

8-2

To change a decimal to a fraction, write the decimal as a fraction with a denominator as a power of ten. Then write the fraction in simplest form.

To change a fraction to a decimal, divide the numerator by the denominator. You can indicate that a decimal has repeating digits by placing a bar over the digits that repeat.

Write each decimal as a fraction or mixed number in simplest form.

9. 0.10

10. 0.5

11. 0.24

12. 3.75

13. 2.96

Write each fraction as a decimal.

14. $\frac{3}{5}$

15. $\frac{75}{100}$

16. $\frac{7}{8}$

17. $\frac{1}{3}$

18. $\frac{5}{6}$

19. Writing Describe a situation in which you would use a fraction, and a situation in which you would use a decimal.

Adding and Subtracting Fractions

8-4

To add or subtract fractions first find a common denominator and then add or subtract the numerators.

Find each sum or difference.

20. $2\frac{1}{3} + \frac{3}{4}$

21. $16\frac{4}{5} - 9\frac{2}{3}$

22. $8\frac{1}{6} + 7\frac{3}{12}$

23. $11\frac{5}{6} - 5\frac{3}{8}$

Multiplying and Dividing Fractions

8-6, 8-7

To multiply fractions, you multiply their numerators and then multiply their denominators. To divide fractions, you multiply by the reciprocal of the divisor. To find $\frac{2}{3} \div \frac{5}{6}$, you multiply $\frac{2}{3} \cdot \frac{6}{5}$.

Find each product or quotient.

24. $\frac{3}{5} \cdot 1\frac{1}{2}$

25. $2\frac{2}{3} \cdot 3\frac{3}{8}$

26. $5\frac{1}{4} \div \frac{7}{8}$

27. $\frac{4}{5} \div 1\frac{1}{3}$

Solving Equations

8-5, 8-10

To solve equations, use the properties of equality.

28. $1\frac{7}{8} + n = 3\frac{3}{4}$

29. $q - 3\frac{1}{5} = 5\frac{3}{10}$

30. $5p = 18$

31. $\frac{x}{5} = 7\frac{1}{4}$

Write an equation and solve each problem.

32. The 70 students graduating are $\frac{1}{5}$ of the total school population. How many students attend the school?

33. Jon's height was $68\frac{1}{2}$ in. in June. He had grown $1\frac{5}{8}$ in. during the school year. How tall was he when school started?

Customary Measurement

8-9

To change from a larger unit to a smaller unit, you *multiply*. To change from a smaller unit to a larger unit, you *divide*.

Complete.

34. 30 in. = ■ ft

35. 54 oz = ■ lb

36. 20 yd = ■ ft

37. $3\frac{1}{2}$ c = ■ fl oz

Strategies and Applications

8-8, 8-11

To solve some problems you may have to work backward.

38. Lien wants to be at school at 7:30 A.M. It takes her $\frac{3}{4}$ h to get dressed, $\frac{1}{2}$ h to fix and eat breakfast, and 15 min to walk to school. What time should she get up?

39. John bought a pair of shoes during a "$\frac{1}{4}$-off" sale. The original price was $34. After he paid for the shoes he had $14.26. How much money did he start with?

GETTING READY FOR CHAPTER 9

Which fraction does not equal the others in each set?

1. $\frac{1}{2}, \frac{8}{16}, \frac{4}{6}$

2. $\frac{3}{4}, \frac{15}{24}, \frac{5}{8}$

3. $\frac{10}{18}, \frac{4}{9}, \frac{15}{27}$

4. $\frac{24}{30}, \frac{8}{10}, \frac{3}{5}$

PUTTING IT ALL TOGETHER

follow Up

Investing in Stocks

The Young Investors Club has asked you to prepare a report recommending a stock for the club to buy. You can make a written or an oral report that includes the following information.

✓ a description of the company
✓ a graph of the stock's price over a period of time
✓ your analysis of the stock's potential

The problems preceded by the magnifying glass (p. 319, #33, p. 325, #36, p. 355, #14) will help you complete the investigation.

HEAVENS TO HAMBURGERS

An international fast food restaurant claims to have served over 90 billion hamburgers. If all these hamburgers were placed end to end, would they reach around the Earth at the equator? If they were all stacked one on top of the other, would they reach the Moon? A hamburger measures about 4" in diameter by $1\frac{1}{4}$" high.

Oatmeal Cookies

$\frac{3}{4}$ c vegetable shortening

$1\frac{1}{4}$ c brown sugar

$\frac{1}{4}$ c granulated sugar

1 egg

$\frac{1}{3}$ c water

1 tsp vanilla

3 c uncooked oats

1 c all-purpose flour

1 tsp salt

$\frac{1}{2}$ tsp baking soda

Preheat oven to 350°F. Beat together shortening, sugars, egg, water, and vanilla. Add remaining ingredients, and mix well. Drop by rounded teaspoonfuls onto greased cookie sheet. Bake for 12 to 15 min. Makes 5 dozen cookies.

Bakers often double or triple the amount of the ingredients in a recipe. What would you do to the recipe in order for each member of your class to get six cookies? List the amount of each ingredient you would need.

Rolling Fractions Game

Two or more players

Materials: 10- or 6-sided die or spinner with numbers 1-10, pencil, paper

To Play:

1) Each player copies the form shown.
2) Any player rolls the die.
3) Each player secretly writes the number rolled in any box on the form.
4) Roll the die again. Write that number in any remaining blank box. Continue rolling the die until all the boxes are filled.
5) Players add the fractions on their forms. The player with the greatest number gets 1 point. If there is a tie, the tying players score 1 point. The first player to score 4 points wins.

Variations: A) Expand the form to add three fractions. B) Subtract, multiply, or divide the fractions. C) The answer nearest zero gets a point.

1. **Writing** Explain how to order $\frac{1}{2}$, $\frac{3}{4}$, $\frac{2}{5}$, and $\frac{9}{10}$ from least to greatest.

2. **Choose A, B, C, or D.** Which fraction is closest to 0.92?

   A. $\frac{14}{15}$ **B.** $\frac{9}{10}$ **C.** $\frac{11}{12}$ **D.** $\frac{19}{20}$

3. Write 0.84 as a fraction in simplest form.

4. Write $\frac{5}{9}$ as a decimal.

5. You jog $8\frac{1}{2}$ times around the block. The distance around the block is 770 yd. About how many miles have you jogged? (1 mi = 1,760 yd)

6. Find each sum or difference.

   a. $8\frac{2}{5} + 5\frac{3}{5}$ **b.** $7\frac{5}{8} - 4\frac{1}{8}$

   c. $4\frac{3}{4} + 5\frac{1}{5}$ **d.** $9\frac{3}{8} - 5\frac{1}{4}$

   e. $1\frac{2}{3} - \frac{3}{4}$ **f.** $4\frac{2}{3} + 1\frac{5}{6}$

7. **Choose A, B, C, or D.** In which equation is the value of x less than 1?

   A. $\frac{3}{8} = x - \frac{3}{4}$ **B.** $x - \frac{1}{3} = \frac{3}{4}$

   C. $x - 1\frac{1}{3} = 2\frac{1}{3}$ **D.** $x + 1\frac{1}{5} = 1\frac{3}{5}$

8. Jake worked $12\frac{1}{2}$ h at $6.50 per hour. After he was paid, he spent $24.99 on a pair of jeans. He now has $389.23. How much money did he have before he was paid?

9. A rectangle is $4\frac{3}{4}$ ft long and $2\frac{1}{2}$ ft wide. What is its perimeter?

10. Genex Co. stock started trading at $2\frac{7}{8}$ this morning and closed at $1\frac{1}{4}$ this afternoon. If you owned 100 shares, how much would the total value of your shares have decreased today?

11. Find each product or quotient.

    a. $\frac{4}{5} \cdot \frac{1}{4}$ **b.** $\frac{4}{5} \div \frac{1}{4}$

    c. $1\frac{2}{3} \cdot 1\frac{1}{4}$ **d.** $1\frac{2}{3} \div 1\frac{1}{4}$

    e. $150 \div 2\frac{2}{3}$ **f.** $5\frac{3}{8} \cdot 3\frac{3}{4}$

12. Complete.

    a. 38 in. = ■ ft   **b.** 60 oz = ■ lb

    c. $3\frac{3}{4}$ qt = ■ c   **d.** $1\frac{2}{3}$ mi = ■ ft

13. Solve.

    a. $15y = 33$ **b.** $12 = 8x$

    c. $\frac{y}{12} = 2\frac{1}{2}$ **d.** $\frac{1}{4}y = 10$

    e. $w + 4\frac{3}{5} = 6\frac{1}{2}$ **f.** $k - 2\frac{3}{4} = 9$

14. You are an employee in a store having a "$\frac{1}{3}$-off" sale. Employees get an additional $\frac{1}{5}$ off the sale price. How much would you pay for a jacket that originally cost $60?

15. Compare using <, >, or =.

    a. 5.4 ■ $\frac{26}{5}$ **b.** $\frac{5}{6}$ ■ $\frac{24}{25}$

16. The two legs of a right triangle are $1\frac{1}{2}$ ft and 2 ft long. What is the length of the hypotenuse?

Choose A, B, C, or D.

1. Estimate $6\frac{3}{4} \cdot 3\frac{1}{5}$.

   A. 18   **B.** 21   **C.** 24   **D.** 27

2. Which sequence is *neither* arithmetic nor geometric?

   A. 3, 6, 12, 21, . . .   **B.** 3, 6, 9, 12, . . .

   C. 3, 6, 12, 24, . . .   **D.** 3, 9, 15, 21, . . .

3. You want to buy some birthday presents for your little brother. You have $21. You know you will need about $1 for sales tax. What should you buy?

   A. book and video

   B. model and video

   C. book and soccer ball

   D. model and soccer ball

Item	Cost
Book	$7.95
Model	$8.99
Video	$11.49
Soccer Ball	$12.50

4. Find the value of $\frac{xy}{x-y}$ when $x = -3$ and $y = -6$.

   A. -6 **B.** -3 **C.** 6   **D.** 3

5. The area of a rectangle is 12 ft². One side is $3\frac{3}{8}$ ft long. Which equation could you use to find the length of the other side?

   A. $x + 3\frac{3}{8} = 12$

   B. $x\left(3\frac{3}{8}\right) = 12$

   C. $2x + 2 \cdot 3\frac{3}{8} = 12$

   D. $\dfrac{x}{3\frac{3}{8}} = 12$

6. Which function is graphed at the right?

   A. $f(n) = n$

   B. $f(n) = 2n$

   C. $f(n) = n + 1$

   D. $f(n) = 2n + 1$

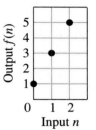

7. Which decimal is *not* 4.01 when rounded to the nearest hundredth?

   A. 4.0086   **B.** 4.0049

   C. 4.0149   **D.** 4.0140

8. Write the numbers 0.361×10^7, 4.22×10^7, and 13.5×10^6 in order from least to greatest.

   A. 13.5×10^6, 0.361×10^7, 4.22×10^7

   B. 4.22×10^7, 13.5×10^6, 0.361×10^7

   C. 0.361×10^7, 13.5×10^6, 4.22×10^7

   D. 13.5×10^6, 4.22×10^7, 0.361×10^7

9. Henry plans to build a set of steps for his attic stairway. The steps must reach a height of $8\frac{1}{2}$ ft. Each step can be no more than $7\frac{3}{4}$ in. high. What is the least number of steps he must build.

   A. 11   **B.** 12

   C. 13   **D.** 14

10. Which sum is closest to 1?

    A. $\frac{1}{3} + \frac{1}{5}$ **B.** $\frac{5}{8} + \frac{5}{9}$

    C. $\frac{2}{3} + \frac{3}{11}$ **D.** $\frac{3}{4} + \frac{3}{5}$

9 Reasoning with Proportions

A POOR STATE OF AFFAIRS

- The number of children living below the poverty line in the United States increased in the 1980s by 16%.
- There are 13.4 million poor children in the United States.
- The children in the United States who suffer from hunger number 5.5 million.
- A family of three living in the United States needs $964/mo to live.

Source: *U.S. News and World Report*

Teen Survey

	"Yes"
I'm pretty close with my sibling(s).	75%
I'm close with one sibling, but not the other(s).	27%
My parent(s) pay more attention to my sibling(s) than they do to me.	20%
I'd rather have been an only child.	15%
My parent(s) expect me to help out too much with my sibling(s).	13%

Source: *Seventeen*

America's Shrinking Households

Year	Number of Households	Number of People/Household
1930	29,905,000	4.11 people
1940	34,949,000	3.67 people
1950	43,554,000	3.37 people
1960	52,799,000	3.33 people
1970	63,401,000	3.14 people
1980	80,776,000	2.76 people
1990	93,347,000	2.63 people
1991	94,312,000	2.63 people

Sources: *Information Please Almanac*

WORLD VIEW

Today 12% of Japanese children live in households that include grandparents as well as parents. In 1960, 25% of Japanese children lived in such households.

BEDRO
9 FT-8
X
11 FT-3

MASTER
BEDRO
11 FT-8
X
11 FT-3

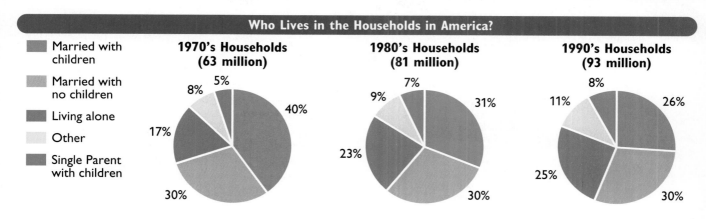

Who Lives in the Households in America?

- Married with children
- Married with no children
- Living alone
- Other
- Single Parent with children

1970's Households (63 million)
5%
8%
40%
17%
30%

1980's Households (81 million)
7%
9%
31%
23%
30%

1990's Households (93 million)
8%
11%
26%
25%
30%

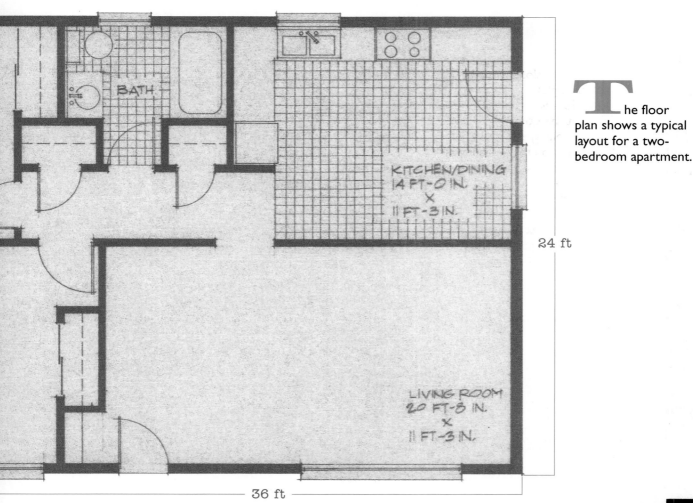

BATH

KITCHEN/DINING
14 FT-0 IN.
X
11 FT-3 IN.

LIVING ROOM
20 FT-8 IN.
X
11 FT-3 IN.

24 ft

36 ft

The floor plan shows a typical layout for a two-bedroom apartment.

investigation

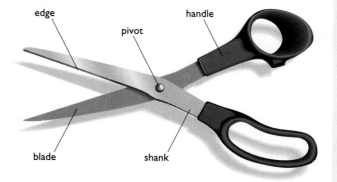

Project File

Memo

The vice president for new product development for the Skizzer Scissor Company received a letter from an unhappy customer. The customer wrote that while Skizzers are the best scissors on the market they don't work for left-handed people. For lefties, the scissors' reverse-design finger holes make them difficult and even painful to use. After reading the letter, the vice-president began to wonder: Is there a market for left-handed scissors?

Left-handed scissors

edge

pivot

handle

blade

shank

Mission: Do some research to help the vice president decide whether there is a market for left-handed scissors. Write a letter to the vice president of the Skizzer Scissor Company describing your research and supporting your recommendation.

LeADs tO FoLLoW

✓ How many lefties are there in your group? in your class?

✓ Do the lefties in your class have a need for left-handed scissors?

✓ What other items might you design for lefties?

Exploring Ratios

WHAT YOU'LL NEED

✓ Calculator

*The U.S. Census Bureau predicts that by the year 2000 there will be about 48 million people under the age of 18 and 45 million people 65 and older in the United States. **Use this information to write a ratio in three ways.***

THINK AND DISCUSS

The United States Census Bureau predicts that in the year 2000 there will be about 96 males for every 100 females. You can compare the number of males to the number of females by writing a **ratio,** which is a comparison of two numbers. You can write a ratio in three ways.

$$96 \text{ to } 100 \qquad 96 : 100 \qquad \frac{96}{100}$$

The table below shows the ratio of males to females for different years and different age groups.

Ratio of Males to Females by Age Group
(Each entry compares the number of males to 100 females.)

Year	10 to 14 year olds	30 to 34 year olds	60 to 64 year olds
1970	104 (to 100)	97	88
1980	104	99	86
1990	105	100	87

Source: *Statistical Abstract of the United States*

1. Look at the ratios for 10 to 14-year-olds. What was the ratio of males to females in 1970? in 1990?

2. Write the ratio of males to females for the 60 to 64-year-olds in 1990 in three ways.

3. The United States Census Bureau predicts that in the year 2000 there will be about 57 males for every 100 females who are 75 years old or older.

   a. A student reported the ratio of males to females as 100 : 57. Is this correct? Explain.

   b. **Discussion** What is the importance of the order of the numbers when stating a ratio?

4. In the table, **Ratio of Males to Females by Age Group**, how does the ratio of males to females change as people get older?

5. **Critical Thinking** How do you think a jeans manufacturer would use the data displayed in the table, **Ratio of Males to Females by Age Group**?

You find equal ratios by multiplying or dividing each term by the same nonzero number.

$$\frac{12}{15} \; \overset{\times 2}{\underset{\times 2}{=}} \; \frac{24}{30} \qquad\qquad \frac{12}{15} \; \overset{\div 3}{\underset{\div 3}{=}} \; \frac{4}{5}$$

The ratios $\frac{12}{15}$, $\frac{24}{30}$, and $\frac{4}{5}$ are equal.

6. Which of the above ratios is in simplest form? How do you know?

7. Write three ratios equal to $\frac{10}{16}$. Include the simplest form.

8. Find the ratio of males to females in your classroom.

We sometimes express ratios as decimals. The comparison is always to 1. For example, the ratio of the length to the width of an official United States flag is 1.9 (meaning 1.9 to 1).

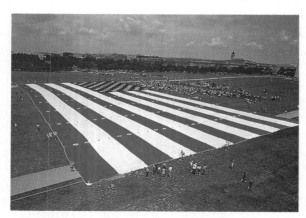

*The largest United States Flag is shown on the Ellipse in Washington, D.C., on Flag Day. It weighs 3,000 lb. **Estimate the number of people you think are required to hold up the flag. Explain.***

Source: *The Boston Globe*

Relative Lengths and Widths of United States Flags					
Length	1.9	4.37	8.74	■	28.5	■
Width	1	2.3	■	5.4	■	100

9. **Calculator** Copy the table. Use a calculator to find the missing values.

10. The largest United States flag measures 505 ft by 244 ft.

   a. What is the ratio of the flag's length to its width? Round your answer to the nearest tenth.

   b. Is the largest United States flag an official United States flag? Explain.

11. **a.** Survey your class to find the month in which each person was born.

   b. Write the ratio of the number of people born in each month to the number of people in class.

   c. Discussion How do you think you could use the data to estimate the number of students in your school who were born in August?

Write the ratio for each situation in three ways.

12. About 24 out of 25 Californians live in a metropolitan area.

13. About 1 out of 5 people in the United States is school age.

14. About 1 out of 3 people swims at least 6 times each year.

15. Find the ratio of the area covered by the community pool to the paved area in the drawing at the right.

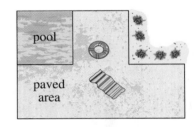

16. Investigation (p. 364) Ask 25 people whether they are left-handed or right-handed. Write the ratio of the number of left-handed people to the number of right-handed people and the ratio of the number of left-handed people to the total number of people surveyed.

17. Use the chart below.

Room number	Girls	Boys
101	12	16
104	9	20
107	9	12

   a. Which two rooms have the same ratio of girls to boys?

   b. The students in Room 101 and Room 104 have one class together. What is the ratio of girls to boys for the combined class? Write the ratio in simplest form.

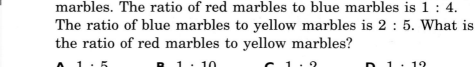

Mixed REVIEW

Estimate.

1. 412 • (−83)

2. 654 ÷ 48

Round to the nearest hundredth.

3. 4.883   4. 6.1252

5. A swimsuit that has a regular price of $38.00 is now on sale for $\frac{1}{4}$ off. What is its sale price?

6. How much colder is a temperature of −2°F than a temperature of 86°F?

Antifreeze (qt)	Water (qt)
8	4
7.5	3
12	8
3.5	1
9	18

18. **Choose A, B, C, or D.** A bag contains red, blue, and yellow marbles. The ratio of red marbles to blue marbles is 1 : 4. The ratio of blue marbles to yellow marbles is 2 : 5. What is the ratio of red marbles to yellow marbles?

 A. 1 : 5   **B.** 1 : 10   **C.** 1 : 2   **D.** 1 : 12

Choose Use a calculator, paper and pencil, or mental math.

19. Sports A softball diamond measures 65 ft by 65 ft. A baseball diamond measures 90 ft by 90 ft.

 a. Find the ratio of the length of a side of a softball diamond to the length of a side of a baseball diamond. Write the ratio in simplest form.

 b. Find the ratio of the area of a softball diamond to the area of a baseball diamond. Write the ratio in simplest form.

 c. Writing Why do you think the ratio of the sides and the ratio of the areas are not the same?

20. Writing Sara's math class included 15 girls and 10 boys. Sara said the ratio of girls to boys was 3 to 2. Two new students, a girl and a boy, enrolled in the class. Sara says the ratio is still 3 to 2. Is she correct? Why or why not?

21. Cars A jack for a car requires a force of 120 lb to lift a 3,000 lb car. What is the ratio of the car's weight to the force required to lift the car? Write the ratio in simplest form.

22. Cars Car owners use antifreeze to protect their cars' radiators from freezing or overheating. Prestone Antifreeze recommends mixing at least 2 parts antifreeze with every 1 part water for protection to −82°F.

 a. Which of the ratios of antifreeze to water at the left provide protection to −82°F?

 b. Critical Thinking A car's radiator can hold 15 qt. How much antifreeze and how much water should be added to give protection to −82°F?

23. Data File 8 (pp. 314–315) Write as a decimal the ratio of consumption of red meat to consumption of fish and shellfish in 1991. Round to the nearest tenth.

Rates and More Rates

■ WHAT YOU'LL NEED

✓ **Watch with second hand or stopwatch**

✓ **Newspaper article**

✓ **Calculator**

During a speech in December 1961, President John F. Kennedy delivered a passage at the rate of 327 words/min, the fastest rate recorded for a public speaker.

Source: *Guinness Book of Records*

⌐WORK TOGETHER

Suppose you plan to try out for a part in a radio commercial. The casting director is looking for someone who can speak clearly but *very* fast.

• Work in pairs to time each other as you read aloud as fast as you can for two minutes.

• After the two minutes, count the number of words that you read.

⌐THINK AND DISCUSS

To find who reads fastest, the casting director first writes the reading rates. A **rate** is a ratio that compares two quantities measured in different units. Suppose you read 233 words in two minutes. Your reading rate would be $\frac{233 \text{ words}}{2 \text{ min}}$.

1. What is your reading rate? your partner's?

A **unit rate** is the rate for one unit of a given quantity.

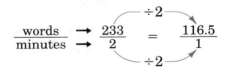

$$\frac{\text{words}}{\text{minutes}} \rightarrow \frac{233}{2} = \frac{116.5}{1}$$

The unit rate is $\frac{116.5 \text{ words}}{1 \text{ min}}$, or 116.5 words/min (words per minute).

2. a. Find the unit reading rates for your partner and yourself.

b. Suppose you and your partner continued reading for 5 min. About how many words would each of you read?

c. Who would the casting director select from your class based on the unit reading rate?

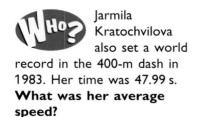

3. a. We measure the speed of a car in miles per hour. How is speed an example of a rate?

b. Write two other examples of rates that are speeds.

Sometimes we write measures in mixed units such as minutes and seconds. To find the unit rate, you first need to write the mixed units as the same unit.

Example 1

In 1983, Jarmila Kratochvilova of Czechoslovakia set a new world record for the women's 800-m race. Her time was 1:53.28 (1 min 53.28 s). What was her average speed in meters per second? Round to the nearest hundredth of a meter.

• Write 1 min 53.28 s in seconds.

   1 min 53.28 s = 60 s + 53.28 s ← 1 min = 60 s
   　　　　　　 = 113.28 s

• Write the ratio of distance to time. Find the unit rate.

   Estimate $\dfrac{m}{s}$ → $\dfrac{800}{113.28} \approx \dfrac{800}{100} = 8$

   $\dfrac{800}{113.28} = 800$ ÷ 113.28 = 7.0621469

   $\dfrac{800}{113.28} \approx 7.06$

Jarmila Kratochvilova's average speed was about 7.06 m/s.

A unit price is the price per unit of an item. The unit price can help you determine the better buy.

Example 2

A 10.2 fl oz bottle of Shine shampoo costs $5.98. The 16 fl oz bottle costs $9.95. Find each unit price. Which is the better buy?

• $\dfrac{cost}{fl\ oz}$ → $\dfrac{\$5.98}{10.2} \approx \$.59/fl\ oz$

• $\dfrac{cost}{fl\ oz}$ → $\dfrac{\$9.95}{16} \approx \$.62/fl\ oz$

The 10.2 fl oz size is the better buy.

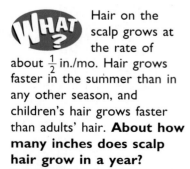

Write the unit rate for each situation.

4. travel 1,200 mi in 4 h

5. score 210 points in 10 games

6. earn $34 in 8 h

7. type 6,750 words in 2 h 30 min

8. A school has 35 teachers and 945 students. What is the student-to-teacher ratio? Express your answer as a unit rate.

9. Eight pens cost $9.20. What is the unit price?

ON YOUR OWN

Find the unit price. Then determine the better buy.

10. detergent: 32 fl oz for $1.99
               50 fl oz for $2.49

11. walnuts: 1 lb for $3.49
          10 oz for $2.49

12. popcorn: 15 oz for $1.69
          30 oz for $2.99

13. ribbon: 1 yd for $.49
        3 yd for $1.95

FLASHBACK
1 lb = 16 oz

Choose **Use a calculator, paper and pencil, or mental math.**

14. A 17-min telephone call from Boston to Chicago costs $2.38. What is the cost per minute?

15. A plane travels 2,250 km in 3 h. What is its average speed?

16. a. *Population density* indicates the average number of people per unit of area. Alaska has the lowest population density of any state in the United States. What is its population density? Round to the nearest person per square mile.

ALASKA

Population:
550,043

Area:
570,833 mi²

Source: *The Information Please Almanac*

    b. **Critical Thinking** New Jersey has 1,042 people/mi². It has the highest population density of any state. Can you conclude that 1,042 people live in every square mile in New Jersey? Explain.

    c. **Writing** Explain how you could find the population density of your classroom.

17. a. Travel The driving distance from Chicago to San Francisco is 2,142 mi. The Marten family left Chicago on a Monday morning. They averaged 50 mi/h and drove 6 h each day. On what day did they reach San Francisco?

b. The Martens' car used 119 gal of gasoline on the trip. What was the car's fuel efficiency (mi/gal)?

18. Consumer Issues At one store, Rice Krispies costs $1.79 for a 7.2-oz box. The larger box that weighs 1 lb 4.25 oz costs $3.69.

a. Which size is the better buy? Why?

b. Explain how you got your answer to part (a).

19. Sports Use the table below.

Distance	Time (s)	Record Holder
100 m	9.86	Carl Lewis, USA
200 m	19.72	Pietro Mennea, Italy
400 m	43.29	Butch Reynolds, USA
800 m	1:41.73	Sebastian Coe, UK

Source: *Runner's World*

a. Find the average speed for each record holder. Round to the nearest hundredth of a meter per second.

b. Critical Thinking Is it fair to compare the speeds? Explain.

20. Activity Have a member of your family count the number of times you blink in 3 min while you are watching television.

a. What is your blinking rate in blinks per minute?

b. About how many times will you blink in an hour while watching television?

c. Critical Thinking Suppose you were reading or playing a sport. Do you think your blinking rate would be the same as your rate while watching television? Explain.

21. Sports Susan Butcher and her dog team won the 1990 Iditarod Trail Sled Dog Race. They completed the 1,158-mi race from Anchorage to Nome in 11 da 2 h. What was their average speed, rounded to the nearest mile per hour?

Solve.

1. $72 = 8x$ **2.** $\frac{n}{6} = 4$

Write as a ratio in three ways.

3. 3 students to 8 students

4. 2 wins to 11 losses

5. Data File 3 (pp. 90–91) Write a ratio in simplest form for the number of NBA titles won by the Celtics to the number won by the Pistons.

6. Jordan has a collection of nickels, dimes, and quarters, totaling 8 coins. More than $\frac{1}{2}$ of his coins are quarters and less than $\frac{1}{4}$ are dimes. What are the possible amounts of money Jordan has?

• Solving proportions

• Using proportions to solve word problems

✓ **Calculator**

The bones in your fingers are examples of a very special ratio called the golden ratio. For the bones, the following proportion is true:

$$\frac{a}{b} = \frac{b}{c} \text{ and } \frac{b}{c} = \frac{c}{d}$$

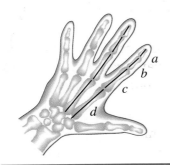

Source: *Fascinating Fibonaccis*

Proportions

THINK AND DISCUSS

A **proportion** is an equation that states that two ratios are equal.

1. Which of the pairs of ratios could form a proportion?

   a. $\frac{3}{8}, \frac{6}{16}$ **b.** $\frac{6}{9}, \frac{4}{6}$ **c.** $\frac{4}{8}, \frac{5}{9}$ **d.** $\frac{6}{10}, \frac{9}{15}$

Think about the proportion $\frac{6}{8} = \frac{9}{12}$.

2. **a.** What is the product of 6 and 12? of 9 and 8?

   b. What is true of the products you found in part (a)?

   c. Why do you think the products of the circled terms are called the cross products?

The *cross products* of a proportion are always equal. You can use cross products to find if two ratios form a proportion.

3. What numbers will you multiply to find the cross products for the proportion $\frac{2}{3} = \frac{6}{9}$?

4. Use cross products to show that $\frac{6}{15}$ and $\frac{4}{10}$ form a proportion.

Solving a proportion means finding a value that makes the proportion true. You can use cross products to solve a proportion.

Example 1   Solve $\frac{n}{9} = \frac{10}{15}$.

$15n = 9 \cdot 10$ ← **Write the cross products.**

$15n = 90$

$\frac{15n}{15} = \frac{90}{15}$ ← **Divide both sides by 15.**

$n = 6$

You can use proportions and cross products to solve problems.

Example 2

The Concorde flies the 3,630 mi from New York to Paris in about 2.7 h. About how many hours would it take the Concorde to fly 5,687 mi from Paris to Rio de Janeiro? Round to the nearest tenth of an hour.

The Concorde stretches about 10 in. as it travels at about twice the speed of sound, its top speed. **Use a reference book to find the speed of sound. Then find the Concorde's top speed.**

Sources: Air France and *3-2-1 Contact*

- $\dfrac{\text{mi}}{\text{h}} \rightarrow \dfrac{3{,}630}{2.7} = \dfrac{5{,}687}{n}$

  $3{,}630n = 2.7 \cdot 5{,}687$

  $\dfrac{3{,}630n}{3{,}630} = \dfrac{2.7 \cdot 5{,}687}{3{,}630}$

  Let n represent the number of hours it takes to fly from Paris to Rio de Janeiro.

2.7 ⊠ 5687 ⊟ 3630 ▭ *4.23*

$n \approx 4.2$

The Concorde takes about 4.2 h to travel from Paris to Rio de Janeiro.

5. Write the calculator steps you would use to solve the proportion $\dfrac{254}{28} = \dfrac{7{,}265}{n}$.

⌐T R Y THESE

6. **Choose A, B, or C.** Work in pairs. "It takes Mr. Simon 3 h to travel 125 mi. How long will it take him to travel 200 mi traveling at the same rate?" Which of the proportions will *not* help you solve the problem? Explain why.

   A. $\dfrac{3}{125} = \dfrac{n}{200}$ **B.** $\dfrac{3}{125} = \dfrac{200}{n}$ **C.** $\dfrac{125}{3} = \dfrac{200}{n}$

Mental Math **Which pairs of ratios form a proportion?**

7. $\dfrac{45}{9}, \dfrac{10}{2}$ 8. $\dfrac{6}{8}, \dfrac{4}{3}$ 9. $\dfrac{40}{12}, \dfrac{95}{4}$ 10. $\dfrac{8}{18}, \dfrac{20}{45}$

11. **Travel** A Boeing 747 airplane takes about $4\frac{3}{4}$ h to fly 2,475 mi from New York City to Los Angeles. About how many hours will it take the Boeing 747 to fly 5,470 mi from Los Angeles to Tokyo? Round to the nearest tenth.

12. A florist sells holiday bouquets that use roses and carnations in a ratio of 2 to 7. She receives a shipment of 343 carnations. How many roses will the florist need?

13. **Art** An artist mixes 2 parts red paint with 3 parts yellow paint to get the shade of orange she wants.

    a. How many quarts of red paint must she mix with 12 quarts of yellow paint?

    b. **Writing** To solve part (a), one student wrote the proportion $\frac{2}{3} = \frac{12}{n}$. Explain why this proportion is incorrect and how you would help the student to write a correct proportion.

14. **Health** You would burn about 200 calories by walking for 60 min. About how many calories would you burn if you walk for 15 min?

15. **Choose A, B, or C.** A recipe requires $1\frac{3}{4}$ c of cheese to make 8 servings of enchiladas. Which of the proportions would help you find the cheese needed to make 12 servings?

    A. $\frac{1\frac{3}{4}}{12} = \frac{n}{8}$ **B.** $\frac{1\frac{3}{4}}{8} = \frac{12}{n}$ **C.** $\frac{1\frac{3}{4}}{8} = \frac{n}{12}$

Choose **Use a calculator, paper and pencil, or mental math. Find the value of n in each proportion.**

16. $\frac{6}{9} = \frac{n}{12}$ 17. $\frac{20}{n} = \frac{4}{5}$ 18. $\frac{14}{21} = \frac{35}{n}$

19. $\frac{\frac{1}{2}}{7} = \frac{n}{42}$ 20. $\frac{45}{12} = \frac{30}{n}$ 21. $\frac{n}{12} = \frac{7.5}{8}$

22. Raymond types 84 words in 2 min. He estimates that his history essay is 420 words long. What is the least amount of time it will take Raymond to type his essay?

23. The ratio of boys to girls in a gym class is 5 : 3. There are 27 girls in the class. How many boys are in the class?

24. **Social Studies** Franklin D. Roosevelt won his first election for President in 1932 with about 22,800,000 votes. The ratio of the number of votes he received to the number the other candidates received was 4 : 3. About how many votes did the other candidates receive?

25. Write directions for solving the proportion $\frac{8}{3} = \frac{30}{n}$.

26. A class of 28 students ate only 6 of the 8 large pizzas they had ordered. The Environment Club plans to order pizza. How many large pizzas do you think the Environment Club should order for 45 members? Explain.

Use the data at the left. Round your answers to the nearest pound.

27. **Physical Science** An astronaut weighs 120 lb on Earth. Use proportions to find what her weight would be on Mars and on Jupiter.

28. **Physical Science** An astronaut would weigh 60 lb on Mercury. Find his weight on Earth.

29. **Physical Science** Choose three planets. Find how much you would weigh on each.

30. **Entertainment** A video cassette recorder uses 2 m of tape in 3 min when set on extended play. The tape is about 240 m long. How many hours can you record using extended play?

Astronaut Weight Chart	
Planet	**Weight (lb)**
Earth	100
Mercury	37
Venus	88
Mars	38
Jupiter	264
Saturn	115
Uranus	117
Neptune	118
Pluto	5

CHECKPOINT

Write two ratios equal to each ratio.

1. $2 : 50$ 2. $\frac{3}{5}$ 3. 4 to 12   4. $\frac{6}{9}$

5. **Choose A, B, C, or D.** Which has the most calories per ounce?

 A. cheese: 230 cal/2 oz   B. chicken: 240 cal/6.2 oz

 C. beef: 185 cal/3 oz   D. yogurt: 230 cal/8 oz

Find the value of x in each proportion.

6. $\frac{3}{8} = \frac{57}{x}$ 7. $\frac{4}{3} = \frac{x}{21}$ 8. $\frac{x}{15} = \frac{5}{6}$

9. A high-speed train in Japan takes 50 min to travel 106.3 mi from Morica to Sendi. Suppose a train travels at the same rate from Washington, D.C., to Boston, a distance of 416 mi. How long would the trip take? Round to the nearest minute.

Exploring Similarity

WHAT YOU'LL NEED

✓ Scissors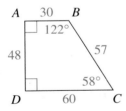

✓ Ruler

THINK AND DISCUSS

The word *similar* is often used in everyday language to compare things. Explore the figures below to discover the mathematical definition for similar.

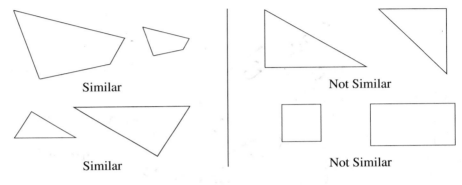

Similar

Not Similar

Similar

Not Similar

1. a. Are similar figures the same shape?

   b. Do similar figures have to be the same size?

2. Examine the similar trapezoids at the left.

   a. ∠B and ∠F are *corresponding angles*. ∠B and ∠E are not corresponding angles. What appears to be true of corresponding angles?

   b. List the pairs of corresponding angles for the trapezoids.

   c. Complete the sentence: Similar figures have corresponding angles that are ■.

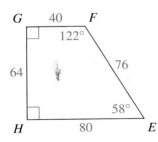

3. a. ∠A corresponds to ∠G, and ∠B corresponds to ∠F. So $\overline{AB}$ corresponds to $\overline{GF}$. $\overline{AB}$ and $\overline{GF}$ are called *corresponding sides*. List the other pairs of corresponding sides.

   b. Write the ratios of the length of each side of *ABCD* to the length of the corresponding side of *GFEH*. What is true of these ratios?

   c. Complete the sentence: The ratios of the lengths of corresponding sides of similar figures are ■.

Figures that are similar have two important properties.

- **The corresponding angles are congruent.**
- **The ratios of the lengths of corresponding sides are equal.**

The symbol for *is similar to* is ~. For the trapezoids on page 377, you can write *ABCD* ~ *GFEH*. The length of $\overline{AB}$, written as *AB*, is the distance from *A* to *B*.

You can use proportions to find missing measures in similar figures since the ratios of corresponding sides are equal.

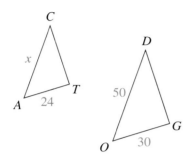

Example △*CAT* ~ △*DOG*. Find the value of *x*.

- Write a proportion.

$$\frac{CA}{DO} = \frac{AT}{OG}$$ $\overline{CA}$ corresponds to $\overline{DO}$.
$\overline{AT}$ corresponds to $\overline{OG}$.

$$\frac{x}{50} = \frac{24}{30}$$ **Substitute.**

$30x = 50 \cdot 24$ **Write the cross products and solve.**

$$\frac{30x}{30} = \frac{1{,}200}{30}$$

$$x = 40$$

4. Suppose *DG* is 36. What is *CT*?

Traditional Russian stacking dolls are similar in shape so that they will nest inside one another.

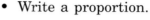 **WORK TOGETHER**

5. Work with a partner. Similar figures will nest inside of each other like the rectangles on the right. The diagonals of similar figures will align.

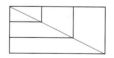

- **a.** Draw rectangles with the dimensions 2 in. by 3 in., 4 in. by 5 in., 1 in. by $1\frac{1}{2}$ in., 4 in. by 6 in., and 6 in. by $7\frac{1}{2}$ in.

- **b.** Cut out the rectangles and nest them to determine which rectangles are similar. Make a list for each group of similar rectangles.

- **c.** Use proportions to confirm that the rectangles in each of your lists are similar.

6. Describe how to determine the corresponding sides in similar figures when you know which angles are corresponding angles.

Each pair of figures is similar. Find the value of *x*.

7.

8.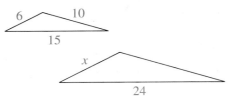

9. Judging by appearance, is *LMNO* ~ *PQRS*? Justify your answer.

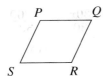

10. △*ABC* ~ △*PQR*. Complete.

a. ∠*A* corresponds to ■.

b. ∠*Q* corresponds to ■.

c. $\overline{AC}$ corresponds to ■.

d. $\overline{PQ}$ corresponds to ■.

e. What is the ratio of the lengths of the corresponding sides?

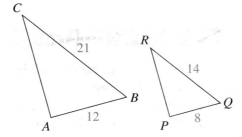

11. Social Studies Students at Horace Mann Middle School want to enlarge a copy of the flag of the Philippines for International Day. They found a copy of the flag in an encyclopedia. To enlarge the flag so that the longest side measures 6 ft, how wide will the students need to make the flag?

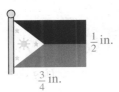

$\frac{1}{2}$ in.

$\frac{3}{4}$ in.

Complete with <, >, or =.

1. −4 + 7 ▪ 11 − (−7)

2. −8 − 14 ▪ 23 − 41

Evaluate each expression for x = 3.

3. 2x + 6   4. 5 − 4x

Solve each proportion.

5. $\frac{13}{x} = \frac{39}{60}$ 6. $\frac{4}{9} = \frac{7}{y}$

7. Two angles of a triangle measure 76° and 22°. Classify the triangle by its angles.

Choose Use a calculator, paper and pencil, or mental math. The pairs of figures below are similar. Find the values of *x* and *y*.

12.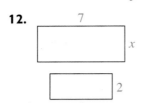

13.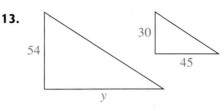

14.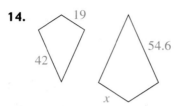

15.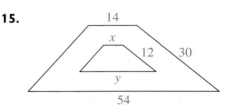

16. **Writing** Are two congruent figures similar? Explain.

17. **Critical Thinking** The ratio of the corresponding sides of two similar triangles is 4 : 9. The sides of the smaller triangle are 10 cm, 16 cm, and 18 cm. Find the perimeter of the larger triangle.

18. Maria wants to know the height of a Saguaro cactus. The triangle formed by the cactus and its shadow is similar to the triangle Maria forms with her shadow. How tall is the cactus in feet?

Draw a pair of polygons to fit each description. If the polygons described cannot be drawn, explain why.

19. rectangles that are similar

20. rectangles that are not similar

21. squares that are not similar

22. regular polygons that are similar

23. regular polygons that are not similar

24. isosceles right triangles that are similar

25. isosceles right triangles that are not similar

Solve. The list at the left shows some possible strategies you can use.

PROBLEM SOLVING STRATEGIES
Make a Table
Use Logical Reasoning
Solve a Simpler Problem
Too Much or Too Little Information
Look for a Pattern
Make a Model
Work Backward
Draw a Diagram
Guess and Test
Simulate a Problem
Use Multiple Strategies
Write an Equation

1. The product of the page numbers on the two facing pages of an opened textbook is 72. What is the page number of the page on the left?

2. **Cooking** A recipe that makes 2 dozen oatmeal cookies calls for $\frac{3}{4}$ c of flour. How much flour will be needed to make 5 dozen cookies?

3. **Sports** Jen-Min is training for the track team. Every day she does sit-ups and runs 3 mi. How many sit-ups does she do in a week?

4. Examine the figures below.

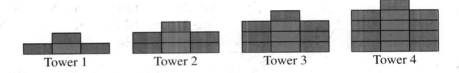

Tower 1   Tower 2   Tower 3   Tower 4

   a. Draw Towers 5 and 6.

   b. Make a chart showing the number of red bricks, the number of blue bricks, and the total number of bricks in each tower.

   c. How many blue bricks will be in Tower 36?

   d. How many red bricks will be used in Tower 10? in Tower 22?

   e. The total number of bricks in a tower is 25. How many blue bricks are in the tower?

   f. **Writing** How can you find the total number of bricks used in any tower if you are given the tower number?

5. Aimee, Bob, and Carl work as an artist, a banker, and a conductor. Aimee and the artist play tennis together. The conductor helped Carl plant his garden. Bob is not the conductor, and he does not know Aimee. What does each person do for a living?

9-5

Exploring Maps and Scale Drawings

THINK AND DISCUSS

A **scale drawing** is an enlarged or reduced drawing of an object. Maps and floor plans are smaller than the actual size. A scale drawing of a human cell is larger than the actual size.

You use a map's scale and proportions to find actual distances. The map distance from Tijuana to Monterrey is 5.1 cm. The proportion below will help you find the actual distance.

$$\frac{\text{map (cm)}}{\text{actual (km)}} \rightarrow \frac{2}{700} = \frac{5.1}{n}$$

1. Find the actual distance from Tijuana to Monterrey.

2. Find the actual distance from Tijuana to Mexico City.

3. Suppose you are making a map of the United States and Mexico. The actual distance from San Francisco to Mexico City is about 1,890 mi. What is the map distance if the scale of the map is 2 in. : 420 mi?

 The first known map was made in Babylon more than 4,000 y ago. It was scratched into a clay tablet and then baked. The map would fit in the palm of your hand.

Source: *Britannica Junior Encyclopedia*

The actual length of the wheel base for the all-terrain vehicle is 234 cm.

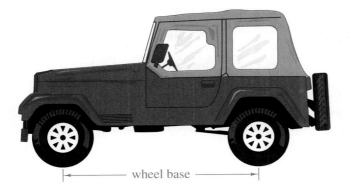

4. **a.** Measure the length of the wheel base to the nearest millimeter, and find the scale of the drawing.

b. Measure the length of the vehicle from the front to the end of the spare tire extension. Find the actual length of the all-terrain vehicle.

WORK TOGETHER

5. **a.** Make a scale drawing of the floor plan of your classroom. Compare your drawing with other groups.

b. Do the scale drawings have the same shape even if the scales are not the same? Explain.

ON YOUR OWN

The scale of a map is 2 cm : 15 km. Find the actual distances for the following map distances.

6. 8 cm   **7.** 1.3 cm   **8.** 5 mm   **9.** 24.4 m

A scale drawing has a scale of $\frac{1}{2}$ in. : 10 ft. Find the length on the drawing for each actual length.

10. 20 ft   **11.** 10 ft   **12.** 5 ft   **13.** 45 ft

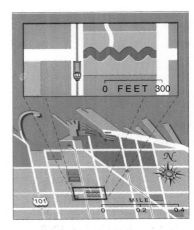

Lombard St. in San Francisco is popular with tourists. It is 412.5 ft long.

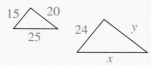

Mixed REVIEW

1. Find the values of x and y in the similar triangles.

15 20
25 24 y
x

Estimate.

2. $16.12 \div 5.1$

3. $8.2 \cdot 17.3$

Solve.

4. $3x + 2 = 17$

5. $\frac{x}{5} + 5 = 21$

6. A class of 23 students includes 11 students who are in the Computer Club and 14 who are in the Math Club. Five students belong to both clubs. How many students are *not* members of either club?

14. **Writing** Describe what you would do to draw a map of the route from your home to school. What scale would you use?

15. **Critical Thinking** Ramon plans to make a scale model of the solar system. The average distance from the Sun to Mercury is 3.6×10^7 mi. The average distance from the Sun to Pluto is 3.7×10^9 mi. What do you suggest Ramon use for a scale? Why?

16. **Architecture** The scale drawing shows the first floor of a house. The dimensions of the carport are 20 ft by 25 ft.

  a. Complete: The scale is ■ : 5 ft.

  b. Copy the floor plan on your paper. Write the actual dimensions in place of the scale dimensions.

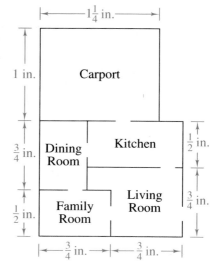

A space suit, which includes a helmet and a backpack that supplies oxygen, weighs 247 lb on Earth. The ratio of an object's weight on Earth's surface to its weight on the Moon's surface is 6 : 1. **Estimate how much the space suit weighs on the Moon.**

Far-Out Clothes

Computers help designers save time and money as they improve space suits for future space travelers.

Clothes designed for space must allow astronauts to move and breathe in an airless environment. An astronaut's suit must protect the astronaut from the sun's harsh rays as well as from micrometeorites, tiny bits of matter that travel at speeds up to 150,000 mi/h.

For a computer image that is $\frac{1}{8}$ of the actual size, the designer knows that all other dimensions will have the same ratio.

17. a. Suppose the computer image of the pants of a space suit is 5 in. long. How long are the pants?

  b. An astronaut's arm measures 24 in. long. Find the arm length in the computer image for a space suit.

9-6

Modeling Percents

THINK AND DISCUSS

A **percent** is a ratio that compares a number to 100. You can write the ratio $\frac{25}{100}$ as 25%.

1. Each graph below contains 100 squares. Write a ratio and a percent to describe the shaded part.

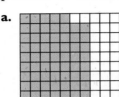   **a.**   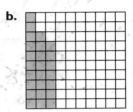   **b.**   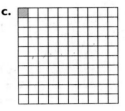   **c.**

2. Write a ratio and a percent to describe the unshaded part of each figure above.

$$\frac{75}{100} = \frac{3}{4} = 75\%$$

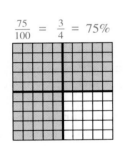

You can rewrite any ratio as a percent. The figure at the left shows that $\frac{3}{4} = \frac{75}{100}$, which is 75%. You can use equal ratios to change ratios to percents.

$$\frac{3}{4} \overset{\times 25}{\underset{\times 25}{=}} \frac{75}{100} = 75\%$$

Write each ratio as a percent.

3. $\frac{1}{4}$ **4.** $\frac{1}{2}$ **5.** $\frac{3}{5}$ **6.** $\frac{14}{20}$

Some percents are less than 1%.

7. a. Which color represents 0.5%?

    b. Which color represents 5%?

    c. Which color represents 50%?

    d. How many times larger is 50% than 0.5%?

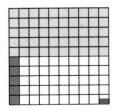

You can model percents greater than 100% using two graphs.

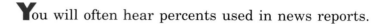

100%   +   25%   = 125%

8. Use graph paper to model 258%.

You will often hear percents used in news reports.

9. Write the percents in each passage using numerals.

   a. Consumer Issues Prices on consumer goods rose a tenth of a percent during the month of March.

   b. Biology The number of nesting pairs of bald eagles in the lower 48 states has increased over three hundred percent since the Environmental Protection Agency listed bald eagles as an endangered species in 1978.

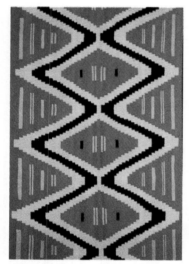

The design is from a Navajo Indian blanket made between 1880 and 1890. **Estimate the percent of red in the design.**

WORK TOGETHER

Work with a partner to shade 3 squares on a 10 × 10 square of graph paper so that the total area of the 3 squares covers 50% of the graph.

10. How big is each square?

ON YOUR OWN

Write the percent of each figure that is shaded.

11. 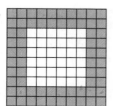   **12.** 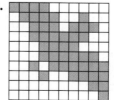   **13.**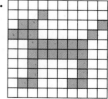

Draw figures on 10 × 10 squares of graph paper that represent each of the following percents.

14. 35%   **15.** 78%   **16.** 187%

17. a. What percent of the square at the right does the yellow part represent? the green part?

   b. What fraction of the square is the yellow section?

   c. What fraction equals $33\frac{1}{3}\%$?

   d. What fraction equals $66\frac{2}{3}\%$?

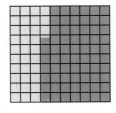

Rewrite each ratio as a percent.

18. $\frac{3}{5}$ **19.** $\frac{1}{2}$ **20.** $\frac{21}{25}$ **21.** $\frac{7}{10}$

Find what percent of a dollar each set of coins makes.

22. 2 quarters   **23.** 5 quarters and 2 dimes

24. 3 quarters, 2 dimes, and 1 nickel

Estimate the percent that is shaded in each figure.

25. 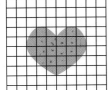   **26.** 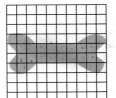   **27.**

28. a. Writing Describe a situation that requires a percent less than 1%.

   b. Describe a situation that requires a percent greater than 100%.

29. a. Draw and shade the first letter of your name on a 10 × 10 square of graph paper so that more than 30% of the graph is shaded.

   b. Draw and shade the last letter of your name on a 10 × 10 square of graph paper so that less than 30% of the graph is shaded.

30. A triangle with a height of 8 units and a base of 4 units is drawn and shaded on a 10 × 10 square. What percent of the square is shaded?

Mixed REVIEW

Write each number in scientific notation.

1. The speed of light is 299,790,000 m/s.

2. The star Alpha Centauri is about 40.6 trillion km from our solar system.

A floor plan has the scale 1.5 in. : 1 ft.

3. What are the actual dimensions of a room that measures 21 in. × 24 in. on the floor plan?

4. What are the floor plan dimensions of a room measuring 12 ft × 15 ft?

5. Seven teams are in the tennis-doubles playoffs. Each team plays every other team twice. What is the total number of games played?

9-7

Fractions, Decimals, and Percents

THINK AND DISCUSS

You can use fractions or percents to compare the calories from fat in a slice of cheese pizza.

1. Write the number of calories from fat in a cheese pizza as a fraction.

To write the data as a percent, use the fraction you found in Problem 1 and proportions.

$$\frac{\text{calories from fat}}{\text{total calories}} \longrightarrow \frac{36}{145} = \frac{n}{100}$$

$$36 \cdot 100 = 145n \quad \textbf{Write the cross products.}$$

$$n \approx 24.82758621$$

Fat accounts for 24.8% of the calories in one slice of cheese pizza.

2. Suppose you are writing an article about the nutrition found in pizza. Would you use fractions or percents? Why?

You can rewrite a percent as a fraction.

One slice of a 12 in. cheese pizza has 145 calories. There are 36 calories from fat.

Example 1

A sheep sleeps 25% of a day. A lion sleeps $83\frac{1}{3}$% of a day. What fraction of a day does each animal sleep?

• Write each percent as a fraction with the denominator of 100.

• $25\% = \frac{25}{100} = \frac{1}{4}$

• $83\frac{1}{3}\% = \frac{83\frac{1}{3}}{100}$

$$= 83\frac{1}{3} \div 100$$

$$= \frac{250}{3} \times \frac{1}{100}$$

$$= \frac{250}{300}, \text{ or } \frac{5}{6}$$

A sheep sleeps $\frac{1}{4}$ of a day. A lion sleeps $\frac{5}{6}$ of a day.

3. An elephant sleeps 12.5% of a day. What fraction of a day does an elephant sleep?

FLASHBACK

Dividing by a number is the same as multiplying by its reciprocal.

To write a decimal as a percent, write the decimal as a fraction. Then multiply or divide the numerator and denominator by the same power of 10 to change the denominator to 100.

Example 2

Paper occupies 0.5 of an average landfill. Fast food packaging occupies 0.0025 of an average landfill.

What percent of space does each take in a landfill?

- $0.5 = \dfrac{5}{10}$

  $= \dfrac{5 \times 10}{10 \times 10}$

  $= \dfrac{50}{100}$

  $0.5 = 50\%$

- $0.0025 = \dfrac{25}{10{,}000}$

  $= \dfrac{25 \div 100}{10{,}000 \div 100}$

  $= \dfrac{0.25}{100}$

  $0.0025 = 0.25\%$

Paper occupies 50% of a landfill's space. Fast food packaging occupies 0.25% of a landfill's space.

To write a percent as a decimal, first write it as a fraction with a denominator of 100.

Example 3

Write $37\frac{1}{2}\%$ as a decimal.

- $37\frac{1}{2}\% = \dfrac{37\frac{1}{2}}{100}$

  $= \dfrac{37.5}{100}$ Write the fraction in the numerator as a decimal.

  $= \dfrac{37.5 \times 10}{100 \times 10}$ Multiply the numerator and the denominator by 10 so that there is no decimal in the numerator.

  $= \dfrac{375}{1{,}000}$

  $37\frac{1}{2}\% = 0.375$

FLASHBACK

$\frac{1}{2} = 0.5$

WORK TOGETHER

Work with a partner. Find each of the following.

4. What percent of the students in your class wear glasses?

5. What percent of the students in your class are wearing blue shirts?

6. What percent of the students in your class play a musical instrument?

⌐T R Y THESE

Mental Math **Write each decimal number as a percent.**

7. 0.28   **8.** 1.25   **9.** 0.33   **10.** 2.89

Write each fraction as a percent.

11. $\frac{27}{50}$ **12.** $\frac{17}{20}$ **13.** $\frac{33}{40}$ **14.** $\frac{5}{8}$

15. **Choose A, B, C, or D.** Examine the figure at the left. Which set of numbers below represents the part of the graph that is shaded?

    A. 3.8%, $\frac{38}{100}$, 0.38   **B.** 38%, $\frac{38}{100}$, 0.38

    C. 38%, $\frac{38}{100}$, 0.038   **D.** 0.38%, $\frac{38}{100}$, 0.038

16. **Nutrition** The Delux brand vitamin tablet supplies 0.5% of the Recommended Daily Allowance (RDA) for phosphorus.

    a. Write the percent as a fraction.

    b. Write the percent as a decimal.

    c. Which way do you prefer to see the number for the Recommended Daily Allowance for phosphorus, as a fraction, as a decimal, or as a percent? Why?

Mixed REVIEW

Complete.

1. $4 \cdot 3 = 3 \cdot$ ■

2. $5 - (-2) = 5 +$ ■

Use graph paper to model each percent.

3. 45%   **4.** 11.5%

Solve.

5. $\frac{3}{5} = \frac{9}{x}$ **6.** $\frac{8}{3} = \frac{x}{24}$

7. A club has 100 members. Each of the 5 officers calls 6 other members to help them decorate for a club party. What percent of the club members help decorate?

⌐O N YOUR OWN

17. **Nutrition** The table below gives nutritional information for one serving of oatmeal.

	Protein	Iron	Calcium	Vitamin A	Copper
% U.S. RDA	6	50	20	25	8

    a. Write each percent as a fraction and as a decimal.

    b. How many servings of oatmeal would you need to eat in order to have all the recommended vitamin A for a day?

18. **Writing** Does 0.4 equal 0.4%? Explain.

Choose Use a calculator, paper and pencil, or mental math to write each percent as a fraction in simplest form and as a decimal.

19. 45%   **20.** 62.5%   **21.** 173%   **22.** $12\frac{1}{2}\%$

Write each number as a percent. Round to the nearest tenth of a percent where necessary.

23. $\frac{7}{8}$ **24.** 0.375   **25.** $\frac{17}{33}$ **26.** 2.5

27. Activity Collect 5 examples of percents used in a newspaper. Display your examples in class.

28. Nutrition Before a race, runners usually eat foods high in carbohydrates. A gram of fat has 9 calories. A gram of protein and a gram of carbohydrates each have 4 calories.

  a. How many calories does one serving of macaroni and cheese have? one serving of spaghetti with meatballs?

  b. What percent of the calories in each meal is carbohydrates? Round to the nearest percent.

  c. Which meal is the better choice for a runner? Why?

29. Investigation (p. 364) One left-handed person stated, "This is a right-handed world." Interview at least 5 left-handed people. What percent agree with the statement? Ask each person who agrees to name 4 products, like right-handed scissors, that cause them to have this opinion.

Macaroni and Cheese
Protein	17 g
Fat	33 g
Carbohydrates	40 g

Spaghetti with Meatballs
Protein	19 g
Fat	12 g
Carbohydrates	39 g

CHECKPOINT

1. A map's scale is 1 in. : 15 mi. Two towns are 3.5 in. apart on the map. What is the actual distance between them?

2. $\triangle ABC \sim \triangle FDE$. Find x and y.

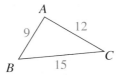

Write each fraction as a percent.

3. $\frac{4}{5}$ **4.** $\frac{1}{250}$ **5.** $\frac{1}{3}$ **6.** $\frac{14}{25}$

What's Ahead

- Solving problems using more than one strategy

9-8

Use Multiple Strategies

Sometimes you may need to use more than one strategy to solve a problem.

> Jack and his cousin Sam live in west Texas. Their homes are 50 mi apart. One spring day, Jack called Sam suggesting that they each ride their bicycles to a state park that is halfway between their homes. Sam averages 10 mi/h on his bicycle, and Jack averages 12 mi/h. In order to meet at 1 P.M., what time should each boy leave his home?

READ

Read and understand the given information. Summarize the problem.

Read the problem carefully.

1. How far apart do Jack and Sam live?

2. What rate does each boy average when riding his bicycle?

PLAN

Decide on a strategy to solve the problem.

Decide on strategies.   Write an equation to find how long each boy should ride.

Work backward to find what time each boy should leave his home.

SOLVE

Try out the strategy.

Each boy travels halfway, which is 25 mi. Let x represent the number of hours that Jack should ride his bicycle.

$$12x = 25$$
$$\frac{12x}{12} = \frac{25}{12}$$
$$x = 2\frac{1}{12}$$

Jack should ride his bicycle $2\frac{1}{12}$ h, which is 2 h 5 min.

Work backward to find what time Jack should leave home.

Jack should leave at 10:55 A.M.

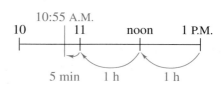

3. What time should Sam leave his home to meet Jack at 1 P.M.?

4. Did you solve the problem correctly? Add the traveling time to the starting time for Jack and Sam. Will both boys arrive at the state park at 1:00 P.M.? You will have to think, "One hour past 12:00 can be expressed as 1:00 or 13:00."

◄ **LOOK BACK**

Think about how you solved this problem.

TRY THESE

Use any strategy to solve each problem. Show all your work.

5. **a.** A fenced-in rectangular area has a perimeter of 40 ft. The fence has a post every 4 ft. How many posts are there?

   b. Since there must be a post at the corners, what do you think the length and width of the field are?

   c. Are there any other possible answers to part (b)? Explain.

6. A kite and its tail total 32 ft in length. The tail is 18 ft longer than the length of the kite's body. How long is the kite's tail?

7. A grocer stacks oranges in the shape of a square pyramid. How many oranges will she use if one side of the base has 6 oranges?

The smaller the ratio of the weight of a kite to its surface area the better the kite will fly. **Which will fly better, a kite that weighs 5 oz with a surface area of 2 ft² or one that weighs 14 oz with a surface area of 16 ft²?**

Source: *Scholastic Dynamath*

ON YOUR OWN

Use any strategy to solve each problem. Show all your work.

8. **Consumer Issues** Tanya, the Science Club treasurer, found that the bill for 18 sweatshirts ordered by the club had two digits blurred by water damage. Tanya was sure that the first and last digits were the same. What do you think the total price is? Explain your choice.

$■68.9■

9. **Social Studies** At the beginning of every new term, each of the nine judges on the Supreme Court shakes hands with every other judge. How many handshakes take place?

10. Find a two-digit even number such that the difference of the digits is prime and the sum of the digits is also prime.

11. How many triangles are in the design at the left?

12. a. What is the sum of the three consecutive numbers 8, 9, and 10?

b. Find three consecutive numbers that have a sum of 48.

c. Can you find three consecutive numbers that have any given sum? Why or why not?

13. In a magic square all the rows, columns, and major diagonals have the same sum. Find the value of x and y.

15	$4x$	13
$5x$	12	14
11	16	$y + 2$

Mixed REVIEW

Find each answer.

1. $|-6| + 12$

2. $-3 \cdot 8 \div (-4)$

Find the perimeter of each figure.

3. a regular pentagon with sides 4.6 cm

4. a rectangle with length 4.2 m and width 3.8 m

5. Data File 3 (pp. 90–91) What percent of his field goal attempts did Shaquille O'Neal make in 1991–1992? Round to the nearest percent.

6. Write $66\frac{2}{3}\%$ as a fraction.

7. How many different ways can you make a rectangle with 12 toothpicks? Draw and label the rectangles.

14. Using only the digits 1, 2, 3, and 4, find all the 4-digit numbers that are divisible by 4. You may use a digit only once in each number.

15. Examine the numbers below and look for patterns.

row 1	1
row 2	1 3
row 3	1 3 5
row 4	1 3 5 7
row 5	1 3 5 7 9
row 6	■

a. Write the sixth row.

b. What is the last number in the 11th row? in the 23rd row?

c. What is the sum of the numbers in the 4th row? in the 10th row?

d. How can you find the sum of any row when you know the row number?

• Finding the percent of a number using proportions

• Finding what percent one number is of another using proportions

Percents and Proportions

THINK AND DISCUSS

You will often find percent data presented in graphs.

1. What did most of the people surveyed have on their gift list?

2. What do about $\frac{1}{3}$ of the people have on their list? $\frac{1}{4}$ of the people?

3. How many people were surveyed?

4. Why do you think the sum of the percents is greater than 100%?

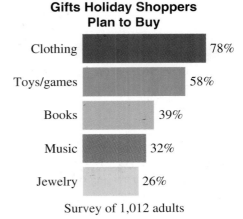

Gifts Holiday Shoppers Plan to Buy

Clothing 78%
Toys/games 58%
Books 39%
Music 32%
Jewelry 26%

Survey of 1,012 adults

Source: *USA Today*

In 1991, global toy sales totaled $54 million. The average spent on each child in the United States was $348; in Japan, $282; in Germany, $441.

Source: *U.S. News & World Report*

To find the number of the people surveyed who have clothing on their gift list, find 78% of 1,012, the total number of people surveyed. Think of the people who have clothing on their list as *part* of the *whole* group surveyed. Use the following proportion.

$$\frac{\text{part}}{\text{whole}} \rightarrow \frac{n}{1{,}012} = \frac{78}{100} \leftarrow 78\% = \frac{78}{100}$$

5. **a.** Solve the proportion to find the number of people who have clothing on their gift list.

   b. Look back at your answer to part (a). Should you round your answer to the nearest whole number? Why or why not?

6. About how many people have music on their gift list?

7. **Critical Thinking** Would a department store manager be more interested in the percents or in the actual number of people who responded in each category? Explain.

Suppose you have data that you want to express as a percent. You can use a proportion.

Example Eighteen students in a class of 25 students plan to go on a class hiking trip. What percent of the students plan to go on the trip?

- $\dfrac{\text{part}}{\text{whole}} \ \begin{array}{c}\rightarrow\\\rightarrow\end{array}\ \dfrac{18}{25} = \dfrac{n}{100}$ Write a proportion to solve.

$18 \cdot 100 = 25n$ Write the cross products and solve.

$\dfrac{1{,}800}{25} = \dfrac{25n}{25}$

$n = 72$

The United States has 13,592 mi of National Scenic Trails, which are continuous protected trails for non-motorized travel. The American Discovery Trail is waiting for congressional approval. The trail is 4,920 mi long stretching from Delaware to San Francisco.

72% of the students plan to go on the trip.

⌐WORK TOGETHER

Take two surveys of 20 students. You may survey the same students twice. Ask which gifts they would like to receive. Use the categories clothing, toys/games, books, music, and jewelry.

- In the first survey, allow the students to choose more than one category.

- In the second survey, allow the students to choose only one category.

8. a. For both surveys, express the results as percents and show the results in a graph.

  b. What difference does the wording of your survey make in the appearance of the graphs?

  c. Compare the results of your first survey with the **Holiday Gift List** graph on page 395. Are there any similarities between what the students want and what the adults in the survey plan to buy? Explain.

⌐TRY THESE

9. Choose the proportion that will help you find 45% of 80. Explain your choice.

      A. $\dfrac{45}{80} = \dfrac{n}{100}$ **B.** $\dfrac{n}{80} = \dfrac{45}{100}$ **C.** $\dfrac{80}{n} = \dfrac{45}{100}$ **D.** $\dfrac{n}{45} = \dfrac{100}{80}$

10. Choose the proportion that will help you find what percent 13 is of 20. Explain your choice.

A. $\frac{13}{20} = \frac{n}{100}$ **B.** $\frac{n}{20} = \frac{13}{100}$ **C.** $\frac{13}{n} = \frac{100}{20}$ **D.** $\frac{n}{13} = \frac{20}{100}$

11. a. Discussion The number of students in this year's seventh grade class is 110% of the number in last year's class. When you write 110% as a ratio, what number is in the denominator? Why?

b. Do you think there will be more or fewer students in this year's class? Why?

c. There were 260 students in last year's class. How many students are in this year's class?

ON YOUR OWN

Write a proportion. Use mental math to solve.

12. What is 8% of 25?

13. What percent of 230 is 23?

14. Find 30% of 40.

15. 24 is what percent of 32?

Choose Use a calculator, paper and pencil, or mental math.

16. Social Studies In 1992, voters elected 105 new members to the House of Representatives. The total number of people in the House of Representatives is 435. What percent were new members? Round to the nearest percent.

17. What percent of the numbers from 1 to 20 are prime?

18. What is 120% of 34?

19. Find 37.5% of 12.

20. 5 is what percent of 15?

21. What percent of 25 is 23?

22. Social Studies Mesa, Arizona, is one of the fastest growing cities in the United States. By 1990, the population had grown 460% from its 1970 total of 63,000. What was the population in 1990?

23. Writing Write a word problem that you could solve by using the proportion $\frac{n}{60} = \frac{12}{100}$.

Mixed REVIEW

Estimate each answer.

1. $\frac{3}{8} \cdot 30\frac{4}{5}$

2. $123 \div (-43)$

Find the area of each figure.

3. a triangle with base 5 in. and height 4.8 in.

4. a square 26.3 cm on each side

5. A student spends $\frac{3}{8}$ of her money on a sweatshirt and $\frac{1}{2}$ of the remaining amount on a cassette. She now has $15. How much money did she have originally?

24. **Data File 9 (pp. 362–363)** For the Teen Survey, 2,046 teens with one or more brothers and/or sisters responded.

    a. How many teens are close to their sibling(s)? Why should you round your answer to the nearest whole number?

    b. **Critical Thinking** How many teens responded that they would "rather have been an only child?" Does this mean that the rest of the teens were happy to have sibling(s)? Why or why not?

    c. **Writing** Write a question that can be answered by analyzing the survey.

25. **Investigation (p. 364)** Use the results of your survey on left-handed people, Exercise 16, page 367. Suppose the ratio of left-handed people to the total number of people in the United States is the same as the ratio you found in your survey of 25 people. About how many left-handed people are there? The population of the United States is about 249 million.

What do children spend the most on?

The Super Shoppers—Kids!

A survey of 1,440 American families reveals the purchasing power of children from ages 4 to 12. Children in the United States have an estimated income of $14.4 billion. They save $5.5 billion and spend $8.9 billion. Children spend the largest portion of their money on snacks, $3.2 billion. They buy $2.6 billion worth of toys, games, and craft supplies. Children spend $1.2 billion on new clothes. For entertainment—movies, sports events, and video arcades—children spend $1.4 billion. Other unspecified items account for $0.5 billion of children's spending.

26. **a.** **Consumer Issues** What percent of $8.9 billion do children spend for each category? Round to the nearest percent.

    b. Make a graph of the data.

    c. What type of graph did you use? Why?

    d. **Writing** Which is a better way of communicating the information about the children's purchasing power, an article or a graph? Explain.

More About Percents

 Many schools and businesses are recycling paper. Every ton of recycled paper saves 17 trees. **If your school recycled a ton of paper a month, how many trees would be saved in a school year?**

THINK AND DISCUSS

Recycle! Those of us who live in the United States recycle about 25.6% of our paper waste. We recycle about 18.4 million tons of paper each year. About how much paper waste do we generate?

In this question, you are to find the whole, or the total amount of paper waste. You know the part, 18.4 million tons of paper. You can use a proportion to solve the problem.

$$\frac{\text{part}}{\text{whole}} \rightarrow \frac{18.4}{n} = \frac{25.6}{100} \leftarrow 25.6\% = \frac{25.6}{100}$$

$$18.4 \cdot 100 = 25.6n$$

$$18.4 \; \boxed{\times} \; 100 \; \boxed{\div} \; 25.6 \; \boxed{=} \; \textit{71.875}$$

We generate about 71.9 million tons of paper waste each year.

1. People in the United States recycle about 62.5% of the aluminum beverage cans they use. About 55 million cans are recycled each year. How many cans are used each year?

You must read percent problems carefully. Ask yourself, "Do I want to find the part, the whole, or the percent?" Keep this question in mind as you read each problem below.

Problem A   A class has 15 girls. Girls make up 48% of the class. How many students are in the class?

Problem B   A class has 30 students. There are 18 girls in the class. What percent of the class is girls?

Problem C   A class has 24 students. Boys make up 55% of the class. How many boys are in the class?

2. Which problem requires a percent sign in the answer?

3. Which problem asks you to find a part of the class?

4. Which problem asks you to find the total number of students in a class?

You can use proportions to find information about sales.

Example 1

The sale price of a winter coat is $72. This is 80% of the original price. What was the original price?

- $\dfrac{\text{part}}{\text{whole}} \longrightarrow \quad \dfrac{72}{n} = \dfrac{80}{100}$ The sale price is *part* of the original price.

$$72 \cdot 100 = 80n$$

$$\dfrac{7{,}200}{80} = \dfrac{80n}{80}$$

$$90 = n$$

The original price of the coat was $90.

Price cut 40%

Price is now
$14.95

Advertisements like "40% off" or "Price reduced 40%" tell you the percent a price was reduced. To find the original price, you must do two steps.

- First, find the percent the new price is of the original price by subtracting the percent the price is reduced from 100%.

- Then use proportions to find the original price.

Example 2

Use a calculator to find the original price of the telephone. Round to the nearest cent.

- $100\% - 40\% = 60\%$ ← The sale price is 60% of the original price.

- $\dfrac{\text{part}}{\text{whole}} \longrightarrow \dfrac{14.95}{n} = \dfrac{60}{100}$

$$14.95 \cdot 100 = 60n$$

14.95 ☒ 100 ÷ 60 = *24.916667*

The original price of the telephone was $24.92.

TRY THESE

Write a proportion and solve.

5. 80% of what number is 15?   **6.** 80% of 15 is what number?

7. Sneakers cost $36.74, which is 25% off the original price.

   a. What percent of the original price is the sale price?

   b. What was the original price?

Write a proportion and solve.

8. What percent of 25 is 21?   9. 54 is 75% of what number?

10. What is 225% of 48?   11. 48 is what percent of 144?

12. Find 65% of 320.   13. $12\frac{1}{2}$% of what number is 424?

Choose Use calculator, paper and pencil, or mental math.

14. **Consumer Issues** The sale price of a shirt is $18. This is 80% of the original price. Find the original price.

15. The average daily attendance at Randolph Middle School is 92% of the school's enrollment. The average attendance is 422 students. What is the school's enrollment?

16. **a.** 50 is what percent of 75?   **b.** 75 is what percent of 50?

  c. Which results in a percent greater than 100%, part (a) or (b)? Why?

17. **Consumer Issues** The price of a new version of a computer game is 120% of the price of the first version. The new version costs $48. What was the cost of the first version?

18. **Consumer Issues** The regular price of a calculator is $15.40. It goes on sale for 30% off of the regular price. What is the sale price?

19. **Consumer Issues** Natasha bought a new tape player on Friday. It cost $72. On Monday, she found that the tape player was on sale. The sale price is $54.

  a. What percent of the original price was the sale price?

  b. The store will give Natasha a refund of the difference between the price she paid for the tape player and the sale price. How much money will she get as a refund?

20. **a.** **Consumer Issues** What was the original price of the television in the advertisement at the right?

  b. Rewrite the ad using percents.

  c. **Writing** Which do you think is more effective, using "Save $30" or using percents? Why?

Solve each equation.

1. $y + 5 = 9$

2. $3x = 6$

Use Data File 7
(pp. 278–279)

3. About how many cameras were sold in 1991?

4. What percent of the cameras sold in 1991 were instant cameras?

5. Myra and Leah leave home at the same time walking in opposite directions. They each walk at the rate of 6 mi/h. How far apart are they after 20 min?

TECHNOLOGY

Percent of Change

• Using percents to describe increases and decreases

• Using computers to explore percent of change

WHAT YOU'LL NEED

✓ **Computer**

✓ **Spreadsheet software**

✓ **Tape measure**

Pythons can grow as long as 33 ft and swallow prey weighing up to 120 lb.

THINK AND DISCUSS

A 10-foot snake and a computer may not seem to have much in common, but zoologists use computers to help study all kinds of animals. The computer spreadsheet shows the length, in inches, of a python called Scooter.

	A	B	C	D
	Year	**Start of Year**	**End of Year**	**Change**
1				
2	1st	20	40	20
3	2nd	40	50	10
4	3rd	50	64	■
5	4th	64	80	■
6	5th	80	100	■
7	6th	100	121	■

1. **a.** How do you find the numbers in the **Change** column?

   b. Write a formula to have the computer find the entries for the **Change** column.

   c. **Computer** Print out the completed spreadsheet.

2. The drawing shows Scooter's growth during both the first and fifth years. In which year was Scooter's growth the more noticeable? Why?

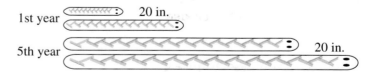

1st year ⟨⟩ 20 in.

5th year ⟨⟩ 20 in.

3. **a.** Write a ratio of the change in Scooter's growth in her first year to her length at the start of that year.

   b. **Mental Math** Write the ratio you found in part (a) as a percent.

You have found the *percent of increase* in Scooter's growth for her first year. **Percent of change** is the percent something increases or decreases from its original measure or amount. Finding percent of change requires two steps.

• Subtract to find the amount of change.
• Use the proportion $\dfrac{\text{amount of change}}{\text{original amount}} = \dfrac{\text{percent of change}}{100}$.

4. a. Use a calculator to find the percent of increase in Scooter's growth for her second year.

b. Write the calculator steps you used in part (a).

You can use the formula (D3*100)/B3 to have the computer find the percent of change for Scooter's growth in the second year.

	A	. . .	E
			% of
1	**Year**	. . .	**Change**
2	1st	. . .	
3	2nd	. . .	
4	3rd	. . .	
5	4th	. . .	
6	5th	. . .	
7	6th	. . .	

5. a. How is the formula for finding the percent of change like the calculator steps you wrote in 4(b)?

b. Add column E to your spreadsheet. Find the percent of increase in Scooter's growth for each year.

c. Make bar graphs of the data in columns D **(Change)** and E **(% of Change)**. How do the two graphs show change differently?

The percent a price decreases when an item goes on sale is an example of *percent of decrease*.

6. The sale price for the aquarium advertised at the right is $60.

a. What is the ratio of the amount of decrease to the original, or regular, price?

b. Find the percent of decrease.

WORK TOGETHER

Work in pairs. Measure each other's height when each of you is relaxed. Then measure each other's height again when each of you is stretching to stand as tall as you can.

7. Find the percent of change in your height. Round to the nearest percent.

Evaluate for $m = 8$ and $n = -2$.

1. $6m + 8 + 5n$
2. $18 - 3(m - n)$

Write as a mixed number.

3. $\frac{19}{6}$ 4. $\frac{24}{5}$

Find each answer.

5. What is 40% of 360?

6. 45 is what percent of 360?

7. A student is participating in a 100-mi fund-raising walk. She walks 40% of the distance the first day and $\frac{1}{3}$ of the remaining distance the second day. How many more miles does she have to walk?

ON YOUR OWN

Find the percent of change. State whether the change is an increase or a decrease.

8. **Business** A worker earning $5.00/h receives a raise. He now earns $6.50/h.

9. **Social Studies** The population of Fresno, California, was 762,565 in 1980. The population in 1990 was 836,231. Round to the nearest tenth of a percent.

10. **Sports** A football player gained 1,200 yd last season and 900 yd this season.

11. **Business** The High Hopes Kite Store opened five years ago. The owner uses a computer to keep track of yearly sales, but the computer has a bug. Some cells print @@@ instead of numbers. Copy the spreadsheet. Fill in the correct numbers.

	A	B	C	D
	Year	Sales ($)	Change From Last Year ($)	Change From Last Year (%)
1				
2	1	200,000	(not open last year)	(not open last year)
3	2	240,000	40,000	@@@
4	3	@@@	@@@	25
5	4	330,000	30,000	@@@

12. **Writing** How you would find the percent of change in the number of students in your school from last year to this year?

CHECKPOINT

1. **Data File 4 (pp. 142–143)** What percent of the items reported lost to the East Japan Railway Co. in 1989 were umbrellas? Round to the nearest percent.

2. What percent of 72 is 54?   3. 7 is 35% of what number?

4. A $30 sweater is marked down to $12. What is the percent of decrease?

Practice

Write each ratio in simplest form.

1. $\frac{6}{15}$
2. 8 to 14
3. 3 : 15
4. $\frac{8}{36}$
5. 24 to 6

Find the unit rate.

6. earn $63.00 in 15 h
7. travel 396 mi on 22 gal of fuel
8. 12 lb lost in 8 wk

Find the value of *n*.

9. $\frac{3}{5} = \frac{n}{15}$
10. $\frac{10}{n} = \frac{15}{21}$
11. $\frac{n}{9} = \frac{8}{6}$
12. $\frac{12}{9} = \frac{20}{n}$

Find the missing lengths in the similar figures.

13.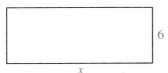

14.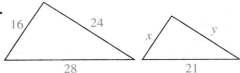

Write each number as a percent.

15. $\frac{18}{25}$
16. $\frac{3}{10}$
17. $\frac{45}{60}$
18. 0.03
19. 0.734

Write each percent as a decimal and as a fraction in simplest form.

20. 64%
21. 3%
22. 0.5%
23. $24\frac{1}{2}\%$
24. $56\frac{1}{4}\%$

Write a proportion and solve.

25. What is 6% of 50?
26. What percent of 48 is 30?
27. 24 is 80% of what number?

28. What is $66\frac{2}{3}\%$ of 180?
29. What percent of 25 is 40?
30. 96 is 120% of what number?

31. a. While practicing for the swim team competitions, a student's time for the 50-m freestyle changed from 45 s to 38 s. What was her percent of change? Round to the nearest tenth of a percent.

  b. Was the percent of change an increase or a decrease?

9-12 **C**ircle Graphs

What's Ahead

• Analyzing and constructing circle graphs

1991 World Production of Automobiles

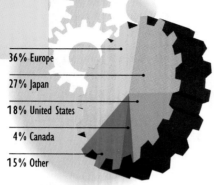

36% Europe

27% Japan

18% United States

4% Canada

15% Other

World Total: 48,400,000

⚡ FLASHBACK

A *central angle* is an angle whose vertex is at the center of a circle.

THINK AND DISCUSS

Wheels! Not only do automobiles fascinate most of us, but motor vehicles are also an important part of world commerce.

1. Where were the most automobiles produced in 1991?

2. Canada's production was what fraction of the United States production?

3. About how many automobiles were produced in the United States in 1991? in Japan?

A circle graph shows the parts of a whole. To make a circle graph, you must know the sum of the measures of the central angles of a circle.

4. **a.** What is the sum of the measures of the central angles in the circle at the right?

   b. What percent is each angle of the whole circle?

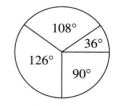

You use a circle graph to display data that represent parts of a whole.

Example The "Big Three" automakers have export sales of $23 billion. General Motors has 43%, Ford 37%, and Chrysler 20% of the sales. Show the data in a circle graph.

• Find the measure of each central angle. Round to the nearest degree.

General Motors	**Ford**	**Chrysler**
$\dfrac{n}{360} = \dfrac{43}{100}$	$\dfrac{n}{360} = \dfrac{37}{100}$	$\dfrac{n}{360} = \dfrac{20}{100}$
$n = 154.8$	$n = 133.2$	$n = 72°$
$n \approx 155°$	$n \approx 133°$	

Use a compass to draw a circle. Draw the central angles with a protractor.

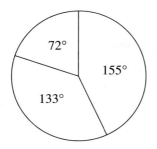

72°

155°

133°

Label each section. Add any necessary information.

Export Sales of the Big Three Automakers

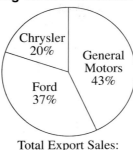

Chrysler 20%

General Motors 43%

Ford 37%

Total Export Sales: $23 Billion

In the year 1900, 38% of U.S. cars were electric, only 22% gasoline, and the rest were powered by steam. The next century will see a popular return of electric cars. By the year 2003, 10% of all the new cars in California must be pollution-free. Only electric cars meet this standard.

T R Y THESE

Find the measure of the central angle that you would draw to represent each percent in a circle graph. Round to the nearest degree.

5. 28%

6. 25%

7. 62%

8. 12.5%

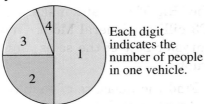

9. In the graph below, the angle measure for the portion of the graph that represents 4 people in a vehicle is 20°.

Survey of Commuter Traffic

4

3

1

2

Each digit indicates the number of people in one vehicle.

Total Vehicles: 538

a. What percent of the whole circle represents 4 people in a vehicle? Round to the nearest tenth of a percent.

b. How many vehicles contained 4 people? Why must you round your answer?

Minimum Driving Ages

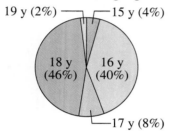

19 y (2%) — 15 y (4%)

18 y (46%) 16 y (40%)

17 y (8%)

ON YOUR OWN

10. Use the data below to draw a circle graph. The data represent the power sources for cars in the United States in 1900.

Power Source	Steam	Electricity	Gasoline
Percent	40%	38%	22%

11. Use the data below to draw a circle graph. The data represent student responses for how they get to school.

Transportation Mode	Walk	Bicycle	Bus	Car
Number of Students	252	135	432	81

12. The age at which you can obtain a driver's license without a driver's education course varies. The circle graph at the left displays the percent of states requiring the indicated minimum ages.

   a. The graph does not tell the total number of states. What is the total number of states? Do you think the total should be part of the graph? Explain.

   b. What is the most common minimum age for obtaining a license? How many states require this age?

DECISION MAKING

Buying a Car

Deciding what kind of car to buy can be difficult. There are many choices of cars. Also there are many factors to consider when buying a car, such as price, size, and fuel efficiency.

COLLECT DATA

1. Ask each member of your family to make a list of the most important factors to consider when buying a car.

2. Gather data about three car models that you like. Use magazine articles, newspaper advertisements, and buying guides for automobiles.

13. The Miller family wants to buy a new car. Mr. Miller made a graph of how the family spends their monthly income of $2,400.

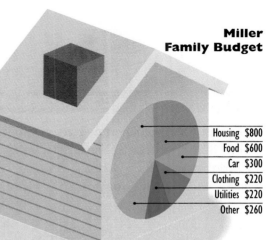

Miller Family Budget

Housing	$800
Food	$600
Car	$300
Clothing	$220
Utilities	$220
Other	$260

   a. What percent of the budget is car expenses?

   b. Mr. Miller estimates that payments on a new car will increase their monthly car expenses to $480. What percent of their monthly budget will car expenses be if the Millers buy a new car?

   c. **Critical Thinking** What changes do you think the Miller family should make in their budget so that they can buy a new car? Make a circle graph that shows the changes you suggest.

14. **Choose A, B, or C.** Which circle graph shows 25%, 5%, 40%, and 30%?

   A.   **B.**   **C.**

15. **Writing** Suppose you took two surveys asking people what they consider important safety features on a car. In the first survey, you allow people to give more than one response. In the second survey, you allow people to give only one response. Which survey results can you show in a circle graph? Why?

ANALYZE DATA

3. Use the lists from your family members to make a chart that rates each factor from 1 (not important) to 10 (very important). From your chart make a circle graph showing the importance each factor should have in the decision for buying a car.

4. Use your chart to grade the cars about which you have collected data.

MAKE DECISIONS

5. Determine which car best fits the needs and desires of your family.

*The average cost per mile of owning, maintaining, and operating a car in 1980 was 27.95¢. In 1990, the cost was 41.0¢/mi. **What was the percent of increase?***

Wrap Up

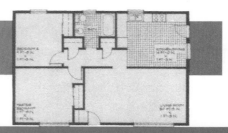

Ratios, Rates, and Proportions
9-1, 9-2, 9-3

A *ratio* is a comparison of two numbers.

A *rate* is a ratio that compares two quantities measured in different units.

A *proportion* is an equation that states that two ratios are equal.

1. In the 1992 Summer Olympics, the United States won 108 medals, including 37 gold medals. Write the ratio of gold medals to total medals in three ways.

2. Find the unit price for each item and tell which has the lower unit price, a 10-oz box of cereal for $2.79 or a 13-oz box for $3.99?

Find the value of *n* in each proportion.

3. $\frac{3}{7} = \frac{n}{28}$

4. $\frac{3}{5} = \frac{15}{n}$

5. $\frac{n}{18} = \frac{12}{72}$

6. $\frac{32}{n} = \frac{4}{17}$

7. In 1992, Michael Jordan of the Chicago Bulls scored 2,004 points in 80 games. How many games would it take him to break Kareem Abdul-Jabbar's lifetime record of 38,387 points if he had continued to score points at the same rate as he did in 1992?

Similarity and Scale Drawings
9-4, 9-5

If two figures are *similar,* corresponding angles are congruent and the ratios of the lengths of corresponding sides are equal.

A *scale drawing* is an enlarged or reduced drawing of an object.

Each pair of figures is similar. Find *x* and *y*.

8.

9.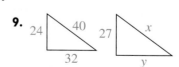

10. The scale on a map is 1.5 in. : 500 mi. The map distance from Chicago to Tokyo is 12 in. Find the actual distance between the cities.

11. A drawing's scale is 0.5 in. : 10 ft. A room is 15 ft long. How long is the room in the drawing?

Percent and Proportions

A *percent* is a ratio that compares a number to 100.
You can use a proportion to express data as a percent.

12. Write $62\frac{1}{2}\%$ as a fraction. **13.** Write 1.8% as a decimal. **14.** Write $\frac{3}{8}$ as a percent.

Write a proportion and solve.

15. What percent of 40 is 28? **16.** 38 is 80% of what number? **17.** What is 60% of 420?

Percent of Change and Circle Graphs

A *percent of change* is the percent something increases or
decreases from its original measure or amount.

You can make a circle graph of data that represent the parts of
a whole.

18. An answering machine costs $54 on sale. The original price
is $80. Find the percent of change.

19. **Writing** Tell how you would make a
circle graph of the data at the right.

| Who Drives | | | |
Age group	19 and under	25–49	50–69	79 and over
Percent	6	34	41	19

Strategies and Applications

Sometimes you use more than one strategy to solve a problem.

20. Choose A, B, C, or D. A rectangular lot is worth $9,000.
What is the value of a similar lot whose length and width
are each 50% greater than the dimensions of the first lot?

  A. $2,250 **B.** $4,000 **C.** $13,000 **D.** $20,250

GETTING READY FOR CHAPTER 10

Find each product.

1. $\frac{2}{3} \cdot \frac{1}{5}$ **2.** $\frac{3}{4} \cdot \frac{5}{8}$ **3.** $\frac{3}{4} \cdot \frac{4}{5}$ **4.** $\frac{5}{6} \cdot \frac{2}{3}$ **5.** $\frac{3}{8} \cdot \frac{2}{7}$ **6.** $\frac{5}{12} \cdot \frac{4}{11}$

7. You are having your picture taken with three friends. In
how many ways can you line up for the photograph?

PUTTING IT ALL TOGETHER

Follow Up

Left-Handed Scissors

The vice president of the Skizzer Scissors Corporation must decide whether to market left-handed scissors. This is your last chance to make a case for or against the proposal. Revise your letter to the vice president based on your research. The following suggestions may help.

✓ Design a map showing the proportion of lefties in the United States population.

✓ Make a circle graph.

✓ Create an ad for left-handed Skizzers.

If you worked the problems preceded by the magnifying glass (p. 367, # 16; p. 391, # 29; and p. 398, # 25), the data you collected will also help.

Marketing a new product is always risky. A company must invest a lot of money to develop a new product. If the company overestimates the demand for the product, it can lose its investment. To guard against such a disaster, companies conduct extensive surveys of public opinion before beginning product development.

Excursion: Lefty Louie's makes products exclusively for left-handers. Turquoise Trinkets designs jewelry exclusively for people with blue eyes. Which company do you think will be more successful? Explain the reasons for your answer.

Use Your Shadow

On a sunny day, you and your partner can use proportions to find the height of a tall building or tree or flagpole. First measure your partner's height. Then have your partner stand near a tall object while you measure the length of your partner's shadow and the length of the object's shadow. Use the height and the shadow lengths to write a proportion. Find out how tall the object is. Make a poster about your activity to exhibit in class.

Savings On Sale

Look at a sale flyer from a clothing store. Select a new outfit from the sale items shown. List each item. Show the original and sale prices. How much money could you save if you bought your items on sale? What percent of the original cost is saved? How many hours must you work at minimum wage to earn that amount? Discuss your findings with your family.

Percent Game

Two or more players.

Materials: Two ten-sided dice or two spinners divided into ten equal parts.

To Play:
1) Agree on a target number greater than 20.
2) Roll the dice then choose which die represents the percent. A roll of 1 on the "percent die" is 10%, 2 is 20%, and so on. Find the percent one die is of the other.
3) Add the results of each roll to previous turns. The first player to reach the target number is the winner.

FIND THE TIME

Between 4:00 P.M. and 5:00 P.M., what will be the minute reading on the clock when the minute hand passes the hour hand?

1. Write a ratio in three ways for the following data: Forty-nine out of 50 homes have at least one television.

2. Four cars were tested to find their fuel efficiency. Which car gets the most miles per gallon?

Car	Miles	Gallons
A	225	14
B	312	15
C	315	10
D	452	16

3. Find the value of n in each proportion.

   a. $\frac{6}{5} = \frac{n}{7}$ b. $\frac{3.5}{n} = \frac{14}{15}$

4. The ratio of teachers to students in Jefferson Middle School is 2 to 25. There are 350 students in the school. Find the number of teachers.

5. The two triangles in the figure below are similar. Find x and y.

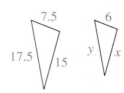

6. A map with a scale 350 mi : 2 in. shows two cities to be 5 in. apart. How many miles apart are the cities?

7. Use graph paper to model $12\frac{1}{2}\%$ and 285%.

8. Write 35% as a decimal and as a fraction in simplest form.

9. A hot air balloon is 2,100 ft in the air. It is scheduled to land at 3:30 P.M. It descends 15 ft every 10 s. When should the balloonist start descending?

10. Write a proportion and solve.

    a. Find 35% of 150.

    b. What percent of 80 is 50?

    c. 40 is what percent of 25?

11. Shea bought a sweater for $18.75, which was 25% off the regular price. What was the regular price?

12. In 1990, there were about 1.7 million registered nurses in the United States. By the year 2000, the United States Labor Department predicts there will be 2.5 million registered nurses. What percent of change does the Labor Department expect? Round to the nearest tenth of a percent.

13. **Writing** The price of a popular tape was $8.95 last week. This week the price is $7.16. Explain how to find the percent of change and tell whether the percent of change is an increase or decrease.

14. Students earned the following amounts of money to pay the transportation costs of a class trip. Make a circle graph for the data.

Fund Raiser	Money
Car Wash	$150
Paper Drive	$75
Book Sale	$225
Food Stand	$378

Choose A, B, C, or D.

1. What can you conclude from the scatterplot?

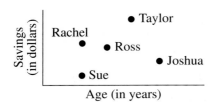
Age (in years)

A. There is positive correlation between age and savings.

B. Joshua is the oldest.

C. Joshua has the most in savings.

D. Taylor and Rachel are the same age.

2. Which number is closest to 35% of 1,291?

A. 200   B. 300

C. 400   D. 450

3. Which product is *closest* to $(2.7^2)(10.5)$?

A. $(3^2)(10)$ B. $(4^2)(10)$

C. $(2^2)(11)$ D. $(3^2)(11)$

4. Which equation is *not* equivalent to $2x - 3 = 5$?

A. $2x = 8$ B. $x - 1.5 = 2.5$

C. $2x - 4 = 4$ D. $4x - 3 = 10$

5. What are the next two terms of the sequence:
1, 2, 4, 5, 7, 8, 10, 11, 13, 14, . . . ?

A. 16, 17   B. 17, 19

C. 17, 18   D. 16, 18

6. Which statement is *not* true?

A. $\dfrac{12}{16} = \dfrac{9}{12}$ B. $\dfrac{12 + 16}{16} = \dfrac{9 + 12}{12}$

C. $\dfrac{12}{9} = \dfrac{16}{12}$ D. $\dfrac{12 + 1}{16} = \dfrac{9 + 1}{12}$

7. Which point on the number line shows the product $\left(1\frac{7}{8}\right)\left(2\frac{1}{5}\right)$?

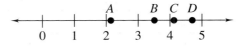

8. *ABCD* is a rhombus. What is the area of the shaded region?

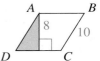

A. 64   B. 56

C. 24   D. 48

9. What dimensions of a single sheet of wrapping paper could you use to wrap a 4 in. × 8 in. × 12 in. box?

A. 10 in. by 40 in

B. 8 in. by 24 in.

C. 8 in by 32 in.

D. 12 in. by 20 in.

10. Which statement is false?

A. Some rhombuses are rectangles.

B. All squares are rhombuses.

C. All isosceles triangles have three congruent sides.

D. A trapezoid has exactly one pair of parallel sides.

Data File 10

the largest egg
is about the size
of a pinhead

The Monarch
butterfly lives only about
30–35 days from the time
the egg is laid. In good
weather conditions,
however, Monarchs can
live for 6 months.

Source: Entomology Laboratory,
Harvard University

egg
(enlarged)

5 days

caterpillar

stops growing
at $1\frac{4}{5}$ inch,
after increasing
its weight
3,000 times

2-3 weeks

Life Expectancy Around the World

Afghanistan
Australia
Brazil
Canada
China
France
India
Japan
Mexico
Nigeria
United States

■ Male
■ Female

0 10 20 30 40 50 60 70 80 90 100
Years

Source: *Junior Scholastic*

What Are the Odds that Someone Living in the United States will Live to be 100?

At Age:	Odds Are:
0 (birth)	1 to 87
1 y	1 to 86
30 y	1 to 84
45 y	1 to 81
65 y	1 to 67
85 y	1 to 24
90 y	1 to 12
99 y	1 to 1.4

Source: *Boston Globe*

WHAT YOU WILL LEARN

- how to find simple probabilities and odds
- how to use probability to make predictions
- how to use technology to explore experimental probability
- how to solve problems by simulating a problem

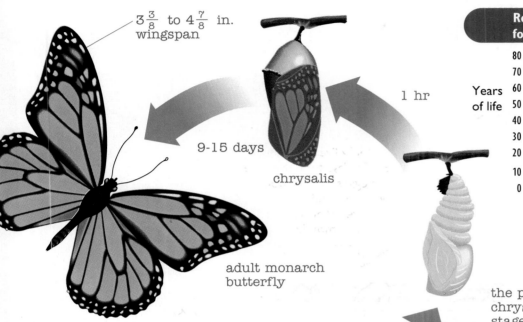

$3\frac{3}{8}$ to $4\frac{7}{8}$ in. wingspan

9-15 days

1 hr

chrysalis

adult monarch butterfly

beginning of pupa or chrysalis stage

the pupa or chrysalis stage lasts approximately 1 week

$\frac{1}{2}$ in. in diameter

$1\frac{1}{5}$ in. long

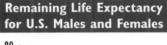

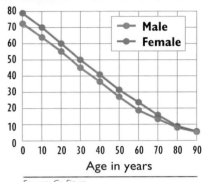

Remaining Life Expectancy for U.S. Males and Females

Years of life (vertical axis): 0 10 20 30 40 50 60 70 80

Age in years (horizontal axis): 0 10 20 30 40 50 60 70 80 90

- Male
- Female

Source: *Go Figure*

WORLD VIEW

There are 92 countries that have birth rates higher than India, and 134 countries that have birth rates higher than China. However, $\frac{1}{3}$ of the world's births occur in these two countries.

Average Life Expectancy of Some Animals

Animal	Number of Years	Animal	Number of Years
Galapagos tortoise	100	rhesus monkey	15
African elephant	60	house cat	13
Asian elephant	60	dog	12
European catfish	60	sheep	12
condor	52	goat	10
hippopotamus	40	gray squirrel	10
gorilla	35	chipmunk	6
giraffe	25	red fox	5
horse	25	white rabbit	5
moose	18	guinea pig	4
tiger	16	white mouse	3
cow	15	opossum	1

Source: *Macmillan Illustrated Almanac for Kids*

in)vestigation

Memo

Professor Mergatroid had a theory. "Two people with the same birthday must have very similar personalities," he said. "Now all I have to do is find two such people to check out my theory."

His assistant Labcoat replied, "But that will take ages! You may have to ask 365 people before you find two with the same birthday."

"I don't think so," said the professor with a knowing look in his eye. "I have a feeling it will be far simpler than that."

Mission: Estimate the number of people you would have to ask at random before you would find two with the same birthday. How did you make your estimate?

LeADs tO FOLLow

✓ Do you know two people with the same birthday?

✓ What experiment could you perform to help you make your estimate?

Probability and Odds

THINK AND DISCUSS

• There's a 40% chance of rain.

• Your little brother almost always gets a cold every winter.

• The driver of a red car is more likely to be involved in an accident than the driver of a blue car.

• The Sun is sure to rise tomorrow.

All of these involve ideas from *probability*.

Have you ever seen a 12-sided die? When you toss a 12-sided die, there are 12 possible **outcomes:** 1, 2, 3, 4, 5, 6, 7, 8, 9, 10, 11, and 12. Each outcome is **equally likely.**

1. a. What are the outcomes of tossing a coin?

b. Are all the outcomes equally likely?

2. a. List all the outcomes for spinning the spinner at the left.

b. Is it equally likely that the spinner will land on red or blue? Explain.

An **event** is any group of outcomes. When all outcomes are equally likely, the **probability** that an event E will happen, $P(E)$, is the following ratio.

Probability of an Event
The probability that an event E will occur is given by: $$P(E) = \frac{\text{number of favorable outcomes}}{\text{total number of possible outcomes}}$$

On average, children get six to eight colds per year, while adults suffer from two to four. Boys catch more colds than girls, but women catch more colds than men.

Source: *What Are the Chances?* and *Journal of the American Medical Association*

3. Use the spinner at the left above.

a. What is $P(\text{blue})$?

b. What is $P(\text{red})$?

c. Why are the probabilities in parts (a) and (b) not equal?

You can write the ratio for a probability as a fraction, a decimal, or a percent.

Example 1 Find the probability of rolling an even number on a 12-sided die.

There are six favorable outcomes: 2, 4, 6, 8, 10, 12.

$$P(\text{even}) = \frac{\text{number of favorable outcomes}}{\text{number of possible outcomes}} = \frac{6}{12} = \frac{1}{2}$$

The probability of rolling an even number is $\frac{1}{2}$ or 0.5 or 50%.

4. Determine the probability of each event using a 12-sided die. Write each probability as a fraction, a decimal, and a percent.

   a. $P(\text{number less than 9})$ **b.** $P(\text{multiple of 6})$

FLASHBACK

Ratios are usually written in one of the following three ways:

1 to 10   1 : 10 $\frac{1}{10}$

You can use **odds** to compare favorable outcomes to unfavorable outcomes. You usually write the ratio for odds as a fraction or a phrase that uses the word "to."

Odds in Favor of an Event
The odds in favor of an event occurring are given by: $$\text{odds in favor of an event} = \frac{\text{number of favorable outcomes}}{\text{number of unfavorable outcomes}}$$

5. **a.** How are odds and probability similar? different?

   b. The odds in favor of winning a door prize at a party are 1 to 10. What does this mean?

Example 2 What are the odds in favor of spinning an 11?

There is one favorable outcome. There are 19 unfavorable outcomes.

$$\text{Odds} = \frac{\text{number of favorable outcomes}}{\text{number of unfavorable outcomes}} = \frac{1}{19}.$$

The odds in favor of spinning an 11 are 1 to 19.

6. Find the probability of spinning an 11. Then use $<$, $>$, or $=$ to compare the probability with the odds found in Example 2.

A game is **fair** if all the players are equally likely to win. Play the following game with a partner. Before you play, read the directions and decide if you think the game is fair or unfair.

- Take turns rolling two number cubes. Find the product of the two numbers. If the product is even, Player A scores a point. If the product is odd, Player B scores a point.

- After 15 rolls each, the player with more points wins.

Product Chart

	1	2	3	4	5	6
1	1	2	3	▪	▪	▪
2	2	4	▪	▪	▪	▪
3	▪	▪	▪	▪	▪	▪
4	▪	▪	▪	▪	▪	▪
5	▪	▪	▪	▪	▪	▪
6	▪	▪	▪	▪	▪	▪

7. Play the game twice. Based on your results, do you think the game is fair?

8. **a.** Copy and complete the Product Chart at the right.

   b. What is the total number of even products? the total number of odd products?

   c. Find P(even) and P(odd).

9. **Discussion** How could you award points differently to make this a fair game?

A number cube is rolled once. Find each probability.

10. $P(4)$ 11. P(multiple of 3)   12. P(number less than 3)

13. Ten thousand programs are printed for the baseball game. Only one of them displays the winning number. What are the odds in favor of your winning if you buy one program? if you buy two programs?

14. A spinner lettered A–Z is spun. Find the odds in favor of the spinner landing on the first letter of your first name.

Do you agree or disagree with each statement? Explain.

15. You toss a penny ten times with these results: 3 heads and 7 tails. So heads and tails are not equally likely outcomes.

16. The odds in favor of winning a contest are 1 to 7. So the probability of winning the contest is $\frac{1}{8}$.

In 1991, the Toronto Blue Jays set a record for season attendance at home games with crowds totaling 4,001,527 fans. Suppose one out of every 10,000 fans won a prize. **How many prizewinners would there have been?**

Source: *Guinness Book of Records*

Find the measure of the central angle that would represent each percent in a circle graph.

1. 40%   **2.** 15%

Find each difference.

3. $1 - \frac{5}{6}$ **4.** $1 - 0.52$

Write a variable expression for each word phrase.

5. one third of the sum of a number y and 8

6. the quotient of a number x divided by 3

7. If you start with a number, subtract 7, then divide by 13, the result is 21. What was the original number?

Exercise results in a 45% lower risk of heart attack for people with an active lifestyle. Quitting smoking lowers risk 50–70%. Maintaining a healthy body weight reduces risk 55%.

Source: *Harvard Medical School Health Letter*

ON YOUR OWN

A spinner numbered from 1 to 10 is spun. Each outcome is equally likely. Write each probability as a fraction, a decimal, and a percent.

17. $P(5)$ **18.** $P(\text{odd})$ **19.** $P(\text{number less than 11})$

20. You buy a raffle ticket to win a computer. One of 200 tickets will be drawn from a box to determine the winner. Find the probability and the odds that you will win.

Use the spinner shown.

21. Estimate $P(\text{X})$, $P(\text{Y})$, and $P(\text{Z})$.

22. Which of the events X, Y, or Z is most likely? least likely?

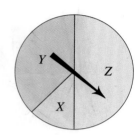

23. A bag contains five green marbles, seven clear marbles, and three orange marbles.

    a. Find the probability of drawing a green marble.

    b. What marbles could you add or remove so that the probability of drawing a green marble is $\frac{1}{2}$?

24. Writing Suppose you have 3 nickels, 3 dimes, and 3 quarters in your pocket. Are you equally likely to select a dime as a quarter from your pocket? Explain.

A box contains cards numbered from 1 to 100. Find each probability.

25. selecting a prime number   **26.** selecting an even number

27. Health Odds are often used with medical treatments. The odds in favor of recovery using a new medicine are 1 to 3. A patient is thinking about using the new medicine.

    a. Writing Explain to the patient how to interpret the odds.

    b. Find the probability of recovery using the medicine.

28. Writing You are given a choice of two medical treatments, *A* and *B*. The odds in favor of recovery are 5 : 4 for *A* and 4 : 3 for *B*. Which medical treatment would you choose? Explain.

Exploring Probabilities

The national weather service has an 85% accuracy rate in its predictions for rain.

Source: "Why They Still Can't Predict the Weather." *Readers Digest*

THINK AND DISCUSS

On the news you hear that there is a 40% chance of rain.

1. What is the probability of rain? of no rain?

2. How can you use $P(\text{rain})$ to find $P(\text{no rain})$?

3. Complete: $P(\text{rain}) + P(\text{no rain}) = $ ■.

The event "no rain" is the *complement* of the event "rain." The probability of an event plus the probability of its complement always equals 1, or 100%.

4. a. When rolling a number cube, what is $P(6)$? What is $P(\text{not } 6)$?

   b. What is $P(1, 2, 3, 4, \text{ or } 5)$?

There is more than one way to find the probability of events that cannot occur at the same time, such as "rolling a 1" and "rolling a 2" on a number cube.

5. a. Find $P(1 \text{ or } 2)$, the probability of rolling a 1 or 2.

   b. Find the sum of $P(1)$ and $P(2)$.

   c. Describe two ways of finding the probability of rolling a 1 or a 2.

6. What is the probability of the complement of $P(1 \text{ or } 2)$?

$P(1) = $ ■
$P(1 \text{ or } 2) = $ ■
$P(1, 2, \text{ or } 3) = $ ■
$P(1, 2, 3, \text{ or } 4) = $ ■
$P(1, 2, 3, 4, \text{ or } 5) = $ ■
$P(1, 2, 3, 4, 5, \text{ or } 6) = $ ■

7. a. Copy and complete the table at the left.

   b. On a number line, graph each probability: $P(1), P(1 \text{ or } 2), \ldots$

   c. What is the probability of rolling a 7?

   d. Between what two whole numbers do the probabilities lie?

   e. What is the least number a probability can be? the greatest number?

A *certain* event will always happen. The probability of a certain event is 1. An *impossible* event will never happen. The probability of an impossible event is 0.

8. Give an example of a certain event.

9. Give an example of an impossible event.

 WORK TOGETHER

Work in small groups. Draw a number line like the one below on a big piece of paper.

Label the number line with each of the following:

- the probabilities 0, $\frac{1}{4}$, $\frac{1}{2}$, $\frac{3}{4}$, and 1
- the probabilities 0%, 10%, 20%, . . . , 100%
- the words "certain" and "impossible"

The words at the left describe probabilities. As a group, decide where to write each word or phrase on the number line. For example, write "no chance" at 0 because an event that has no chance of happening has probability of 0. Have each group member think of at least one more word or phrase that describes a probability. Write your word or phrase on the number line.

PROBABILITY WORDS

no chance, slight chance, unexpected, always, likely, maybe, even chance, expected, unlikely, possible, probably not, indefinite, uncertain, certain

---

M*ix*ed REVIEW

1. How long is a diagonal of a 5 m × 12 m rectangle?

Write the prime factorization.

2. 625   **3.** 7,200

The rule for a function is $f(n) = -2n - 4$**. Find:**

4. $f(-3)$ **5.** $f(2)$

6. What is the probability of rolling a number less than 5 on a number cube?

ON YOUR OWN

You draw a chip at random from the bag.

10. Find each probability.
    a. $P(\text{red})$ **b.** $P(\text{blue})$
    c. $P(\text{red}) + P(\text{blue})$
    d. $P(\text{red or blue})$

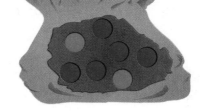

11. Complete: $P(\text{not red}) = P(\blacksquare)$, and $P(\text{not blue}) = P(\blacksquare)$.

12. a. You add six yellow chips to the bag. What is $P(\text{yellow})$?
    b. What is the complement of the event "yellow"?

Use the spinner at the right to find each probability.

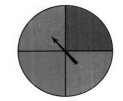

13. P(not green)   **14.** P(red or blue)   **15.** P(white)

16. A bag contains an unknown number of chips. You know P(red) $= \frac{1}{4}$ and P(green) $= \frac{3}{4}$.

   a. Are all the chips either red or green? How do you know?

   b. How many chips of each color might be in the bag? Is your answer the only possibility? Explain.

17. a. Complete: The probability of a certain event is ■.

   b. Complete: The complement of a certain event is a(n) ■ event.

18. Your teacher selects one student at random from your class.

   a. What is the probability that you are selected?

   b. What is the probability that a girl is not selected?

   c. Find P(girl or boy is selected).

19. Data File 10 (pp. 416–417) What is the *probability* that someone who is 1 year old will live to be 100?

20. a. Suppose $P(E) = 0.3$. Find P(not E).

   b. Suppose P(not E) $= 65\%$. Find $P(E)$.

21. Choose A, B, C, or D. The forecast for tomorrow is an 80% chance of rain. Which conclusion is most appropriate?

   A. 80% of the region will receive rain.

   B. It will rain on 8 of the next 10 days.

   C. It will rain for 9.6 h of the next 24 h.

   D. On similar days in the past, 8 out of 10 have had rain.

22. Writing Describe an event E that has not occurred but may occur in the future. Use words to describe the probability that E will occur in your lifetime.

23. Critical Thinking Review the definition of "complement" when referring to angles. How is the use of the word "complement" when used with angles similar to its use in probability?

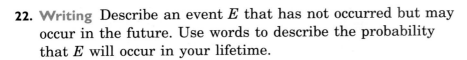

The weather map shows a weather pattern in which there is a 40% chance of snow in the Northeast. **What is the probability that it will not snow?**

10-3 **S**ample Spaces

> When you have eliminated the impossible, whatever remains, however improbable, must be the truth.
> —Sir Arthur Conan Doyle (1859–1930)

T H I N K A N D D I S C U S S

An outcome is one of the possible things that can occur as the result of an experiment. The set of all possible outcomes is the **sample space.**

1. Give the sample space for each situation. How many possible outcomes are there?

a. You toss a coin.

b. You spin the spinner once.

c. You toss a coin *and* spin the spinner once.

2. Discussion How can you organize your thinking so that you find *all* possible outcomes?

Example 1 Make a table to find the sample space for rolling two number cubes. Write the outcomes as ordered pairs.

	1	2	3	4	5	6
1	(1, 1)	(2, 1)	(3, 1)	(4, 1)	(5, 1)	(6, 1)
2	(1, 2)	(2, 2)	(3, 2)	(4, 2)	(5, 2)	(6, 2)
3	(1, 3)	(2, 3)	(3, 3)	(4, 3)	(5, 3)	(6, 3)
4	(1, 4)	(2, 4)	(3, 4)	(4, 4)	(5, 4)	(6, 4)
5	(1, 5)	(2, 5)	(3, 5)	(4, 5)	(5, 5)	(6, 5)
6	(1, 6)	(2, 6)	(3, 6)	(4, 6)	(5, 6)	(6, 6)

There are 36 possible outcomes.

3. What is the probability of rolling "doubles" (the same number on both number cubes)?

4. What is the probability of rolling a sum that is even?

5. a. How many ways can you roll a sum of 7?

b. What is the probability of rolling a sum of 7?

6. What is the probability of rolling a sum of 10?

7. a. Copy and complete the table to find the sample space for tossing two coins.

b. Find the probability of tossing two heads.

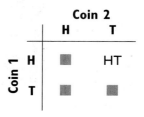

Coin 2

	H	T
H	▪	HT
T	▪	▪

Coin 1

You can also draw a *tree diagram* to find a sample space.

Example 2

You toss three coins. What is the sample space?

Make a tree diagram in which you consider the outcomes one coin at a time.

Coin 1	Coin 2	Coin 3	Outcomes

H — H — H ——— H H H
H — H — T ——— H H T
H — T — H ——— H T H
H — T — T ——— H T T
T — H — H ——— T H H
T — H — T ——— T H T
T — T — H ——— T T H
T — T — T ——— T T T

There are eight possible outcomes: HHH, HHT, HTH, HTT, THH, THT, TTH, and TTT.

8. Use the tree diagram in Example 2.

a. Find P(at least two heads).

b. Find P(exactly two heads).

9. a. Four coins are tossed. Draw a tree diagram to find the sample space.

b. Find P(three heads and one tail).

10. Critical Thinking Ten coins are tossed. You want to find the sample space. Would you make a table or draw a tree diagram? Explain your choice.

To find the number of possible outcomes, you can make a table or make a tree diagram, and count the number of outcomes. When the number of outcomes is very large, you may find it more convenient to use the *counting principle*.

P(girl) P(boy)

In 1991, there were 4,011,000 children under the age of one in the United States. In this group, P(girl) is 0.488, and P(boy) is 0.512.

Source: *Statistical Abstract*

DELI BUTTON Deli Sandwiches

BREADS RYE, WHEAT, WHITE, PITA OR BULKY ROLL

MEATS ROAST BEEF, TURKEY, HAM, PASTRAMI, SALAMI, OR LIVERWURST

The number of outcomes for an event is the product of the number of outcomes for each stage of the event.

Example 3

To order a Deli-Button sandwich, a customer chooses one bread and one meat. How many different sandwiches are available at the Deli-Button?

Bread		**Meat**
number of choices	$\times$	number of choices
5	$\times$	6

There are 30 different sandwiches available.

11. Why is it helpful to use the counting principle instead of a tree diagram to solve this problem?

12. The manager of the Deli-Button decides to add chicken to the list of meat choices. How many different sandwiches are now available?

13. What information does a tree diagram or a table give you that the counting principle does not?

CITY MOVIE THEATER

Popcorn
small $1.25
medium $1.50
large $2.00

Fruit Punch or Lemonade
small $1.00
medium $1.25
large $1.75
jumbo $2.25

T R Y THESE

Use the information at the left for Exercises 14–18.

14. List all the possible beverage orders.

15. You order lemonade and popcorn at the City Movie Theater.
   a. Draw a tree diagram to find the sample space.
   b. Show that the counting principle gives the same number of outcomes as your tree diagram.

16. How many possible orders are there for popcorn and a beverage?

17. **Discussion** A manager used the counting principle to find that P(small popcorn, medium lemonade) $= \frac{1}{24}$. Do you agree? Why or why not?

18. Suppose popcorn choices are plain, buttered, and cheese. Find P(medium plain popcorn, medium fruit punch).

19. Education Cuong is taking art and music as electives. There are 4 art teachers and 3 music teachers. How many possible outcomes are there for the two teachers Cuong will have?

20. a. A teacher uses a seating chart for students. Rows are numbered 1 through 6, and columns are lettered A through D. One possible seat for a student is 3A. Make a table to display the sample space for the seats.

    b. Use the counting principle to find the number of seats. Does your answer agree with the number of seats in your table?

21. Travel On your vacation you will travel from home to camp. You will go to Chicago, then to northern Minnesota. You can get to Chicago by car, bus, plane, or train. You can get to camp in northern Minnesota by car or bus. Draw a tree diagram to display all possible travel arrangements.

22. Writing Use your own words to explain "sample space" and how to use the counting principle to find the number of outcomes in a sample space.

23. Fashion Steven has four shirts (white, blue, green, and tan) and four pairs of socks in the same colors.

    a. How many different shirt-socks outfits does Steven have?

    b. Suppose he grabs a shirt and a pair of socks without looking. What is the probability that they will not match?

24. Seven people are eligible for three different positions on the student council. Their names are placed in a bag.

    a. How many people are eligible for the first position?

    b. How many people are eligible for the second position once the first has been selected? the third position once the first two have been selected?

    c. Use the counting principle to find the number of ways three people out of seven can be selected for the three positions on the student council.

25. Investigation (p. 418) Find a list of birthdays of the presidents of the United States. How many presidents have there been? How many have had the same birthday?

Mixed REVIEW

1. Find 30% of 50.

2. Suppose the probability of rain today is 60%. What is the probability of no rain today?

Write each number in scientific notation.

3. 21 million   **4.** 543

Find each sum.

5. $\frac{1}{2} + \frac{2}{3}$ **6.** $\frac{1}{8} + \frac{3}{4}$

7. The odds of winning a contest are 1 : 999,999. What is the probability of losing the contest?

Use any strategy to solve each problem. Show all your work.

1. Karla has an average of 88 on three tests. What grade will she have to make on the fourth test to have a 90 average?

2. On Monday the low temperature at the South Pole fell 9°F below Sunday's low. On Tuesday it fell another 7°, then rose 13° on Wednesday and rose 17° more on Thursday. Friday it dropped 8° to −50°F. What was Sunday's low temperature?

3. How many triangles can you draw using the vertices of a pentagon?

4. A bowling lane is 78 ft long and 42 in. wide. How many square feet of flooring are needed to resurface the 12 lanes at the local bowling club?

5. In 1989, Robert Commers jumped 13,783 revolutions of a jump rope in 1 h. How many revolutions did he jump per minute?

6. Data File 2 (pp. 44–45) Suppose you helped conduct the survey of *Science World* readers. What is the probability that you would have interviewed a reader who thinks space explorers will prove that life once existed on Mars?

7. Of 28 students in a math class, 15 have a brother, 12 have a sister, and 4 have a brother and a sister. How many of the 28 students do not have either a brother or a sister?

8. Four students are sitting in one row. Jana is behind Nathan. Tae is ahead of Robin. Nathan is behind Robin. Write the names of the students in order.

9. The sum of two numbers is 13. Twice the lesser number plus 1 equals the greater number. Find the two numbers.

10. A lottery winner gave his daughter half of his winnings and his brother half as much as he gave his daughter. He kept $50. How much did his daughter and brother each get?

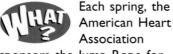 Each spring, the American Heart Association sponsors the Jump Rope for Heart. This health awareness program encourages exercise and raises money for charity. In 1993, over 1.5 million students, parents, and teachers from 17,533 different schools participated.

Source: American Heart Association

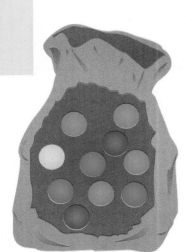

WORK TOGETHER

Work in pairs. Suppose you have a bag of marbles like the one at the left, and you draw a marble at random.

1. What is the probability that you would draw a red marble?

2. a. Before you draw a second marble, you drop the first one back in the bag and shake it. What is the probability that you select a red marble on the second draw?

b. Suppose that the first marble you draw is red. Suppose that you do not put the first marble back in the bag. How does this affect the sample space for the second draw? What is the probability of drawing a red marble on your second draw?

THINK AND DISCUSS

Two events are **independent** if the outcome of one event has no effect on the outcome of the other. In the Work Together activity, there were 4 ways out of 10 to select a red marble on the first draw. If you drop the red marble back in the bag, there are still 4 ways out of 10 to select a red marble on the second draw. The first selection does not affect the second selection so the events (red and red) are independent. Events are **dependent** if the outcome of the first event affects the outcome of a second event.

3. a. When the first marble is not returned to the bag before the second marble is drawn, the events (red, then red) are dependent. Explain why.

b. Laurie pulls a coin out of her change purse and a bill out of her wallet. Are these events independent or dependent? Explain why.

4. a. Describe two events that are dependent.

b. Describe two events that are independent.

 The chances of a fair coin landing heads up 50 times in a row are very low. If one million coins were tossed 10 times/min for 40 h/wk, then 50 consecutive heads would happen only once every 9 centuries.

Source: *Mathematics*

Carnivals began as festivals in Europe hundreds of years ago. In the United States, traveling carnivals began after transportation improved in the late 1800s. Today there are about 500 different carnivals that travel across the country.

Probability of Two Independent Events

If A and B are independent events, $P(A \text{ and } B) = P(A) \times P(B)$.

Example 1

To play the carnival game "Spin Your Initials," you spin a wheel lettered A–Z twice. To win, you must spin your first initial, then spin your last initial. Find the probability of winning if your initials are B and Z.

- The two events are independent.

$$P(\text{B and Z}) = P(\text{B}) \times P(\text{Z})$$

$$= \frac{1}{26} \times \frac{1}{26} = \frac{1}{676}$$

The probability of winning is $\frac{1}{676}$.

5. Two number cubes are rolled. Find $P(6 \text{ and } 6)$.

Probability of Two Dependent Events

If A and B are dependent events, then

$$P(A, \text{ then } B) = P(A) \times P(B \text{ after } A).$$

Example 2

To play the carnival game "Draw Your Initials," you draw two cards from a bucket that contains cards lettered A–Z. To win, the cards must be your initials. Find the probability of winning if your initials are R and M.

- The two events are dependent.

$$P(\text{R, then M}) = P(\text{R}) \times P(\text{M after R})$$

$$= \frac{1}{26} \times \frac{1}{25} = \frac{1}{650}$$

The probability of winning is $\frac{1}{650}$.

6. Explain why $P(\text{M after R}) = \frac{1}{25}$.

7. The names of all the students in your class are in a hat. Your teacher draws one name, then draws a second name without replacing the first. Why are these events dependent?

Are the two events independent or dependent?

8. You toss a coin and draw a card from a deck of cards.

9. You toss a nickel, and you toss a dime.

10. You draw a card, replace it, then draw another card.

11. You grab a sock from the dryer, then grab another sock from the dryer.

Imagine drawing two marbles from the bag at the right.

12. Suppose you replace the first marble before drawing the second one. What is P(two green marbles)?

13. Suppose you do not replace the first marble before drawing the second. What is P(two green marbles)?

O N YOUR OWN

14. In the game Yahtzee™ you roll five number cubes. One objective of the game is to get five of a kind in one roll of the dice. What is the probability of getting five ones?

A box contains the letters M I S S I S S I P P I.

15. What is the probability that if you reach in you will select the letter I?

16. What is the probability of selecting a consonant?

17. What is the probability of selecting an S, then a P, if:

  a. the first letter is not replaced before selecting the second letter?

  b. the first letter is replaced before selecting the second letter?

18. Make up a problem about the letters in the box. Solve it.

You roll one number cube twice. What is the probability of each of the events?

19. P(6, then 4)   **20.** P(double 5's)   **21.** P(6, then 7)

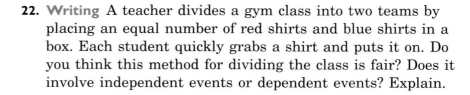

Mixed REVIEW

Write each fraction in simplest form.

1. $\frac{27}{243}$ 2. $\frac{52}{78}$

3. Find the area of a square with a perimeter of 18 ft.

A spinner is equally likely to land in any section of a circle. The sections are numbered from 1 to 20.

4. Find P(prime number).

5. Find P(square number).

6. How many different pairs of students can be formed in a group of 5 students?

22. **Writing** A teacher divides a gym class into two teams by placing an equal number of red shirts and blue shirts in a box. Each student quickly grabs a shirt and puts it on. Do you think this method for dividing the class is fair? Does it involve independent events or dependent events? Explain.

23. John is tossing a coin. He says, "I got three tails in a row! My next toss will be heads for sure." Do you agree? Explain.

24. Five girls and seven boys want to be the announcers for a variety show. The show will have only two announcers. To be fair, a teacher put the names of the twelve students in a hat and drew two.

    a. Find the probability that both hosts are boys.

    b. Find the probability that both hosts are girls.

    c. **Critical Thinking** Use what you know about complements to find the probability that the hosts are a boy and a girl.

    d. One of the girls suggests that the teacher draw one girl's name from a hat and one boy's name from a different hat. Do you think this is a better method? Explain.

CHECKPOINT

Use the wheel at the left. Write each probability as a fraction, a decimal, and a percent.

1. P(not 4)   2. P(2 or 3)   3. P(prime number)

The letters M A T H E M A T I C S are written on a set of cards.

4. Find the odds in favor of selecting an M.

5. Find the probability of selecting a vowel, replacing it, then selecting another vowel.

6. Find the probability of selecting an A, then a T, from the lettered cards above if the first letter is not replaced before selecting the second one.

7. The cafeteria has 3 sandwich choices, 2 beverage choices, and 4 dessert choices. How many different meals consisting of sandwich, beverage, and dessert does the cafeteria offer?

What's Ahead

10-5 **S**imulate a Problem

- Solving problems by simulation

READ
PLAN
LOOK BACK
SOLVE

WHAT YOU'LL NEED

✓ **Number cubes**

You have probably played video games in which you pilot an aircraft or drive a car. Some computer games encourage you to pretend you're the owner of a small roadside business or a scientist conducting an experiment. Models of real-world situations like these are called **simulations.**

> Kayley Karl wants to collect the six different model dinosaurs being given as prizes in boxes of Crispy Crunchy cereal. Each box of cereal contains one model, and there is an equally likely chance of any one of the prizes being in any one box. Kayley has enough money to buy 20 boxes. Is she likely to get all six prizes in those 20 boxes?

READ

Read and understand the given information. Summarize the problem.

Think about the problem.

1. **a.** What is the least number of boxes of cereal Kayley may need to buy to collect all six dinosaurs?

    b. After buying 20 boxes of cereal, what is the fewest types of dinosaurs that she could have collected?

    c. Guess the number of boxes you think she may need to buy.

PLAN

Decide on a strategy to solve the problem.

Instead of actually buying boxes of cereal, Kayley can *simulate* the problem to estimate how many boxes she will need to buy to get all six dinosaurs.

2. Into how many congruent sections should a spinner be divided to simulate the cereal problem?

3. Suppose Kayley uses a number cube to simulate the problem. Rolling a 1 means Kayley gets a brontosaurus model. Rolling a 2 means Kayley gets a stegosaurus, and so on. How many different numbers will Kayley have to roll to receive all six different dinosaur models?

Number	Roll
1	II
2	IIII
3	I
4	II
5	II
6	III
Total	■

One *trial* for a simulation is completed once you get all possible responses once. You may get some responses more than once.

4. Kayley simulated the problem by rolling a number cube. The tally she made during the first trial is at the left.

   a. How many times did she have to roll the number cube to get all six numbers?

   b. According to this trial, how many boxes of cereal would Kayley have to buy to get all six model dinosaurs?

   c. Do you think a second trial of the problem would have the same results? Why or why not?

SOLVE ▶

Try out the strategy.

Simulate the problem by rolling a number cube.

5. a. Roll a number cube as many times as necessary to receive all six dinosaurs. Keep a tally of your results.

   b. According to your trial, about how many boxes of cereal would Kayley need to buy to get all six prizes?

   c. Make nine more trials. Then find the mean of the number of boxes Kayley would need to buy.

LOOK BACK ▶

Think about the data you collected.

6. How close was your guess in Question 1 (c) to the mean number of boxes you found in Question 5 (c)?

7. The more trials you have the better your estimate is. Find the mean number of boxes Kayley needs to buy based on the results of the trials for your class.

8. a. Do you think Kayley is likely to get all six prizes if she buys 20 boxes of cereal? Explain.

   b. Do you know for sure that Kayley will get all six prizes after she buys 20 boxes of cereal?

 In the late 1980s Ralston–Purina put model cars in some cereal boxes. The models included scale Corvettes, which were redeemable for the actual car.

Source: *Marketing News*

TRY THESE

Simulate the problem to solve.

9. A fast-food restaurant gives away a model car with each purchase. You are equally likely to get any of three different cars. Estimate the number of purchases you would need to make to get all cars.

10. Explain how you would simulate the following problem: Suppose you are given a matching quiz in a language you do not know. There are five questions and five answers. Estimate the number of guesses you need to make before getting a match.

ON YOUR OWN

Use any strategy to solve each problem. Show your work.

11. The Booster Club hired a rock band for a fund-raiser. The club guaranteed the band a fee of $1,500 plus $4.50 for each ticket sold. There are 1,132 seats in the auditorium. What is the greatest possible amount of money the band can earn for a performance? the least amount?

12. The largest window in the world is in Paris, France, at the Palace of Industry and Technology. The window measures 715.2 ft wide by 164 ft high. How many square yards of glass are in this window?

13. The longest-lived comic strip is "The Katzenjammer Kids." It was created by Rudolph Dirks and first published in the *New York Journal* on December 12, 1897. Use today's date to calculate the age of this comic strip.

14. A juice company advertises that under each bottle cap is a winning letter. There are five different letters: J, U, I, C and E. To win a prize, you must collect all five caps to spell JUICE. Estimate the number of juice bottles you will need to buy to win a prize.

15. **Data File 8 (pp. 314–315)** What is the probability that a 13-year-old male has eaten at a "fast food" restaurant in the last seven days?

16. A store puts a sweater on sale. During the sale the store reduces the sweater's price by 30%. After the sale, the store manager increases the sale price of the sweater by 30%. Is the price before and after the sale the same? Explain.

 17. **Investigation (p. 418)** Ask your friends and neighbors their birth date. Keep a record. How many birthdays did you need to check before finding two that are the same?

Mixed REVIEW

1. Find the radius of a circle that has a circumference of 75.36 in.

Express as unit rates.

2. 560 words typed in 8 min

3. 850.5 km driven in 9 h

Assume that events A and B are independent. Find P(A and B).

4. $P(A) = \frac{1}{2}$, $P(B) = \frac{2}{5}$

5. $P(A) = \frac{2}{9}$, $P(B) = \frac{3}{4}$

6. A student counts 18 legs on the chairs and the three-legged stools as she waits at the doctor's office. How many chairs and how many stools does she see?

10-6 **Experimental Probability and Simulations**

■ **WHAT YOU'LL NEED**

✓ Crumpled papers

✓ Waste basket

✓ Computer

✓ Software with random number and graphing capabilities

┌**WORK TOGETHER**

Have you ever tossed a crumpled piece of paper into a waste basket? What is the probability that you will make a basket? To find this probability, you need to experiment. The **experimental probability** that you will make a basket is the following ratio.

$$P(\text{basket}) = \frac{\text{number of baskets made}}{\text{number of baskets attempted}}$$

Work with a partner to collect data. First decide on the number of baskets you will attempt for your experiment. Also agree on any necessary rules or procedures. While you attempt to make baskets, your partner records the data. Then switch roles.

1. Find $P(\text{basket})$ for both you and your partner.

2. Why do you need to experiment to find this probability?

┌**THINK AND DISCUSS**

Tonia is on the girls' basketball team. One day at practice, Tonia collected the data at the left on her free throws.

3. a. What is the experimental probability that Tonia will make a basket when she shoots a free throw?

  b. Write her experimental probability as a percent.

4. a. Tonia shoots 12 free throws in the next game. How many do you expect her to make?

  b. Will she make this same number every time she attempts 12 free throws? Explain.

When a player makes many baskets in a row, people may call this a *hot streak*. This means that the results are better than usual.

5. Tonia made 4 baskets in a row during a game. Do you think that a sequence of 4 baskets is a hot streak for Tonia?

TONIA'S FREE THROWS							
M = Miss			B = Basket				
M	M	B	B	B	M	B	M
M	B	M	B	B	M	M	B

 In 1992 Ginny Doyle, a senior at the University of Richmond, set a record for college basketball by making 66 consecutive free throws.

Source: *New York Times*

One way to simulate an activity is to use random numbers. Because they are **random,** all the numbers used are equally likely to occur. You can use a computer to simulate Tonia's shots by randomly generating a set of two digits, such as 0 and 1. Let 0 represent making a basket and let 1 represent a miss.

6. Computer Simulate 20 of Tonia's free throws.

  a. How many sequences of 4 or more baskets in a row do you see in the data?

  b. Judging from your list of random numbers, how often do you expect Tonia to make a sequence of 4 baskets in a row?

  c. Do you think Tonia's 4 baskets is a hot streak?

7. a. Computer Continue simulating Tonia's free throws. Make a spreadsheet like the one shown below. Let the spreadsheet calculate the probability in column D.

	A	B	C	D
1	**Number of Baskets**	**Number of Misses**	**Number of Free Throws**	**P(basket)**
2			20	
3			40	
4			60	
5			80	
6			100	

On April 14, 1993, Don Calhoun of Bloomington, Illinois, sank a basket from 79 ft away. The challenge was part of a promotion held during a Chicago Bulls–Miami Heat game. For his efforts Calhoun won $1 million. Neither Scottie Pippen nor Michael Jordan could make the 79-ft shot.

Source: *Sports Illustrated*

  b. Make a line graph of the data in columns C and D of your spreadsheet. What does the graph show?

  c. What happens to *P*(basket) as the number of free throws increases?

  d. What is the advantage of collecting a large amount of data?

8. a. Sam tossed a penny 100 times. He found the experimental probability of getting heads was 55%. Susan thought the probability of getting heads was 50%. Why are Sam's results different from what Susan expects?

  b. How do you think a thousand tosses would affect Sam's results?

1. A right triangle has sides 9 cm, 12 cm, and 15 cm long. Find its area.

Evaluate for $x = \frac{1}{2}$.

2. $-16x^2 - \frac{7}{8}$

3. $x^3 + 5x$

4. A bag contains 1 red marble and 3 white marbles. What is the probability that a marble drawn is red?

5. Mr. and Mrs. Medeiros have two boys. What is the probability that their next child will be a girl?

RANDOM NUMBER TABLE

```
23948 71477 12573 05954
65628 22310 09311 94864
41261 09943 34078 70481
34831 94515 41490 93312
09802 09770 11258 41139
66068 74522 15522 49227
00458 48800 33785 67694
45713 06400 87143 19586
57648 49551 40424 72908
21397 31604 84615 40513
```

9. **Data File 3 (pp. 90–91)** Find P(free throw) for Shaquille O'Neal during the 1990–91 season. Was he more likely to make a field goal or a free throw?

10. **Writing** Give an example of a probability that you can find only by doing an experiment.

11. **Language** Do an experiment to find the probability that a randomly selected word in this book contains the letter e.

    a. List your data, and explain how you generated the data.

    b. How many words did you look at to find $P(e)$? If you looked at twice as many words, would your results be different? Would they be better? Explain.

12. **Science** The probability that a male is colorblind is 8%. Suppose you interview 1,000 males. About how many do you think will be colorblind? Do you think you will get exactly this number? Why or why not?

13. A game at the carnival is called "Spin Your Age." To play, you spin a wheel numbered 0–9 twice. To win, you must spin the two digits of your age in order. For example, if you are 13, you must spin a 1, then a 3.

    a. Calculate the probability that you will win.

    b. Consider the digits in the random number table two at a time. Use the table to find the experimental probability that you will win.

    c. Write the probabilities you found in part (a) and part (b) as percents. Round to the nearest tenth. Is the experimental probability you found in part (b) close to the probability you calculated in part (a)?

14. **Sports** Patrick Ewing of the New York Knicks makes about 75% of his free throws. Use the random number table at the left. Let 1–6 represent making a basket, and 7 and 8 represent missing a basket. Skip 9 and 0.

    a. How does the plan for using the random number table reflect Patrick Ewing's free throw probability?

    b. What kind of basket streaks do you find?

    c. How many baskets must Patrick Ewing make in a row for you to consider him to be on a streak?

ractice

A number cube is rolled. Find each probability.

1. $P(5)$ **2.** $P(\text{not } 5)$ **3.** $P(4 \text{ or } 5)$ **4.** $P(4 \text{ or not } 4)$

A wheel numbered from 1 to 8 is spun. Each outcome is equally likely. Write each probability as a fraction, a decimal, and a percent.

5. $P(9)$ **6.** $P(\text{odd number})$ **7.** $P(1 \text{ or } 5)$ **8.** $P(1) + P(5)$

9. $P(\text{not } 5)$ **10.** $P(\text{not } 2 \text{ and not } 3)$ **11.** $P(0)$ **12.** $P(\text{number less than } 8)$

Find the odds in favor of each event when using the spinner at the right.

13. in favor of a 4

14. in favor of a multiple of 3

15. in favor of a 7 or 9

16. in favor of an odd number

The events *A* and *B* are independent. Find *P*(*A* and *B*).

17. $P(A) = \frac{2}{3}$, $P(B) = \frac{3}{5}$ **18.** $P(A) = \frac{1}{2}$, $P(B) = \frac{3}{4}$ **19.** $P(A) = \frac{2}{9}$, $P(B) = \frac{1}{6}$

A box has 4 red cards, 2 blue cards, 1 yellow card, and 1 green card in it. Find the probability of each pair of events.

20. A: Draw a red card. Keep it.   B: Draw a red card.

21. A: Draw a blue card. Keep it.   B: Draw a green card.

22. A: Draw a blue card. Replace it.   B: Draw a yellow card.

23. Draw a grid or a tree diagram to show all the outcomes in the sample space for rolling a number cube and tossing a coin.

24. There are 7 ways to do task Q. There are 3 ways to do task R. Find the number of ways to do task Q, then task R.

25. A bag contains the letters P R O B A B I L I T Y. What is the probability that if you reach in and take out two letters, one after the other without replacement, you will select a T, then an I?

Permutations and Combinations

WORK TOGETHER

Play the game STOP with your group. You have one minute in which to write as many words as possible that use all four letters in the word STOP. A word counts only if it is in a dictionary. The player who has the greatest number of words wins.

1. **Discussion** What strategies did you use to find every possible arrangement of the four letters?

2. Make an organized list that includes every arrangement of the four letters.

   a. How many of these arrangements are in your list?

   b. How many of these arrangements are real words you can find in a dictionary?

THINK AND DISCUSS

You can use the counting principle to find the number of arrangements of the letters S, T, O, and P.

FLASHBACK

To use the counting principle, multiply by the number of choices for each decision.

first letter		second letter		third letter		fourth letter	
4	×	3	×	2	×	1	= 24

3. **a.** Why are there 4 choices for the first letter but only 3 choices for the second letter?

   b. What is the probability that when the letters S, T, O, and P are scrambled, a real word is formed?

An arrangement in which order is important is a **permutation.** The permutation STOP is different from the permutation POTS because the order of the letters is different.

4. How many permutations of the letters A, B, and C are there?

5. Use the four letters S, T, O, and P. Make an organized list of all the three-letter permutations.

You can also use the counting principle to find the number of three-letter permutations of the four letters S, T, O, and P.

first letter		second letter		third letter	
4	×	3	×	2	= 24

6. Use the counting principle to find the number of two-letter permutations of the letters S, T, O, and P. To check your work, make an organized list of all possible arrangements.

7. Use your list from Question 6. How many permutations contain the letters S and T? T and P? S and O? O and T?

An arrangement in which order does *not* matter is a **combination.** Suppose Tom, George, and Martha are standing in a line. The arrangement Tom, George, then Martha is different from the arrangement George, Martha, then Tom. Arranging people in a line involves permutations. Selecting three people for a committee, on the other hand, involves combinations. Tom, George, Martha is the same committee as George, Martha, Tom.

Scrabble® is a popular word game where players try to form words with lettered tiles. There are over 3.3 billion permutations of the alphabet when you use 7 different letters at a time. **How many permutations are there for one set of 7 letters?**

Example   You own five sweaters and you are taking two to summer camp. In how many ways can you choose two sweaters from the five?

Let the numbers 1, 2, 3, 4, 5 represent the five sweaters. List all the possible arrangements.

(1, 2) (1, 3) (1, 4) (1, 5) (2, 1) (2, 3) (2, 4) (2, 5)
(3, 1) (3, 2) (3, 4) (3, 5) (4, 1) (4, 2) (4, 3) (4, 5)

Underline only the different arrangements.

<u>(1, 2)</u> <u>(1, 3)</u> <u>(1, 4)</u> <u>(1, 5)</u> (2, 1) <u>(2, 3)</u> <u>(2, 4)</u> <u>(2, 5)</u>
(3, 1) (3, 2) <u>(3, 4)</u> <u>(3, 5)</u> (4, 1) (4, 2) (4, 3) <u>(4, 5)</u>

You have 10 different choices.

8. In how many ways can a coach choose a team of three gymnasts from a group of five gymnasts?

9. You and three friends want to have a picture taken together. If you line up shoulder to shoulder, in how many ways can the picture be taken?

10. Which question, 8 or 9, involves permutations?

1. Name four fractions which are equivalent to $\frac{3}{5}$.

Write each decimal as a fraction and simplify it.

2. 0.096   3. 0.875

4. A rectangle has a perimeter of 48 m. Make a list of all of the possible dimensions that are whole meter units. Which dimensions give you the largest area?

Find the square root.

5. 625   6. 196

7. Give an example of a probability problem that can be solved by a computer simulation. Explain how this can be done.

Problem Solving Hint

Find the ways one accessory can be selected, then two, then three.

TRY THESE

11. You decide to pin photos of six friends in a row on a bulletin board. In how many ways can you arrange the photos?

12. **Critical Thinking** You have 4 books and select 2 of them. Are there more possible combinations or permutations? Why?

13. A club of 10 students chooses officers. One student will be president and another student will be vice president. How many different outcomes are possible?

14. Twelve students volunteer to help organize a class trip. Two of them are assigned to collect money for the trip. In how many ways can these two students be chosen?

ON YOUR OWN

15. Suppose you have five different CDs to play. Your CD player can play three CDs in a row.

    a. How many different sets of three CDs can you play?

    b. You decide on which three CDs to play. In how many different orders can you play them?

16. **Choose A, B, C, or D.** Andrea plans to buy a bicycle, a helmet, a water bottle, and a lock. She will buy the bicycle and some accessories. How many different sets of one or more accessories can she select?

    A. 3   **B.** 5   **C.** 4   **D.** 7

17. **Writing** Use your own words and an example to explain the difference between a permutation and a combination.

18. The combination to open your lock has three numbers: 10, 45, and 6. You cannot remember the order of the numbers.

    a. List all the possible combinations for your lock.

    b. You decide to start trying different combinations. If you are as unlucky as possible, how many will you have to try before you open the lock?

    c. **Language** Are you concerned about mathematical *combinations* or *permutations* when you have a combination lock?

19. Write all the four-letter permutations of the letters C, A, T, and S. How many of the permutations form real words?

20. **Investigation (p. 418)** Professor Mergatroid's assistant Labcoat rushed in to tell the professor that he had found two couples that were married in June. Why was the professor not amazed by Labcoat's discovery?

More Area Codes in 1995

Three-digit area codes were first developed in 1947. At that time only 86 of them were used. The first digit could not be 0 or 1 because 0 and 1 were used for contacting telephone operators. The second digit was always 0 or 1 to indicate a long distance phone call. Now, all but a few area codes are in use.

New technology has been developed so that 792 area codes will be possible. The new area codes will be in use beginning in 1995.

21. How many different area codes were available in 1947?

22. If there were no restrictions on the digits used for three-digit area codes, how many would be possible?

Telstar,
the first communications satellite, was launched in 1962. Telstar allowed the first television pictures to be transmitted across the Atlantic and ushered in a new age of telephone, telegraph, telephoto, and facsimile transmissions.

Source: *Encyclopedia Britannica*

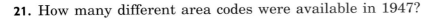
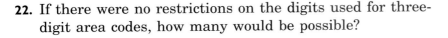

Tell whether each situation is a combination or a permutation. Then solve the problem.

1. Find the number of ways of selecting 2 soloists from a chorus group of 6.

2. **Calculator** Find the number of ways of arranging 9 books on a shelf.

3. **a.** How could you simulate randomly selecting two club officers from the choices Liz, Janis, Alex, and Maurice?

b. Is the selection of officers an independent or dependent event? Explain.

What's Ahead

- Using the capture/recapture method to estimate population size

10-8 Estimating Population Size

Marked deer wear *their visible collars for life. The collars are made of a strong plastic-vinyl material. A symbol is painted on each collar so that the collar serves as an identification tag.*

THINK AND DISCUSS

One project of the Montana Department of Fish, Wildlife, and Parks is to manage the mule deer population in the Bridger Mountains near Bozeman. They use the *capture/recapture* method to estimate the size of the population each winter. Researchers place a visible collar around the necks of a number of deer. The deer with collars are called marked deer. The researchers fly over a specific area and count the number of marked deer and the total number of deer they see. Then they solve the proportion below for an estimate of the deer population.

$$\frac{\text{marked deer counted}}{\text{total deer counted}} = \frac{\text{number of marked deer}}{\text{estimate of deer population}}$$

1. Suppose researchers know that there are 55 marked deer in an area. They fly over the area and count 48 marked deer and a total of 638 deer. Estimate the deer population.

Data collected in one area of the Bridger Mountains by the Montana Department of Fish, Wildlife and Parks are given below.

Date	Conditions	Total Deer Counted	Marked Deer Counted	Number of Marked Deer
3/79	Patchy snow, −7°C	1173	65	101
3/80	Patchy snow, −4°C; deer scattered	1017	42	83
3/81	Mostly bare, dry, −1°C; deer scattered	1212	32	60
3/82	Light snow cover, 1°C; deer at low elevation	1707	30	36
3/83	Mostly bare, −4°C; deer at low elevation	1612	68	89
3/84	Bare, dry, 6°C; large deer groups at low elevation	1590	37	59
3/85	Mostly bare, dry; deer at low elevation	1417	42	54
3/86	Mostly bare, dry; deer at low elevation	1608	85	110
3/87	2 cm snow cover; deer normally distributed	1469	52	83

2. Use a proportion to estimate the total number of deer for each year from 1979 to 1987. Complete a table with these column headings: Date, Total Deer Counted, Marked Deer Counted, Number of Marked Deer, and Deer Population Estimate.

3. Analyze your table. How did the population of deer change over the eight years?

Researchers also calculate aerial counting efficiency by finding the ratio of marked deer counted to the number of marked deer.

4. a. Calculate aerial counting efficiency for each year from 1979 to 1987. Write the ratio as a decimal rounded to the nearest thousandth. Include these numbers in the table you made in Exercise 2.

b. In which years did researchers count a high percent of the deer?

c. Discussion Explain how this might affect the estimate of the deer population.

Deer population data are collected in the winter. Each winter, the same families of deer settle in the same areas. Researchers have determined seven distinct "population habitat units" in the Bridger Mountains. A clear, snowy winter day provides ideal conditions for seeing and counting the deer from a helicopter or airplane.

WORK TOGETHER

Try out the capture/recapture technique with your group. Place an unknown number of square tiles in a bag. As a group decide on the number of tiles to remove from the bag. Then follow the steps below.

- Remove the decided upon number of tiles from the bag. Mark each tile with an X.
- Replace the marked tiles in the bag and shake it.
- Take a sample from the bag.
- Record the number of marked tiles in the sample. Record the total number of tiles in the sample.
- Write and solve a proportion to find the number of square tiles in the bag.

1. 2,000 sheets of paper stack 635 mm high. How thick is 1 piece of paper?

2. How many ways can you arrange 4 books on a shelf?

3. How many different 5-digit license plates can be made using the digits 1–9 without repeating a digit?

4. Solve $\frac{1}{2}n + 5 = -20$.

5. A $75 coat is on sale for $52.50. What percent of the regular price is the sale price?

ON YOUR OWN

5. In a study of catfish in Beaver Lake, workers for the state extension service caught, tagged, and set free 124 catfish. A few weeks later the workers caught 140 catfish. Thirty-five had tags. Estimate the number of catfish in the lake.

6. **a.** An ecology class is helping the local conservation society determine the squirrel population in the city's park. In early October, the students and society members captured, tagged, and set free 68 squirrels. Three weeks later, 84 squirrels were captured, and 16 had tags. Estimate the number of squirrels in the park.

   b. Critical Thinking Suppose some of the squirrels lost their tags. How do you think this would affect your estimation of the squirrel population?

DECISION MAKING

Too Many to Count

Experiment with the capture/recapture method. For members of the population, use any convenient objects that you can mark.

COLLECT DATA

Your goal is to find how many objects you need in a sample to get an accurate measure of the number of objects in the population. Count out 200 objects for the total population and mark 20 of them. You will take several samples and use the capture/recapture method to estimate the number of objects in the total population.

1. Decide how to take samples of different sizes. Explain how you plan to collect your data.

2. Take at least five different-sized samples and record your data. Complete a table like the one below.

	Marked Objects Present	Total Objects Counted	Marked Objects Counted
Sample 1	20	■	■
Sample 2	20	■	■

Officials Consider Closing Flathead

The Montana Department of Fish, Wildlife, and Parks is proposing to close Flathead Lake to sockeye salmon fishing. Their plan seeks to help the ailing salmon populations rebuild.

Once a mainstay of fishing in Flathead Lake, the sockeye salmon have all but disappeared from the lake in recent years despite efforts to save them. When the department released a quarter-million of them into the lake this summer, lake trout gobbled up many of them.

The department is seeking public comment on the sockeye salmon proposal and a dozen other changes to fishing in northwest Montana.

 Scientists use capture/ recapture methods to estimate many populations—bird, mammal, fish, reptile, insect, and others.

7. **Writing** Use what you have learned to explain how the Montana Department of Fish, Wildlife and Parks might have researched the issue discussed in the news article above.

NALYZE DATA

3. For each sample, solve a proportion to estimate total objects present. Add a column to your table for these values.

4. How well do you think the capture/recapture method works?

5. Analyze your results. Do you think the size of the sample affects how close the estimate is to the actual population? Make a hypothesis and test it by taking more samples.

6. Do you think the number of marked objects affects the population estimate? Make a hypothesis and test it.

AKE DECISIONS

7. Decide on an ideal sample size for estimating a population of about 200. Explain why the sample size should not be too small or too large.

8. Suppose you mark 40 objects. Will this affect the size of the sample you need? Try an experiment and then explain.

To predict election results, pollsters carefully choose sample sizes in order to collect valid data.

Wrap Up

Probability and Odds   10-1, 10-2

The **probability** of an event is the ratio of favorable outcomes to the total number of possible outcomes. The **odds** in favor of an event is the ratio of favorable to unfavorable outcomes.

The sum of the probability of an event and the probability of its complement is 1.

Find the probability of each event if a card is drawn at random.

| T | R | U | M | P | E | T |

1. selecting a P
2. selecting a T
3. not selecting a P

Use the cards above to find the odds in favor of each event.

4. selecting a T
5. selecting an E
6. selecting a consonant

Sample Space and the Counting Principle   10-3

The **sample space** is the set of all possible outcomes of an event.

The **counting principle** enables you to find the number of outcomes for an event with more than one step by multiplying the number of outcomes for each step.

7. **a.** At the China Panda, if you order the Happy Family Dinner, you choose one appetizer, one soup and one main dish from the menu below. Use a tree diagram or grid to find the sample space of all the possible dinners. How many dinners are there?

Appetizers	Soups	Main Dishes
Egg rolls	Won-ton	Almond Chicken
Fried Won-tons	Sizzling Rice	Sweet & Sour Pork
		Beef Broccoli

   b. Use the counting principle to find all of the possible dinners.

8. Use the counting principle to determine the number of ways the offices of president, vice president, secretary, and treasurer can be chosen from the 12 member student council.

Independent and Dependent Events

Two events are **independent** if the outcome of the first event *does not* affect the outcome of the second event.

Two events are **dependent** if the outcome of the first event *does* influence the outcome of the second event.

9. A jar contains 5 blue, 3 red, and 2 green marbles. You select a blue marble and replace it. What is the probability of selecting a green marble?

10. **Choose A, B, C, or D.** A jar contains 5 blue, 3 red, and 2 green marbles. What is the probability of choosing a red marble and then another red marble when none is replaced?

   A. $\frac{1}{5}$ **B.** $\frac{1}{15}$ **C.** $\frac{3}{100}$ **D.** $\frac{3}{10}$

Permutations and Combinations

A **permutation** is an arrangement of a set of objects where order is important. A **combination** is an arrangement of objects where order does not matter.

11. Five students compete on a relay team. Only four of them can race at a time. How many different teams are possible?

12. Four students are selected for a relay team. In how many ways can they line up for the race?

Strategies and Applications

You can simulate some problems. For other problems, you can use the capture/recapture method to estimate population size.

13. Charlie usually makes one out of two baskets that he attempts. Describe a simulation to find the probability that he will make four out of five baskets.

14. Researchers marked 22 lions in an area. They make an aerial count of 68 lions, 16 of which are marked. Estimate the lion population.

GETTING READY FOR CHAPTER 11

Copy each figure on graph paper. Then show what each figure would look like if you "flip" it over the red line.

1.

2.

3.

4.

PUTTING IT ALL TOGETHER

fOllow Up

The Birthday Hypothesis

Professor Mergatroid is uncertain of whether to begin a search for two people with the same birthday. He has asked for your opinion on the matter. At the beginning of the chapter you estimated the number of people whose birthdays the professor might have to check. Look back at your estimate. Revise it if necessary based on your study of the chapter. Then write a letter to the professor with your recommendation. In your letter you should include how you made your estimate.

The problems preceded by the magnifying glass (p. 429, # 25; p. 437, # 17; and p. 445, # 20) will help you complete the investigation.

Excursion: Labcoat found that he had to ask 333 people before he located another person with his birthday, July 17. "See," he said to Professor Mergatroid, "I told you it would be hard." How was Labcoat's search different from the one the professor is thinking of making?

NUMBER EXPLORATION "AVERAGE NUMBERS"

Even numbers are numbers which end with the digits 0, 2, 4, 6, or 8. Odd numbers are numbers which end with the digits 1, 3, 5, 7, or 9. When we count by two, we name all the even numbers.

- What do you think the average of the first four consecutive even numbers (2, 4, 6, 8) is? Make a prediction then check your estimate.

- Now find the average of the first seven consecutive even numbers. Notice anything?

Explore finding the averages of sets of consecutive even numbers starting with 2. Have you noticed a pattern? Can you predict the average of the first twenty-four consecutive even numbers? Use a calculator to check your prediction.

Extension: Can you predict the average of the first four consecutive odd numbers? Explore sets of consecutive odd numbers as you did above. What do you notice?

Enough!!!

This game is for two or three people. You need two number cubes numbered 1 through 6 and paper for keeping score. Take turns rolling the cubes. Each person rolls the cubes as many times as s/he wants to in each turn. The total of all the numbers rolled, no matter how many times the cubes have been rolled during the turn, is awarded to that player. When the player thinks s/he has enough points for that turn, say "Enough" and pass the cubes on to the next person. Add the scores at the end of each round. The first person to reach or go over 100 points is the winner. Sounds easy?

The catch: When the number "1" shows up during a turn, all the points rolled in that turn go back to "0", the turn is over, and nothing is scored for that player during that round.

FAIR GAME

Toy companies develop new games every year. Once created, the games must be tested to find out if they are "fair" to every player.

Get together with one or two friends and create a new game. Think of a theme or goal for the game. You may use spinners, number cubes, or a set of cards that you make to determine moves. If your game requires a game board, make an interesting one. Write out the rules for others to follow. When your game is finished, play it a few times to make sure it is a fair game. Be prepared to fix it if needed. When the game is ready, share it with others.

PAPER CUPS

Experiment with paper cups and their landing position (up, upside down, or sideways). Suppose the size or material of the cup changes. Does the probability of the landing position change? Design different experiments with different cups so you can compare the results. Experiment with Styrofoam, plastic, and paper cups as well as with cups of different sizes.

Strategy

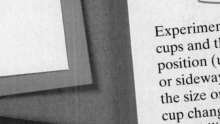

The following game is for two players. You place ten pennies in a circle. The first player picks up one or two adjacent pennies. The next player does the same. You continue back and forth until there are no more pennies left. The player who picks up the last penny wins. Play the game several times. Are you more likely to win if you are the first player or the second? Will your answer change if you use 9 or 11 pennies?

1. The odds in favor of snow tomorrow are 1 to 4. Find the probability that it will snow tomorrow.

2. Factory workers test 80 batteries made in the factory. Four batteries are defective. Find the probability that any battery from the factory will be defective. Write the probability as a fraction, a decimal, and a percent.

3. Javier is buying a new car. He has a choice of 3 models, 8 colors, and 2 interiors. How many different car choices are there?

4. There are six open containers arranged as shown. A ball is tossed and falls into one of the containers. Find the probability of each event.

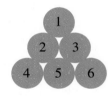

   a. $P(4)$ **b.** P(even number)

   c. P(a number greater than 4)

5. Suppose you have a bag that contains 6 blue, 3 red, 2 green and 1 white marble. All marbles are equally likely to be drawn from the bag. Find each probability.

   a. P(blue)   **b.** P(white)

   c. P(blue or white)

   d. P(blue, then white when blue is not replaced)

6. Suppose that the probability that you make a basket each time you shoot is 0.2. What is the probability that you will not make a basket?

7. The letters of the word HALLOWEEN are written on a set of cards. You are equally likely to get any card. What is the probability of selecting an L, then a W if the first card is not replaced before selecting the second card?

8. **a.** Find the number of two-letter permutations of the letters A, B, C.

   b. Find the number of two-letter combinations of the letters A, B, C.

9. **Writing** Fifty students in a school were chosen at random. They were asked what kind of pizza crust they liked best. Fifteen of them said that they preferred thick crust. If there are 940 students in the school, how many of them would you expect to prefer thick crust? Explain.

10. **Choose A, B, C, or D.** You are equally likely to get one of four prizes when you buy Good Morning cereal. You want to find out how many boxes of cereal you should buy to get all four prizes. Which of the following is *not* a true statement?

    A. You can simulate buying the cereal by using a spinner divided into four equal sections. One trial ends when the spinner has stopped in each of the sections at least once. Average the results of several trials.

    B. The result of the simulation is the exact number of boxes you will need to buy.

    C. The more trials you have, the better your results.

    D. A possible answer is 4 boxes.

Cumulative Review

Choose A, B, C, or D.

1. Which jar of peanut butter is the best buy?

   A. an 18 oz jar for $1.69

   B. a 30 oz jar for $2.59

   C. a 32 oz jar for $2.89

   D. a 24 oz jar for $2.09

2. Sarah bought a remnant of fabric $5\frac{1}{8}$ yards long to make pennants for the school fair. How many pennants can she make if $\frac{3}{4}$ yard is needed for each pennant?

   A. 5   **B.** 6   **C.** 7   **D.** 8

3. **Estimation** If the area of the shaded region is 4 in.^{2}, what is the best estimate for the area of the unshaded region?

   A. 4 in.^{2}

   B. 8 in.^{2}

   C. 12 in.^{2}

   D. 16 in.^{2}

4. Which event does *not* have a 50% probability of occurring?

   A. getting heads on one toss of a coin

   B. drawing a red marble from a bag that has 3 red, 2 blue and 1 yellow marble

   C. rolling a number cube and getting an even number

   D. rolling a number cube and getting either a 5 or a 6

5. Which one does not equal the others?

   A. 4% of 3,000   **B.** 40% of 30

   C. 40% of 300   **D.** 30% of 400

6. Rectangle *ABCD* and rectangle *AXYZ* are similar. How long is $\overline{XY}$?

   A. 2.5 cm

   B. 2 cm

   C. 1.6 cm

   D. 1.5 cm

   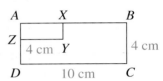

7. If the two spinners are each spun once, what is the probability that the sum of the numbers spun is 10?

   A. 0   **B.** $\frac{1}{4}$ **C.** $\frac{1}{2}$ **D.** 1

8. The lowest common denominator of three fractions is 42. Two of the fractions are $\frac{5}{3}$ and $\frac{6}{7}$. Which fraction could be the third one?

   A. $\frac{10}{21}$ **B.** $\frac{1}{35}$ **C.** $\frac{17}{284}$ **D.** $1\frac{9}{14}$

9. What is the volume of a rectangular prism that has dimensions 1 in., 2 in., and 3 in.?

   A. 27 in.^{3} **B.** 18 in.^{3}

   C. 6 in.^{3} **D.** 12 in.^{3}

10. A circle has circumference 56.52 ft. What is its area? Use 3.14 for π.

    A. 254.34 ft^2 **B.** 56.52 ft^2

    C. 28.26 ft^2 **D.** 1,017.36 ft^2

Data File 11

Ratios of Exposed to Submerged Areas of Icebergs

Iceberg type	Ratio (exposed:submerged)
Flat top	1:6
Rounded top	1:4
Typical iceberg	1:3
Single peak	1:2
Double peaked	1:1

Source: *Encyclopedia Britannica*

Average Temperature at Different Latitudes

North latitudes	Average Temperature (°C)	(°F)
90°	−22.7	−8.9
80°	−17.2	1.0
70°	−10.7	12.7
60°	−1.1	30.0
50°	5.8	42.4
40°	14.1	57.4
30°	20.4	68.7
20°	25.3	77.5
10°	26.7	80.1
Equator	26.2	79.2
10°	25.3	77.5
20°	22.9	73.2
30°	18.4	65.1
40°	11.9	53.4
50°	5.8	42.4
60°	−3.4	25.9
70°	−13.6	7.5
80°	−27.0	−16.6
90°	−33.1	−27.6
South latitudes		

Source: *Encyclopedia Britannica*

Iceberg Sightings in the North Atlantic South of 48°N

Number of Icebergs (y-axis: 0 to 80)

Jan. Feb. Mar. Apr. May June July Aug. Sept. Oct. Nov. Dec.

Source: *The Times Atlas and Encyclopedia of the Sea*

WHAT YOU WILL LEARN

- how to graph points and lines
- how to interpret slope
- how to use technology to graph mathematical models
- how to solve problems by writing an equation

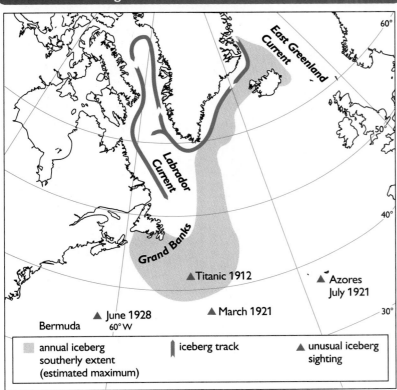

Iceberg Movements in the North Atlantic

East Greenland Current

Labrador Current

Grand Banks

▲ Titanic 1912

▲ Azores July 1921

▲ June 1928

Bermuda 60° W

▲ March 1921

60°
50°
40°
30°

annual iceberg southerly extent (estimated maximum)

iceberg track

▲ unusual iceberg sighting

WHERE IN THE WORLD ARE YOU?

We locate places on a globe by measuring degrees of latitude and longitude. We measure latitude starting at the equator, which is 0° latitude. The imaginary lines above it are given as degrees north, and those below it are given as degrees south. Longitude is based upon a line called the prime meridian, which runs from the North Pole, through Greenwich, England to the South Pole. This location is 0° longitude. The imaginary lines are placed east and west of it. Ocean vessels use latitude and longitude to give their location while at sea.

WORLD VIEW

If the Antarctic ice sheets were to melt completely, sea levels throughout the world would rise about 220 ft. If the Greenland icecap also melted, the sea levels would rise an additional 24 ft.

Arctic icebergs usually break away from glaciers near Greenland. About 12,500 icebergs break away each year. Of these, about 375 float into the Atlantic Ocean.

Sources: *The Times Atlas and Encyclopedia of the Sea, Encyclopedia Britannica*

investigation

Memo

There are many ways to get from the bottom of a mountain to the top. In Colorado, motorists drive to the top of Mount Evans and Pikes Peak. In Albuquerque, New Mexico, skiers take a cable car to the top of Sandia Peak. In Pittsburgh, commuters ride funiculars—train cars pulled by cables—up the city's hills. A few mountains, including Whiteface Mountain in New York's Adirondack Mountains, have elevators to the top! The steepness of a mountain determines how difficult it is to climb—by foot, car or elevator!

Mission: Find the steepness of an imaginary line running from the base of one wall of your classroom to the top of the opposite wall. Describe your findings in mathematical terms.

LEADS tO FOLLoW

✓ What tools can you use to measure steepness?

✓ How can you express how steep something is?

✓ What changes as a line grows steeper and steeper?

- Writing the coordinates of a given point

- Graphing points on the coordinate plane

■ WHAT YOU'LL NEED

✓ **Graph paper**

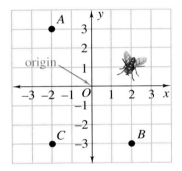

TH**I**N**K** **A**N**D** **D**I**S**C**U**S**S**

An old legend says that the French mathematician and philosopher Rene Descartes (1596–1650) was lying on his bed one day, staring up at the ceiling, when he noticed a fly crawling across it. Descartes began thinking about how to describe the exact position of the fly on the ceiling. His thoughts generated the *coordinate plane.*

The intersection of a horizontal number line (called the **x-axis**) and a vertical number line (called the **y-axis**) forms the **coordinate plane.** The axes intersect at a point called the *origin.*

You can describe all locations on the coordinate plane by using the numbers along the axes. The first number, or *x*-coordinate, tells you how far to move horizontally. The second number, or *y*-coordinate, tells you how far to move vertically. You write the coordinates as an *ordered pair* (x, y).

Example Write the coordinates for the fly at the left.
1
- The fly is 2 units to the right of the *y*-axis. Movement left and right is shown by the *x*-coordinate. So the *x*-coordinate is 2.

- The fly is 1 unit above the *x*-axis. Movement up and down is shown by the *y*-coordinate. So the *y*-coordinate is 1.

The ordered pair for the location of the fly is (2, 1).

1. What are the coordinates of the origin?

2. a. On the *x*-axis, which direction is positive? negative?

  b. On the *y*-axis, which direction is positive? negative?

Example What point has coordinates $(2, -3)$?
2
- Start at the origin. Move 2 units to the right and 3 units down.

Point *B* has coordinates $(2, -3)$.

Did you ever wonder why it's so difficult to hit a fly with a flyswatter? The common housefly has over 4,000 eye facets, providing it with a wide field of vision. The mosaic effect of all those eye facets make it difficult for the fly to see shapes clearly, although movement is seen very quickly.

Source: *Collier's Encyclopedia*

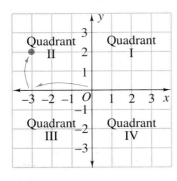

The *x*- and *y*-axes divide the coordinate plane into four *quadrants,* as shown at the left.

Example In which quadrant is the point $(-3, 2)$ located?
3
- Start at the origin (O). Move 3 units to the left and 2 units up.

The point $(-3, 2)$ is in the second quadrant.

3. What is true of the signs of the *x*- and *y*-coordinates of all the points in the first quadrant?

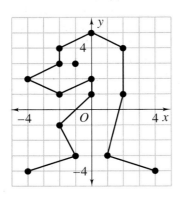

WORK TOGETHER

Make a dot-to-dot drawing (such as the one at the left) on a coordinate plane. On a separate sheet of paper, write the coordinates of the dots in the order in which you connected them. Without showing your drawings, exchange lists of ordered pairs with your partner. Recreate your partner's drawing by graphing the coordinates given to you.

TRY THESE

Name the point with the given coordinates.

4. $(-5, 3)$ **5.** $(4, 0)$

6. $(-6, 2)$ **7.** $(5, -3)$

8. $(0, 5)$ **9.** $(6, 2)$

Write the coordinates of each point.

10. *G*   **11.** *K*

12. *J*   **13.** *H*

14. *M*   **15.** *L*

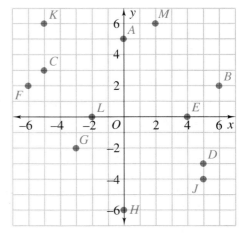

16. Which of these points is *not* the vertex of a square formed by the other four: $(-1, -3)$, $(-1, 0)$, $(2, -3)$, $(4, -2)$, and $(2, 0)$?

17. In which quadrant are both coordinates of a point negative?

Identify the quadrant in which each point lies.

18. $(3, -15)$ **19.** $(-2,000, 12)$ **20.** $(-0.05, -0.39)$ **21.** $\left(\dfrac{17}{2}, \dfrac{3}{21}\right)$

22. In which quadrant(s) do the coordinates of a point have different signs?

23. a. Graph the points $(-3, -2)$, $(-3, 2)$, $(-3, -6)$, and $(-3, 6)$.

   b. What do you notice about these four points?

   c. Give the coordinates of two other points that fit the pattern.

24. a. A horizontal line is shown in red at the right. List the ordered pairs of 3 points that fall on the line.

   b. Which coordinate of an ordered pair stays the same for all points on the line? which coordinate changes?

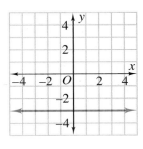

25. Writing Describe how to find the point $(5, -1)$ on a coordinate plane.

26. A robot arm must move the black peg in the diagram onto the white square, but the peg must be moved around—not over—the red walls. List the coordinates of the vertices of a path the robot arm might follow to move the peg.

27. Choose A, B, C, or D. Which of the following groups of ordered pairs are *not* the vertices of a rectangle?

   A. $(-4, 1)$, $(4, 1)$, $(-4, -1)$, and $(4, -1)$

   B. $(-1, 0)$, $(-5, -3)$, $(-1, -4)$, and $(-5, 0)$

   C. $(3, 6)$, $(6, 6)$, $(3, 9)$, and $(6, 9)$

   D. $(-3, 8)$, $(3, 8)$, $(3, -8)$, and $(-3, -8)$

Mi$x$ed **REVIEW**

Find each sum.

1. $5 + (-9)$

2. $-10 + (-6)$

3. A bag contains an unknown number of marbles. You pick 15 at random and mark them. You put back the marked marbles and mix the contents. You pick 30 marbles. If 10 are marked, predict the number of marbles in the bag.

4. Find two integers whose sum is -3 and whose difference is 7.

By the year 2000 there may be over 60,000 robots in use in the United States.

Source: *Robotics*

11-2 **G**raphing Linear Equations

T H I N K A N D D I S C U S S

Ronelle Moore makes tire swings for local day-care centers during her summer vacations. One swing requires enough rope to reach the tree branch plus another 5 ft for the knots around the tire and the branch.

1. Suppose you want a swing to hang 8 ft below the branch. How much rope do you need?

2. Suppose you have 17 ft of rope. How far below the branch will the swing hang?

Ronelle let x represent the distance the swing hangs below the tree and y represent the length of rope needed. She wrote the equation $y = x + 5$. Then she found some possible lengths.

3. Copy and complete Ronelle's table.

x	$x + 5$	y	(x, y)
8	8 + 5	13	(8, 13)
10	10 + 5	■	(■, ■)
12	■	■	(■, ■)

An equation like $y = x + 5$ is an equation in two variables. A solution of an equation in two variables is an ordered pair that makes the equation true. Each of the ordered pairs in the table is a solution of the equation $y = x + 5$.

Example 1 Is the ordered pair (40, 45) a solution of the equation $y = x + 5$?

• $y = x + 5$
$y = 40 + 5$ ← Substitute 40 for x in the equation.
$y = 45$

The ordered pair (40, 45) is a solution of the equation $y = x + 5$.

4. Is (30, 38) a solution of the equation $y = x + 5$? Explain.

An equation is called a *linear equation* when all its solutions lie on a line.

5. **a.** Graph the ordered pairs from the table on page 462. Draw a line through the points.

   b. Is the equation $y = x + 5$ a linear equation? Explain why or why not.

Example 2

Find three solutions of the equation $y = 2x$.

- Choose three values for x. Try 0, 5, and 10.
- Make a table to organize your data.

x	$2x$	y	(x, y)
0	2(0)	0	(0, 0)
5	2(5)	10	(5, 10)
10	2(10)	20	(10, 20)

The ordered pairs (0, 0), (5, 10) and (10, 20) are solutions of the equation $y = 2x$.

6. **a.** Find one other solution of $y = 2x$.

   b. Graph all four solutions on a coordinate plane.

   c. Is $y = 2x$ a linear equation? Explain.

 A relationship exists between a person's age and his or her heart rate. Let a represent your age and let r represent your maximum heart rate. Then the equation that describes the relationship between them is $r = 220 - a$. **Is this equation a linear equation?**

Source: *Aerobic Dance Exercise Instructor Manual*

The graph of a linear equation in two variables is the graph of all points whose coordinates are solutions of the equation.

Example 3

Graph the equation $y = x + 1$.

- Choose three values for x. Make a table.

x	$x + 1$	y	(x, y)
0	0 + 1	1	(0, 1)
-2	-2 + 1	-1	(-2, -1)
3	3 + 1	4	(3, 4)

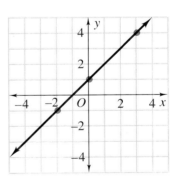

- Graph the points.
- Draw a line through the points.

7. Use the equation $y = x + 1$ to find two more points on the line.

Tell whether each ordered pair is solution of $y = x + 12$.

8. $(-12, 24)$ **9.** $(12, 24)$ **10.** $(0, -12)$ **11.** $(-12, 0)$

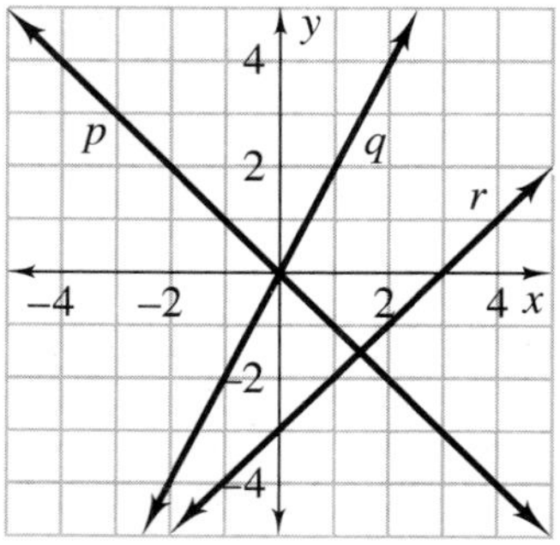

Match each equation with a line on the graph at the left.

12. $y = x - 3$ **13.** $y = 2x$ **14.** $y = -x$

15. a. Copy and complete the table below. Show five different solutions of the equation $y = x - 7$.

x	$x - 7$	y	(x, y)
0	$0 - 7$	-7	$(0, -7)$
10	■	3	■
■	■	2	■
■	■	■	■
■	■	■	■

b. Graph the ordered pairs on a coordinate plane, and draw a line through them.

On which of the following lines does each point lie? (A point may lie on more than one line.)

I. $y = x + 6$

II. $y = -x - 6$

III. $y = 2x + 3$

16. $(-2, -1)$ **17.** $(-6, 0)$ **18.** $(-3, -3)$

19. $(0, -6)$ **20.** $(0, 0)$ **21.** $(3, 9)$

Graph each equation on a coordinate plane.

22. $y = 2x - 4$ **23.** $y = 2x$ **24.** $y = 2x + 1$

25. Choose A, B, or C. The three lines you graphed in Exercises 22–24 appear to be:

A. perpendicular **B.** parallel **C.** intersecting

M$i\chi^e$d REVIEW

1. Point Z is the midpoint of $\overline{XY}$. If $\overline{XY}$ is 46 cm long, what is the length of $\overline{XZ}$?

2. Write $5 \times 5 \times 5$ in exponential form.

Identify the quadrant in which each point lies.

3. $(5, -39)$ **4.** $(-0.4, -3)$

5. At 8:00 A.M., Jim's watch was running 1 min late. Every hour it lost another 2 s. At what time was his watch running 3 min late?

26. a. Graph the equations $y = x$ and $y = -x$ on the same set of axes.

   b. Find the ordered pair that is a solution of both equations.

   c. Do these lines appear to be perpendicular or parallel? Explain.

27. Choose A, B, C, or D. The graph of which equation passes through the second quadrant?

   A. $y = x - 5$ **B.** $y = 2x$ **C.** $y = x + 3$ **D.** $y = x$

Use the graph at the right for Exercises 28 and 29.

28. Substitute the x- and y-coordinates for point P into the equation for line j to show that this ordered pair is not a solution of the equation.

29. What are the coordinates of the point that is a solution of the equations of both lines j and k?

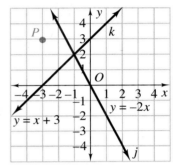

30. Writing What is the minimum number of solutions of a linear equation you must graph in order to draw a line? Describe why you think this number of points will be enough, and give an example.

Cushions of Corn

The Popcorn Institute reports that sales of popcorn have increased recently. One reason is that many companies now use popcorn instead of Styrofoam to cushion packages.

Environmentally friendly popcorn is easy to produce. A hot-air popper about the size of a microwave oven can make about $\frac{1}{2}$ lb of popcorn in 1 min, or about 30 lb in 1 h.

31. a. Let x represent the number of minutes the popper is on and let y represent the popper's output in pounds. Then the equation $y = \frac{1}{2}x$ describes the relationship between x and y. Create a table for the equation. Find 3 solutions.

   b. Graph the points from your table. Draw the line that represents the equation.

   c. Critical Thinking Does it make sense to extend the line into the third quadrant? Why or why not?

11-3 Discovering the Effect of Slope

WORK TOGETHER

1. Work with a partner to graph these equations on the same coordinate plane: $y = 3x$ $y = x$ $y = \frac{1}{2}x$.

2. a. Through which point do all the lines pass?

   b. Suppose you were riding a bicycle up a hill. Which equation represents the hill you would most likely choose? Which represents a hill you wouldn't choose? Explain.

THINK AND DISCUSS

On your graph, some of the lines you drew are steeper than others. *Slope* measures the steepness of a line. In the equation $y = mx$, the value of m represents the slope of the line.

3. **Discussion** List the equations of the lines you graphed in order of the steepness of the lines. What do you notice?

4. The graph at the left shows lines p and q. Which is steeper?

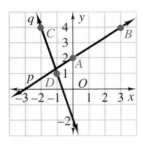

The **slope** of line p at the left is the ratio of the vertical change to the horizontal change. As you move from point $A(0, 2)$ to point $B(3, 4)$, the vertical change is 2 units up and the horizontal change is 3 units to the right.

$$\text{slope} = \frac{\text{vertical change}}{\text{horizontal change}} = \frac{2}{3}$$

Another way to use the coordinates of two points on a line to find the slope is to write the ratio of the difference in the y-coordinates to the difference in the x-coordinates. The slope of the line through $C(-2, 4)$ and $D(-1, 1)$ is

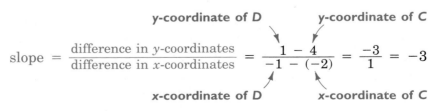

5. a. Graph the points $(1, 2)$ and $(4, -2)$. What is the vertical change? the horizontal change?

b. Use subtraction to find the slope of the line through $(1, 2)$ and $(4, -2)$.

c. What do you notice about your answers to parts (a) and (b)?

6. a. Name two points on line j; on line k.

b. Find the slope of lines j and k.

c. Which line has negative slope?

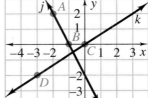

Mi**xe**d **REVIEW**

Find the area of each quadrilateral.

1. square: $s = 12$ m

2. rectangle: $l = 9$ ft, $w = 8$ ft

Create a table for each equation. Find three solutions.

3. $y = x + 9$

4. $y = 2x^2$

5. Lily is twice as tall as Bob. The sum of their heights is 7 ft 9 in. How tall is Lily?

O N YOUR OWN

Graph the given points. Determine the slope of the line through the points.

7. $(4, 8)$, $(5, 10)$ **8.** $(2, 2)$, $(1, 1)$ **9.** $(4, -1)$, $(-4, 1)$

10. Choose A, B, C, or D. A line contains two points with coordinates $(1, 3)$ and $(2, 5)$. Which expression can you use to find the slope of the line?

A. $\dfrac{2 - 1}{5 - 3}$ **B.** $\dfrac{5 - 3}{2 - 1}$ **C.** $\dfrac{1 - 2}{1 - 5}$ **D.** $\dfrac{5 - 3}{1 - 2}$

Find the slope.

11. $y = -3x$ **12.** $y = 27x$ **13.** $y = -x$

14. $y = \dfrac{1}{3}x$ **15.** $y = -\dfrac{1}{6}x$ **16.** $y = \dfrac{1}{5}x$

17. In the graph at the right, what is the slope of line t? of line s?

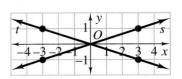

18. Kenji found the slope of the line through the points $(4, 2)$ and $(5, -1)$ to be 3. Wesley found the slope to be -3. What mistake was made? Who made it?

19. Writing Describe how to find the slope of a line.

20. Investigation (p. 458) Let a corner of your room represent the point $(0, 0)$. Walk five feet from the corner along one wall. Let this be the point $(5, 0)$. Standing at this point, have someone measure the vertical distance from the floor to the top of your head. Express this point as an ordered pair. Find the slope of a line from $(0, 0)$ to the ordered pair that you wrote.

Solve. The list at the left shows some possible strategies you can use.

PROBLEM SOLVING STRATEGIES

Make a Table
Use Logical Reasoning
Solve a Simpler Problem
Too Much or Too Little Information
Look for a Pattern
Make a Model
Work Backward
Draw a Diagram
Guess and Test
Simulate a Problem
Use Multiple Strategies
Write an Equation

1. **Money** Manouk withdraws $20 from his bank account. He uses some of this money to buy lunch for $4.75, a ticket to the movies for $7.50, and a snack after the movie for $3.45. He has $14.23 left in his account. How much money did he have before he withdrew the $20?

2. **Weather** The temperature at 6:00 A.M. was 48°F. At 9:00 A.M. it was 60°F. The temperature climbed at a constant rate from 6:00 A.M. to 11:00 A.M. What was the temperature at 10:00 A.M.?

3. **Sports** The Blazers lost 35% of the 20 games they played this season. How many games did they win?

4. A rubber ball is dropped from a height of 16 ft. Each bounce sends it halfway back up. After how many bounces does the ball rise only 1 ft off the ground?

5. Find two numbers whose sum is 28 and whose product is 96.

6. Sonia had a package of graph paper for math class that she shared with three friends. She gave $\frac{1}{4}$ of the pack to Naomi. Eartha got $\frac{1}{3}$ of what was left. Then Arissa took $\frac{1}{6}$ of what was left in the pack. Sonia had 30 sheets left. How many sheets were in the package?

7. A worm is at the bottom of a 40-m hole. It can crawl upward at the rate of 4 m in one day, but at night it slips back 3 m. At this rate, how long will it take the worm to crawl out of the hole?

8. What fractional part of the square at the left is shaded? The area of the square is 64 square units. Point C is the midpoint of $\overline{AD}$. Point B is the midpoint of $\overline{AC}$.

9. It takes a man 1 h to dig a hole 2 m long, 2 m wide, and 2 m deep. How long would it take the same man to dig a hole 4 m long, 4 m wide, and 4 m deep if he works at the same rate?

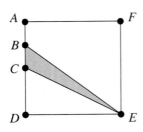

What's Ahead

• To use linear graphs to understand or make decisions about finances

WHAT YOU'LL NEED

✓ Graph paper

11-4 Using Linear Equations

WORK TOGETHER

You, your partner, and the rest of your school's Bicycle Club are trying to raise money for a trip by selling apples and oranges at school. Your *expenses* are $10 per week for the fruit. Your **profit** is the amount of money you make after you meet your expenses. After a discussion, you and your partner decide to charge $.50 for each piece of fruit.

1. a. How many pieces of fruit do you have to sell each week to cover the cost of the fruit?

  b. Let x represent the number of pieces of fruit sold and let y represent your profit. Then $y = 0.5x - 10$ describes the relationship between the fruit sold and your profit. Graph this equation.

2. Suppose you sell 60 pieces of fruit in one week. What is your profit?

THINK AND DISCUSS

Companies and other groups, like the Bicycle Club, use equations to predict profits based on their expenses.

3. Suppose your group decides they want to make more money. After much discussion, you decide to raise the price of a piece of fruit to $.75. The equation that gives the profit, y, changes to $y = 0.75x - 10$.

  a. About how many pieces of fruit must you sell to cover your expenses?

  b. After you raise the price, you sell only an average of 45 pieces of fruit in 1 week. What is your profit?

  c. Was it a good idea to raise the price of the fruit? Explain.

4. Discussion Through what quadrant(s) does the graph of the equation *not* pass? Why does this make sense?

Many people have bicycled across the United States, but Deepak Lele of India unicycled 3,963 mi from New York to Los Angeles. She began on June 4, 1984, and arrived in Los Angeles on September 25, 1984.

Source: *The Guinness Book of Records*

The graph at the left compares Carrie's savings to her brother Ian's savings over a ten-week time period.

5. **a.** Negative savings means a person is in debt. Who was in debt at the beginning of the 10-wk period shown?

   b. How many weeks did it take to pay back the debt?

6. Who had more savings after ten weeks?

7. How many weeks did it take Ian to catch up with Carrie?

8. **Critical Thinking** Who saves more money each week? How do you know?

9. **Investigation (p. 458)** Two of the world's steepest streets are Filbert Street and 22nd Street in San Francisco, both of which have a 31.5% slope.

   a. Write 31.5% as a decimal. Round it to the tenths' place.

   b. Graph a line whose slope is about 31.5%. Use the decimal you found in part (a). Start at (0, 0).

Graph labels: savings (dollars) on vertical axis; time (weeks) on horizontal axis with marks at 2, 4, 6, 8. Lines labeled Carrie and Ian.

GREAT EXPECTATIONS

Fashion Retailer

I'm not sure what I want to be, but I think I might like to be a business woman. To be a business woman would be a challenge.

I might have to go to college to get a job with a clothing company. I'd like working with a clothing company. One of the ways I might have to use math in my job is to figure my profits. I'd have to compare my company's prices with those of other stores. I'd have to do cost analysis. I'd have to predict what kinds of clothes will be in style. I'd have to figure out the amount of my paycheck and my employees paychecks. My employees might be seamstresses, designers, delivery people and maybe even a personal secretary. To save money, I might design clothes myself.

Daniela Pisciuneri

10. At the right is a graph of two plans for making and selling the drink, the Apple-Smoothie, at the school fair. Suppose the *x*-values represent the number of drinks sold, and *y*-values represent the profits.

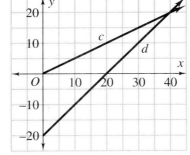

a. Which line shows no expenses for the drink?

b. Which line represents the greater price per drink?

c. When is the profit the same for both plans?

11. a. Maia's father pays her to make his lunches. He eats 4 or 5 sandwiches a week. He is giving her the choice of two payment plans. Let *x* be the number of sandwiches and *y* be the payment in dollars. The two payment plans are $y = 2x - 5$ and $y = x - 1$. Graph the two equations.

b. Writing How does the graph help you decide which payment plan is better?

M$i$$x$$e$d REVIEW

Find the value of x.

1. $\frac{3}{4} = \frac{x}{12}$

2. $\frac{9}{x} = \frac{3}{27}$

Graph the given points. Find the slope of the line through the points.

3. (3, 2), (2, 0)

4. (4, −2), (1, 5)

5. A freelance photographer charges $15/h for herself and $10/h for her assistant. The bill came to $70. If the assistant worked 2 h, how long did the photographer work?

Dear Daniela,

Becoming a business woman with a clothing company is a wonderful idea!

In my business, we often use the four basic math operations. We find our expenses, such as employees' salaries, taxes, materials, telephone bills, and rent. Then, we determine how much money we earned by totalling how many things we have sold.

We use percents to show estimates of how many sales we will have in the future. This helps us make sure we will have enough clothing in stock.

Sometimes we use graphs and charts to show how we divide our money to cover our expenses.

Good luck, Daniela.

Carolyn Elman,
National Business Women's Association

Women's Clothing Sales in the United States

Exploring Nonlinear Relationships

WORK TOGETHER

Mr. Wethers came to you and your partner with this question: "I have a 1 ft by 1 ft window that doesn't let in quite enough light. How will the amount of light change as I enlarge the window?"

1. Copy and complete the following table, where x is the length of one side of a square window and y is its area. Graph the ordered pairs and connect the points as smoothly as possible.

x	x^2	y	(x, y)
1	$(1)^2$	1	■
2	$(2)^2$	■	■
3	■	■	■
4	■	■	■

2. How is this graph different from the graph of $y = x$?

3. Which window dimensions will let in 4 times the original amount of light of the 1 ft by 1 ft window?

THINK AND DISCUSS

Not all solutions of an equation in two variables fall on a line. The curve you graphed in the Work Together is half of a *parabola*. The equation for the entire parabola is $y = x^2$.

4. **a.** How is the right side of the parabola at the right different from the curve you drew in the Work Together?

   b. The equation of this parabola is $y = \frac{1}{2}x^2$. What part of the equation causes the differences between this parabola and the curve you drew?

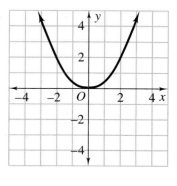

Declination of the Sun

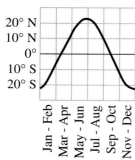

 This graph shows the declination of the Sun over the course of a year. The axis on the graph indicates the equator. **During what months is the Sun highest in the sky north of the equator? south of the equator?**

Source: *The Information Please Almanac*

Salary Options	
Option 1	$y = x$
Option 2	$y = x^2$

(x = hours worked and
y = dollars earned)

5. **Writing** Suppose you were paid by the hour for stuffing pillows at a pillow factory. Which of the equations at the right would you prefer to use to calculate your salary? Explain.

6. **a.** Make a table for the equation $y = -x^2$. Use at least 6 values for x, some positive and some negative.

b. Graph the ordered pairs and connect the points as smoothly as possible.

c. How is this parabola different from the others you have seen?

7. **a.** Two greedy but polite friends share a box of popcorn at a movie. Each time one reaches for the box, she carefully counts the remaining pieces and takes exactly half. Copy and complete the table until only one piece is left.

x number of reaches for the box	y number of pieces left	(x, y)
1	64	(1, 64)
2	32	■
3	■	■

b. Graph the ordered pairs and connect the points with a smooth curve.

c. Describe how the graph you just drew is different from the graph of $y = x^2$.

Use the graph at the right for Exercises 8 and 9.

8. The graph at the right shows the equation $y = |x|$. List the coordinates of each point shown.

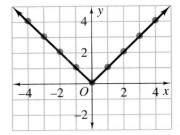

9. In the graph of the equation $y = |x|$, what general statement can you make about the y-coordinates? Will there ever be points in quadrants III and IV? Why or why not?

Express each fraction as a percent.

1. $\frac{3}{4}$ **2.** $\frac{5}{20}$

3. Melanie earns $2.50 for every hour she baby-sits her younger sister. Let x be the number of hours she baby-sits. Let y be the dollars earned. Write an equation that describes Melanie's earnings.

4. Mike vacuums his room every 6 days. At the end of a year, how many times will he have vacuumed?

10. **Data File II (pp. 456–457)** Graph the temperature and latitude data on a coordinate plane. Let the x-axis represent the latitude and let the y-axis represent the average temperature in degrees Celsius. Draw a smooth curve through the points.

11. Match each graph with an equation.

I.

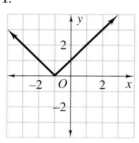

II.

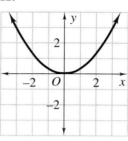

III.

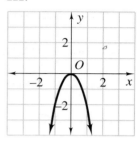

a. $y = |x + 1|$ **b.** $y = |x| - 1$ **c.** $y = \frac{1}{2}x^2$

d. $y = \frac{1}{3}x^2$ **e.** $y = x^2 - 8$ **f.** $y = -2x^2$

Problem Solving Hint

Substitute values for x into the equations to find coordinates of points.

CHECKPOINT

Name the point with the given coordinates.

1. $(-4, 1)$ **2.** $(3, -3)$ **3.** $(0, 2)$

Name the coordinates of each point.

4. F **5.** C **6.** A **7.** E

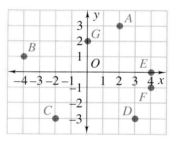

8. **Choose A, B, or C.** The graph of which equation passes through the first quadrant?

A. $y = -1$ **B.** $y = -x$ **C.** $y = 4 + x$

9. **a.** Make a table for the equation $y = x + (-2)$.

    b. Graph the equation.

    c. What is the slope of the line?

10. **a.** Make a table for the equation $y = -x^2 + 9$.

    b. Graph the equation.

An electro-cardiograph, or EKG, is a device that measures and graphs heart activity. By studying the differences between resting and exercising results, doctors learn a great deal about their patients' health.

Source: *Academic American Encyclopedia*

TECHNOLOGY

11-6 **M**athematical Models

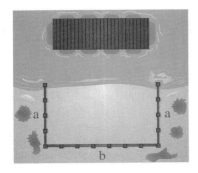

WORK TOGETHER

As director of this year's *Bands on the Bay* concert, you need to find a way to fence off an area of the shore for the audience. The city has 1,600 ft of fencing and you need fencing on three sides. How can you arrange the fencing to make room for the greatest number of people?

1. a. Find five different rectangular enclosures like the one at the left that each require 1,600 ft of fencing for three sides. Organize your data to show the lengths of side a and side b, as in the table at the right.

a	b	Length (ft) $2a + b$
500	600	$2(500) + 600 = 1,600$

b. Calculator Add a column to your table for area. Find the area for each set of dimensions.

c. Suppose you need to provide 10 ft² of area for each person. How many people will each set of dimensions allow at the concert?

d. Which set of dimensions allows the greatest attendance?

e. Write ordered pairs (side a, area) and graph them on a coordinate plane like the one at the left. To make the graphing simpler, let each unit for side a represent 100 ft and each unit for the area represent 10,000 ft².

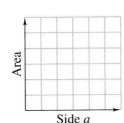

2. a. Computer Graph the equation $y = -2x^2 + 16x$.

b. What do you notice about the points you plotted for Question 1(e) and the graph you made in part (a) for $y = -2x^2 + 16x$?

c. Does x represent side a or the area? What does y represent?

d. What is the highest point on the graph? How many square feet of area does this represent?

e. What is the value of x when y is the greatest?

f. What values of a and b result in the greatest area?

THINK AND DISCUSS

Mathematical modeling, like the modeling you did in the Work Together, is a powerful tool used by scientists, engineers, and business people to find relationships among observed data.

3. Paula Glider's favorite pastime is hang gliding. Using her handy pocket watch and altimeter, Paula found that 2 min after jumping from a cliff, she was 128 m from the ground. After 4 min, she was 32 m from the ground.

   a. Write Paula's time and height as ordered pairs, where time is the x-value and height is the y-value.

   b. **Computer** The graphs of the equations $y = -8x^2 + 160$ and $y = -48x + 224$ contain the ordered pairs you wrote. Graph each equation.

   c. Which equation do you think better models Paula's hang gliding experience? Why?

   d. Suppose Paula also found that after 3 min she was 88 m from the ground. Which equation models her flight?

   e. Use the graph of the equation you chose to find the height of the cliff and about how long Paula's flight lasted.

ON YOUR OWN

Use a computer or make the graphs by hand.

4. a. Graph each of the following equations.

   $$y = x^2 - 5 \qquad y = 5x - 9 \qquad y = 4x - 8$$

   b. Which equation is a good model for data that include the points $(3, 4)$, $(1, -4)$, and $(5, 12)$?

5. In 1787, Jacques Charles, a French scientist, observed that a fixed amount of gas expands with a rise in temperature. For air, an equation that expresses this is $y = \frac{5}{3}x + 445$, where x is the temperature of the air in degrees Celsius and y is the volume of the air in cubic centimeters.

   a. Graph the equation.

   b. Use the graph to estimate the volume of the air when the temperature is 90°C.

   c. What is the volume when the temperature is 0°C?

6. The year is 2153. Jesse from planet Earth and Zachmar from planet Krayter are radio pals. Jesse sends messages over a shortwave radio set. Zachmar has much more sophisticated equipment. She decides to send Jesse a radio-screen so they can see each other when they talk. Zachmar sends the radio-screen on a spaceship programmed to fly to Earth, drop the present, turn around, and return home again. The curved path of the spaceship is modeled by the equation $y = \frac{1}{2}(x - 3)^2$, where x is the amount of time the spaceship has been in flight and y is its distance from the Earth in light years, the distance light travels in one year.

a. Copy and extend Jesse's table to $x = 0$ to model the spaceship's path.

x	$\frac{1}{2}(x - 3)^2$	y	(x, y)
5	$\frac{1}{2}(5 - 3)^2$	2	$(5, 2)$
4	$\frac{1}{2}(4 - 3)^2$	■	■
3	■	■	■

b. Graph the ordered pairs to see when the spaceship will turn around.

c. Which point represents the spaceship landing on Earth?

7. Calculator A local theater group is trying to decide how much to charge for tickets to an upcoming play. They know that as the price goes down, more tickets are sold. What price should they charge to make the most money?

a. Copy and extend the table at the right.

b. How many tickets must the theater group sell for the greatest total revenue?

c. Graph the ordered pairs of the price and the total revenue.

d. Writing Should the theater group set a limit on how low the ticket price can go? Why or why not?

8. Investigation (p. 458) Use a protractor, paper tube, and weight on a string to construct an angle-measuring device, as shown. Use the device to measure the steepness of objects of your choosing. Express the steepness in degrees.

Express each percent as a fraction or mixed number in reduced form.

1. 48%   **2.** 175%

3. 5%   **4.** 87.5%

5. Find two prime numbers whose sum is 30 and whose product is 221.

6. Sketch a graph to show the relationship between the amount of time spent studying and the grades on a test.

Price per Ticket	Tickets Sold	Total Revenue
$30.00	400	$12,000
$29.00	420	■
$28.00	440	■
■	460	■

What's Ahead

• Solving problems by writing an equation

There is an enclosure at the city zoo that contains both ostriches and elephants. The number of ostriches in the enclosure is 17 more than twice the number of elephants. There are 29 ostriches in the enclosure. How many elephants are there?

READ

Read and understand the given information. Summarize the problem.

1. Think about the information and what you are asked to find.

   a. What information are you given about the ostriches?

   b. What do you need to find?

PLAN

Decide on a strategy to solve the problem.

Since you're given the relationship between numbers, an equation may help simplify the situation.

Let e represent the number of elephants. A number sentence that relates the number of ostriches and the number of elephants is

$$\text{number of ostriches} = 17 + 2e.$$

You know the number of ostriches, so you can include this information in the number sentence.

$$29 = 17 + 2e$$

SOLVE

Try out the strategy.

Now you have an equation that describes how the given numbers are related to each other. You can solve this equation for e.

$$29 + (-17) = 17 + (-17) + 2e$$
$$12 = 2e$$
$$\frac{12}{2} = \frac{2e}{2}$$
$$6 = e$$

2. How many elephants are there?

Another advantage of using an equation to solve a problem is that if any aspect of the problem changes, only a small adjustment needs to be made to the equation.

◀ LOOK BACK

Think about how you solved the problem.

3. Suppose there were 33 ostriches in the enclosure, not 29.

   a. How would the equation change?

   b. Write and solve the new equation.

4. Suppose the number of ostriches was 11 more than twice the number of elephants instead of 17 more.

   a. How would the equation change?

   b. Write and solve the new equation.

⌐**TRY** THESE

Write an equation to solve each problem. Show your work.

5. **Money** A pair of boots cost $5 more than twice the cost of a pair of shoes. The boots cost $42.90. Find the price of the shoes.

6. The perimeter of a rectangle is 64 cm. The length is 20 cm. Find the width.

7. Jason and Judy read mystery novels. Judy has read 3 less than five times as many as Jason. She has read 17. How many has Jason read?

8. The school booster club sold $\frac{3}{4}$ of their raffle tickets. They had 175 tickets left over. How many tickets were printed?

9. A piggy bank contains $4.30 in dimes and quarters. The bank has $2.80 in dimes. How many quarters does the bank contain? (*Hint:* Let n be the number of quarters. Since each quarter has a value of $.25, the value of n quarters is $0.25n$).

⌐**ON** YOUR OWN

Use any strategy to solve each problem.

10. **Money** With the $5.75 in her pocket, Tia decided to treat herself to lunch. How much can she spend on lunch so she still has enough left to leave a 15% tip for the waitress?

Mix²ed REVIEW

Find each sum or difference.

1. $\frac{4}{5} + \frac{3}{4}$

2. $\frac{9}{10} - \frac{5}{6}$

3. $2\frac{1}{2} - 1\frac{3}{4}$

Solve.

4. $5b = 23$

5. $81c = 27$

6. Anika is going to make popcorn. The instructions say $\frac{1}{2}$ c of kernels makes one serving. How many cups should she use to serve three people?

7. Graph the equation $y = -x^2$.

11. JoAnne's kitchen measures 11 ft by $13\frac{1}{2}$ ft. She wants to tile the floor using square ceramic tiles that are 6 in. on each side. How many tiles does she need?

12. Ravi, Jasper, and Holly are all less than 45 years old. The mode of their ages is 35. The range is 13. What is the mean of their ages? What is the median of their ages?

13. The sum of two numbers is 31. Twice the lesser number is 6 less than twice the greater number. What are the numbers?

14. The local library operates a research desk where people can call in and ask questions. The following numbers of calls were received on 13 consecutive days.

117 104 116 110 98 128 112 125 95 101 123 130 97

    a. Find the median number of calls.

    b. At the end of the next day, the median number of calls was 114. How many calls had the library received that day?

15. Jamie has a coordinated wardrobe consisting of four blouses, three skirts, and two pairs of slacks. How many different two-piece outfits can she make?

16. **Environment** "Guess what!" Morris ran into the room waving the newspaper. "The town council just passed a zoning ordinance that guarantees a minimum of 2 acres of land per house! Isn't that great?"

    "I don't know, Morris," said Gretchen. "If every town in the world had ordinances like that, we wouldn't have enough room for everyone and still have space to grow food."

    "Nonsense," said Morris. "The Earth has plenty of space!"

    "Yes," agreed George, "and most of it's in Siberia and Antarctica!"

    "Do either of you know how much land is available for each person?" asked Gretchen.

    "I don't," admitted Morris. "Let's figure it out."

    a. Use the Earth Facts at the left. How many acres of land will there be per person in the year 2000 not including Antarctica and Siberia?

    b. **Writing** Do you agree with Gretchen, Morris, or George about the space available on the Earth? Explain your reasoning.

EARTH FACTS

The surface of the Earth is about 196,800,000 mi^2, and water covers about 71% of it.

1 mi^2 = 640 acres

The estimated world population for the year 2000 is 6,261,000,000.

Antarctica has an area of about 5,400,000 mi^2.

Siberia has an area of about 4,929,000 mi^2.

Name the point with the given coordinates.

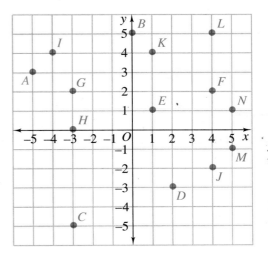

1. $(1, 4)$ **2.** $(-3, -5)$ **3.** $(2, -3)$

4. $(5, -1)$ **5.** $(0, 5)$ **6.** $(-4, 4)$

Write the coordinates of each point.

7. N **8.** E **9.** H

10. A **11.** J **12.** F

Identify the quadrant in which each point lies.

13. $(23, -12)$ **14.** $(1, 11)$ **15.** $(-9, 4)$

16. $(-3, 3)$ **17.** $(12, 11)$ **18.** $(-7, -29)$

Graph the points. Determine the slope of the line through the points.

19. $(5, 4), (0, 9)$ **20.** $(2, 7), (8, 3)$ **21.** $(-3, -3), (4, -3)$ **22.** $(-10, -6), (4, 5)$

Graph each equation on a coordinate plane.

23. $y = x - 1$ **24.** $y = 2x + 1$ **25.** $y = \frac{1}{2}x + 1$ **26.** $y = \frac{1}{3}x^2$

27. Inez paid $10 to park her car in a parking garage. The garage charges $4 for the first hour and $2 for each additional hour. How many hours was her car parked?

28. Minh is renting a sound system for a dance. There are two stores that rent sound systems. One charges a fee of $30 plus $10 for each hour the sound system is rented. The other charges a fee of $20 plus $15 for each hour.

  a. Let x represent the number of hours the sound system is rented and let y represent the cost of the rental. The equations describing their relationship are $y = 10x + 30$ and $y = 15x + 20$. Graph both equations on the same plane. At what time are costs of both systems the same?

  b. The dance will last at least 3 hours. If Minh is interested in minimizing costs, which store should he choose? Why?

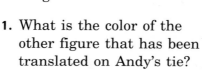

Movements of figures on a plane are **transformations.** A transformation can be a slide, a flip, or a turn. The pattern in Andy's new tie was created by sliding a single purple shape into new positions, as shown below. Another name for a slide is a **translation.**

Figure *ABCD* has been translated to figure *A'B'C'D'*. The figure you get after a translation is the **image** of the original. You use *prime notation (A')* to identify an image.

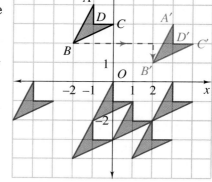

1. What is the color of the other figure that has been translated on Andy's tie?

2. **a.** What are the coordinates of points *A*, *B*, *C*, and *D*?

   b. What are the coordinates of *A'*, *B'*, *C'*, and *D'*?

3. **a.** By what value did the *x*-coordinate of each point of the figure change to form the image points?

   b. By what value did the *y*-coordinate of each point change?

4. Point *F*(4, 1) at the left has been translated up 2 units.

   a. What point is the image of point *F*?

   b. What are the coordinates of the image?

5. Suppose that point *F* had been translated to the left 2 units. What would be the coordinates of its image?

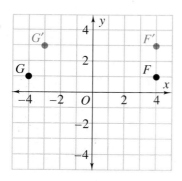

To show a translation, you can use arrow notation. For the translation of *G* to *G'* on the graph at the left, you can write *G*(−4, 1) ➝ *G'*(−3, 3).

6. Write the translation of *F* to *F'* using arrow notation.

To translate geometric figures, first translate the vertices of the figure. Then connect the images of the vertices to form the image of the geometric figure.

Example 1 A metal rod rests on the coordinate plane with its ends at $(0, 0)$ and $(2, 2)$. Draw its image after a translation of 3 units up.

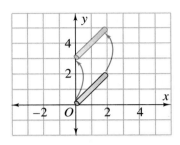

- $(0, 0) \rightarrow (0, 3)$ Translate each endpoint.
  $(2, 2) \rightarrow (2, 5)$

Graph the translated endpoints on the same coordinate plane as the original rod. Then draw the image, as shown on the graph at the right.

To find the coordinates of an image after a translation, you can read the coordinates from a graph of the image. Another way to find the image coordinates is to add or subtract the amount of movement from the coordinates of the original figure.

7. Suppose you translate a point to the left 2 units and down 1 unit. Would you add or subtract to find the x-coordinate of the image? the y-coordinate of the image?

Example 2 Write a rule for the translation of $\triangle ABC$ to $\triangle A'B'C'$.

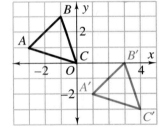

- The horizontal change from A to A' is 4 units to the right, so $x \rightarrow x + 4$.
- The vertical change from A to A' is 3 units down so $y \rightarrow y - 3$.

The rule for the translation is $(x, y) \rightarrow (x + 4, y - 3)$.

8. Suppose a figure is translated to the right 2 units and up 6 units. Complete the general rule to show how to find the image: $(x, y) \rightarrow (x + \blacksquare, y + \blacksquare)$.

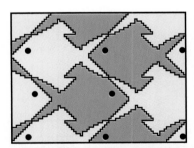

WORK TOGETHER

Art The two patterns at the right show how designs for fabric or wrapping paper can be created from geometric shapes. Work with a partner to create and color a design by translating and tracing a cardboard cutout.

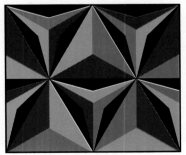

TRY THESE

Use the graph at the right for Exercises 9 and 10.

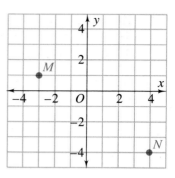

9. Give the coordinates of point *M* after it is translated right 5 units.

10. Give the coordinates of point *N* after it is translated up 4 units.

11. Suppose $P(3, 4) \rightarrow P'(-2, -3)$. What is the horizontal change? the vertical change?

12. Triangle *RST* has coordinates $R(2, -5)$, $S(1, 1)$, $T(-3, -1)$. Point $R(2, -5) \rightarrow R'(5, -7)$. Give the coordinates of S' and T'.

13. Suppose you translated a shape to the left 2 units and up 1 unit. Complete the general rule to show how to find the image: $(x, y) \rightarrow (x - \blacksquare, y + \blacksquare)$.

ON YOUR OWN

Describe the translation shown in each graph.

14.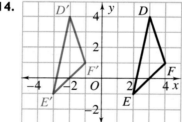

15.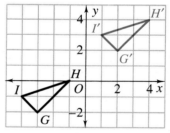

Use graph paper to graph the image of figure *ABCD* after each translation. Name the coordinates of *A'*, *B'*, *C'*, and *D'*.

16. left 3 units   17. up 2 units   18. right 1 unit, down 4 units

19. Does moving a point up and down affect the *x*-coordinate or the *y*-coordinate? What about left and right?

20. **Writing** When you translate a sentence from English to Spanish, you are telling what the English words mean in Spanish. How is this use of the word *translation* similar to the mathematical use of the word?

21. **Choose A, B, or C.** On the graph at the right, which shape is a translation of $\triangle XYZ$?

   A. $\triangle ABC$ **B.** $\triangle JKL$

   C. $\triangle PQR$

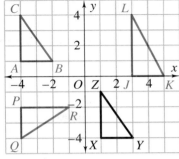

22. The vertices of $\triangle DEF$ are $D(-1, 2)$, $E(-1, -1)$, and $F(2, -1)$.

   a. Graph the triangle.

   b. Graph its translation right 2 units and down 1 unit.

   c. Write the coordinates of D', E', and F'.

23. **Aviation** Three airplanes are flying in a triangular formation. In 1 min, airplane P moves as shown in the graph at the right. The planes remain in formation as they fly.

   a. Give the original and the new coordinates of each airplane.

   b. How far in each direction did the airplanes move?

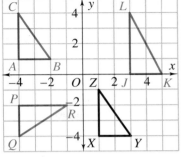

Mixed REVIEW

Graph each point. Tell in which quadrant each point is located.

1. $(4, 5)$ **2.** $(-2, -9)$

3. $(-3, 1)$ **4.** $(6, -1)$

Find each product.

5. $\frac{9}{20} \times 5\frac{1}{4}$

6. $7\frac{3}{4} \times 1\frac{1}{8}$

7. The length of a rectangle is 48 cm. The perimeter of the rectangle is 120 cm. Write and solve an equation to find the width.

CHECKPOINT

Graph the given points. Determine the slope of the line through the points.

  1. $(8, 2), (4, 3)$ **2.** $(3, 5), (5, 9)$ **3.** $(1, 2), (6, -2)$

  4. **Choose A, B, or C.** The graph of which equation is steepest?

     A. $y = \frac{1}{3}x$ **B.** $y = -3x$ **C.** $y = \frac{1}{2}x$

  5. Samantha delivers pizzas for Amram's Pizza Pad in Newton. Amram pays Samantha $1 for each pizza she delivers.

    a. Let p represent the number of pizzas Samantha delivers and let e represent her earnings. Write an equation to find how much Samantha earns.

    b. Samantha uses $10 worth of gas each week. Write an equation to find Samantha's weekly profit.

    c. How many pizzas must Samantha deliver to make a profit of $38 in one week?

• Recognizing and graphing reflections

• Identifying lines of symmetry

WHAT YOU'LL NEED

✓ **Graph paper**

✓ **Ruler**

✓ **Scissors**

✓ **Colored pencils**

When a drop of water vapor freezes, it becomes a snowflake, like the one at the right. Although they don't know for sure, scientists think that each snowflake is one of a kind. Part of what makes a snowflake so beautiful is its *symmetry*. A figure is *symmetrical* when one side is a mirror image of the other side. The vertical red line drawn down the center of the snowflake is called a *line of symmetry*.

1. Some objects have more than one line of symmetry, and not all lines of symmetry are vertical. What other lines of symmetry do you see in the snowflake?

2. Identify the lines of symmetry in each of these photographs.

3. Name two items in your classroom that have a line of symmetry.

4. **a.** Name at least one capital letter of the alphabet that has a horizontal line of symmetry.

   b. Name at least one capital letter of the alphabet that has a vertical line of symmetry.

   c. Discussion What capital letters of the alphabet have both horizontal and vertical lines of symmetry?

5. Draw a figure that has both horizontal and vertical symmetry. Draw its lines of symmetry.

Wilson Bently, better known as "the snowflake man," recorded the varying shapes of snowflakes by photographing 5,381 patterns during his lifetime.

Source: *Backpacker Magazine*

You can create symmetry on the coordinate plane. A *reflection*, or flip, is a second kind of transformation. The image $\triangle A'B'C'$ is the reflection of $\triangle ABC$ across the *y*-axis. Using arrow notation, $\triangle ABC \rightarrow \triangle A'B'C'$. The *y*-axis is called the *line of reflection*.

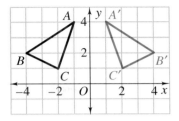

6. a. What are the coordinates of *A* and *A'*? *B* and *B'*? *C* and *C'*?

  b. What do you notice about the *x*-coordinate of each vertex of $\triangle ABC$ and its image?

7. a. Copy the coordinate plane and $\triangle ABC$. Reflect $\triangle ABC$ across the *x*-axis to form a new reflection image.

  b. Identify the line of symmetry in your graph.

  c. What do you notice about the *y*-coordinate of each vertex of $\triangle ABC$ and its image?

WORK TOGETHER

You and your partner operate a custom window design company. Mrs. Smith, your favorite customer, has asked you to design a stained glass window for her to give to her husband for their wedding anniversary. Her only requirement is that the design on the window be symmetrical.

8. a. Create a design for a window. Use at least 4 colors.

  b. Mark the line or lines of symmetry on your design.

ON YOUR OWN

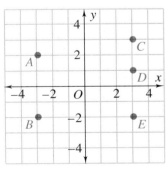

Use the graph at the right for Exercises 9–11.

9. For which two points is the *x*-axis the line of reflection?

10. For which two points is the *y*-axis the line of reflection?

11. Points *C* and *E* are *not* reflections over the *x*-axis. Why not?

A person's face is not perfectly symmetrical. There are slight differences between the left and right sides. The top picture was created by replacing the right side of the photo by a mirror image of the left side. The bottom picture was made from the right side of the photo and its mirror image. **Do these look like the same person or more like sisters?**

**△*A'B'C'* is a reflection of
△*ABC* over the *y*-axis.
Complete each statement.**

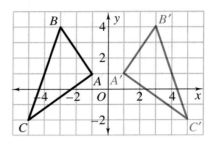

12. $A(-1, 1) \rightarrow A'(\blacksquare, \blacksquare)$

13. $B(-3, 4) \rightarrow B'(\blacksquare, \blacksquare)$

14. $C(-5, -2) \rightarrow C'(\blacksquare, \blacksquare)$

**Graph the image point after each reflection. Name the
coordinates of the image.**

15. (3, 7) across the *x*-axis   **16.** (−5, 12) across the *y*-axis

**Trace each figure and draw the line(s) of symmetry. If
there are no lines of symmetry, write *none*.**

17.   **18.**   **19.**   **20.**

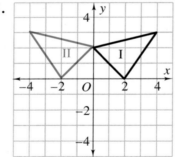

Mixed REVIEW

**Write the missing terms
in each sequence.**

1. −10, −6, −2, ▪, ▪

2. 2, 3, 5, 8, ▪, ▪

△*ABC* has vertices
A(2, 6), *B*(1, 2), and
C(4, 5).

3. Graph △*ABC* and its
image after a translation of
6 units to the left and 4
units down.

4. Give the coordinates of
the vertices of △*A'B'C'* in
Exercise 3.

5. Last month, Vu had $27
in his bank account. He
deposited $31, $14, and
$11.80. He earned interest
of $.14. How much money
does he have in his
account this month?

**Tell whether the graph shows a reflection or a translation.
Name the line of reflection or describe the translation.**

21.   **22.**

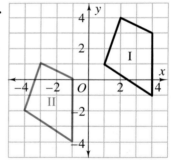

23. a. Graph the line $y = -2x$.

   b. Draw the reflection of this line across the *y*-axis. (*Hint:*
   Reflect several points and then draw a line through these
   points.)

24. Data File 10 (pp. 416–417) How many lines of symmetry do
you see in the butterfly?

25. Writing Explain the difference between a translation and a
reflection. Use examples.

11-10 Rotations

THINK AND DISCUSS

Suppose the blades of this windmill are revolving counterclockwise. One full turn of the blades brings the blade at position *A* back to its original position.

1. How much of a turn brings the blade at position *A* to the *A'* position? the *A"* position? the *A'''* position?

A rotation is a transformation that turns a figure about a fixed point (*O*). Point *O* is the *center of rotation*. In this text, all rotations are counterclockwise.

A figure has **rotational symmetry** when an image after a rotation fits exactly on top of the original figure. The windmill blades have 90° rotational symmetry because after a turn of 90° the blades look like they did before the turn.

Example 1

Does the lily at the right have rotational symmetry?

• Rotate petal 1 to the position of each of the other petals.

• The lily looks the same at each position.

The lily has rotational symmetry.

2. **Discussion** Does star *A* at the right have rotational symmetry? How do you know? What about star *B*? Explain.

3. Name a capital letter in the alphabet that has rotational symmetry. Name one that does *not* have rotational symmetry.

A   *B*

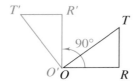

The figure at the left, $\triangle TRO$, has been rotated $90°$ around point O. Using arrow notation, $\triangle TRO \rightarrow T'R'O'$. The *center of rotation* is point O.

Example 2

Draw the image of $\triangle TRO$ after a rotation of:

a. $180°$ about O.

b. $270°$ about O.

a.

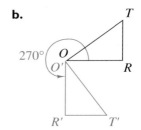

b.

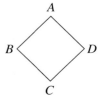

4. a. In the square at the right, what rotation will move point A to the position held by point B? A to C? A to D?

b. Does the square have rotational symmetry?

TRY THESE

Which figures have rotational symmetry?

5.

6.

7.

Draw the image of each figure after a rotation of $90°$, $180°$, and $270°$ about point O.

8.

9.

10.

11. Which figures in Exercises 8–10 have rotational symmetry?

Which figures below have rotational symmetry? Explain.

12.   **13.**   **14.**   **15.**

16. Engineering A *cam* is a useful roller that is not round. The small black wheel rolls along the edge of the rotating cam shown at the right, causing the rod to move up and down. Does the cam have rotational symmetry? Explain.

17. Which figure(s) could be a rotation of the figure at the right?

A. 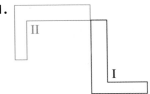 **B.** **C.** **D.**

18. a. On graph paper, draw rectangle *ABCD* with vertices at *A*(3, 1), *B*(−3, 1), *C*(−3, −1), and *D*(3, −1).

b. On a coordinate plane, draw three images formed by rotating the rectangle 90°, 180°, and 270° about the origin.

Figure II is the image of Figure I. Identify the transformation as a translation, a reflection, or a rotation.

19.  **20.**

21. 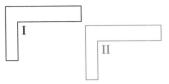 **22.**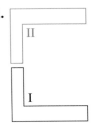

23. Writing Describe an object in your classroom that has rotational symmetry.

Wrap Up

The Coordinate Plane and Linear Equations   11-1, 11-2

The **coordinate plane** is formed by the intersection of the **x-axis** and the **y-axis.** This allows every point on the plane to be described by an *ordered pair* of numbers (x, y) called **coordinates.** An equation is *linear* if all of its solutions lie on a straight line.

Use the graph below for Exercises 1 and 2.

1. Name the point with the given coordinates.

   a. $(-3, 2)$ **b.** $(2, -1)$

2. Write the coordinates of each point.

   a. B **b.** C

   c. D **d.** F

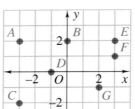

3. Which of the following ordered pairs are solutions of the equation $y = 3x - 5$?

   a. $(5, 10)$ **b.** $(-2, -1)$ **c.** $(1, -2)$

4. **a.** List three ordered pairs that are solutions to $y = x + 4$.

   b. Graph the equation.

Exploring Slope   11-3

The **slope** of a line is determined by a ratio.

$$\text{slope} = \frac{\text{difference in } y\text{-coordinates}}{\text{difference in } x\text{-coordinates}}$$

5. **Choose A, B, C or D.**
   Which of the equations below describes the graph at the right?

   A. $y = 3x$ **B.** $y = -3x$

   C. $y = \frac{1}{3}x$ **D.** $y = -\frac{1}{3}x$

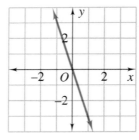

Determine the slope of the line through the points.

6. $(-2, 6), (4, 3)$ 7. $(-3, 2), (-1, 5)$

8. $(0, 5), (9, 8)$ 9. $(6, 2), (-3, 4)$

Strategies and Applications   11-7

Some problems describe relations between numbers. Using an equation can simplify these problems and help in finding a solution.

10. The school band sold $377 worth in tickets to their spring concert. Each ticket cost $3.25. How many tickets were sold?

Mathematical Models

11-4, 11-6

You can use equations and graphs to predict profit based on income and expenses.

11. Use the graph at the right. At what time is the difference between income and expenses the greatest?

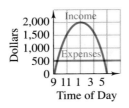

12. **Writing** How might modeling situations with equations and graphs help you in solving problems?

Exploring Nonlinear Relationships

11-5

13. Which equation, $y = x^2 - 4$ or $y = |2x| + 4$, is a good model for the data that include $(-2, 0)$, $(0, -4)$ and $(-4, 12)$? Explain your reasoning.

14. Which of the following equations has the greatest value for y at $x = 3$? at $x = 12$?

I. $y = |3x + 5|$

II. $y = x^2 - 6$

III. $y = -2x^2 + 26$

Transformations

11-8, 11-9, 11-10

There are three different ways that you can move a figure on a plane. You can slide it, flip it, or turn it. The names for these *transformations* are **translations, reflections** and **rotations.**

15. Name an everyday object that has at least two lines of symmetry. Draw the object and its lines of symmetry.

16. Draw the image of △*SUN* after the translation $(x, y) \rightarrow (x + 3, y - 4)$

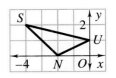

Figure II is the image of Figure I. Is the transformation a translation, a reflection, or a rotation?

17.

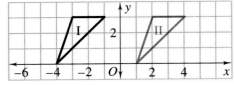

18.

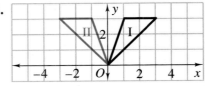

19.

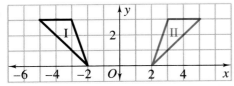

20.

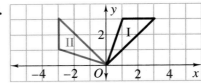

PUTTING IT ALL TOGETHER

follow Up

How Steep Is It?

At the beginning of the chapter you found the steepness of an imaginary line running from the base of one wall of your classroom to the top of the opposite wall. Look back at your findings. Revise or expand on them if you wish, based on your study of the chapter. Then express the steepness of the line in as many ways as you can. Use both general descriptive terms and precise mathematical expressions. Explain how you determined each expression. The problems preceded by the magnifying glass (p. 467, # 20; p. 470, # 9; and p. 477, # 8) will help you complete the investigation.

Steepness is an example of a property that can be expressed in a number of different ways. Practice looking at things in different ways. You will be developing a powerful tool that will help you not only in mathematics but in every discipline.

Excursion: Suppose the imaginary line in your classroom were the bottom of a mile-long kite string. How high above the ground would the kite be?

What's the Relationship?
Square and Triangular Numbers

Square numbers can be put into a square formation on graph paper. They also form a pattern. This is a sequence of square numbers:

$$1, 4, 9, 16, 25, 36, 49, \ldots$$

There are also triangular numbers, which can be formed into triangles on triangle dot paper. They form this pattern:

$$1, 3, 6, 10, 15, 21, \ldots$$

It is interesting that every square number is the sum of two triangular numbers. Is there a way to predict the next triangular number in a sequence? Can you find which triangular numbers make up 100? Can you find the 100th triangular number?

Make a poster showing square and triangular numbers as well as their relationship.

Copy This

Make a simple sketch by connecting ten to thirty points on a coordinate plane. On a separate sheet of paper, list these points as ordered pairs but reverse the x- and y-coordinates. Give the list of ordered pairs to a friend. Ask this friend to plot the points on a coordinate plane and connect them. Compare your original drawing with your friend's. What do you discover about the two drawings?

How High Can You Throw a Ball

Can you throw a softball higher in the air than you can throw a basketball?

Galileo is a famous Italian mathematician and scientist who proved that heavy objects fall at the same speed as light objects. Legend has it that he demonstrated this by dropping a cannonball and a small stone at the same time off the Leaning Tower of Pisa.

Now you can investigate whether throwing objects of different weights directly upward affects how high you can throw them. You can use the formula below to find the height of a ball when you know the number of seconds it is in the air.

$$T^2 \times 4 = H$$

T = *time* (in seconds); H = *height* of the throw

Toss a basketball straight up into the air. Have a friend use a stopwatch to measure the length of time the ball was in the air to the nearest tenth of a second. It may take some practice to get the timing right. Take turns timing and recording your results. Use the formula to find out how high you threw the ball. Graph your results. Try the experiment again with a softball and compare your results with the basketball experiment. What did you find?

TIC-TAC-GRID

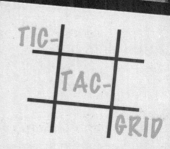

Play this game with one other player. Make a coordinate grid to use as your playing board. Players take turns naming an ordered pair, then initialing that point on the grid. Play continues back and forth until one player has four points in a row, either horizontally, vertically, or diagonally.

1. Determine whether each ordered pair is a solution of the equation $y = -2x + 5$.

   a. $(3, -5)$
   b. $(0, 5)$
   c. $(4, -3)$
   d. $(2.5, 0)$

2. Determine the slope of the line through the points.

   a. $E(7, 1), F(-3, 3)$

   b. $G(-2, 6), H(0, 0)$

   c. $L(-4, 0), M(0, 2)$

   d. $S(8, 5), T(1, -1)$

3. **Choose A, B, C, or D.** Which set of ordered pairs does *not* describe the vertices of an isosceles triangle?

   A. $(-2, 4), (-5, 6), (-8, 4)$

   B. $(0, 5), (5, 0), (5, 10)$

   C. $(6, -2), (7, -7), (2, -6)$

   D. $(-4, 0), (0, 0), (-6, -3)$

4. Trevor and Tyne are planning to start a grocery delivery service. Trevor wants to charge $1.00 plus $1.25 per bag of groceries. Tyne wants to charge $2.00 plus $.75 per bag of groceries.

   a. Write equations to describe both Trevor's and Tyne's proposed fees for the grocery service.

   b. Make tables for both equations and graph the equations.

   c. **Writing** Decide which of the two options is better. Explain your decision.

5. Find the slope of the line you would graph for the equation $y = \frac{4}{3}x + 4$.

6. In which quadrant(s) are both coordinates of a point negative?

7. Find four solutions of each equation.

   a. $y = x^2$

   b. $y = |x|$

8. Graph each of the following equations.

   a. $y = x - 3$

   b. $y = 3x - 4$

9. **a.** Graph $\triangle ABC$ with vertices $A(1, 3)$, $B(5, 8)$, and $C(7, 1)$. Then connect the vertices in order.

   b. Find the coordinates of the reflection of $\triangle ABC$ over the x-axis. Graph the reflection.

   c. Find the coordinates of the vertices of the image of $\triangle ABC$ after a translation of 12 units to the left and 10 units down. Graph the translation.

   d. Graph the image of $\triangle ABC$ after a 90° rotation about the origin. Write the coordinates of the image of $\triangle ABC$.

10. Match each equation with its graph.

    a. $y = -x + 2$

    b. $y = x + 2$

    c. $y = 2$

    d. $x = 2$

    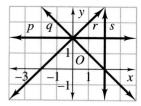

11. **Writing** Give an example of a rotation, a reflection, and a translation you might see in everyday objects.

Choose A, B, C, or D.

1. Which rule best describes the function in the table?

n	f(n)
0	0
1	1
2	4
3	9

   A. $f(n) = n + 2$

   B. $f(n) = n$

   C. $f(n) = 2n$

   D. $f(n) = n^2$

2. How many two-letter permutations of the letters of CAR contain the letter R?

   A. 2   **B.** 3

   C. 4   **D.** 6

3. What situation is described by the linear equation $P = 7.5x - 150$?

   A. A bus company's profit if x people buy tickets for a trip at $7.50 each, but it costs $150 to run the bus.

   B. The total price of renting a restaurant for a party if the restaurant charges $150 plus $7.50 per person, and x people attend.

   C. The price of a home video game machine if it costs $150, but you have x coupons, each of which says, "deduct $7.50."

   D. The total profit made by putting on a concert if the profit is $7.50 per person for each person and x people more than 150 attend.

4. A muffin recipe uses $2\frac{1}{4}$ c of flour and makes 12 muffins. How many muffins can you make with 6 c of flour?

   A. 24   **B.** 30

   C. 32   **D.** 45

5. What is the unit's digit of 7^{23}?

   A. 3   **B.** 5   **C.** 7   **D.** 9

6. What is the *best estimate* for the percent of the figure that is shaded?

   A. 10%   **B.** 25%

   C. 50%   **D.** 75%

7. For which linear equation is $(-3, 0.5)$ *not* a solution?

   A. $x - 2y = -4$

   B. $4y = 3x + 11$

   C. $x = -6y$

   D. $-x + 6y = 0$

8. What is the probability of spinning red or blue on the spinner?

   A. $P(\text{red}) - P(\text{blue})$

   B. $P(\text{red}) + P(\text{blue})$

   C. $P(\text{blue}) - P(\text{red})$

   D. $P(\text{red}) \times P(\text{blue})$

9. What percent of the letters of the alphabet are vowels?

   A. about 15%   **B.** about 19%

   C. about 30%   **D.** about 33%

10. Which translation takes $\triangle ABC$ to $\triangle A'B'C'$?

   A. $(x, y) \rightarrow (x - 3, y)$

   B. $(x, y) \rightarrow (x + 3, y)$

   C. $(x, y) \rightarrow (x, y + 3)$

   D. $(x, y) \rightarrow (x, y - 3)$

   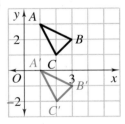

Chapter 1
Extra Practice

The stem-and-leaf plot shows daily high temperatures on Mt. Washington, NH, during three weeks in January.

0	1 2 3 3 4 4 5 7
1	0 0 1 1 1 5 6
2	0 2 8 8
3	1 1

2 | 0 means 20

1. Create a frequency table for the data.

2. Create a line plot for the data.

3. Find the mean, median, mode, and range of the data.

4. How many days was the temperature above 10 degrees?

Exercises 5–8 refer to the graph at the right.

5. Which team has won the most matches?

6. Which team has won the fewest matches?

7. Which team has won almost the same number of matches as they lost?

8. About how many more matches has Team A won than Team D?

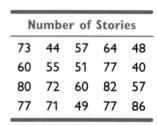

The data set at the right shows the number of stories in some notable tall buildings in the United States.

9. Display the data in a stem-and-leaf plot.

10. Find the mean, median, and mode of the data.

11. How many buildings have less than the mean number of stories?

Number of Stories				
73	44	57	64	48
60	55	51	77	40
80	72	60	82	57
77	71	49	77	86

12. **Writing** The graph at the right shows the growth of personal computer purchases, with the percentages representing the percent of households with PCs.

   a. Describe the data as presented in the graph.

   b. Tell whether you feel the graph is misleading or fair.

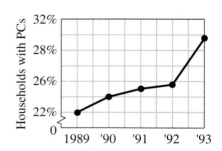

Chapter 2
Extra Practice

1. Draw the next figure for the pattern.

Find each missing angle measure. Then classify each triangle by its angles.

2.

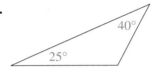

40°

25°

3.

36°

54°

4.

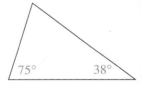

75°   38°

Match each description with its picture.

5. angle bisector

6. vertical angles

7. supplementary angles

8. complementary angles

9. nonadjacent angles

a.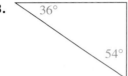

60°
30°

b.

55°   55°

c.

65°
65°

d.

88°
88°

e.

140° 40°

10. Draw a circle *O*. Draw, label, and identify a diameter, a chord, a radius, and an arc that is not a semicircle.

11. $\triangle ABD \cong \triangle CED$. Which of the following statements must be true?

   a. $\overline{AB} \cong \overline{CE}$ **b.** $\overline{AD} \cong \overline{ED}$ **c.** $\angle A \cong \angle C$

   d. $\angle BDA$ and $\angle EDC$ are congruent angles   **e.** $\overline{BD} \cong \overline{EC}$

12. Critical Thinking At one point in a race Lars was 15 ft behind Paul and 18 ft ahead of Jorge. Jorge was trailing Simon by 30 ft. How far ahead of Simon was Paul?

Chapter 3
Extra Practice

Order from greatest to least.

1. 0.092, 0.095, 0.102, 0.099   **2.** 1.01, 1.12, 1.02, 1.101   **3.** 0.55, 0.505, 0.52, 0.56

Estimation **Use any method to estimate.**

4. $32.13 ÷ 6.15   **5.** 1.2 + 2.4 + 0.86   **6.** $34.50 − $10.80 + $2.10

7. 0.054 + 0.901 + 0.62   **8.** $18.95 × 3.5   **9.** 2.7236 − 0.6512

Choose **Use a calculator, paper and pencil, or mental math to find each value.**

10. 100^0 **11.** 5^3 **12.** 3^5 **13.** 15^2 **14.** 8^4

Mental Math **Use the distributive property to evaluate.**

15. 2(8 − 4.5)   **16.** 3(99)   **17.** 6(20 + 4)   **18.** 4(7 + 4)

Use a calculator or paper and pencil to find each answer. Use a bar to show repeating decimals.

19. 3.2 ÷ 1.2   **20.** 4.86 − 2.161   **21.** 4(1.4 ÷ 3)   **22.** 3.5 × 4.4

23. 2.1 + 3.62 + 1.003   **24.** 127 ÷ 2.4   **25.** 37 ÷ 11.1   **26.** 3(6.1 + 0.461)

Compare. Use <, >, or =.

27. 0.101 ■ 0.10   **28.** 15.55 ■ 15.555   **29.** 1.16 ■ 1.160   **30.** 29.08 ■ 29.10

31. Write an expression for 5 less than twice a number.

32. Write an expression for 6 more than a number divided by 2.

33. Complete the table below. Substitute the value indicated on the left for the variable in the expression at the top of each column, and evaluate.

	3(x − 1)	$3x^2$	3x − 1	$2x^3$
x = 2.3	■	■	■	■
x = 3.2	■	■	■	■

Extra Practice

Write the integer represented by each model.

1.

2.

3.

Write the equation represented by each model. Then solve the equation.

4.

5.

6.

Write *true* or *false*.

7. $|5| > |-5|$

8. $|-3| \leq |-2|$

9. $|10| = |-10|$

10. $|6| < |8|$

Choose Use a calculator, paper and pencil, or mental math to find each value.

11. $-45 \div (-3)^2$

12. $-110 + 5 - (-5)$

13. $4(2 - 7)^2$

14. $3(-4 \cdot 3)$

15. $-(1^{20}) + 1$

16. $(-3)(-2)(-1)$

17. $9^2 + 3^2$

18. $2(-2) - 4$

19. Amah has 3 each of 15¢, 20¢ and 25¢ stamps. In how many different ways can she get the exact postage for an overseas letter that will cost $1.05 to mail?

Solve.

20. $-3 + t = -10$

21. $7 + x = -7$

22. $\frac{a}{4} = 12$

23. $\frac{x}{2} = -4(-2)$

24. $2x - 2 = 12$

25. $3x + 1 = -11$

26. $3^2 + x = 6$

27. $\frac{y}{-6} = 3$

28. $112p + 7 = 231$

29. $\frac{r}{-6} + 4 = -3$

30. $12m + 24 = 0$

31. $-6 + \frac{d}{2} = 12$

32. a. Write an equation to describe the following relationship: A pair of boots costs $6 more than 3 times as much as a pair of shoes. The price of the boots is $87.99.

b. Write a step-by-step explanation for how you would solve this two-step equation.

c. How much do the shoes cost?

Extra Practice

Find the area and perimeter of each figure.

1.

5.4

5.4

2.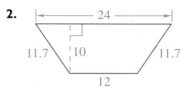

24

11.7 10 11.7

12

3.

4

3

4.

1.5

6

5.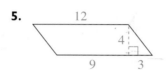

12

4

9   3

6.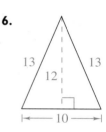

13   13

12

10

Calculator Use a calculator to find each quantity to the nearest tenth of a unit.

7. length of the sides of a square with area of 136 in.²

8. length of the hypotenuse of a right triangle with legs of 8 cm and 13 cm

9. volume of a cube with an edge of 3.4 ft

10. diameter of a circle with a circumference of 12 m

11. perimeter of a right triangle with legs of 7 in. and 12 in.

A rectangular swimming pool is shown.

12. How many cubic feet of water would you need to fill the pool to within 1 ft of the top?

13. If a gallon of pool paint covers 230 ft², how many gallons of paint should you buy to put two coats on the bottom and sides?

14. A square tile is 12 in. on a side. How many tiles would you need to make a walkway one tile wide around the perimeter of the pool?

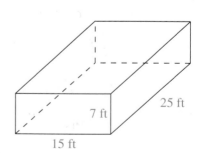

7 ft   25 ft

15 ft

15. Suppose you were to swim diagonally across the pool. To the nearest tenth, what is the length of the diagonal?

Extra Practice

Compare. Use <, >, or =.

1. 7.03×10^4 ■ $70,000$

2. 100 ■ 1.02×10^2

3. 6.1×10^6 ■ $610,000$

4. 2^5 ■ 5^2

5. 4.8×10^2 ■ 9.6×10^2

6. 13^4 ■ $28,200$

7. $20,000,000$ ■ 2×10^7

8. 250 ■ 4^5

9. $54,000$ ■ 5.4×10^4

Identify each sequence as arithmetic, geometric, or neither. Then find the next three terms in the sequence.

10. $1, 2, 5, 6, 9, \ldots$

11. $1,215, 405, 135, 45, \ldots$

12. $50, 25, 48, 24, \ldots$

13. $3.25, 3.55, 3.85, 4.15, \ldots$

14. $0, -2, -4, -6, \ldots$

15. $1, 1.2, 1.44, 1.728, \ldots$

16. a. Write a rule for the function represented by the table at the right.

   b. Using this rule, find $f(0)$, $f(-1)$, $f(-2)$, and $f(-3)$.

   c. Do the values for $f(0)$, $f(-1)$, $f(-2)$, and $f(-3)$ form an arithmetic or a geometric sequence?

n	$f(n)$
1	1
2	4
3	7
4	10

17. a. Describe the pattern for the units digit of the powers of 8.

   b. What is the units digit of 8^{19}?

Use a calculator or a computer. Use the formula $A = p(1 + r)^n$. Calculate how much will be in the account for each situation.

18. \$1,200 invested for 6 y at an interest rate of \$.12 for every dollar in the account each year

19. \$1,200 invested for 6 y at an interest rate of \$.01 for every dollar in the account each month

20. \$100 invested for 24 months at an interest rate of \$.01 for every dollar in the account each month

21. On her trip to the library, Arlene walked two blocks to the bus stop in five minutes. She rode the bus for 15 min. The bus stopped three times, for a minute each time. Make a graph to represent Arlene's trip.

Extra Practice

Write a fraction in simplest form for each part that is shaded.

1.
2.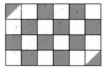
3.
4.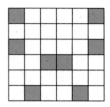

Find two fractions that are equivalent to each fraction.

5. $\frac{21}{24}$ 6. $\frac{65}{100}$ 7. $\frac{6}{9}$ 8. $\frac{40}{80}$ 9. $\frac{12}{36}$

Find the GCF of each set of numbers.

10. 35, 49   11. 11, 12   12. 28, 40   13. 17, 34   14. 16, 26   15. 10, 30

Write each fraction in its simplest form.

16. $\frac{15}{75}$ 17. $\frac{16}{36}$ 18. $\frac{110}{225}$ 19. $\frac{72}{108}$ 20. $\frac{45}{315}$ 21. $\frac{54}{96}$

Write each mixed number as an improper fraction.

22. $7\frac{7}{8}$ 23. $3\frac{5}{7}$ 24. $3\frac{1}{4}$ 25. $4\frac{2}{5}$ 26. $10\frac{1}{6}$ 27. $2\frac{2}{5}$

Write each improper fraction as a whole number or a mixed number.

28. $\frac{76}{15}$ 29. $\frac{136}{12}$ 30. $\frac{76}{4}$ 31. $\frac{13}{4}$ 32. $\frac{28}{8}$ 33. $\frac{100}{6}$

Write the prime factorization of each number.

34. 80   35. 240   36. 720   37. 48   38. 186   39. 150

Write each fraction in its simplest form, and draw a model for each.

40. $\frac{4}{10}$ 41. $\frac{14}{28}$ 42. $\frac{15}{18}$ 43. $\frac{9}{24}$ 44. $\frac{80}{100}$

Write the first five multiples of each number.

45. 3   46. 9   47. 12   48. 8   49. 17

Extra Practice

Compare. Use <, >, or =.

1. $\frac{1}{4}$ ■ $\frac{2}{9}$ 2. $\frac{3}{7}$ ■ $\frac{1}{2}$ 3. $\frac{2}{5}$ ■ $\frac{4}{10}$ 4. $\frac{5}{6}$ ■ $\frac{7}{8}$ 5. $\frac{3}{5}$ ■ $\frac{2}{3}$

Write each fraction as a decimal. Write each decimal as a fraction.

6. $\frac{4}{5}$ 7. 0.365   8. $\frac{7}{8}$ 9. 0.42   10. $\frac{9}{11}$ 11. 0.7

Estimate each sum, difference, product, or quotient.

12. $\frac{2}{3} + \frac{7}{9}$ 13. $15\frac{1}{5} - 5\frac{4}{7}$ 14. $3\frac{12}{13} \cdot \frac{1}{4}$ 15. $99\frac{9}{10} - \frac{1}{5}$ 16. $7\frac{4}{5} \div 1\frac{2}{3}$

Find each sum, difference, product, or quotient. Write the answer in simplest form.

17. $\frac{2}{3} + \frac{9}{5}$ 18. $1\frac{5}{8} \cdot 6\frac{1}{3}$ 19. $\frac{4}{5} \div \frac{9}{10}$ 20. $12 - 1\frac{3}{5}$ 21. $3\frac{1}{8} + 3\frac{3}{4}$

Solve each equation.

22. $\frac{n}{3} = -18$ 23. $1\frac{1}{3} + m = 2\frac{5}{6}$ 24. $\frac{2}{7} = y - \frac{1}{2}$ 25. $64t = 16$

Complete.

26. $\frac{3}{4}$ gal = ■ c   27. $6\frac{1}{8}$ T = ■ lb   28. $\frac{3}{8}$ mi = ■ yd   29. $12\frac{2}{3}$ lb = ■ oz

30. Darlene is making costumes for Halloween. The pattern she has chosen requires $2\frac{2}{3}$ yd of felt at \$3.69/yd, and $1\frac{3}{4}$ yd of artificial fur at \$5.50/yd. If Darlene makes a matching costume for her sister, what is the total cost of material for the two costumes?

31. **Choose A, B, C, or D.** Which expression has the greatest value?

   A. $\frac{5}{6}$ of 14   **B.** $21\frac{1}{4} - 10\frac{1}{8}$ **C.** $5\frac{1}{3} + 6\frac{1}{7}$ **D.** $\frac{1}{3}$ of 35.46

32. A recipe requires $1\frac{3}{4}$ c of flour. How much flour will you need if you triple the recipe?

Chapter 9

Extra Practice

Find the unit rate.

1. a. 32 oz for $2.29
    b. 48 oz for $3.19

2. a. earn $200 in 8 h
    b. earn $364 in 14 h

3. a. fly 2,250 km in 3 h
    b. fly 6,000 km in 7.5 h

Find the value of n in each proportion.

4. $\dfrac{12}{n} = \dfrac{3}{5}$

5. $\dfrac{n}{12} = \dfrac{4}{16}$

6. $\dfrac{7}{8} = \dfrac{n}{4}$

7. $\dfrac{7}{10} = \dfrac{14}{n}$

Write each fraction as a percent; write each percent as a fraction.

8. $\dfrac{5}{6}$

9. $37\dfrac{1}{2}\%$

10. $\dfrac{11}{5}$

11. 87.5%

12. 64%

Write a proportion and solve.

13. 54 is 40% of what number?

14. What is 5% of 48?

15. What percent of 200 is 120?

Find the missing lengths in the similar figures.

16.

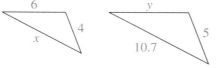

17.

18. Sandra's Photo Studio charges $8.95 for either one 11 × 14 enlargement, two 8 × 10 enlargements, or three 5 × 7 enlargements. Which is the best buy in terms of cost per square unit?

19. Costs for the Middle School picnic have increased a total of 30% in three years. There is $235 in the school picnic fund. If juice cost $57.25 and food cost $129.80 three years ago, is there enough money in the fund to pay this year's bill? Explain your answer.

20. The scale on an architectural drawing is 0.5 in. : 15 ft. If the dimensions of a room in the original drawing are 0.75 in. by 1.2 in., how big is the actual room?

Extra Practice

A number cube is rolled. Find each probability.

1. $P(3 \text{ or } 4)$ **2.** $P(\text{not } 3)$ **3.** $P(5)$ **4.** $P(1 \text{ and } 7)$

A box has 6 green marbles, 8 blue marbles, and 3 red marbles in it. Find $P(B)$ after A has happened.

5. A: Draw a green marble. Keep it. B: Draw a red marble.

6. A: Draw a blue marble. Replace it. B: Draw a red marble.

7. A: Draw a red marble. Keep it. B: Draw a red marble.

The events A and B are independent. Find $P(A \text{ and } B)$.

8. $P(A) = \frac{1}{5}, P(B) = \frac{3}{4}$ **9.** $P(A) = \frac{1}{6}, P(B) = \frac{5}{6}$ **10.** $P(A) = 1, P(B) = 0$

11. a. Flip two coins, and spin a wheel with congruent sections colored red, white, and blue. Draw a grid or a tree diagram to find the sample space.

    b. Find $P(\text{exactly two heads and blue})$ and $P(\text{at least one tail and red})$.

Use the data at the right for Exercises 12 and 13. A student is chosen at random from the students in this school.

School Enrollment	
Freshmen	156
Sophomores	152
Juniors	138
Seniors	144

12. What is the probability the student is a freshman?

13. What is the probability the student is *not* a senior?

14. In how many ways can a committee of 3 be chosen from a club of 9 members?

15. In how many ways can a president, a vice-president, and a treasurer be elected from a club of 9 members?

16. A box contains the letters S T A T I S T I C S. What is the probability that if you take out two letters, one after the other without replacement, you will select an S, then a T?

17. Audubon Society volunteers marked 25 sea gulls in a nesting area. Later in the summer they counted 500 gulls, 19 of which were marked. Estimate the sea gull population.

Chapter 11

Extra Practice

Use the graph at the right for Exercises 1–11. Name the point with the given coordinates.

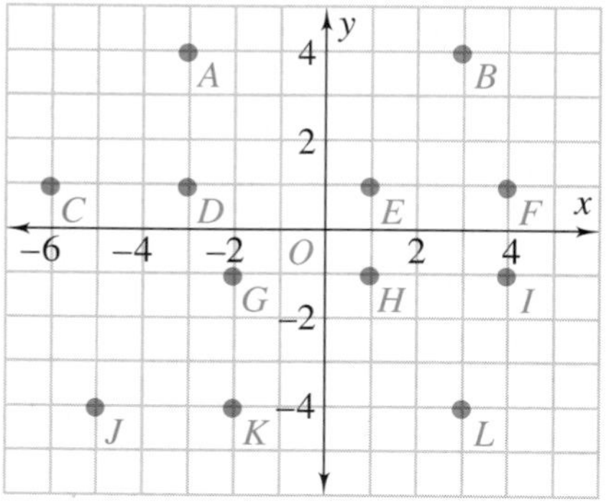

1. $(-2, -1)$ **2.** $(1, 1)$ **3.** $(3, -4)$

Write the coordinates of each point.

4. A **5.** I **6.** J

Determine the slope of the line through the points.

7. A and E **8.** G and E **9.** B and F

10. Is the triangle formed by points E, B, and F a reflection, a rotation or a translation of the triangle formed by points H, L, and I?

11. Write a rule for the translation of the triangle formed by points C, A, and D to the triangle formed by points J, G, and K.

12. Kenyatta accumulated a total of 28 points to win a wrestling tournament. The scoring system was 4 points for each win at the first level (3 matches maximum), 5 points for a quarter-final win, 7 points for a semi-final win, and 8 points for winning in the finals. How many matches did Kenyatta win at the first level?

13. Choose A, B, or C. Which equation has the greatest value for y at $x = -2$?

A. $y = x^2 + 3$ **B.** $y = 3x + 9$ **C.** $y = |x - 4|$

14. Choose A, B, or C. Which equation is a good model for data that include the points $(0, -2)$, $(-1, -4)$, and $(3, 4)$?

A. $y = x^2 - 2$ **B.** $y = \frac{x}{2} - 2$ **C.** $y = 2x - 2$

15. a. Graph the square $ABCD$ with vertices $A(2, -3)$, $B(4, -5)$, $C(6, -3)$, and $D(4, -1)$. Then connect the vertices in order.

b. Graph the reflection of $ABCD$ over the y-axis. Find the coordinates of the reflection.

c. Find the coordinates of the vertices of the image of $ABCD$ after a translation of 3 units to the left and 4 units up. Graph the translation.

Tables

Table 1 Measures

Metric

Length

10 millimeters (mm) = 1 centimeter (cm)

100 cm = 1 meter (m)

1,000 m = 1 kilometer (km)

Area

100 square millimeters (mm^2) = 1 square centimeter (cm^2)

10,000 cm^2 = 1 square meter (m^2)

Volume

1,000 cubic millimeters (mm^3) = 1 cubic centimeter (cm^3)

1,000,000 cm^3 = 1 cubic meter (m^3)

Mass

1,000 milligrams (mg) = 1 gram (g)

1,000 g = 1 kilogram (kg)

Liquid Capacity

1,000 milliliters (mL) = 1 liter (L)

United States Customary

Length

12 inches (in.) = 1 foot (ft)

3 feet = 1 yard (yd)

36 in. = 1 yd

5,280 ft = 1 mile (mi)

1,760 yd = 1 mi

Area

144 square inches ($in.^2$) = 1 square foot (ft^2)

9 ft^2 = 1 square yard (yd^2)

4,840 yd^2 = 1 acre

Volume

1,728 cubic inches ($in.^3$) = 1 cubic foot (ft^3)

27 ft^3 = 1 cubic yard (yd^3)

Weight

16 ounces (oz) = 1 pound (lb)

2,000 lb = 1 ton (T)

Liquid Capacity

8 fluid ounces (fl oz) = 1 cup (c)

2 c = 1 pint (pt)

2 pt = 1 quart (qt)

4 qt = 1 gallon (gal)

Time

1 minute (min) = 60 seconds (s)

1 hour (h) = 60 min

1 day (da) = 24 h

1 year (y) = 365 da

Table 2 — Formulas

Circumference of a circle

$C = \pi d$ or $C = 2\pi r$

Area		
	parallelogram:	$A = bh$
	rectangle:	$A = bh$
	trapezoid:	$A = \frac{1}{2}h(b_1 + b_2)$
	triangle:	$A = \frac{1}{2}bh$
	circle:	$A = \pi r^2$

Volume		
	cylinder:	$V = \pi r^2 h$
	rectangular prism:	$V = lwh$

Table 3 — Symbols

Symbol	Meaning	Symbol	Meaning
$>$	is greater than	$\perp$	is perpendicular to
$<$	is less than	$\cong$	is congruent to
$\geq$	is greater than or equal to	$\sim$	is similar to
$\leq$	is less than or equal to	$\approx$	is approximately equal to
$=$	is equal to	$\overline{AB}$	segment AB
$\neq$	is not equal to	$\overrightarrow{AB}$	ray AB
$^\circ$	degrees	$\overleftrightarrow{AB}$	line AB
$\%$	percent	$\triangle ABC$	triangle ABC
$f(n)$	f of n	$\angle ABC$	angle ABC
$a : b$	ratio of a to b, $\frac{a}{b}$	$m\angle ABC$	measure of angle ABC
$\lvert -5 \rvert$	absolute value of negative 5	AB	length of segment AB
$P(E)$	probability of an event E	$\overarc{AB}$	arc AB
π	pi		

Table 4   Squares and Square Roots

N	N^2	$\sqrt{N}$	N	N^2	$\sqrt{N}$
1	1	1	51	2,601	7.141
2	4	1.414	52	2,704	7.211
3	9	1.732	53	2,809	7.280
4	16	2	54	2,916	7.348
5	25	2.236	55	3,025	7.416
6	36	2.449	56	3,136	7.483
7	49	2.646	57	3,249	7.550
8	64	2.828	58	3,364	7.616
9	81	3	59	3,481	7.681
10	100	3.162	60	3,600	7.746
11	121	3.317	61	3,721	7.810
12	144	3.464	62	3,844	7.874
13	169	3.606	63	3,969	7.937
14	196	3.742	64	4,096	8
15	225	3.873	65	4,225	8.062
16	256	4	66	4,356	8.124
17	289	4.123	67	4,489	8.185
18	324	4.243	68	4,624	8.246
19	361	4.359	69	4,761	8.307
20	400	4.472	70	4,900	8.367
21	441	4.583	71	5,041	8.426
22	484	4.690	72	5,184	8.485
23	529	4.796	73	5,329	8.544
24	576	4.899	74	5,476	8.602
25	625	5	75	5,625	8.660
26	676	5.099	76	5,776	8.718
27	729	5.196	77	5,929	8.775
28	784	5.292	78	6,084	8.832
29	841	5.385	79	6,241	8.888
30	900	5.477	80	6,400	8.944
31	961	5.568	81	6,561	9
32	1,024	5.657	82	6,724	9.055
33	1,089	5.745	83	6,889	9.110
34	1,156	5.831	84	7,056	9.165
35	1,225	5.916	85	7,225	9.220
36	1,296	6	86	7,396	9.274
37	1,369	6.083	87	7,569	9.327
38	1,444	6.164	88	7,744	9.381
39	1,521	6.245	89	7,921	9.434
40	1,600	6.325	90	8,100	9.487
41	1,681	6.403	91	8,281	9.539
42	1,764	6.481	92	8,464	9.592
43	1,849	6.557	93	8,649	9.644
44	1,936	6.633	94	8,836	9.695
45	2,025	6.708	95	9,025	9.747
46	2,116	6.782	96	9,216	9.798
47	2,209	6.856	97	9,409	9.849
48	2,304	6.928	98	9,604	9.899
49	2,401	7	99	9,801	9.950
50	2,500	7.071	100	10,000	10

Tables

Student Study Guide and Glossary

A

Absolute value (p. 145)	A number's distance from zero on the number line is called its absolute value.
Example	The absolute value of -3 is 3 because -3 is 3 units from zero on the number line.

Acute angle (p. 50)	An acute angle is any angle that measures less than 90°.
Example	$0° < m\angle 1 < 90°$

Acute triangle (p. 54)	A triangle that contains all acute angles is an acute triangle.
Example	$m\angle 1, m\angle 2, m\angle 3 < 90°$ 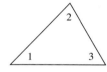

Addition property of equality (p. 172)	If the same number is added to each side of an equation, the results are equal.
Example	If $a = b$, then $a + c = b + c$.

Adjacent angle (p. 50)	Adjacent angles are two angles that share a vertex and one common side but have no interior points in common.
Example	$\angle 1$ and $\angle 2$ are adjacent angles. 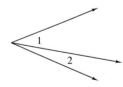

Angle (p. 49)	An angle is made up of two rays with a common endpoint.
Example	$\angle 1$ is made up of $\overrightarrow{GP}$ and $\overrightarrow{GS}$ with common endpoint G. 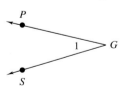

| **Angle bisector (p. 76)** | An angle bisector is the ray that divides the angle into two congruent angles. |
| | **Example** $\overrightarrow{DB}$ bisects $\angle ADC$ so that $\angle 1 \cong \angle 2$. 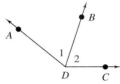 |

| **Arc (p. 71)** | An arc is part of a circle. A semicircle is an arc that is half of a circle. |
| | **Example** $\overset{\frown}{AB}$ is an arc of circle O. $\overset{\frown}{ABC}$ is a semicircle of circle O. |

| **Area (p. 194)** | The number of square units inside a figure is the area. |
| | **Example** $l = 6$ ft, and $w = 4$ ft, so the area is 24 ft². Each square equals 1 ft². |

| **Arithmetic sequence (p. 245)** | A sequence of numbers in which each term is the result of adding the same number to the preceding term is called an arithmetic sequence. |
| | **Example** The sequence 4, 10, 16, 22, 28, 34, . . . is an arithmetic sequence. |

| **Associative property of addition (p. 102)** | Changing the grouping of the addends does not change the sum. |
| | **Example** $(2 + 3) + 7 = 2 + (3 + 7)$
$(a + b) + c = a + (b + c)$ |

| **Associative property of multiplication (p. 110)** | Changing the grouping of the factors does not change the product. |
| | **Example** $(3 \times 4) \times 5 = 3 \times (4 \times 5)$
$(a \times b) \times c = a \times (b \times c)$ |

B

| **Bar graph (p. 10)** | A bar graph compares amounts. |
| | **Example** This bar graph represents class sizes for grades 6, 7, and 8. 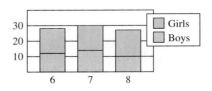 |

Student Study Guide

Base (p. 120)	When a number is written in exponential form, the number that is used as a factor is the base.
Example	$5^4 = 5 \times 5 \times 5 \times 5$

Biased question (p. 32)	A question is biased if it makes assumptions about the person being questioned or if it makes one answer seem better than another.
Example	"Do you prefer good food or junk food?"

C

Central angle (p. 70)	A central angle is an angle with its vertex at the center of a circle.
Example	$\angle AOB$ is a central angle of circle O.

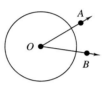

Chord (p. 70)	A chord is a segment that has both endpoints on the circle.
Example	$\overline{CB}$ is a chord of circle O.

Circle (p. 70)	A circle is a set of points on a plane that are all the same distance from a given point, called the center.
Example	Circle O

Circle graph (p. 406)	A circle graph shows the parts of a whole.
Example	This circle graph represents the different types of plays William Shakespeare wrote.

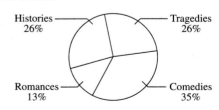

Histories 26%   Tragedies 26%   Romances 13%   Comedies 35%

Circumference (p. 206)	Circumference is the distance around a circle. You calculate the circumference of a circle by multiplying the diameter by pi, or π ($C = \pi d$). Pi is approximately equal to 3.14.
Example	The circumference of a circle with a diameter of 10 cm is approximately 31.4 cm.

10 cm
about 31.4 cm
O

Combination (p. 443)	An arrangement in which order does not matter is a combination.
Example	You choose two vegetables from spinach, carrots, and peas. The possible combinations are spinach and carrots, spinach and peas, and carrots and peas.
Commutative property of addition (p. 102)	Changing the order of the addends does not change the sum.
Example	$a + b = b + a$
Commutative property of multiplication (p. 109)	Changing the order of the factors does not change the product.
Example	$ab = ba$
Compatible numbers (p. 98)	Estimating quotients is easier when you use compatible numbers. Compatible numbers are numbers close in value to the numbers you want to divide, and that are easy to divide mentally.
Example	Estimate the quotient of 151 and 14.6. $151 \approx 150$ $14.6 \approx 15$ $150 \div 15 = 10$ $151 \div 14.6 \approx 10$
Complementary angles (p. 49)	Two angles are complementary if the sum of their measures is 90°.
Example	$\angle BCA$ and $\angle CAB$ are complementary angles.

C
A
B

Composite number (p. 292)	A whole number that has more than two factors is called a composite number.
Example	24 is a composite number that has 1, 2, 3, 4, 6, 8, 12, and 24 as factors.
Congruent angles (p. 54)	Congruent angles are angles that have the same measure.
Example	$\angle C$ and $\angle B$ are both 60° so $\angle C$ is congruent to $\angle B$.

C 60°   60° B

Congruent figures (p. 61)   Figures that have the same size and shape are congruent.

Example $AB = QS$, $CB = RS$, and $AC = QR$.
$m\angle A = m\angle Q$, $m\angle C = m\angle R$, and
$m\angle B = m\angle S$. Triangles ABC and QSR
are congruent.

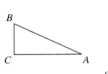

Congruent polygons (p. 61)   Polygons whose corresponding parts (sides and angles) are
congruent are congruent polygons.

Example $\triangle HOT \cong \triangle PIE$

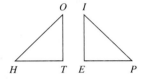

Congruent segments (p. 54)   Congruent segments are segments that have the same length.

Example $\overline{AB} \cong \overline{WX}$ $A \bullet \!\!\!-\!\!\!-\!\!\!-\!\!\!-\!\!\!\bullet\, B$

$W \bullet \!\!\!-\!\!\!-\!\!\!-\!\!\!-\!\!\!\bullet\, X$

Converse of the Pythagorean   In any triangle with sides of lengths a, b and c, if $a^2 + b^2 = c^2$,
Theorem (p. 214)   then the triangle is a right triangle.

Example The triangle shown has sides
of lengths 5, 12 and 13. Since
$5^2 + 12^2 = 25 + 144 = 169 = 13^2$,
the triangle is a right triangle.

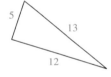

Coordinate plane (p. 459)   A coordinate plane is formed by the intersection of a horizontal
number line called the x-axis, and a vertical number line called
the y-axis.

Example

Coordinates (p. 459)   Each point on the coordinate plane is identified by a unique
ordered pair of numbers called coordinates. The first coordinate
tells you how far from the origin to move along the x-axis. The
second coordinate tells you how far from the origin to move along
the y-axis.

Example The ordered pair $(-2, 1)$ describes the point that
is 2 units to the left of the origin and one unit
above the x-axis.

Correlation (p. 21)

Two sets of related data have a positive correlation if, in general, as the values of one set of data increase, the values of the other set increase also. Two sets of related data have a negative correlation if, in general, as the values of one set increase, the values of the other set decrease. Two sets of related data have little or no correlation if the data do not show a consistently increasing or decreasing trend.

Example

Positive   Negative   No Correlation

Counting principle (p. 428)

The number of outcomes for an event is the product of the number of outcomes for each stage of the event.

Example Flip a coin and roll a number cube. The total number of possible outcomes = 2 × 6 = 12.

Cylinder (p. 224)

A cylinder is a space figure with two circular, parallel, and congruent bases.

Example

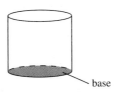

base

D

Dependent events (p. 431)

Events are dependent if the outcome of the first event affects the outcome of a second event.

Example When a marble is drawn from a bag containing red and blue marbles, and not returned, the events (red, then blue) are dependent.

Diameter (p. 70)

A diameter is a segment that passes through the center of a circle and has both endpoints on the circle.

Example $\overline{RS}$ is a diameter of a circle O.

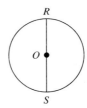

Distributive property (p. 117)	Each term inside a set of parentheses can be multiplied by a factor outside the parentheses.
Example	$2(3 + 5) = 2 \cdot 3 + 2 \cdot 5$; $a(b + c) = ab + ac$

Division property of equality (p. 176)	If both sides of an equation are divided by the same nonzero number, the results are equal.
Example	If $a = b$ and $c \neq 0$, then $\frac{a}{c} = \frac{b}{c}$.

Double bar graph (p. 13)	Double bar graphs compare two sets of data.

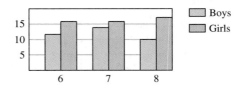

Example	This double bar graph shows class sizes for grades 6, 7, and 8 for both boys and girls.

Double line graph (p. 12)	Double line graphs compare changes over time of two sets of data.

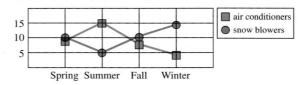

Example	This double line graph represents seasonal air conditioner and snow blower sales (in thousands) for a large chain of department stores.

E

Equilateral triangle (p. 54)	An equilateral triangle is a triangle with three congruent sides.
Example	$\overline{SL} \cong \overline{LW} \cong \overline{WS}$

Equivalent decimals (p. 94)	Decimals that name the same amount are equivalent decimals.
Example	$0.6 = 0.60$

Equivalent equation (p. 172)	When the same number is added to or subtracted from each side of an equation, the result is an equivalent equation.
Example	$(23 + x) - 23 = 34 - 23$ is equivalent to $(23 + x) = 34$.

Equivalent fractions (p. 285)	Fractions that are equal to each other are equivalent fractions.
Example	$\frac{1}{2} = \frac{25}{50}$

Event (p. 419)	An event is any group of outcomes.
Example	There are six possible outcomes for a roll of a number cube. The event (Even Number) is made up of three outcomes: 2, 4, and 6.

Experimental probability (p. 438)	Experimental probability is an estimate based on the relative frequency of positive outcomes occurring during an experiment.
Example	If 2 out of the first 10 widgets off of an assembly line are defective, you can estimate that 5 out of 25 will be defective.

Exponent (p. 120)	An exponent tells you how many times a base is used as a factor.
Example	$3^4 = 3 \times 3 \times 3 \times 3$

F

Factor (p. 284)	One number is a factor of another if it divides that number with no remainder.
Example	1, 2, 3, 4, 6, 9, 12, 18, and 36 are factors of 36.

Factor tree (p. 293)	A factor tree is used to find a number's prime factors.
Example	

Fair game (p. 421)	A game is fair if any player is equally likely to win.
Example	Players A and B roll a number cube. Player A gets a point if the number is even; player B gets a point if the number is odd. This game is fair.

Frequency table (p. 5)	A frequency table lists items together with the number of times, or frequency, that they occur.
Example	This frequency table shows the number of household telephones for a class of students.

Phones	Tally	Frequency
1										8
2								6
3						4

Student Study Guide

Front-end estimation (p. 97)	To use front-end estimation to estimate sums, first add the front-end digits. Then adjust by estimating the sum of the remaining digits. Add the two values.
Example	Estimate $3.49 + $2.29. $3 + 2 = 5$ $0.49 + 0.29 \approx 1$ $\$3.49 + 2.29 \approx \$5 + \$1 = \$6$
Function (p. 259)	A function is a relationship in which each member of one set is paired with exactly one member of a second set.
Example	Earned income is a function of the number of hours worked (h). If you earn $5/h, then your income is expressed by the function $f(h) = 5h$.

 G

Geometric sequence (p. 246)	In a geometric sequence, each term is the result of multiplying the preceding term by the same number.
Example	The sequence 1, 3, 9, 27, 81, . . . is a geometric sequence.
Gram (p. 230)	A gram is the basic unit of mass, or weight, in the metric system.
Example	A paper clip weighs about 1 g.
Greatest common factor (GCF) (p. 289)	The greatest common factor of two or more numbers is the greatest number that is a factor of all the numbers.
Example	12 and 30 have a GCF of 6.

H

Histogram (p. 6)	A histogram is a special type of bar graph used to show frequency. The height of each bar gives the frequency of the data.
Example	This histogram gives the frequency of board game purchases at a local toy store. 
Hypotenuse (p. 212)	The hypotenuse is the longest side of a right triangle. It is the side opposite the right angle.
Example	$\overline{AC}$ is the hypotenuse of $\triangle ABC$.

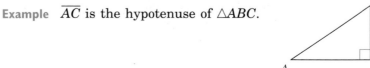

Identity property of addition (p. 102)	The sum of any number and 0 is that number.
	Example $a + 0 = a$

Identity property of multiplication (p. 109)	The product of 1 and any number is that number.
	Example $a(1) = a$

Image (p. 482)	A point, line, or figure that has been transformed to a new set of coordinates is the image of the original point, line, or figure.
	Example $A'B'C'D'$ is the image of $ABCD$. 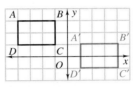

Independent events (p. 431)	Events are independent if the outcome of one event does not affect the outcome of the other.
	Example When a marble is drawn from a bag containing red and blue marbles, and returned, the events (red and blue) are independent.

Integers (p. 145)	Integers are the set of whole numbers and their opposites.
	Example $-3, -2, -1, 0, 1, 2, 3$ are integers.

Inverse operations (p. 164)	Operations that undo each other, such as addition and subtraction, are inverse operations.
	Example $15 + 3 = 18$, and $18 - 3 = 15$.

Isosceles triangle (p. 54)	An isosceles triangle is a triangle with at least two congruent sides.
	Example $\overline{LM} \cong \overline{LB}$ 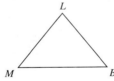

Least common denominator (LCD) (p. 317)	The least common denominator of two or more fractions is the least common multiple of their denominators.
	Example The least common denominator of $\frac{1}{5}$ and $\frac{2}{3}$ is 15. $\frac{1}{5} + \frac{2}{3} = \frac{3}{15} + \frac{10}{15} = \frac{13}{15}$

Student Study Guide

Legs of a right triangle (p. 212)	The two shorter sides of a right triangle form a right angle and are called the legs of the triangle.
Example	$\overline{AB}$ and $\overline{BC}$ are the legs of $\triangle ABC$.

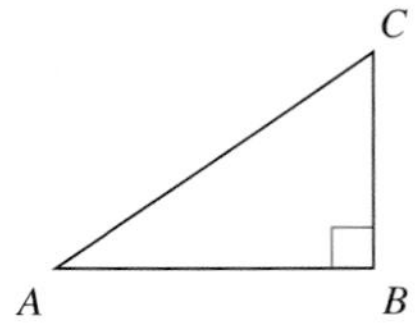

Line graph (p. 10)	A line graph shows how an amount changes over time.
Example	This line graph shows the amount of time a student spends reading each night for a week.

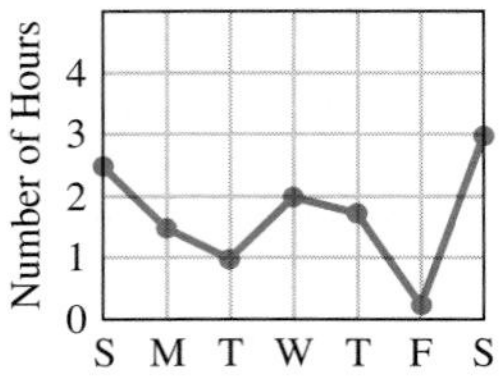

Linear equation (p. 463)	An equation is a linear equation when the graphs of all its solutions lie on a line.
Example	$y = \frac{1}{2}x + 3$ is linear because the graphs of its solutions lie on a line.

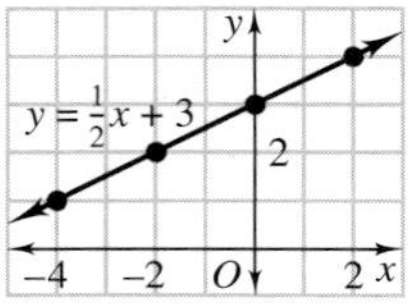

Liter (p. 225)	A liter (L) is the basic unit of capacity, or volume, in the metric system.
Example	A pitcher holds about 2 L of juice.

M

Mean (p. 16)	The mean of a set of data is the sum of the data divided by the number of pieces of data.
Example	The mean temperature (°F) for the set of temperatures 44, 52, 48, 55, 60, 67 and 58 is: $\frac{44 + 52 + 48 + 55 + 60 + 67 + 58}{7} \approx 54.86°F$

Median (p. 16)	The median is the middle number in a set of data when the data are arranged in numerical order. If there is an even number of data items, the median is the mean of the two middle items.
Example	Temperatures (°F) for one week arranged in numerical order are 44, 48, 52, 55, 58, 60, and 67. 55 is the median because it is the middle number in the set of data.

Meter (p. 200)	A meter (m) is the basic unit of length in the metric system.
Example	A doorknob is about 1 m from the floor.

Midpoint (p. 75)	The midpoint of a segment is the point that divides the segment into two congruent segments.
Example	$\overline{XM} \cong \overline{MY}$. M is the midpoint of $\overline{XY}$. 

Mode (p. 17)	The mode is the data item that appears most often.
Example	The mode of the set of wages $2.50, $3.75, $3.60, $2.75, $2.75, $3.70, is $2.75.

Multiple (p. 284)	A multiple of a number is the product of that number and any nonzero whole number.
Example	Multiples of 13 are 13, 26, 39, 52, and so on.

Multiplication property of equality (p. 176)	If both sides of an equation are multiplied by the same number, the results are equal.
Example	If $a = b$, then $a \cdot c = b \cdot c$.

O

Obtuse angle (p. 50)	An obtuse angle is any angle whose measure is greater than 90° and less than 180°.
Example	

Obtuse triangle (p. 54)	A triangle that contains one obtuse angle is an obtuse triangle.
Example	$90° < m\angle J < 180°$ 

Odds (p. 420)	Odds are used to compare favorable outcomes to unfavorable outcomes. The odds in favor of an event $= \dfrac{\text{number of favorable outcomes}}{\text{number of unfavorable outcomes}}$.
Example	The odds in favor of getting a 4 when spinning the wheel are $\frac{1}{7}$.

Opposite numbers (p. 145)	Numbers that are the same distance from zero on the number line but in opposite directions are opposite numbers.
Example	-17 and 17 are opposites.

Student Study Guide

Order of operations (p. 121)	**1.** Do all operations within parentheses. **2.** Do all work with exponents. **3.** Multiply and divide from left to right. **4.** Add and subtract from left to right.
Example	$2^3(7 - 4) = 2^3 \cdot 3 = 8 \cdot 3 = 24$

Ordered pair (p. 459)	An ordered pair is a pair of numbers that describe the location of a point on a coordinate plane. The first value is the x-coordinate and the second value is the y-coordinate.
Example	$(-2, 1)$ is an ordered pair. The x-coordinate is -2; the y-coordinate is 1. 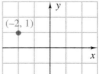

Origin (p. 459)	The point of intersection of the x- and y-axes on a coordinate plane is called the origin.
Example	The ordered pair that describes the origin is $(0, 0)$.

Outcomes (p. 419)	Outcomes are the possible results or consequences of an action.
Example	The outcomes of rolling a number cube are 1, 2, 3, 4, 5, or 6.

Outlier (p. 17)	An item of data that is much higher or lower than the rest of the data is an outlier.
Example	An outlier in the list 6, 7, 9, 10, 11, 12, 14, 52, is 52.

P

Parallel lines (p. 66)	Parallel lines are lines in the same plane that do not intersect.
Example	$\overleftrightarrow{EF} \parallel \overleftrightarrow{HI}$ 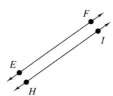

Parallelogram (p. 66)	A parallelogram has both pairs of opposite sides parallel.
Example	$\overline{KV}$ is parallel to $\overline{AD}$, and $\overline{AK}$ is parallel to $\overline{DV}$, so $KVDA$ is a parallelogram. 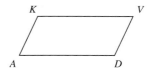

| **Percent (p. 385)** | A percent is a ratio that compares a number to one hundred. The symbol for percent is %. |
| | **Example** $50\% = \frac{50}{100}$ |

| **Percent of change (p. 403)** | Percent of change is the percent something increases or decreases from its original measure or amount. |
| | **Example** If a school's population increased from 500 to 520 students, the amount of change is 20. Use the proportion $\frac{20}{500} = \frac{\text{percent of change}}{100}$ to find that the percent of increase is 4%. |

| **Perfect square (p. 210)** | A perfect square is a whole number that is equal to the second power of an integer. |
| | **Example** $25 = 5^2$ |

| **Perimeter (p. 193)** | Perimeter is the distance around a figure. |
| | **Example** The perimeter of rectangle $ABCD$ is 12 ft. |

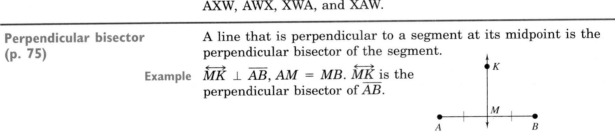

| **Permutation (p. 442)** | An arrangement in which order is important is a permutation. |
| | **Example** There are six permutations of the letters W, A, and X: WAX, WXA, AXW, AWX, XWA, and XAW. |

| **Perpendicular bisector (p. 75)** | A line that is perpendicular to a segment at its midpoint is the perpendicular bisector of the segment. |
| | **Example** $\overleftrightarrow{MK} \perp \overline{AB}$, $AM = MB$. $\overleftrightarrow{MK}$ is the perpendicular bisector of $\overline{AB}$. |

| **Perpendicular lines (p. 75)** | Perpendiuclar lines are lines that intersect to form right angles. |
| | **Example** $\overleftrightarrow{DE} \perp \overleftrightarrow{RS}$ |

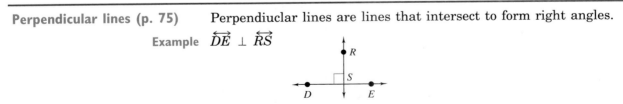

| **Population (p. 31)** | A population is a collection of objects or group of people about whom information is gathered. |
| | **Example** A quality control inspector examines a sample of the population, which is the output of a factory. |

Prime factorization (p. 293)	Writing a composite number as the product of its prime factors is called prime factorization.
Example	The prime factorization of 30 is $2 \times 3 \times 5$.

Prime numbers (p. 292)	A number that has exactly two factors, 1 and the number itself, is a prime number.
Example	13 is a prime number because its only factors are 1 and 13.

Prism (p. 80)	A prism is a three-dimensional figure with two parallel and congruent polygonal faces, called bases. A prism is named by the shape of its base.
Example	

Rectangular   Triangular

Probability (p. 419)	When all outcomes are equally likely, the probability that an event E will happen is: $P(E) = \dfrac{\text{number of favorable outcomes}}{\text{number of possible outcomes}}$
Example	The probability of getting a 4 on spinning the wheel is $\frac{1}{8}$.

Proportion (p. 373)	A proportion is an equation stating that two ratios are equal.
Example	$\frac{3}{12} = \frac{12}{48}$ is a proportion.

Pyramid (p. 81)	Pyramids are three-dimensional figures with only one base. The base is a polygon and the other faces are triangles. A pyramid is named by the shape of its base.
Example	

Triangular   Rectangular

Pythagorean Theorem (p. 213)	In any right triangle, the sum of the squares of the lengths of the legs (a and b) is equal to the square of the hypotenuse (c): $a^2 + b^2 = c^2$
Example	The right triangle shown has legs 3 and 4 and hypotenuse 5: $3^2 + 4^2 = 5^2$

Q

Quadrant (p. 460)

The *x*- and *y*-axes divide the coordinate plane into four regions, called quadrants.

Example

R

Radius (p. 70)

A radius is a segment that has one endpoint at the center and the other endpoint on the circle.

Example $\overline{OA}$ is a radius of circle *O*.

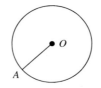

Range (p. 5)

The range of a set of numerical data is the difference between the greatest and least values of the set.

Example The range of the data 1, 3, 4, 2, 6, 1, 3 is 6 − 1 = 5.

Rate (p. 369)

A rate is a ratio that compares two quantities measured in different units.

Example A student typed a 1,100 word essay in 50 min. The student's typing rate is 1100 words per 50 min, or 22 words/min.

Ratio (p. 365)

A ratio is a comparison of two numbers by division.

Example A ratio can be written in three different ways: 72 to 100, 72 : 100, and $\frac{72}{100}$

Rectangle (p. 66)

A rectangle is a parallelogram with four right angles.

Example

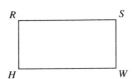

| **Reflection** (p. 487) | A reflection flips a figure across a line. |
| | **Example** $K'L'M'N'$ is a reflection of *KLMN* over the y-axis. |

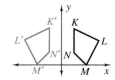

| **Regular polygon** (p. 66) | A regular polygon has all sides congruent and all angles congruent. |
| | **Example** *ABDFEC* is a regular hexagon. |

| **Repeating decimal** (p. 113) | A repeating decimal is a decimal in which a digit or a sequence of digits keeps repeating. The symbol for a repeating decimal is a bar drawn over the digit, or digits, that repeat. |
| | **Example** $0.8888\ldots$, or $0.\overline{8}$ |

| **Rhombus** (p. 67) | A rhombus is a parallelogram with four congruent sides. |
| | **Example** |

| **Right angle** (p. 50) | A right angle is an angle with a measure of 90°. |
| | **Example** $m\angle D = 90°$ |

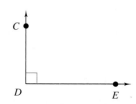

| **Right triangle** (p. 54) | A right triangle is a triangle with a right angle. |
| | **Example** $m\angle B = 90°$ |

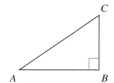

Rotation (p. 489)	A rotation is a transformation that turns a figure about a fixed point, called the center of rotation.
Example	$\triangle RST$ has been rotated 180° about the origin (O) to $\triangle R'S'T'$. 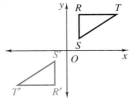

Rotational symmetry (p. 489)	A figure has rotational symmetry when an image after a rotation fits exactly on top of the original figure.
Example	This figure has 60° rotational symmetry.

S

Sample (p. 31)	A sample of a group is a smaller subgroup selected from within the group. A representative sample of a group is a subgroup that has the same characteristics as the larger group. A random sample of a group is a subgroup selected so that each member of the group has an equal chance of being chosen.
Example	A representative sample of last week's math quizzes would include quizzes from each of several math classes. A random sample could be obtained by shuffling all the quizzes together and selecting a certain number of them without looking at them.

Sample space (p. 426)	The set of all possible outcomes of an event is called the sample space.
Example	The sample space for tossing 2 coins is HH, HT, TH, TT.

Scale drawing (p. 382)	A scale drawing is an enlarged or reduced drawing of an object that is proportional to the original object.
Example	A map is a scale drawing.

Scalene triangle (p. 54)	A scalene triangle is a triangle with no congruent sides.
Example	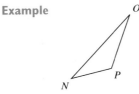

Scatter plot (p. 20)		In a scatter plot two related sets of data are graphed as points.

Example This scatter plot shows amounts spent on advertising (in dollars) versus product sales (in thousands of dollars).

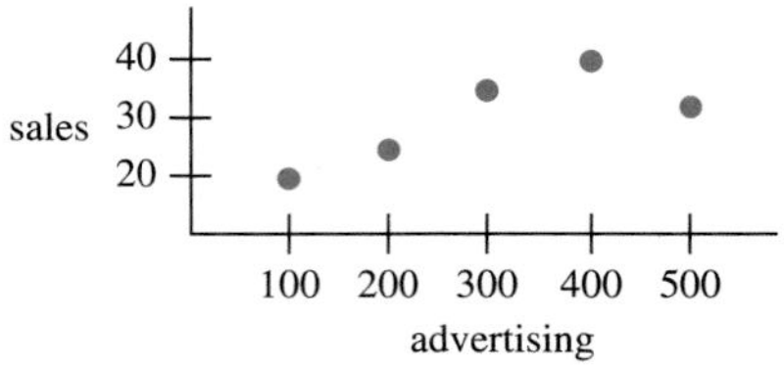

Scientific notation (p. 249)

A number is expressed in scientific notation when it is written as the product of a number greater than or equal to 1 and less than 10, and a power of 10.

Example 37,000,000 is written as 3.7×10^7 in scientific notation.

Segment bisector (p. 75)

A segment bisector is a line (or segment or ray) that goes through the midpoint of a segment.

Example $GM = MH$. $\overleftrightarrow{FD}$ is a bisector of $\overline{GH}$.

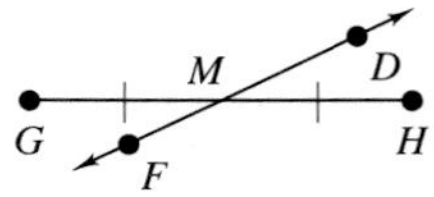

Sequence (p. 245)

A sequence is a set of numbers arranged according to some pattern. Each number is called a term of the sequence.

Example 3, 6, 9, 12, 15 is a sequence.

Similar (p. 378)

Figures that have the same shape are similar.

Example $\triangle ABC \sim \triangle RTS$

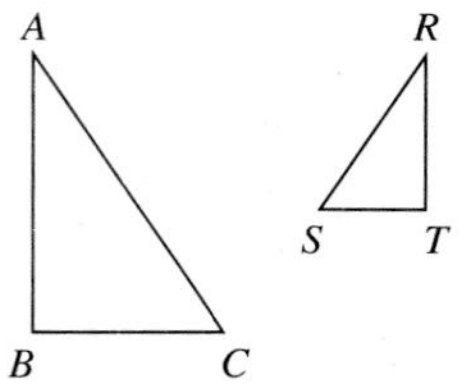

Simplest form of a fraction (p. 288)

A fraction is in simplest form when the only factor common to both the numerator and the denominator is 1.

Example $\frac{1}{3}$ is the simplest form of the fraction $\frac{27}{81}$.

Simulation (p. 435)

A simulation is a model of a real-world situation.

Example A baseball team has an equal chance of winning or losing its next game. We can toss a coin to simulate the outcome.

Slope (p. 466)	Slope is a number that describes the steepness of a line.
	Slope = $\frac{\text{vertical change}}{\text{horizontal change}}$.
Example	The slope of the given line = $\frac{2}{4} = \frac{1}{2}$. 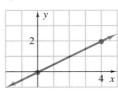

Solution of an equation (p. 170)	A value of the variable that makes the equation true is called a solution of the equation.
Example	4 is the solution of $x + 5 = 9$.

Solution of an equation in two variables (p. 462)	An ordered pair that makes an equation in two variables a true statement is a solution of the equation.
Example	(8, 4) is a solution for $y = -1x + 12$ because $4 = -1(8) + 12$.

Spreadsheet (p. 9)	A spreadsheet is a tool used for organizing and analyzing data. Spreadsheets are arranged in rows and columns. A cell is the box on a spreadsheet where a row and a column meet. The names of the row and column determine the name of the cell. A cell may contain data values, labels, or formulas.
Example	In the spreadsheet shown, column C and row 2 meet at the shaded box, cell C2. The value in cell C2 is 2.75.

	A	B	C	D	E
1	0.50	0.70	0.60	0.50	2.30
2	1.50	0.50	2.75	2.50	7.25

Square (p. 67)	A square is a parallelogram with four right angles and four congruent sides.
Example	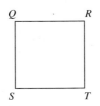

Square root (p. 210)	A square root is one of the two equal factors of a number.
Example	$\sqrt{9} = 3$ because $3^2 = 9$.

Student Study Guide

Stem-and-leaf plot (p. 26)	A display that shows data in order of place value is a stem-and-leaf plot. A leaf is a data item's last digit on the right. A stem represents the digits to the left of the leaf.	
Example	This stem-and-leaf-plot displays recorded times in a race. The stem records the number of seconds. The leaves represent tenths of a second. So 27 I 7 represents 27.7.	

stem leaves

Straight angle (p. 50)	An angle that measures 180° is called a straight angle.
Example	$m\angle TPL = 180°$

180°

T   P   L

Subtraction property of equality (p. 172)	If the same number is subtracted from each side of an equation, the results will be equal.
Example	If $a = b$, then $a - c = b - c$.

Surface area of a prism (p. 220)	The surface area of a prism is the sum of the areas of the faces.	Each square = 1 in.²
Example	4×12 in.² $+ 2 \times 9$ in.² $= 66$ in.²	

Supplementary angles (p. 49)	Two angles are supplementary if the sum of their measures is 180°.	
Example	$\angle A$ and $\angle D$ are supplementary.	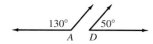

130°   50°

A   D

T

Terminating decimal (p. 113)	A terminating decimal is a decimal that stops, or terminates.
Example	Both 0.6 and 0.7265 are terminating decimals.

Transformations (p. 482)	Movements of figures on a plane are transformations. A transformation can be a translation, reflection, or rotation.	
Example	$K'L'M'N'$ is a reflection of $KLMN$.	

Translation (p. 482)	A translation slides a figure.	
Example	$ABCD$ has been translated to $A'B'C'D'$.	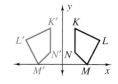

Trapezoid (p. 66)	A trapezoid has exactly one pair of parallel sides.

Example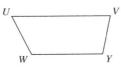

Tree diagram (p. 427)	A tree diagram is a diagram used to show the total number of possible outcomes in a probability experiment.

Example This tree diagram shows the possible outcomes of tossing two coins.

 U

Unit rate (p. 369)	A unit rate is the rate for one unit of a given quantity.

Example If you drive 165 mi in 3 h, your unit rate of travel is $\frac{165\text{ mi}}{3\text{ h}} = 55$ mi/h.

V

Variable (p. 125)	A variable is a symbol, usually a letter, that stands for a number.

Example x is a variable in the equation $9 - x = 3$.

Variable expression (p. 125)	A variable expression is an expression that contains at least one variable.

Example $7 + x$ is a variable expression.

Vertex of a polygon (p. 61)	A vertex of a polygon is any point where two sides of a polygon meet.

Example $C, D, E, F,$ and G are all vertices of this pentagon.

Volume (p. 223)

The volume of a three-dimensional figure is the number of cubic units needed to fill the space inside the figure.

Example The volume of the rectangular prism is 36 in.³

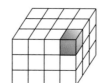

each cube = 1 in.³

W

Whole numbers (p. 145)

The whole numbers are 0, 1, 2, 3, . . .

Example 4, 125, and 3,947 are all whole numbers; -4, 17.5, and $2\frac{1}{2}$ are not whole numbers.

X

x-axis (p. 459)

The x-axis is the horizontal number line that, together with the y-axis, forms the coordinate plane.

Example

Y

y-axis (p. 459)

The y-axis is the vertical number line that, together with the x-axis, forms the coordinate plane.

Example

Z

Zero property of multiplication (p. 109)

The product of zero and any number is zero.

Example $a \times 0 = 0$

Index

Index

Fractions *(cont.)*
   simplifying, 288–291, 294
   subtracting, 326–329
   subtraction equations, 330–333
   unit, 326
Frequency tables, 5–8, 38
Front-end estimation, 97
Functions, 258–261, 263–266
   notation, 263
   representing, 258–261
   rules, 258, 261, 263–266
Function tables, 258, 260, 261, 263–266

Games, fair, 421
GCF (greatest common factor), 289–290, 293, 321, 334
Geometric sequences, 246, 272
Geometry, 44–89
   angles, 49–53
   area, 193–209
   bisectors, 75–78
   circles, 206–209
   congruent triangles, 61–65
   perimeters, 193–197
   Pythagorean theorem, 212–219
   quadrilaterals, 66–69
   reflections, 486–488
   rotations, 489–491
   similar figures, 377–380
   surface area, 220–222
   symmetry, 486–488
   three-dimensional figures, 80–83
   translations, 482–485
   triangles, 54–57
   visual patterns, 47–48
   volume, 223–227
Glossary. *See* Student Study Guide
Goldbach, C., 292
Golden ratio, 306
Graphing
   with computers, 9–11, 72, 304–305

functions, 259
integers, 147
linear equations, 462–465, 469–471
mathematical models, 475–477
non-linear relationships, 472–474, 475–477
points, 459–461
slope, 466–467
symmetry, 486–487
translations, 482–485
Graphs
   bar, 6, 10, 36
   circle, 406–409
   choosing appropriate, 9–11
   double bar, 13, 37
   double line, 12
   histograms, 6
   interpretation, 268–271, 273
   legends for, 12
   line, 10
   misleading, 35
   scatter plots, 20–22
   stem-and-leaf plots, 26–29
Greatest common factor (GCF), 289–290, 293, 321, 334
Guess and test, 228–230, 265

Height, of triangles, 202
   of trapezoids, 202
Hexagons, 66
Histograms, 6
Hypotenuse, 212

Identity property
   of addition, 102
   of multiplication, 109
Images, 482
Impossible events, 424
Improper fractions, 300–303
Independent events, 431–434
Input/output tables, 258, 263–266
Inscribed polygons, 71–73
Inscribed quadrilaterals, 72–73

Integers, 142–189. *See also* Numbers
   absolute values, 145
   adding, 150–153
   comparing and ordering, 145–147
   consecutive, 79, 169
   dividing, 163–166
   graphing, 147
   modeling, 148–149
   multiplying, 163–166
   opposites, 145
   subtracting, 155–159
   writing and solving equations with, 170–173, 175–183
Interdisciplinary connections. *See* Connections
Interest, 255–257
Inverse operations, 164, 171, 182, 330, 349
Investigations, 4, 46, 92, 144, 192, 244, 280, 316, 364, 418, 458
Isosceles triangles, 54

Least common denominator (LCD), 317–318, 326–327
Least common multiple (LCM), 317
Leaves, 26
Legends, 12
Legs, of right triangle, 212
Length
   customary units of measurement, 346
   estimating, 193–195
Linear equations, graphing, 462–465, 469–471
Line graphs, 10
   double, 12
Line plots, 5
Lines
   coplanar, 81
   parallel, 66
   perpendicular, 75
   of reflection, 487
   skew, 81

Lines *(cont.)*
 slope of, 466–467
 of symmetry, 486
Logic. *See* Critical thinking
 exercises, Decision making
 features, *and* Think and
 discuss
Logical reasoning, 23–25

Magic square, 394
Manipulatives
 algebra tiles, 148–149, 150–
 152, 155–156, 170–172,
 175, 177, 181
 compasses, 62–63, 76–77, 78
 dot paper, 53, 68, 69, 82
 fraction bars, 317–318, 326,
 328, 330–333
 graph paper, 5, 6, 12, 20, 53,
 82, 94, 95, 108, 116, 258–
 261, 268–271, 284–285,
 292, 294, 385–387, 459–
 461, 462–467, 469, 472–
 473, 489–491
 number cubes, 148–149, 421,
 435–436
 pattern blocks, 245, 246, 281–
 283, 336, 340
 protractors, 49–50, 52, 489–
 491
 spinners, 422, 425, 426, 432,
 434
 square tiles, 210–211
 tracing paper, 75
Maps, 382–384
Mathematical models, 475–
 477, 493
Means, 16–19, 27, 29
Measurement, 190–241
 of angles, 49–50, 53
 of area, 193–196, 197–200,
 202–205, 206–209, 232–235
 of circles, 206–209
 customary, 345–348
 estimating, 193–196
 of maps and scale drawings,
 382–384
 of perimeter, 232–235

Pythagorean theorem, 212–
 219
 of surface area, 220–222, 232–
 235
 units of, 193, 346
 of volume, 223–227
Medians, 16–19, 27, 29
Mental math, 103, 111, 112,
 124, 126, 140, 153, 156, 157,
 165, 173, 174, 177, 183, 188,
 197, 203, 208, 210, 225, 236,
 240, 250, 286, 294, 332, 337,
 341, 347, 350, 374, 390, 397,
 402, 500
Midpoints, 75
Misleading statistics, 34–37
Mixed numbers, 281, 283, 300–
 303. *See also* Fractions
 adding, 323–325, 326–329
 dividing of, 339–340
 estimating, 323–325
 multiplying, 323–325, 335
 subtracting, 323–325, 326–
 329
Mixed reviews, 8, 11, 13, 19,
 22, 25, 29, 33, 36, 48, 52, 57,
 60, 65, 69, 72, 77, 83, 96,
 100, 103, 106, 111, 114, 118,
 123, 127, 131, 134, 147, 149,
 153, 157, 162, 165, 169, 172,
 177, 179, 183, 196, 200, 204,
 208, 211, 214, 217, 222, 227,
 229, 233, 248, 251, 254, 257,
 261, 265, 270, 283, 287, 290,
 295, 298, 302, 305, 319, 321,
 325, 329, 332, 336, 341, 343,
 347, 350, 354, 368, 372, 375,
 384, 387, 390, 394, 397, 401,
 404, 408, 422, 424, 429, 434,
 437, 440, 444, 448, 461, 464,
 467, 471, 473, 477, 479, 485,
 488, 490
Möbius strip, 115
Modeling
 absolute values, 145
 addition, 148–152, 326, 328
 decimals, 94, 95, 108

distributive property, 116–
 117
 division, 339–340
 equations, 170–172, 175, 177,
 181–182, 330, 332
 exponents, 121
 factors, 293–294
 fractions, 281–283, 285–286,
 304, 317–318, 334, 336, 339–
 340
 functions, 258, 261
 with graphs, 472, 475–477
 improper fractions, 300–302
 integers, 145–146, 148–149
 mathematical, 475–477
 mixed numbers, 300–302
 multiplication, 108, 163, 334,
 336
 outcomes, 427
 patterns, 304
 percents, 385–387, 390
 probability, 421, 427, 435–
 436, 438–440
 Pythagorean theorem, 212–
 213
 sequences, 245
 simulations, 435–436, 438–
 440
 subtraction, 155–157, 326,
 328
 zero, 148
Modes, 16–19, 27, 29
Multiples, 284–286
Multiplication
 associative property, 110
 commutative property, 109,
 163, 324
 of decimals, 108–111, 353
 estimation strategies, 98
 of fractions, 334–337
 identity property, 109
 of integers, 163–166, 185
 of mixed numbers, 323–325,
 335
 zero property, 109
Multiplication equations,
 175–177
 fractions, 349–351

Multiplication property of equality, 176

Negative correlations, 21
Negative numbers, 145. *See also* Integers
  adding, 150–153
  modeling, 148–149
  subtracting, 155–159
Non-linear relationships, graphing, 472–474
Notation. *See also* Scientific notation
  function, 263
  scientific, 249–251
Number lines, 145–146, 151, 163, 166
Number patterns, 245–248, 272. *See also* Patterns
Numbers. *See also* Integers
  absolute value of, 145
  compatible, 98, 324
  composite, 292–295
  consecutive, 79, 169
  divisibility of, 288–290
  factors of, 284–287
  mixed, 281, 283, 300–303
  multiples of, 284–286
  negative, 145
  opposites, 145
  pentagonal, 253
  positive, 145
  prime, 292–295
  random, generating, 439
  reciprocals of, 339, 340
  scientific notation, 249–251
  standard form, 249
Numerators, 285, 288, 294, 301, 305. *See also* Fractions
Numerical expressions, 125, 151

Obtuse angles, 50
Obtuse triangles, 54
Octagons, 66
Odds, 419–422
Operations

inverse, 164, 171, 182, 330, 349
  order of, 117, 121
Opposites, 145
Ordered pairs, 459–465
Ordering
  decimals, 94, 104
  fractions, 317–319
  integers, 145–147
Order of operations, 117
  distributive property, 117
  exponents, 121–122
Origami, 55
Origin, 459
Outcomes
  counting principle and, 427–428
  probability, 419, 426
Outliers, 17

Parabola, 472
Parallel lines, 66
Parallelograms, 66–68
  area of, 197–200
  opposite angles of, 67
Pattern blocks
  dividing fractions with, 340
  making patterns with, 245, 246
  multiplying fractions with, 336
  for understanding fractions, 281–283
Patterns, 47–48
  continuing, 245–248
  finding function rules with, 264
  fractions, 304–306
  geometric figures, 47
  number, 245–248
  in repeating decimals, 112–114
  scientific notation, 249
  sequences, 47–48, 245–247
  solving problems by looking for, 252–254, 296–297
Pentagonal numbers, 253
Pentagons, 66

Percent of change, 402–404
Percents, 385
  decimals and, 389–391
  of decrease, 402–404
  fractions and, 388–391
  of increase, 402–404
  greater than 100, 386
  modeling, 385–387, 390
  probability ratios as, 420
  as proportions, 388–391, 395–401
  ratios as, 385–387, 420
  solving problems with, 399–401
Perfect squares, 210, 236
Perimeters, 193–195, 198–200, 218, 232–235, 236
Permutations, 442–445
Perpendicular bisectors, 75
Perpendicular lines, 75
Pi (π), 114, 206
Points, graphing, 459–462
Polygons
  congruent, 61
  corresponding angles in, 61, 377–378
  corresponding sides in, 61, 377–378
  inscribed, 71–73
  regular, 66
  similar, 377–380
  types of, 66
Populations, sampling, 31
Positive correlations, 21
Positive numbers, 145
Practice, 30, 74, 124, 174, 231, 267, 299, 352 , 405, 441, 481. *See also* Extra practice
Prices, unit, 370
Prime factorization, 292–295
Prime notation (A'), 482
Prime numbers, 292–295
Principal, 256
Prisms, 80
  bases, 80
  faces of, 80, 220
  surface area, 220–222
  volume, 223–224, 225–227

Sample spaces, probability, 426–429
Scale drawings, 382–384
Scalene triangles, 54
Scatter plots, 20–22, 38
Scientific notation, 249–251
Segments
  bisectors, 75–76
  congruent, 54
  midpoints of, 75
Semicircles, 71
Sequences
  arithmetic, 245
  Fibonacci, 248, 306
  geometric, 246
  terms of, 245
Sides, corresponding, 377–378
Similarity, 377–380
Simplest form, of fractions, 288
Simulations, 435–437
Slope, 466–467
Solutions
  of equations, 170–173, 175–177, 181–183
  of proportions, 373–376, 399–401
Solve a simpler problem, 296–298
Spinners, 422, 425, 432, 434
Spreadsheets, 9–11
  exponents, 255
  interest calculations, 255
  percentage changes, 402–404
Square roots, 210–211
Squares, 67
  area of, 197
  perfect, 210
Square tiles, 210–211
Statistics, 34–37
  misleading, 34–37
  See also Data analysis and display *and* Probability
Stem-and-leaf plots, 26–29
Stems, 26
Straight angles, 50
Straightedge, 61–63, 75–78
Student Study Guide, 512–534

Subtraction
  of customary units of measure, 346
  of decimals, 101–104
  of fractions, 326–329
  of integers, 155–159
  of mixed numbers, 323–325
Subtraction equations, 170–173, 330–333
Subtraction property of equality, 172
Supplementary angles, 49
Surface area, 220–222
Surveys, 31–33, 395–396
Symmetry, 486–488
  graphing, 487–488
  lines of, 486–488
  rotational, 489–491

Tables,
  formulas, 510
  frequency, 5–8
  function, 258, 263–266
  measures, 509
  in problem solving, 24, 167–169
  squares and square roots, 511
  symbols, 510
Tally marks, 5
Target groups, sampling, 31
Technology. *See* Calculators *and* Computers
Terminating decimals, 113
Terms, of sequences, 245
Think and discuss. Every lesson except the Problem Solving lesson contains a *Think and Discuss* feature.
Three-dimensional figures, 80–83
  cubes, 81, 220, 225–227
  edges of, 81
  faces, 80, 220
  prisms, 80, 220–227
  pyramids, 81
  surface area of, 220–222
  volume of, 223–227

Translations, 482–485
Trapezoids, 66
  area of, 202–205
  similar, 377–378
Tree diagrams, 427
Trials, 436
Triangles, 54–57, 66
  acute, 54
  area of, 202–205
  base of, 202
  classifying, 54–57
  congruent, 61–65, 302
  equilateral, 54
  height of, 202
  isosceles, 54
  obtuse, 54
  right, 54, 212–219
  scalene, 54
  similar, 378–379
  sum of measures of angles of, 55–57
Two-step equations, 181–183

Unit fractions, 305, 326
Unit prices, 370
Unit rates, 369–371

Values, in spreadsheets, 9
Variable expressions, 125–127, 128–131
Variables, 125, 170, 178, 179
Vertex, of angles, 49
Vertical angles, 50
Visual patterns, 47–48
Volume, 223–227, 237
  applications, 232–234
  of cubes, 225–227, 228–229
  of cylinders, 224–227
  of rectangular prisms, 223–224, 225–227

Weight, customary units of, 346
Whole numbers, 145
Work backward, 342–344
Work together
  Chap. 1: 7, 13, 17, 21, 27, 32, 34

Selected Answers

CHAPTER 1

1-1 pages 5–8
On Your Own
17. a.

Color	Freq.
red	7
pink	2
green	3
blue	9
multi	4

b. 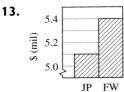 **c.** 7

19. a.

Time	Freq.
5:30–5:59	2
6:00–6:29	5
6:30–6:59	1
7:00–7:29	3
7:30–7:59	3
8:00–8:29	2

b. 6:00–6:29

Mixed Review 1. = **2.** < **3.** 1,000 **4.** 490
5. ×, −, ×

1-2 pages 9–11
On Your Own 9. a. how many movies were made in 1991 in 3 countries **b.** no change over time **11.** bar graph; time is not involved
13.

Mixed Review 1. 32 **3.** 2 **4.** 13 **5.** 108 **6.** 6

1-3 pages 12–14
On Your Own 11. double bar graph

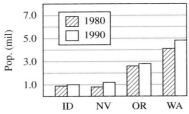

13. Sample: 1965; gasoline prices were high, and more people became interested in fitness

Mixed Review 1. B **2.** $720
3.   **4.**

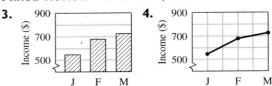

5. $170

Checkpoint 1. B
2.

h	1 2 3 4 5 6 7 8 9
f	2 2 2 2 3 1 2 2 1

```
                x
  x   x   x   x  x         x   x
  x   x   x   x  x   x   x  x   x
  1   2   3   4  5   6   7  8   9
```

Problem Solving Practice page 15
1. 7 **3. a.** one labeled "peaches and plums"
b. peaches labeled "peaches and plums"; plums labeled "peaches"; peaches and plums labeled "plums." **5.** 7 students had no pets

1-4 pages 16–19
On Your Own 13. a. 25 **b.** 11 **15. a.** 74; 71; 63 **b.** yes, 102; raises the mean **c.** 40 y
17. a. 86.8 **b.** sample: no; if Dominic got 100, he would raise his average to only 89

Mixed Review 1. = **2.** < **3.** Sample:
$C = A \cdot B$; $A2 = A1 - 4$, $A3 = A2 - 4$,
$B2 = B1 - 3$, $B3 = B2 - 3$ **4.** 600 **5.** 800

1-5 pages 20–22
On Your Own **9.** pos. corr. **11.** no corr.
13. a.

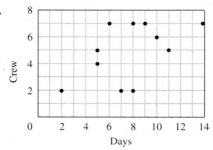

Mixed Review **1.** 84; 85; 85 **2.** 30; lowers the mean **3.** 2 students

1-6 pages 23–25
On Your Own **9.** 1,850 **11.** $3.50 **13.** 5

Mixed Review **1.** pos. corr. **2.** 20 **3.** 360 **4.** 370 **5.** 200 **6.** 1,200

1-7 pages 26–29
On Your Own **13.** 43; 88 **15.** 64; 45

Mixed Review **1.** = **2.** < **3.** 16, 22 **4.** 25, 36, 49 **5.** 15 people

Checkpoint **1.** 117.8; 118; 123; 12; no outliers **2.** about 7.267; 7.5; no mode; 5.3; 3.6 (lowers the mean) **3.**

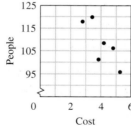

4. Elsa, pink towel and beach ball; Keiko, blue towel and sandwiches; LaTonya, striped towel and iced tea

Practice page 30
3.
```
1 | 0 0 1 1 2 2 2 4 4 5 5 6 7 9
2 | 0 1 3 6 7
3 | 5 8
```
2 | 1 means 21
5. 28 min **7.** Wed. **9.** 95

11.

Speed	Freq.
9	1
14	1
16	1
18	1
25	2
29	1
30	1
33	1
34	2
38	1

13. about 25.4; 27; 25 and 34; 29 **15.** 3

1-8 pages 31–33
On Your Own **7.** fair **9.** fair **11.** Sample: go to the main terminal for the survey

Mixed Review **1.** 10 **2.** 15; 10.5; 10; 24 **3.** mode

1-9 pages 34–37
On Your Own **15. a.** 84; 83; 76 **b.** mean **c.** mode **19.**

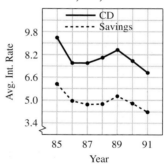

Mixed Review **1.** no; no corr. **2.** yes; pos. corr. **3.** no **4.** 4, 191 **5.** 9 **6.** ×, +, − or ×, ÷, ÷

Wrap Up pages 38–39
1.

2. a. 0.9 **b.** A2

c.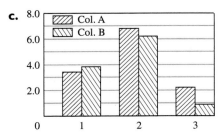

3. a. Sample: line graph, shows change over time
4. Sample: comparing men and women in definite countries; no change over time
5. a. 27.5; 20; 15   **b.** 60 and 65; they raise the mean   **c.** mean   **6.** B

7. 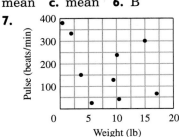   **a.** no corr

8.
```
2 | 4  7
3 | 1  1  2
4 | 6
```
2 | 4 means 2.4
median: 3.1; mode: 3.1
10. Sam, spider, apples; Katie, fish, popcorn; Martin, fox, cookies

Getting Ready for Chapter 2   1. triangle, hexagon, parallelogram, rectangle

Cumulative Review page 43
1. C   **2.** B   **3.** A   **4.** A   **5.** B   **6.** C   **7.** C   **8.** B
9. A   **10.** D

CHAPTER 2

2-1 pages 47–48
On Your Own   5. a. a 5 × 5 dot array;
a 6 × 6 dot array   **b.** a 20 × 20 dot array   **7.** C

Mixed Review   1. 20   **2.** 15, 22   **3.** No. Twice $40 is $80, not $44.   **4.** Wednesday

2-2 pages 49–53
On Your Own   17. straight   **19.** obtuse
21. no; 35°   **25.** $\overline{BC}$, $\overline{HC}$, $\overline{AB}$ **27.** ∠FBA, ∠ABG, ∠FBD, ∠GBD   **29.** ∠KHJ, ∠LHE; ∠JCD, ∠LCA
31. 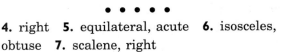   **33.** $m\angle A = 100°$; $m\angle B = 115°$; $m\angle C = 75°$; $m\angle D = 70°$
41. B   **43.** 53°

Mixed Review   1. 1,800   **2.** 39
3.
```
     ×  ×
×  ×  ×  ×  ×
9  10  11  12  13
```
5. (pentagon)   **6.** 11

2-3 pages 54–57
On Your Own   11. 35°   **15.** C   **17.** 70°, 40°
19. a. acute   **b.** No; angles are not cong.   **c.** No; no 2 angles are cong.   **d.** Yes; the triangle is scalene. No 2 sides are cong. if no angles are cong.

Checkpoint   1. (dot triangle)   **2.** acute   **3.** obtuse
4. right   **5.** equilateral, acute   **6.** isosceles, obtuse   **7.** scalene, right

Mixed Review   1.

n	2	3	4	5	6	7	8
f	2	4	2	4	4	3	1

2. obtuse   **3.** adjacent   **4.** Melinda, 13; Jolene, 4

2-4 pages 58–60
On Your Own   9. 12 pencils   **11.** 111117, 211116, 221115, 222114, 222213, 222222, 311115, 321114, 322113, 331113, 411114   **13.** 13 D, 1 Q; 8 D, 3 Q; 3 D, 5 Q   **15.** 225 bulbs   **17.** 10 y and 11 y   **19.** 60°, 28°, 92°

Mixed Review   1. 7   **2.** 5,600   **3.** 86.6; 85; 85
4. 95   **5.** 95°   **6.** obtuse   **7.** 99, 67

2-5 pages 61–65

On Your Own **11.** c, d; b, e; a, f **13. a.** $\angle C$
b. $\angle L$ **c.** $\angle K$ **d.** $\overline{CL}$ **e.** $\overline{LK}$ **f.** $\overline{CK}$ **19.** D
21. b.

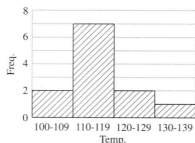

Mixed Review **1.** = **2.** = **3.** 125° **4.** $\angle PSQ$,
$\angle QSR$ **5.** 136

2-6 pages 66–69

On Your Own **9.** rhombus; all sides;
$\angle S \cong \angle Q$; $\angle P \cong \angle R$ **11.** rectangle; $\overline{BC} \cong \overline{AD}$;
$\overline{BA} \cong \overline{CD}$; $\angle B \cong \angle A \cong \angle D \cong \angle C$ **13.** octagon;
no **15.** pentagon; yes **17.** rhombus, parallelo-
gram, rectangle, square; square **19.** trapezoid
23. **25.** Yes, a square has 4 cong. sides
(rhombus) and 4 cong. angles
(rectangle).
29. $\overline{DC}$: 6 cm; $\angle C$: 65° **31.** $\overline{XY}$, $\overline{YZ}$, $\overline{ZW}$: 4 cm
33. No additional information can be determined.

Mixed Review **1.** 9 **2.** 49 **3.** scalene **4.** acute
5. $\angle L$ **6.** $\overline{CA}$ **7.** 30°, 60°

2-7 pages 70–73

On Your Own **15.** Sample: $\overline{FG}$, $\overline{GH}$
17. Sample: $\overline{FH}$ **19.** Sample: $\overparen{FGH}$ **21.** Sample:
$\overline{FH}$ **23.** Sample: $\triangle FGH$ **25.** D **27.** right
triangle

Mixed Review **1.**
4. bicycling

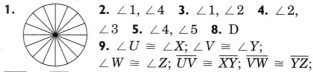

Practice page 74

1. **3.** acute **5.** straight **7.** Sample: $\overleftrightarrow{CF}$,
$\overleftrightarrow{BE}$ **9.** Sample: $\overrightarrow{GB}$, $\overrightarrow{GD}$
11. Sample: $\angle AGC$, $\angle FGD$
13. Sample: $\angle AGC$, $\angle DGC$ **15.** 50°; acute
17. 60°; acute **19.** $\angle F$ **21.** $\overline{EF}$

2-8 pages 75–78

On Your Own **13.** 132°

Mixed Review **1.**

4	3 5 6
5	1 5 6 6 6 9
6	1 3 3

4 | 3 means 43

2.

20	8 9
21	1 2 3 8
22	1 2 5
23	
24	1

3. True

20 | 8 means 208

4. False **5.** 4 angles

Checkpoint **1.** $m\angle 1 = 32°$; $m\angle 2 = 50°$
2. $m\angle 3 = 78°$, $m\angle 4 = 70°$ **7.** $\overrightarrow{OR}$, $\overrightarrow{OQ}$, $\overrightarrow{OP}$
8. $\overrightarrow{RP}$ **9.** $\overparen{PTR}$, $\overparen{RQP}$ **10.** $\overline{RQ}$, $\overline{QP}$, $\overline{PT}$, $\overline{TR}$, $\overline{RP}$
11. $RQPT$ **13.** C

Problem Solving Practice page 79

1. 3 small, 5 large **3.** 18 girls **5.** 13 triangles
7. 22 shirts

2-9 pages 80–83

On Your Own **9.** cone **11.** cylinder
13. hexagonal prism **19.** False

Mixed Review **1.** 36; 68 **2.** No, a rhombus does
not need to have right angles. **3.** midpoint
4. 41° **5.** 6 outfits

Wrap Up page 84

1. **2.** $\angle 1$, $\angle 4$ **3.** $\angle 1$, $\angle 2$ **4.** $\angle 2$,
$\angle 3$ **5.** $\angle 4$, $\angle 5$ **8.** D
9. $\angle U \cong \angle X$; $\angle V \cong \angle Y$;
$\angle W \cong \angle Z$; $\overline{UV} \cong \overline{XY}$; $\overline{VW} \cong \overline{YZ}$;
$\overline{UW} \cong \overline{XZ}$ **10.** a quad. with exactly 1 pair of
parallel sides **11.** a parallelogram with 4 cong.
sides **12.** $\overline{DC}$ **13.** $\overparen{ABC}$ **14.** $\angle BOC$
15. $ABCD$ **16.** $\overparen{AB}$ **18.** $m\angle I = 32°$,
$m\angle T = 116°$

Getting Ready for Chapter 3 **1.** 1,300
2. 32,000 **3.** 54,670 **4.** 200

Cumulative Review page 89

1. B **2.** A **3.** D **4.** A **5.** B **6.** B **7.** C **8.** C
9. A **10.** D

CHAPTER 3

3-1 pages 93–96

On Your Own **11.** 0.769 **13.** 0.564392
15. 18.1, 18.2, 18.3, 18.4, 18.5 **17. b.** Suzanne,
Ayla, Simon, Terri, Max **19. a.** 6 kg; 2 kg
b. about 3 pins **21.** 0.764 or .7640 **23.** Edgar
Martinez; Terry Pendleton **25.** No; many
players would appear to have the same avg.

Mixed Review **1.** 23° **2.** acute **3.** False
4. False **5.** 231 digits

3-2 pages 97–100

On Your Own **17.** $56 **21.** 4,000; rounding
23. 2,100; clustering **25.** 6 **27.** A **29. a.** 80
noodles **b.** compatible numbers; 4,000 and 50
31. 3 m

Mixed Review **1.** 30 **2.** 4.004, 0.403, 0.40,
0.040007, 0.04 **3.** 7.681, 7.6801, 7.618, 7.0681
4. 1,157 **5.** 6,187 **6.** 5 ft, 20 ft

3-3 pages 101–104

On Your Own **15.** 41 **17.** 11.306 mi/h

Mixed Review **1.** rectangle **2.** equilateral
3. 100 **4.** 300 **5.** $4.57

Checkpoint **1.** 8.5, 8.059, 8.05, 8.0499, 8.049,
8.015 **2.** = **3.** > **4.** < **5. a.** $10 **b.** $11
6. 24.6342 **7.** 66.247

3-4 pages 105–107

On Your Own **11.** You need to know how many
died. **13.** swimming, softball, basketball,
volleyball **15.** about 2 y old

Mixed Review **1.**

```
2 | 7  9
3 | 7
4 | 0  6  8
  2 | 7 means 27
```

2.

```
1 | 3  3  4  7
2 | 2  5
  1 | 3 means 1.3
```

3. 65.029 **4.** 4.962 **5.** 0.3 m **6.** 19, 20, 21

3-5 pages 108–111

On Your Own **19.** 0 **21.** 2; 2.4 **23.** 4; 4.4
27. 56.18 cm–67.28 cm

Mixed Review **1.** 33.51682 **2.** 0.619 **3.** obtuse
4. acute **5.** right **6.** obtuse **7.** 24 students

3-6 pages 112–114

On Your Own **11.** $0.\overline{285714}$ **13.** $14.\overline{09}$
15. a. $0.00\overline{4}$, $0.00\overline{5}$, $0.00\overline{6}$ **b.** $0.\overline{36}$, $0.\overline{45}$, $0.\overline{54}$
c. $0.\overline{12}$, $0.\overline{15}$, $0.\overline{18}$ **d.** $0.0\overline{396}$, $0.0\overline{495}$, $0.0\overline{594}$
19. Sample: 163 ÷ 52 ≈ 3.1346

Mixed Review **1.** 1.3 **2.** 1.5 **3.** 13 **4.** 27
5. $1.60

Problem Solving Practice page 115

1. Tessa, sari; Joe, ram's horn; Liz, shell
3. 9:45 A.M. **5.** 60 wk

3-7 pages 116–119

On Your Own **5.** 8(3 + 1), 8 • 3 + 8 • 1; 32
7. 5(2 + 3), 5 • 2 + 5 • 3; 25 **9.** 3, 3 **11.** 7
13. a. 6(5.25) = 6(5) + 6(0.25); $31.50
b. 6(4.75) = 6(5) − 6(0.25); $28.50 **c.** $60
15. 41.2 **17.** 23.2 **19.** + **21.** (4 + 4)
23. (4 − 4) **25.** (4 + 4), (4 − 4) **27. a.** 27 in.^{2}
b. 81 in.^{2} **29.** $3.56

Mixed Review **1.** 42; 420; 4,200; 4,200,000
2. $1.\overline{6}$ **3.** 0.4375 **4.** $0.8\overline{3}$ **5.** $27

3-8 page 120–123

On Your Own **15. a.** 6^4 **b.** 6; 4 **c.** 1,296
17. 0.3^5 **19.** 140.608 **21.** 0.0016 **23.** 32 **25.** 1
27. c **29.** a **31. b.** When the base is 10, the
exponent indicates how many zeros will be in a
number in standard form. **c.** 12 **33.** Sample:
2^5, 4^3 **35. a.** 3^4 **b.** 9^2

Mixed Review **1.** > **2.** > **3.** 4 **4.** 3.8; 3.8
5. C

Practice page 124

1. = **3.** < **5.** < **7.** > **9.** 0.23, 0.234, 0.24, 0.243 **11.** 10.02, 10.2, 10.201 **13.** 2.27 **15.** 11.303 **17.** $4.\overline{6}$ **19.** 15.54 **21.** 80.113 **23.** 152 **25.** 22.5 **27.** 171 **29.** divide **31.** exponents **33.** divide **35.** multiply **37.** 216 **39.** 19.683 **41.** 3.24 **43.** 5 **45.** 1.7 **47.** 50 **49.** 4 **51.** 600

3-9 pages 125–127

On Your Own 9. 23 **11.** 24 **13. a.** 0; 4 **b.** When n = 2; $4n > n^2$ **15.** variable **17.** numerical **19.** 3.7, 1.4, 5.78, 6.8; 4.04, 2.08, 8.3232, 8.16 **21.** Multiply 0.053 by number of dimes. Find distance to moon in inches and compare.

Mixed Review 1. 90° **2.** False **3.** 6^5 **4.** 2.4^4 **5.** $5.45

3-10 pages 128–131

On Your Own 17. 4 divided by n **19.** 8.2 less than n **21. a.** $275b$ **b.** 6,875 **c.** Sample: Approx.; not all shelves have same number of books. **23.** $10a + 8t$ **25.** D

Mixed Review 1. 120 **2.** 40 **3.** 35 **4.** 20 **5.** 192

Checkpoint 1. C **2.** 18.73404 **3.** $3.\overline{3}$ **4.** 41 **5.** 10 **6.** 250 **7.** 34.2 **8.** p times 3 **9.** 14 more than s **10.** t less than 7

3-11 pages 132–135

On Your Own 11. a. 2.9 kW•h **b.** $.32 **13.** (200 • f) ÷ 1,000 • 0.13 **15. a.** $54.65 **b.** $60.43 **c.** $1.95 **17. a.** Winter **b.** Sample: Winters are cold in MN; Joan must have electric heat.

Mixed Review 1. comm. prop. mult. **2.** identity prop. mult. **3.** $r \div 8$ **4.** $c - 15$ **5.** about 105 million

Wrap Up page 136

1. 7; compatible nos. **2.** 6; front-end **3.** 48; clustering **4.** 6; 0.2; distributive prop. **5.** 9.2;

comm. prop. add. **6.** 3; assoc. prop. add. **7.** 5.9; comm. prop. mult. **8.** 3.2; assoc. prop. mult. **9.** 8.1; 6.2; distrib. prop. **10.** 3, 6, 7, 9; 1, 2, 4, 5, 8, 10 **12.** 8 **13.** 6561 **14.** 2187 **15.** 0.008 **16.** 0.0144 **17.** 27 **18.** 43 **19.** 15 **20.** 31 **21.** $8 - n$ **22.** $6c$ **23.** $2n + 6$ **24. a.** You need to know how many kW the refrigerator uses. **b.** $.11

Getting Ready for Chapter 4 1. $8c$ **2.** $d + 2$ **3.** $n - 4$ **4.** $n \div 4$

Cumulative Review page 141

1. C **2.** D **3.** B **4.** C **5.** B **6.** D **7.** D **8.** A **9.** D **10.** C

CHAPTER 4

4-1 pages 145–147

On Your Own 17. a. 22 **b.** −43 **19.** −8
21.

23.

25. > **27.** <
29. a. 8 **33.** −8 or greater **35.** −16 or less

Mixed Review 1. 6.868 **2.** 0.48 **3.** 10.9 **4.** 17 **5.** 10

4-2 pages 148–149

On Your Own 9. 0 **11.** −2 **13.** 2 **15. b.** 0 **21.** −8 **23.** 10 pos. and 2 neg.

Mixed Review 1. 50 **2.** 60 **3.** > **4.** > **5.** = **6.** < **7.** 22

4-3 pages 150–153

On Your Own 23. $2 + (-6); -4$
25. $-2 + (-6); -8$ **27.** $-12 + 19 = 7; 7°F$
29. $-16 + 24 = 8$ **31.** 34 **33.** 38
35. a. 8 P.M. **37.** 5 **39.** 35 ft

Mixed Review 1. 24 **2.** 20 **5.** 13 and 9

Problem Solving Practice page 154

1. a. $3,880 **3.**

R	Y	B	G
G	B	Y	R
Y	R	G	B
B	G	R	Y

G	Y	B	R
B	R	G	Y
R	B	Y	G
Y	G	R	B

5. Sample: numbers in parentheses indicate number of gal in container after each step. 8 gal (3) and 5 gal (5); 5 gal (2) and 3 gal (3); 3 gal (0) and 8 gal (6); 5 gal (0) and 3 gal (2); 8 gal (1) and 5 gal (5); 5 gal (4) and 3 gal (3); 3 gal (0) and 8 gal (4)

4-4 pages 155–159
On Your Own   15. neg   **17.** pos.   **19.** −12
21. 8   **23.** −219   **25.** −136   **27.** 5   **29.** −9
31. 4   **33.** 214°F   **35.** about 130°F   **37.** about 130°F   **39.** −20   **41.** −160   **43.** −120

Mixed Review   1. 4^5 **2.** 1^2 **3.** 9^3 **4.** −3   **5.** 5
6. −9   **7.** 105 mi

4-5 pages 160–162
On Your Own   7. $200
9.

B	C	D	E
1,000	2,000	3,000	4,000
1,830	3,660	5,490	7,320
11,120	11,120	11,120	11,120
6,000	12,000	18,000	24,000
−6,950	−2,780	1,390	5,560

a. 1,000($1.83); B1($1.83)   **c.** $11,120
d. $6(1,000); $6(B1)   **e.** See table.   **f.** $2,073,880

Mixed Review   3. 7   **4.** 9   **5.** 5   **6.** 11, 12

4-6 pages 163–166
On Your Own   29. 6 min
31. 23 ⚹ ✕ 45 ⚹ ═ 1035   **33.** −7   **35.** 2
37. 6,000   **39.** G   **41.** F   **43. a.** 150 cal; 535 cal
b. gain of 385 cal

Mixed Review   1. 2.6   **2.** 29.64   **3.** 79   **4.** 68
5. 24

Checkpoint   1. −1,300   **2.** 83   **3.** 86   **4.** 103
5. −52   **6.** 6   **7.** −180   **8.** 13

4-7 pages 167–169
On Your Own   7. 2 adults, 5 children
9. a. Ludberg, Chester, Topson, Dornville
b. 16.5 mi   **11.** Place 9 mg and 2 mg weights and

wire on one side; 7 mg and 5 mg weights on other side; see if they balance   **13.** 8
15. 29 + 30 + 31; 21 + 22 + 23 + 24;
16 + 17 + 18 + 19 + 20;
6 + 7 + 8 + 9 + ⋯ + 14;
2 + 3 + 4 + 5 + ⋯ + 13   **17.** 28°

Mixed Review   1. F   **2.** T   **3.** 5   **4.** 9   **5.** −480
6. 17   **7.** 27°

4-8 pages 170–173
On Your Own   21. −12   **23.** 0   **25.** 3   **27.** 10
29. 119   **31.** −9   **33.** 128   **35.** A   **37.** Yes; they have the same solution   **39.** add −15 to both sides of the equation

Mixed Review   1.

				×
	×	×		×
×	×	×	×	×	×

```
 7   8   9   10  11  12
```

2.

n	7	8	9	10	11	12
f	1	2	1	2	1	3

3. −6   **4.** 8   **5.** −8   **6.** −60   **7.** 15

Practice page 174
1.
```
-3 -2 -1 0 1 2 3
```
   7. >   **9.** =   **11.** −1   **13.** 3
15. −4   **17.** −4   **19.** −10   **21.** 19   **23.** −9
25. 388   **27.** −24   **29.** 63   **31.** 70   **33.** −27
35. −2   **37.** 1   **39.** −28   **41.** 10   **43.** −5
45. 27   **47.** 17

4-9 pages 175–177
On Your Own   15. 14   **17.** 2   **19.** 960   **21.** 416
23. −800   **25.** 4,800   **29.** C

Mixed Review   1. Dist. Prop.   **2.** Id. Prop.
3. Zero Prop.   **4.** Com. Prop. of Add.   **5.** −10
6. 13   **7.** 12:45 P.M.

4-10 pages 178–180
On Your Own   15. $\frac{n}{6}$ = 8; 48
17. 56 = n − 14; 70   **19.** 30s = 120; 4
21. 48 + n = 88; 40   **23.** 1,000 = 40w; 25 gal

Mixed Review **1.** right **2.** obtuse **3.** 65
4. −7 **5.** 28

4-11 pages 181–183

On Your Own **7.** $3x - 2 = 4$; 2
9. $3(2) + 6 = 12$ **11.** −3 **13.** 121 **15.** −14
17. $\boxed{(}\,67\,\boxed{-}\,12\,\boxed{)}\,\boxed{\div}\,5\,\boxed{=}$; 11 **19.** 8 **21.** B

Mixed Review **1.** right **2.** equil. **3.** $\frac{n}{8} = 9$; 72
4. $n + 15 = 45$; 30 **5.** 10

Checkpoint **1.** 11 **2.** 13 **3.** 36 **4.** 1 **5.** −39
6. −21 **7.** 75 **8.** C

Wrap Up pages 184–185

1. −9 **2.** □ □ □
■ ■ ■ **4.** −6, −3, 0, 1, 7 **5.** < **3. a.** 5 **b.** 2 **c.** 17

6. = **7.** < **8.** > **9.** > **10.** B **11.** $-4 + (-6)$;
−10 **12.** $5 + (-4)$; 1 **13.** $-6 + 7$; 1 **14.** 3
15. −22 **16.** −5 **17.** 29 **18.** −3 **19.** −30
20. 84 **21.** −25 **22.** 2 **24.** −6 **25.** 4 **26.** 35
27. −2 **28.** $n + 17 = -24$; −41 **29.** $\frac{n}{-9} = -6$;
54 **30.** 16 small, no large; 9 small, 5 large; 2
small, 10 large

Getting Ready for Chapter 5 **1.** 30 **2.** 15
3. 20 **4.** 25

Cumulative Review page 189

1. C **2.** B **3.** D **4.** D **5.** A **6.** B **7.** C **8.** B
9. D **10.** A

CHAPTER 5

5-1 pages 193–196

On Your Own **11.** 2 in. **13.** 10.5 cm **15.** in.
17. mm or cm **23. a.** more **b.** 15 **25.** 600 mi^2

Mixed Review **1.** −7 **2.** 6 **3.** 52.5 **4.** 32
5. 26

5-2 pages 197–200

On Your Own **17.** $A = 25$ in.^{2}; $P = 20$ in.
19. $A = 80$ cm^2; $P = 40$ cm **21.** $A = 3$ m^2;
$P = 8$ m **23.** 46 cm **25.** 14 m^2; 26 m^2; 36 m^2;
44 m^2; 50 m^2; 54 m^2; 56 m^2 **27.** $A = 1.5$ m^2 or
15,000 cm^2; $P = 7$ m or 700 cm **31.** about 160

Mixed Review **1.** in. **2.** m^2 **3.** 56 **4.** −72
5. 17 in.^{2}

Problem Solving Practice page 201

1. 42 chips **3.** 15 **5. a.** $9876 \div 45$ **b.** 220
7. −3 and −4

5-3 pages 202–205

On Your Own **15.** $A = 150$ in.^{2}; $P = 60$ in.
17. $A = 130$ cm^2; $P = 52$ cm **19. a.**

b. 1, 16; 2, 8; 4, 4; 8, 2; 16, 1 **c.** length, 3.2;
height, 5 **21.** areas are equal

Mixed Review **1.** 600 **2.** $P = 4.46$ cm;
$A = 1.162$ cm^2 **3.** chord **4.** central **5.** 83

5-4 pages 206–209

On Your Own **9.** $C = 6$ cm; $A = 3$ cm^2
11. $C = 4$ m; $A = 1$ m^2 **13.** $C = 60$ ft;
$A = 300$ ft^2 **15. a.** 98.52 m^2 **b.** 98.47 m^2
17. D **19.** 6.5 ft **21.** about 2 times larger

Mixed Review **1.** −3 **2.** 10 **3.** $A = 28$ cm^2;
$P = 25.6$ cm **4.** $A = 84$ in.^{2}; $P = 44$ in.
5. 18 rungs

5-5 pages 210–211

On Your Own **7.** 169 **9.** 4 **11.** 6 **13.** 5
15. 14 **17.** 11 km **19.** 15 mm **21.** B **23.** 52 ft

Mixed Review **1.** Samples: $\angle$AOF and $\angle$COD;
$\angle$AOB and $\angle$DOE **2.** Samples: $\angle$BOC and
$\angle$COD; $\angle$AOF and $\angle$FOE **3.** $r \approx 4.5$; $d \approx 8.9$
4. $r \approx 7.5$; $d \approx 15.0$ **5.** $4

Checkpoint **5.** $C = 101$ cm; $A = 804$ cm^2
6. $C = 16$ in.; $A = 20$ in.^{2} **7.** $C = 82$ ft;
$A = 531$ ft^2 **8.** 7 **9.** 8 **10.** 20 **11.** 36
12. 225

5-6 pages 212–215

On Your Own **13.** 12 ft **15.** 15 in. **17.** 11 m
19. yes **21.** no **23.** yes **25.** 12 ft

Mixed Review **1.** -19 **2.** -5 **3.** 13 mm
4. 9 in. **5.** 40 in.^{2}

5-7 pages 216–219

On Your Own **17.** $x = 11.2$ m **19.** 1.7 km or
1,700 m **21.** 65 m **23. a.** about 85 ft **b.** about
127 ft **c.** about 95 ft **d.** 150 ft **25. a.** 10
b. $C \approx 31.4$; $A \approx 78.5$ **27. a.** $\overline{AG}$ **b.** the
lengths of $\overline{AB}$ and $\overline{BC}$; the lengths of $\overline{AC}$ and $\overline{GC}$
c. 35 in., 37 in.

Mixed Review **1.** 12 m^2 **2.** 15 cm **3.** -800
4. 10 **5.** about 28.26 in.^{2}

5-8 pages 220–222

On Your Own **11.** 70 m^2 **13.** 880 cm^2
15. 48 m^2 **17. c.** both patterns have the same
set of faces **19.** 7 ft **23. a.** sides and bottom
b. 3,920 ft^2 **c.** $8,428.00

Mixed Review **1.** 6, 7 **2.** 8, 9 **3.** 54 in. **4.** 6

5-9 pages 223–227

On Your Own **17.** 24 cm^3 **19.** 500.3 m^3
21. 4 m **23.** 6 m **25.** 330 ft^3 **27.** yes;
720 in.^{3} $\div$ 231 in.^{3} $\approx$ 3.1 gal **31. a.** 132 in.^{2}
b. 60 in.^{3}

Checkpoint **1.** 24.5 cm **2.** 8.5 in.
3. $SA = 280$ ft^2; $V = 300$ ft^3
4. $SA \approx 1,406.72$ m^2; $V \approx 4,019.2$ m^3 **5.** C

Mixed Review **1.** -18 **2.** 24 **3.** 6 **4.** 202 ft^2
5. how long it takes Peter to mow the lawn

5-10 pages 228–230

On Your Own **9.** four $10 bills, five $5 bills,
four $1 bills **11.** 16¢ **13.** 81 **15.** 39 tricycles,
61 bicycles **17.** 1,080 **19. a.** 64 g **b.** 7 cm
21. 12

Mixed Review **1.** 90° **2.** between 0° and 90°
3. 64 in.^{3} **4.** 5,301 cm^3 **5.** Elicia

Practice page 231

1. $A = 21.16$ cm^2; $P = 18.4$ cm
3. $A = 18.56$ m^2; $P = 18$ m **5.** $A = 29.25$ m^2;
$P = 27.1$ m **7.** $C \approx 78.5$ cm; $A \approx 490.6$ cm^2
9. $C \approx 2.4$ mi; $A \approx 0.4$ mi^2 **11.** 23.5 **13.** 1.4
15. 20 ft **17.** 50 mi **19.** 48.7 in. **21.** yes
23. yes **25.** 240 ft^3

5-11 pages 232–235

On Your Own **11. a.** 52.5 gal to 82.5 gal
b. 598.5 gal to 1,228.5 gal **c.** 50 min **13. a.** 4
b. 6 **c.** part (b); $2.40

Mixed Review **1.** 14, 17, 20 **2.** 23, 33, 45
3. $x + 6 = 112$; 106 **4.** $4x - 2 = 13$; 3.75
5. 5

Wrap Up pages 236–237

1. $P = 22$ cm; $A = 28$ cm^2 **2.** $P = 19.6$ cm;
$A = 19.075$ cm^2 **3.** $P = 144$ in.; $A = 864$ in.^{2}
4. $P = 140$ m; $A = 900$ m^2 **5.** $C = 37.7$ cm;
$A = 113.1$ cm^2 **6.** $C = 50.3$ in.; $A = 201.1$ in.^{2}
7. $C = 125.7$ ft; $A = 1,256.6$ ft^2
8. $C = 56.5$ mm; $A = 254.5$ mm^2 **9.** 9 and 10
10. 121 **11.** 49 **12.** 4 **13.** 8 **14.** 12 **15.** 2
16. B **17.** 9.0 mm **18.** 1.4 m **19.** 11.5 m
20. $V = 87.5$ ft^3; $SA = 130$ ft^2
21. $V = 2,814.9$ cm^3 **22.** 2 m • 3 m • 4 m

Getting Ready for Chapter 6 **1.** 1,000
2. 1,000,000 **3.** 100,000 **4.** no; $3 \cdot 5 + 5 \neq 22$

Cumulative Review page 241

1. A **2.** B **3.** A **4.** C **5.** A **6.** B **7.** D **8.** D
9. A **10.** C **11.** B

CHAPTER 6

6-1 pages 245–248

On Your Own **15.** geo.; start with 1 and
multiply by 2 repeatedly. **17.** neither **19.** geo.;
start with 300 and multiply by 0.2 repeatedly.
21. Jan. 8, Jan. 15, Jan. 22, Jan. 29 **25. a.** 13,
21, 34 **b.** neither **27. a.** 2, 3, 5, 8, 13, 21, 34
b. neither **29.** arith.; start with $4.00 and add
$.50 repeatedly.

Mixed Review 1. obtuse **2.** acute **3.** yes
4. no **5.** 625 **6.** 13.824 **7.** 3

6-2 pages 249–251
On Your Own 13. 3.5×10^5 **15.** 1.9×10^8
17. 227,700,000

Mixed Review 1. mean: 13; median: 15;
mode: 17 **2.** mean: 75.5; median: 75; mode: 75
3. 13, 15, 17 **4.** 81, 243, 729 **5.** 2 mi/da

6-3 pages 252–254
On Your Own 13. 15 color comb. **19.** 8

Mixed Review 1. > **2.** < **3.** 5.7×10^{10}
4. 1.45×10^{13} **5.** 300,000 **6.** 470,000,000
7. 25.2 min

Checkpoint 1. geo.; 3.2, 6.4, 12.8 **2.** arith.;
1, 1.2, 1.4 **3.** arith.; $-19, -27, -35$ **4.** neither;
46, 74, 120 **5.** 6.61×10^3 **6.** 7.38×10^8
7. 8.88×10^7 **8. a.** 1, 6, 15, 20, 15, 6, 1
b. row 10

6-4 pages 255–257
On Your Own 7. $562.43 **9. a.** $1,126.83

Mixed Review 2.

```
7 | 3  4  5  8
8 | 1  1  5
9 | 2  6  6
    9 | 2 means 9.2
```

3. 11 **4.** -21 **5.** 11 and 12

6-5 pages 258–261
On Your Own
13. a.

Distance (mi)	fare $
0	0
0.2	.90
0.4	1.30
0.6	1.70
0.8	2.10
1.0	2.50

b. Carmen's; fares based on 0.2 mi segments

17. a. 1, 4, 9, 16 **b.** **c.** curve

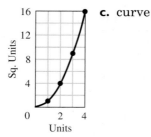

Mixed Review 1. 13 **2.** 22 **3.** $2,552.56

Problem Solving Practice page 262
1. Put 2, 5, 19, and 23 lb items in one box; 10,
11, 13 and 16 lb in other. **3.** Let $b = 0$. Then a
can be any number. **5.** 10 **7.** 243 **9.** 350 cal

6-6 pages 263–266
On Your Own
19.

n	f(n)
1	10
2	8
3	6
4	4

21. a.

n	f(n)
1	3
2	4
3	5
4	6
5	7
6	8

b. $f(n) = n + 2$ **23.** $f(n) = n - 3$
25. $f(n) = 3n + 2$ **27.** $f(n) = 0.5n$
29. a. Add one to the number of dots on the
shorter side. **b.** B

Mixed Review 1. 4 **2.** -2

3.

Time	Distance
(h)	(mi)
1	12
2	24
3	36
4	48

4.

Time	Wages
(h)	($)
1	4.75
2	9.50
3	14.25
4	19.00
5	23.75

5. 4 cm $\times$ 8 cm

Checkpoint 1. a. 4, 8, 12, 16

b.
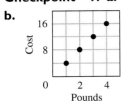

2. $648.96 **3.** $f(n) = -12n$
4. $f(n) = n - 5$
5. $f(n) = 3n - 2$

Practice page 267

1. arith.; 7, 3, -1 **3.** arith.; 0.6, 0.65, 0.7
5. neither; 25, 35, 47 **7.** 5.7×10^4
9. 1.12×10^5 **11.** 7.2×10 **13.** 149
15. 107,000,000,000 **17.** 8 **19.** $463.71 **21.** 5
23. 1 **25.** $f(n) = -9n$ **27.** $f(n) = 4n + 1$

6-7 pages 268–271

On Your Own 9. III **11.** II

13.
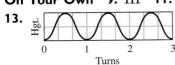

17. a. about 35 ft

b. about 2.8 s **c.** about 32 ft **d.** same height twice, once on way up and once on way down; about 0.4 s and 2.4 s **e.** throwing hand probably 5 ft above ground

Mixed Review 1. 24.68 **2.** 24.0434

3.

n	f(n)
3	3
4	5
5	7
6	9

4.

n	f(n)
3	28
4	49
5	76
6	109

5. 24 in.^{2}

Wrap Up pages 272–273

1. arith.; 23, 27, 31 **2.** geo.; 3, 1.5, 0.75 **3.** geo.; 243, -729, 2,187 **4.** neither; -2, -10, -19
5. start with 48 and multiply by 0.5 repeatedly; start with 3 and multiply by -3 repeatedly.
6. A **7.** 1.524×10^9 **8.** 2.5×10^5
9. 3.83×10^8 **10.** 8.76×10^4 **11.** $1,914.42
13. 249,000,000 **14.** $f(n) = 2n + 2$
15. $f(n) = 0.5n + 3$ **16.** 3, 5, 7, 9
18.
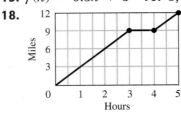

Getting Ready for Chapter 7 1. 2 **2.** 2, 3, 9
3. 3, 5, 9 **4.** 2, 3, 9 **5.** 2, 3, 5, 9, 10 **6.** 2, 5, 10

Cumulative Review page 277

1. D **2.** D **3.** A **4.** C **5.** B **6.** D **7.** A **8.** B
9. C **10.** B

CHAPTER 7

7-1 pages 281–283

On Your Own   7. $\frac{1}{2}$ in.   **9.** $\frac{3}{8}$ **11.** $2\frac{1}{2}$ **13.** $\frac{5}{6}$

15. b. yes

Mixed Review   1. $2n - 4$ **2.** $\frac{1}{2}n + 3$ **3.** >
4. >

7-2 pages 284–287

On Your Own   21. a. 1, 3, 9; 1, 3, 5, 15   **b.** 1
and 3   **23.** D   **25.** A   **27.** B   **29.** D   **33.** 5
35. 45

Mixed Review   1.   **2.**

3. 3, 9   **4.** −2, 1   **5.** 4.56×10^6 **6.** 35   **7.** 13 cm

7-3 pages 288–291

On Your Own   21. 11   **23.** 5   **25.** $\frac{5}{8}$ **27.** $\frac{7}{12}$
29. $\frac{1}{3}$ **31.** $\frac{2}{5}$ **33.** 1   **35.** 1

Mixed Review   1. 288   **2.** −721   **3.** $\frac{8}{10}, \frac{12}{15}, \frac{16}{20}$
4. $\frac{2}{3}, \frac{4}{6}, \frac{8}{12}$ **5.** 15   **6.** −4   **7.** 405 cm²
Checkpoint   1. $\frac{3}{8}$ **2.** $\frac{5}{12}$ **3.** $\frac{1}{4}$ **4.** $\frac{3}{4}$ **5.** $\frac{2}{3}$
6. $\frac{2}{3}$ **7.** $\frac{9}{10}$ **8.** C

7-4 pages 292–295

On Your Own   27. $2^2 \cdot 5^2$ **29.** $5 \cdot 13$
31. 1,225   **33.** 3,250   **35.** 38   **37.** $\frac{3}{5}$ **39.** $\frac{7}{9}$
41. b. $\frac{3}{8}$ **43.** True   **45.** $\frac{11}{37}, \frac{3}{37}$

Mixed Review   1. $\frac{3}{4}$ **2.** $\frac{3}{8}$ **3.** $\frac{5}{6}$ **4.** $\frac{1}{4}$ **5.** 8
6. −10   **7.** 60 months

7-5 pages 296–298

On Your Own   11. 180 handshakes   **13.** Jose;
Jeff, 88 items/h, Jose 90 items/h   **15.** 30 and 31
17. Any number in the form abc,abc is divisible
by 7, 11, 13, 77, 91, 143, and 1,001.

Mixed Review   1. 2,744 in.³   **2.** 1,176 in.²
3. $2^2 \cdot 3^3 \cdot 5$ **4.** $2^4 \cdot 3^2$ **5.** 22   **6.** −4

Practice page 299

1. $\frac{2}{5}$ **3.** $\frac{3}{8}$ **5.**   **9.**

11. 5, 10, 15, 20, 25   **13.** 18, 36, 54, 72, 90
15. 24, 48, 72, 96, 120   **17.** $\frac{2}{5}, \frac{4}{10}$ **19.** $\frac{2}{3}, \frac{24}{36}$
21. $\frac{2}{7}, \frac{4}{14}$ **23.** prime   **25.** prime   **27.** comp.
29. 4, 8   **31.** 4, 8   **33.** none   **35.** 6   **37.** 24
39. 3   **41.** 1   **43.** 5   **45.** 4   **47.** $2^2 \cdot 3^2$
49. $5 \cdot 3^2$ **51.** $2^2 \cdot 3 \cdot 7$ **53.** $\frac{4}{5}$ **55.** $\frac{4}{7}$
57. $\frac{7}{25}$ **59.** $\frac{9}{10}$ **61.** $\frac{3}{4}$ **63.** $\frac{3}{5}$

7-6 pages 300–303

On Your Own   15. $\frac{21}{8}$ **17.** $\frac{13}{12}$ **19.** $\frac{10}{7}$ **21.** $\frac{17}{5}$
23. $5\frac{2}{3}$ **25.** $10\frac{1}{2}$ **27.** $4\frac{5}{8}$ **29.** 12   **31. a.** $\frac{11}{3}$
b. $3\frac{2}{3}$ **33.** 202 slices   **35.** C; $3\frac{1}{8}$ **37.** $2\frac{1}{3}$ **39.** 6
41. no; $\frac{1}{4} \neq \frac{6}{12}$ **43.** $3\frac{45}{60}, 3\frac{3}{4}$

Mixed Review   1. no   **2.** yes   **3.** 56.759
4. 5.526   **5.** 42 bldgs.

7-7 pages 304–306

On Your Own   7. b. numerator, arithmetic
sequence; denominator, geometric sequence

Mixed Review   1. $1\frac{1}{2}$ **2.** $3\frac{1}{3}$ **3.**

4. 69 m   **5.** 24 cm²

Checkpoint   1. comp.   **2.** comp.   **3.** prime
4. comp.   **5.** 9   **6.** $\frac{2}{9}$ **7.** $4\frac{5}{6}$ **8.** $16\frac{2}{5}$ **9.** 3
10. $7\frac{1}{2}$ **11.** $\frac{17}{6}$ **12.** $\frac{37}{9}$ **13.** $\frac{25}{8}$ **14.** $\frac{19}{10}$

Problem Solving Practice page 307

1. 27th day   **3.** 21 volunteers   **5.** Tamara, 1 min
27 s; Janine, 1 min 42 s; Mavis, 1 min 38 s
7. need to know how many cars BJ, Jayda, or
Tony washed or the total no. of cars washed
9. 8 days

Wrap Up pages 308–309

1. $\frac{1}{6}$; $\frac{1}{3}$ **3. a.** 1, 2, 4, 8, 16 **b.** 1, 2, 4, 7, 14, 28
c. 1, 3, 19, 57 **5. a.** $\frac{1}{2}$ **b.** $\frac{1}{4}$ **c.** $\frac{3}{4}$ **6.** B
7. a. prime **b.** comp. **c.** comp. **8. a.** $2^2 \cdot 17$
b. $2^3 \cdot 3^2$ **c.** $2 \cdot 5 \cdot 11$ **9. a.** $\frac{37}{8}$ **b.** $\frac{13}{5}$ **c.** $\frac{52}{9}$
d. $\frac{11}{3}$ **e.** $\frac{21}{4}$ **f.** $\frac{11}{6}$ **10. a.** $1\frac{7}{8}$ **b.** $4\frac{3}{5}$ **c.** 8
d. $4\frac{2}{3}$ **e.** $5\frac{1}{3}$ **f.** $6\frac{1}{2}$ **11.** $\frac{11}{64}, \frac{13}{128}, \frac{15}{256}$ **12.** 210
boxes

Getting Ready for Chapter 8 **1.** $<$ **2.** $>$ **3.** $=$
4. $>$ **5.** $\frac{3}{4}, \frac{2}{4}$ **6.** $\frac{4}{6}, \frac{5}{6}$ **7.** $\frac{3}{8}, \frac{2}{8}$ **8.** $\frac{15}{24}, \frac{14}{24}$

Cumulative Review page 313

1. D **2.** A **3.** D **4.** B **5.** C **6.** C **7.** B **8.** D
9. A **10.** B

CHAPTER 8

8-1 pages 317–319

On Your Own **17.** $<$ **19.** $>$ **21.** $\frac{3}{4}$ in. nails
25. B **27.** C **29.** $\frac{2}{3}$ apple **31.** $\frac{3}{4}$ dollar

Mixed Review **1.** 12 **2.** -26 **3.** 4 **4.** 3
5. about 4,000 rev.

8-2 pages 320–322

On Your Own **11.** $0.8\overline{3}$ **13.** 0.375 **15.** 1.5
19. $\frac{1}{8}$ **21.** $2\frac{1}{2}$ **23. a.** WY **b.** $\frac{1}{4}$ **c.** FL, NY,
MD, ME, OH, KY, CA, OK, AK, WY

Mixed Review **1.** mean, 84.375; median, 86.5;
mode, 93 **2.** 30° **3.** $>$ **4.** $<$ **5.** $w = 28$ ft,
$h = 4$ ft

8-3 pages 323–325

On Your Own **19.** no, $4\frac{3}{4}$ c > 4 c **21.** 4 **23.** 4
25. 8 **27.** 0 **29.** 21 **31.** 10 **33.** yes **35.** C

Mixed Review **1.** 13, 16, 19 **2.** -512; 2,048;
$-8,192$ **3.** $\frac{33}{100}$ **4.** $5\frac{1}{8}$ **5.** Samples: $\frac{1}{4}, \frac{2}{8}$
6. Samples: $\frac{4}{18}, \frac{6}{27}$ **7.** \$3.70

8-4 pages 326–329

On Your Own **23.** $\frac{5}{8}$ **25.** $\frac{2}{3}$ **27. b.** $48\frac{3}{4}$ in.
29. $2\frac{4}{5}$ **31.** $3\frac{5}{6}$ **33.** $9\frac{1}{6}$ **35.** $\frac{1}{2}$ h **37.** $1\frac{1}{6}$ h
39. a. $3\frac{1}{4}$ h **b.** $4\frac{1}{4}$ h **c.** $6\frac{3}{4}$ h **41.** $6\frac{11}{15}$
43. zero **45. b.** $2\frac{3}{8}$

Mixed Review **1.** 30 **2.** -33 **3.** 7 **4.** 4 **5.** 5
6. -9 **7.** 8 students

8-5 pages 330–333

On Your Own **21.** $\frac{1}{8}$ **23.** $7\frac{1}{3}$ **25.** $6\frac{1}{4}$
29. $1\frac{1}{2}$ ft **31.** $\frac{2}{15}$

Mixed Review **1.** 0.4, 0.43, 0.438, 0.4381
2. 11.02, 11.1, 11.2, 11.201 **3.** $\frac{1}{4}$ **4.** $5\frac{1}{9}$ **5.** $\frac{7}{2}$
6. $\frac{17}{3}$ **7.** 73
Checkpoint **1.** $>$ **2.** $<$ **3.** $>$ **4.** $0.4\overline{5}$ **5.** $\frac{18}{25}$
6. 24 **7.** $\frac{1}{2}$ **8.** 3 **9.** $1\frac{5}{8}$ **10.** $4\frac{7}{15}$ **11.** $4\frac{1}{14}$
12. $1\frac{1}{8}$ **13.** $1\frac{7}{15}$ **14.** $1\frac{4}{5}$

8-6 pages 334–337

On Your Own **15.** 21 **17.** 18 **19.** $7\frac{1}{8}$
21. $21\frac{1}{3}$ **23.** $\frac{4}{5}$ **25.** $\frac{2}{5}$ **31.** $\frac{1}{6}$ **33.** about $\frac{6}{25}$
Mixed Review **1.**
```
3 | 7 9
4 | 7
5 | 0 6 8
4 | 7 means 47
```
2.
```
24 | 3 4 8 9
25 | 7
24 | 3 means 2.43
```
3. $5\frac{9}{14}$ **4.** $5\frac{1}{4}$ **5.** $\frac{1}{12}$

Problem Solving Practice page 338

3. Mr. Smith, 34; Mr. Lightfoot, 31 **5.** \$16
7. $\frac{127}{128}$

8-7 pages 339–341

On Your Own **19.** 16 **21.** 18 **25.** $\frac{1}{4}$ **27.** $3\frac{4}{5}$
29. $3\frac{1}{9}$ **31.** $3\frac{1}{3}$ **33. a.** $\frac{3}{4}$ mi **b.** $\frac{1}{4}$ mi **c.** $\frac{1}{2}$ mi
d. $6\frac{3}{4}$ mi

Mixed Review 1. right 2. obtuse 3. $13\frac{7}{8}$
4. $9\frac{3}{8}$ 5. 26; 29

8-8 pages 342–344

On Your Own 9. 1 quarter, 1 nickel, 3 dimes, 5 pennies or 7 nickels, 3 dimes 11. 132 black, 108 white 13. $1,064.41 15. $\frac{5}{6}$ and $\frac{2}{3}$ 17. 5 h

Mixed Review 1. -34 2. -3 3. 11 4. 15
5. 8

8-9 pages 345–348

On Your Own 23. 32 25. 18,480 27. 18
29. about 21,120,000 ft 31. LR, $232\frac{1}{2}$ ft²; MB, $131\frac{1}{4}$ ft²; BR, $108\frac{3}{4}$ ft² 35. 0.75 mi

Mixed Review 1.
2.
3. 421.9 cm³
4. 136.8 cm³ 5. 105

8-10 pages 349–351

On Your Own 15. $2\frac{2}{9}$ 17. 112 19. 1,024
21. 4,396 23. 12 25. 800 27. 72,000 mi²
29. 14

Mixed Review 1. -21 2. -55 3. 4 4. 80
5. 186,000 mi/s

Checkpoint 1. $\frac{1}{2}$ 2. $\frac{3}{4}$ 3. $\frac{1}{8}$ 4. $26\frac{11}{14}$
5. 7:05 A.M. 6. $2\frac{1}{3}$ 7. 136 8. $3\frac{3}{4}$ 9. $3\frac{1}{2}$
10. $6\frac{1}{2}$ 11. 21 12. $\frac{5}{6}$

Practice page 352

1. < 3. < 5. > 7. $0.\overline{27}$ 9. $\frac{2}{5}$ 11. $\frac{7}{8}$ 13. $2\frac{1}{2}$
15. 6 17. 48 19. $3\frac{3}{5}$ 21. $4\frac{1}{2}$ 23. $1\frac{1}{10}$
25. $8\frac{7}{12}$ 27. $\frac{2}{5}$ 29. 25 31. 22 33. $1\frac{1}{8}$ lb

8-11 pages 353–355

On Your Own 11. a. $172.46 b. $114.98
15. a. $56.25 b. less; $10.42 c. $47.49
d. $257.62

Mixed Review 1. $\frac{1}{5}$ 2. 136 3. $3\frac{2}{3}$ 4. 729
5. 15 ft 6. 12 cm

Wrap Up pages 356–357

1. $\frac{1}{4}, \frac{3}{8}, \frac{1}{2}$ 2. $\frac{1}{6}, \frac{7}{12}, \frac{3}{4}$ 3. $\frac{1}{3}, \frac{2}{5}, \frac{7}{15}$ 4. $\frac{8}{20}, \frac{6}{10}, \frac{4}{5}$
5. $2\frac{1}{2}$ 6. $2\frac{1}{2}$ 7. 30 8. 3 9. $\frac{1}{10}$ 10. $\frac{1}{2}$ 11. $\frac{6}{25}$
12. $3\frac{3}{4}$ 13. $2\frac{24}{25}$ 14. 0.6 15. 0.75 16. 0.875
17. $0.\overline{3}$ 18. $0.8\overline{3}$ 20. $3\frac{1}{12}$ 21. $7\frac{2}{15}$ 22. $15\frac{5}{12}$
23. $6\frac{11}{24}$ 24. $\frac{9}{10}$ 25. 9 26. 6 27. $\frac{3}{5}$ 28. $1\frac{7}{8}$
29. $8\frac{1}{2}$ 30. $3\frac{3}{5}$ 31. $36\frac{1}{4}$ 32. 350 33. $66\frac{7}{8}$ in.
34. $2\frac{1}{2}$ 35. $3\frac{3}{8}$ 36. 60 37. 28 38. 6:00 A.M.
39. $39.76

Getting Ready for Chapter 9 1. $\frac{4}{6}$ 2. $\frac{3}{4}$ 3. $\frac{4}{9}$
4. $\frac{3}{5}$

Cumulative Review page 361

1. B 2. A 3. A 4. C 5. B 6. D 7. B 8. C
9. D 10. C

CHAPTER 9

9-1 pages 365–368

On Your Own 13. 1 to 5, 1:5, $\frac{1}{5}$ 15. 1:4
17. a. 101 and 107 b. $\frac{7}{12}$ 19. a. $\frac{13}{18}$ b. $\frac{169}{324}$
21. 25:1 23. 7.6

Mixed Review 1. $-32,000$ 2. 13 3. 4.88
4. 6.13 5. $28.50 6. 88°F

9-2 pages 369–372

On Your Own 11. $.22/oz, $.25/oz; 1 lb for $3.49
13. $.49/yd, $.65/yd; 1 yd for $.49 15. 750 km/h
17. a. the following Monday b. 18 mi/gal
19. a. 10.14 m/s; 10.14 m/s; 9.24 m/s; 7.86 m/s
b. no 21. 4 mi/h

Mixed Review 1. 9 2. 24 3. 3 to 8, 3:8, $\frac{3}{8}$
4. 2 to 11, 2:11, $\frac{2}{11}$ 5. 8:1 6. $1.45 or $1.65

9-3 pages 373–376

On Your Own **13. a.** 8 qt **15.** C **17.** 25
19. 3 **21.** 11.25 **23.** 45 boys **25.** Write the cross products. Divide both sides by 8. **27.** 46 lb on Mars, 317 lb on Jupiter

Mixed Review **1.** 7, 11, 15 **2.** 15, 31, 63 or 13, 21, 31 **3.** 34 mi/gal **4.** $2.35/lb **5.** $\angle A$, $\angle E$; $\angle B$, $\angle F$; $\angle C$, $\angle D$ **6.** 8

Checkpoint **1–4.** Answers may vary. **1.** 1 : 25, 4 : 100 **2.** $\frac{6}{10}$, $\frac{9}{15}$ **3.** 1 to 3, 2 to 6 **4.** $\frac{2}{3}$, $\frac{8}{12}$
5. A **6.** 152 **7.** 28 **8.** 12.5 **9.** 196 min

9-4 pages 377–380

On Your Own **9.** no **11.** 4 ft **13.** 81
15. $x = 5.6$, $y = 21.6$ **17.** 99 cm
21. All sq. are sim. **23.** Sample: reg. pent. and sq. **25.** All isos. rt. triangles are sim.

Mixed Review **1.** < **2.** < **3.** 12 **4.** −7 **5.** 20
6. 15.75 **7.** acute triangle

Problem Solving Practice page 381

1. 8 **3.** too little information **5.** Aimee is a conductor, Bob is a banker, and Carl is an artist.

9-5 pages 382–384

On Your Own **7.** 9.75 km **9.** 18,300 km
11. $\frac{1}{2}$ in. **13.** $2\frac{1}{4}$ in. **17. a.** 40 in. **b.** 3 in.

Mixed Review **1.** $x = 40$, $y = 32$ **2.** 3 **3.** 160
4. 5 **5.** 80 **6.** 3 students

9-6 pages 385–387

On Your Own **11.** 64% **13.** 28%
17. a. $33\frac{1}{3}$%; $66\frac{2}{3}$% **b.** $\frac{1}{3}$ **c.** $\frac{1}{3}$ **d.** $\frac{2}{3}$ **19.** 50%
21. 70% **23.** 145% **25.** about 20% **27.** about 45%

Mixed Review **1.** 2.9979×10^8 m/s
2. 4.06×10^{13} km **3.** 14 ft × 16 ft
4. 18 in. × 22.5 in. **5.** 42 games

9-7 pages 388–391

On Your Own **17. a.** $\frac{6}{100}$ or $\frac{3}{50}$, 0.06; $\frac{50}{100}$ or $\frac{1}{2}$,
0.5; $\frac{20}{100}$ or $\frac{1}{5}$, 0.2; $\frac{25}{100}$ or $\frac{1}{4}$, 0.25; $\frac{8}{100}$ or $\frac{2}{25}$, 0.08

b. 4 servings **19.** $\frac{9}{20}$, 0.45 **21.** $\frac{173}{100}$, 1.73
23. 87.5% **25.** 51.5%

Mixed Review **1.** 4 **2.** 2 **5.** 15 **6.** 64 **7.** 35%

Checkpoint **1.** 52.5 mi **2.** $x = 10$, $y = 6$
3. 80% **4.** 0.4% **5.** $33\frac{1}{3}$% **6.** 56%

9-8 pages 392–394

On Your Own **9.** 36 handshakes **11.** 35
13. $x = 2$, $y = 7$ **15. a.** 1 3 5 7 9 11
b. 21; 45 **c.** 16; 100 **d.** Square the row number.

Mixed Review **1.** 18 **2.** 6 **3.** 23 cm **4.** 16 m
5. 62% **6.** $\frac{2}{3}$ **7.** 3; 1 × 5, 2 × 4, 3 × 3

9-9 pages 395–398

On Your Own **13.** 10% **15.** 75% **17.** 40%
19. 4.5 **21.** 92%

Mixed Review **1.** 12 **2.** −3 **3.** 12 in.^{2}
4. 691.69 cm^2 **5.** $48

9-10 pages 399–401

On Your Own **9.** $\frac{54}{n} = \frac{75}{100}$; $n = 72$
11. $\frac{48}{144} = \frac{n}{100}$; $n = 33\frac{1}{3}$%
13. $\frac{12\frac{1}{2}}{100} = \frac{424}{n}$; $n = 3,392$ **15.** 459 students
17. $40 **19. a.** 75%; **b.** $18

Mixed Review **1.** 4 **2.** 2 **3.** about 20 million
4. 10% **5.** 4 mi

9-11 pages 402–404

On Your Own **9.** 9.7% increase **11.** 20%; 300,000, 60,000; 10%

Mixed Review **1.** 46 **2.** −12 **3.** $3\frac{1}{6}$ **4.** $4\frac{4}{5}$
5. 144 **6.** 12.5% **7.** 40 mi

Checkpoint **1.** 50% **2.** 75% **3.** 20 **4.** 60%

Practice page 405

1. $\frac{2}{5}$ **3.** 1:5 **5.** 4 to 1 **7.** 18 mi/gal **9.** 9
11. 12 **13.** $x = 15$ **15.** 72% **17.** 75%

19. 73.4% **21.** 0.03; $\frac{3}{100}$ **23.** 0.245; $\frac{49}{200}$ **25.** 3
27. 30 **29.** 160% **31. a.** 15.6% **b.** decrease

9-12 pages 406–409

On Your Own **11.**

13. a. 12.5% **b.** 20%

Mixed Review **1.** 23, 30, 37 **2.** $\frac{1}{8}, \frac{1}{32}, \frac{1}{128}$
3. $33\frac{1}{3}\%$ **4.** $66\frac{2}{3}\%$ **5.** 63

Wrap Up page 410–411

1. 37 to 108; 37:108; $\frac{37}{108}$ **2.** \$.28/oz, \$.31/oz;
10-oz box **3.** 12 **4.** 25 **5.** 3 **6.** 136 **7.** 1,533
games **8.** $x = 45$ **9.** $x = 45, y = 36$
10. 4,000 mi **11.** 0.75 in. **12.** $\frac{5}{8}$ **13.** 0.018
14. 37.5% **15.** 70% **16.** 47.5 **17.** 252
18. 32.5% decrease **20.** D

Getting Ready for Chapter 10 **1.** $\frac{2}{15}$ **2.** $\frac{15}{32}$
3. $\frac{3}{5}$ **4.** $\frac{5}{9}$ **5.** $\frac{3}{28}$ **6.** $\frac{5}{33}$ **7.** 24

Cumulative Review page 415

1. B **2.** D **3.** A **4.** D **5.** A **6.** D **7.** C **8.** C
9. A **10.** C

CHAPTER 10

10-1 pages 419–422

On Your Own **17.** $\frac{1}{10}$, 0.1, 10% **19.** $\frac{10}{10}$, 1,
100% **21.** $\frac{1}{8}; \frac{3}{8}; \frac{1}{2}$ **23. a.** $\frac{1}{3}$ **b.** remove all
orange and 2 clear **25.** $\frac{1}{4}$ or 25% **27. b.** $\frac{1}{4}$

Mixed Review **1.** 144° **2.** 54° **3.** $\frac{1}{6}$ **4.** 0.48
5. $\frac{1}{3}(y + 8)$ **6.** $\frac{x}{3}$ **7.** 280

10-2 pages 423–425

On Your Own **11.** blue; red **13.** $\frac{3}{4}$ **15.** 0
17. a. 1 **b.** impossible **19.** $\frac{1}{87}$ **21.** D

Mixed Review **1.** 13 m **2.** 5^4 **3.** $2^5 \cdot 3^2 \cdot 5^2$
4. 2 **5.** -8 **6.** $\frac{2}{3}$

10-3 pages 426–429

On Your Own **19.** 12 **21.**

Car — Car / Bus
Bus — Car / Bus
Plane — Car / Bus
Train — Car / Bus

23. a. 16 **b.** $\frac{3}{4}$ **25.** 41; 2

Mixed Review **1.** 15 **2.** 40% **3.** $2.1 \cdot 10^7$
4. $5.43 \cdot 10^2$ **5.** $\frac{7}{6}$ **6.** $\frac{7}{8}$ **7.** $\frac{999,999}{1,000,000}$

Problem Solving Practice page 430

1. 96 **3.** 10 triangles **5.** 230 rev/min **7.** 5
9. 4, 9

10-4 pages 431–434

On Your Own **15.** $\frac{4}{11}$ **17. a.** $\frac{8}{110}$ or $\frac{4}{55}$ **b.** $\frac{8}{121}$
19. $\frac{1}{36}$ **21.** 0 **23.** no; each toss is independent

Mixed Review **1.** $\frac{1}{9}$ **2.** $\frac{2}{3}$ **3.** 20.25 ft² **4.** $\frac{2}{5}$
5. $\frac{1}{5}$ **6.** 10

Checkpoint **1.** $\frac{4}{5}$; 0.8; 80% **2.** $\frac{2}{5}$; 0.4; 40%
3. $\frac{3}{5}$; 0.6; 60% **4.** 2:9 **5.** $\frac{16}{121}$ **6.** $\frac{2}{55}$ **7.** 24
meals

10-5 pages 435–437

On Your Own **11.** \$6,594; \$1,500 **15.** 79.1%

Mixed Review **1.** 12 in. **2.** 70 words/min
3. 94.5 km/h **4.** $\frac{1}{5}$ **5.** $\frac{1}{6}$ **6.** 3 chairs, 2 stools

10-6 pages 438–440

On Your Own   9. 0.64; free throw   **13. a.** $\frac{1}{100}$
b. Sample: $\frac{1}{50}$ **c.** Sample: 1%; 2%; yes

Mixed Review   1. 54 cm² **2.** $-4\frac{7}{8}$ **3.** $2\frac{5}{8}$ **4.** $\frac{1}{4}$
5. $\frac{1}{2}$

Practice page 441

1. $\frac{1}{6}$ **3.** $\frac{1}{3}$ **5.** 0 **7.** $\frac{1}{4}$, 0.25, 25%
9. $\frac{7}{8}$, 0.875, 87.5% **11.** 0 **13.** $\frac{1}{8}$ **15.** $\frac{2}{7}$ **17.** $\frac{2}{5}$
19. $\frac{1}{27}$ **21.** $\frac{1}{28}$

23.

	Roll cube					
	1	2	3	4	5	6
Coin H	1H	2H	3H	4H	5H	6H
T	1T	2T	3T	4T	5T	6T

25. $\frac{1}{55}$

10-7 pages 442–445

On Your Own   15. a. 10 **b.** 6
19. 24 permutations; 4 **21.** 160 codes

Mixed Review   1. $\frac{6}{10}, \frac{12}{20}, \frac{24}{40}, \frac{48}{80}$ **2.** $\frac{96}{1000}; \frac{12}{125}$
3. $\frac{875}{1000}; \frac{7}{8}$ **4.** 12 m × 12 m **5.** 25 **6.** 14

Checkpoint   1. comb.; 15 **2.** perm.; 362,880
3. a. draw names from hat **b.** dependent

10-8 pages 446–449

On Your Own   5. 496 catfish

Mixed Review   1. 0.32 mm **2.** 24 ways
3. 15,120 plates **4.** -50 **5.** 70%

Wrap Up pages 450–451

1. $\frac{1}{7}$ **2.** $\frac{2}{7}$ **3.** $\frac{6}{7}$ **4.** 2:5 **5.** 1:6 **6.** 5:2
7. a. 12 dinners **b.** 2 • 2 • 3 = 12 **8.** 11,880
9. $\frac{1}{5}$ **10.** B **11.** 5 **12.** 24 **13.** count heads in a trial of 5 flips **14.** about 94 lions

Getting Ready for Chapter 11

1. **2.**

3. **4.**

Cumulative Review page 455

1. B **2.** B **3.** C **4.** D **5.** B **6.** C **7.** B **8.** D
9. C **10.** A

CHAPTER 11

11-1 pages 459–461

On Your Own   19. II **21.** I
23. a.

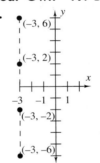

b. fall on a line **c.** $(-3,0)$, $(-3,4)$ **27.** B

Mixed Review   1. -4 **2.** -16 **3.** 45
4. 2 and -5

11-2 pages 462–465

On Your Own   17. I, II **19.** II **21.** I, III
25. B **27.** C **29.** $(-1,2)$
31. a.

x	$\frac{1}{2}$x	y	(x, y)
0	$\frac{1}{2}(0)$	0	(0, 0)
2	$\frac{1}{2}(2)$	1	(2, 1)
4	$\frac{1}{2}(4)$	2	(4, 2)

b.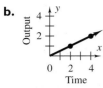

c. no; do not pop popcorn for negative amounts of time

Mixed Review   1. 23 cm   **2.** 5^3 **3.** IV   **4.** III
5. 8:00 P.M.; 2 days later

11-3 pages 466–467

On Your Own   7. 2   **9.** $-\frac{1}{4}$ **11.** -3 **13.** -1
15. $-\frac{1}{6}$ **17.** $-\frac{1}{3}; \frac{1}{3}$

Mixed Review   1. 144 m^2 **2.** 72 ft^2

3.

x	x + 9	y	(x, y)
0	0 + 9	9	(0, 9)
1	1 + 9	10	(1, 10)
2	2 + 9	11	(2, 11)

4.

x	2x²	y	(x, y)
0	$2(0)^2$	0	(0, 0)
1	$2(1)^2$	2	(1, 2)
−2	$2(-2)^2$	8	(−2, 8)

5. 5 ft 2 in.

Problem Solving Practice page 468
1. $34.23   **3.** 13 games   **5.** 4 and 24   **7.** 37 days
9. 8 h

11-4 pages 469–471

On Your Own   5. a. Ian   **b.** 3 wk   **7.** 8 wk
9. a. 0.315; 0.3

Mixed Review   1. 9   **2.** 81   **3.** slope = 2
4. slope = $-\frac{7}{3}$ **5.** 3 h 20 min

11-5 pages 472–474
On Your Own   9. *y*-coordinates are greater than or equal to zero. No; absolute value can never be negative.   **11. I.** a   **II.** d   **III.** f

Mixed Review   1. 75%   **2.** 25%   **3.** $y = 2.5x$
4. 60 times (61 times in a leap year)

Checkpoint   1. B   **2.** D   **3.** G   **4.** (4, −1)
5. (−2, −3)   **6.** (2, 3)   **7.** (4, 0)   **8.** C

9. a.

x	x + (−2)	y	(x, y)
0	0 + (−2)	−2	(0, −2)
2	2 + (−2)	0	(2, 0)
−2	−2 + (−2)	−4	(−2, −4)

b.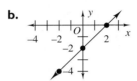

10. a.

x	−x² + 9	y	(x, y)
0	$-(0)^2 + 9$	9	(0, 9)
3	$-(3)^2 + 9$	0	(3, 0)
−2	$-(-2)^2 + 9$	5	(−2, 5)
−1	$-(-1)^2 + 9$	8	(−1, 8)

b.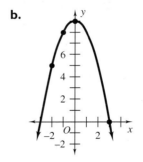

11-6 pages 475–477

On Your Own   5. a.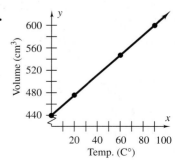

b. about 600 cm^3 **c.** 445 cm^3

7. a.

Price	Tickets Sold	Total Rev
$30.00	400	$12,000
$29.00	420	$12,180
$28.00	440	$12,320
$27.00	460	$12,420
⋮	⋮	⋮
$24.00	520	$12,480

b. 500 tickets **c.**

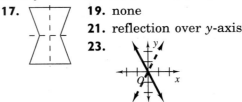

d. Yes; find price that earns greatest revenue

Mixed Review 1. $\frac{12}{25}$ **2.** $1\frac{3}{4}$ **3.** $\frac{1}{20}$ **4.** $\frac{7}{8}$ **5.** 13 and 17

11-7 pages 478–480

On Your Own 11. 594 tiles **13.** 14, 17
15. 20 outfits

Mixed Review 1. $1\frac{11}{20}$ **2.** $\frac{1}{15}$ **3.** $\frac{3}{4}$ **4.** $4\frac{3}{5}$ or 4.6 **5.** $\frac{1}{3}$ **6.** $1\frac{1}{2}$ c

Practice page 481

1. K **3.** D **5.** B **7.** (5,1) **9.** (−3,0) **11.** (4,−2)
13. IV **15.** II **17.** I **19.** −1 **21.** 0
23.

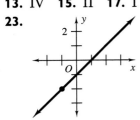

25.

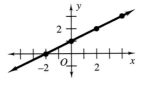

27. 4 h

11-8 pages 482–485

On Your Own 15. $(x, y) \rightarrow (x + 5, y + 4)$
17. $A'(-3, 2), B'(-2, -1), C'(2, -1), D'(1, 2)$
19. y-coord.; x-coord. **21.** A
23. a. $P(-2, 1) \rightarrow P'(2, 4)$; $L(-5, 1) \rightarrow L'(-1, 4)$;
$N(-2, -2) \rightarrow N'(2, 1)$ **b.** planes moved right 4, up 3

Mixed Review 1. I **2.** III **3.** II **4.** IV **5.** $2\frac{29}{80}$
6. $8\frac{23}{32}$ **7.** $2(48 + w) = 120$; 12 cm

Checkpoint 1. $-\frac{1}{4}$ **2.** 2 **3.** $-\frac{4}{5}$ **4.** B
5. a. $e = p$ **b.** profit $= e - 10$ **c.** 48 pizzas

11-9 pages 486–488

On Your Own 9. A, B **11.** not same distance from y-axis **13.** (3,4) **15.** (3,−7)
17. **19.** none
21. reflection over y-axis
23.

Mixed Review 1. 2, 6 **2.** 12, 17 **4.** $A'(-4,2)$, $B'(-5,-2)$, $C'(-2,1)$ **5.** $83.94

11-10 pages 489–491

On Your Own 13. yes **15.** no **17.** A, C, D
19. reflection **21.** rotation

Mixed Review 1. about 38.5 ft^2 **2.** about 63.6 in.^{2} **3.** 96 cm^2 **4.** (5,−1) **5.** (3,4)
6. $2,000

Wrap Up pages 492–493

1. a. A **b.** G **2. a.** (0,2) **b.** (−3,−2)
c. (−1,0) **d.** (3,1) **3.** a, c **4. a.** (0,4), (1,5), (2,6)

b.

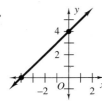

5. B **6.** $-\frac{1}{2}$ **7.** $\frac{3}{2}$ **8.** $\frac{1}{3}$

9. $-\frac{2}{9}$ **10.** 116 tickets

11. 1 P.M. **13.** $y = x^2 - 4$

14. I, II **15.** table; barbell

16.

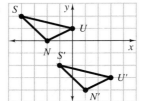

17. translation

18. reflection

19. reflection

20. rotation

Cumulative Review page 497

1. D **2.** C **3.** A **4.** C **5.** A **6.** B **7.** D **8.** B

9. B **10.** D

Extra Practice 1 page 498

1.

Temp.	Freq.
1	1
2	1
3	2
4	2
5	1
7	1
10	2
11	3
15	1
16	1
20	1
22	1
28	2
31	2

3. 13; 11; 11; 30

5. A

7. C

9.
```
4 | 0 4 8 9
5 | 1 5 7 7
6 | 0 0 4
7 | 1 2 3 7 7 7
8 | 0 2 6
    5 | 1 means 51
```

11. 10

Extra Practice 2 page 499

1.

3. 90°; right **5.** c **7.** e **9.** b

11. a, c, d

Extra Practice 3 page 500

1. 0.102, 0.099, 0.095, 0.092 **3.** 0.56, 0.55, 0.52, 0.505 **5.** 4 **7.** 1.5 **9.** 2 **11.** 125 **13.** 225

15. 7 **17.** 144 **19.** $2.\overline{6}$ **21.** $1.8\overline{6}$ **23.** 6.723

25. $3.\overline{3}$ **27.** > **29.** = **31.** $2n - 5$ **33.** 3.9; 15.87; 5.9; 24.334; 6.6; 30.72; 8.6; 65.536

Extra Practice 4 page 501

1. 6 **3.** 0 **5.** $x - 3 = 4$; 7 **7.** F **9.** T **11.** -5

13. 100 **15.** 0 **17.** 90 **19.** 3 **21.** -14 **23.** 16

25. -4 **27.** -18 **29.** 42 **31.** 36

Extra Practice 5 page 502

1. 29.16 units^2; 21.6 units **3.** 6 units^2; 12 units

5. 48 units^2; 34 units **7.** 11.7 in. **9.** 39.3 ft^3

11. 32.9 in. **13.** 9 gal **15.** 29.2 ft

Extra Practice 6 page 503

1. > **3.** > **5.** < **7.** = **9.** =

11. geom.; 15, 5, $1.6\overline{6}$ **13.** arith.; 4.45, 4.75, 5.05

15. geom.; 2.0736, 2.48832, 2.985984

17. a. repeat of 8, 4, 2, 6 **b.** 2 **19.** $2,456.52

21.

Extra Practice 7 page 504

1. $\frac{1}{2}$ **3.** $\frac{1}{3}$ **5.** $\frac{7}{8}, \frac{42}{48}$ **7.** $\frac{2}{3}, \frac{12}{18}$ **9.** $\frac{3}{9}, \frac{4}{12}$ **11.** 1

13. 17 **15.** 10 **17.** $\frac{4}{9}$ **19.** $\frac{2}{3}$ **21.** $\frac{9}{16}$ **23.** $\frac{26}{7}$

25. $\frac{22}{5}$ **27.** $\frac{12}{5}$ **29.** $11\frac{1}{3}$ **31.** $3\frac{1}{4}$ **33.** $16\frac{2}{3}$

35. $2^4 \cdot 3 \cdot 5$ **37.** $2^4 \cdot 3$ **39.** $2 \cdot 3 \cdot 5^2$ **41.** $\frac{1}{2}$

43. $\frac{3}{8}$

45. 3, 6, 9, 12, 15

47. 12, 24, 36, 48, 60

49. 17, 34, 51, 68, 85

Extra Practice 8 page 505

1. > **3.** = **5.** < **7.** $\frac{73}{200}$ **9.** $\frac{21}{50}$ **11.** $\frac{7}{10}$

13. 9 **15.** 100 **17.** $2\frac{7}{15}$ **19.** $\frac{8}{9}$ **21.** $6\frac{7}{8}$

23. $1\frac{1}{2}$ **25.** $\frac{1}{4}$ **27.** 12,250 **29.** $202\frac{2}{3}$ **31.** D

Extra Practice 9 page 506

1. \$.072/oz; \$.066/oz **3.** 750 km/h; 800 km/h

5. 3 **7.** 20 **9.** $\frac{3}{8}$ **11.** $\frac{7}{8}$ **13.** 135 **15.** 60%

17. $1\frac{2}{3}$ **19.** No; cost will be \$243.17.

Extra Practice 10 page 507

1. $\frac{1}{3}$ **3.** $\frac{1}{6}$ **5.** $\frac{3}{16}$ **7.** $\frac{1}{8}$ **9.** $\frac{5}{36}$

11. a.

b. $\frac{1}{12}; \frac{1}{4}$ **13.** $\frac{223}{295}$ **15.** 504 **17.** about 658

Extra Practice 11 page 508

1. G **3.** L **5.** $(4,-1)$ **7.** $-\frac{3}{4}$ **9.** -3

11. down 5, right 1 **13.** A

15.

Acknowledgments

Cover Design
Martucci Studio and L. Christopher Valente

Front Cover Photo Martucci Studio

Back Cover Photo Ken O'Donoghue

Book Design DECODE, Inc.

Technical Illustration ANCO/Outlook

Illustration

Anco/OUTLOOK: 13, 14, 60, 145, 153, 155, 160, 161, 163, 168, 170, 179, 205 B, 209 B, 212, 214, 215, 217, 218, 222, 232, 235, 253, 258, 259, 260, 261, 262, 268, 270, 281, 306, 341, 342, 344, 345, 348, 352, 379, 402, 424, 427, 428, 431, 433, 434, 459, 462, 475, 477, 482, 491

Eliot Bergman: xv B, 18, 37, 94, 98, 132, 166, 173, 367 C, 368, 376, 391, 406, 409

Arnold Bombay: xi B, 8, 22, 103, 150, 159, 220, 266, 288, 304, 320, 344, 353, 383 B, 401, 403

DECODE, Inc.: vii TR, viii TL, ix TL, x TL, xi TL, xii TL, xiii TL, xiv TL, xv TL, xvi TL, xvii TL, 2 TL, , 40 C, 41 BR, 41 CL, 41 TL, 41 TR, 44 T, 86 C, 87 B, 87 TL, 87 TR, 90 TL, 138 CR, 139 BL, 139 BR, 139 TL, 139 TR, 142 TL, 186 B, 187 C, 187 TL, 187 TR, 190 C, 238 BL, 238 BR, 239 B, 239 TL, 239 TR, 242 TL, 274 B, 275 B, 275 T, 278 TL, 310 B, 311 CL, 311 CR, 311 T, 314, TL, 358, 359 C, 359 T, 362 TL, 412 B, 413 BL, 413 BR, 413 T, 416 TL, 452 B, 453 BL, 453 BR, 453 TL, 453 TR, 456 TL, 494 B, 495 CL, 495 CR, 495 T

Jim DeLapine: 7, 55, 111, 130, 388, 435

Tamar Haber-Schaim: 21, 29, 34, 97, 105, 114, 120, 326, 328, 480

Horizon Design/John Sanderson: 146, 337, 371, 382

Joe Lemonnier: 119

Morgan Cain Associates: xv TR, 362–363

Steve Moscowitz: 26, 346

Linda Phinney-Crehan: 16, 322, 355

Matthew Pippin: 469

Precision Graphics: viii TR, x TR, xi TR, xiv TR, xvi TR, xvii TR, 44–45, 91, 143, 190–191, 244, 315, 364, 416–417, 457

Pat Rossi: 260, 431

Schneck-DePippo Graphics: 367 R, 373, 380, 383 T

Schneck-DePippo Graphics and Anco/OUTLOOK: 116, 117

Ned Shaw: 25, 35, 162, 296, 319, 428

Photography

Front Matter: i, ii, iii, Martucci Studio; iv–v, Bill DeSimone Photography; vii TL, Steve Greenberg Photography; vii L, Bob Daemmrich Photography; viii L, Ken O'Donoghue; ix TR; Mitchell Layton/duomo; x L, Chris Bjornberg/Photo Researchers; xii M, Kobal Collection; xii TR; Rick Maiman/Sygma; xiii T, Steve Greenberg Photography; xiii L, PH Photo; xiv L, Wes Thompson, Berenholz, and Donald Johnson/ Stock Market; xvii L, John Madere/Stock Market.

Chapter One: 2, 3, Steve Greenberg; 4, Elena Rooraid/PhotoEdit; 9, The Dinosaur Society; 12, NASA/Science Photo Library/Photo Researchers, Inc.; 19, Faith Barbakoff/AP LaserPhoto; 20, John M. Burnley/Bruce Coleman, Inc.; 31, Rhoda Sidney/ Monkmeyer Press; 33, Bob Daemmrich; 36, D. Strohmeyer/Allsport USA; 38, Steve Greenberg; 40, Menke/ Monkmeyer Press.

Chapter Two: 44, NASA; 50, J. Lotter/Tom Stack & Associates; 51, Ken O'Donoghue; 53 TL, TR, National Fish and Wildlife Forensics Lab; 53 BR, E.R. Degginger/Earth Scenes; 56, Ken O'Donoghue; 59, Frank Siteman/The Picture Cube; 63, Galen Rowell; 64 T, The Bettmann Archive; 64 B, The Granger Collection; 66, Photo Researchers, Inc.; 67, Joyce Photographics/Photo Researchers, Inc.; 68, Kelvin Aitken/Peter Arnold, Inc.; 71, © 1993 The Museum of Modern Art, New York; 73, Orion SVC/TRDNG/FPG International; 80 L, Comstock; 80 M, David Jeffrey/The Image Bank; 80 R, Kal Muller/Woodfin Camp & Associates; 82, Courtesy, Matt Brookhart; 83, Ken O'Donoghue; 84, NASA; 86, John Eastcott/The Image Works.

Chapter Three: 90, Mitchell Layton/© duomo; 92, Aneal Vohra/The Picture Cube; 95, M.P.L. Fogden/Bruce Coleman, Inc.; 99, M.E. Newman/The Image Bank; 100, Tim Rock/Animals Animals; 104 all, Ken O'Donoghue; 107, Pacific Press Service/Photo Researchers, Inc.; 112, The Granger Collection; 115, M.M. Heaton; 116, Alvis Upitus/The Image Bank; 121, Hans Wolf/The Image Bank; 122, Jacques Langevin/Sygma; 125 L, R, Ken O'Donoghue; 126, Courtesy Mike's Movies, Boston, MA. Photo by Ken O'Donoghue; 127, Lee Anderson; 128, M.M. Heaton; 133, Mireille Vautier/Woodfin Camp & Associates; 134, Courtesy, Jill Danek; 135 T, Courtesy, Prentice Hall; 135 BL, Dale O'Dell/The Stock Market; 136, Alan Carey/The Image Works.

Chapter Four: 144, Ken O'Donoghue; 147, Chris Bjornberg/Photo Researchers, Inc.; 148, Wide World Photos; 152, Mark Kelly/Stock Boston; 154, J. Sohm/

The Image Works; **156,** NOAA; **158,** Courtesy, Jason Rodgers; **159,** Mark Gottlieb/FPG International; **164,** The Stock Market; **165,** Garoutte/PDS Bay Island/Tom Stack & Associates; **168,** Bob Daemmrich/The Image Works; **171,** The Granger Collection; **175,** Bettmann; **177,** Michaud/Photo Researchers, Inc.; **180,** Frederik Bodin/Stock Boston; **181,** Erich Lessing/Art Resource; **187,** Bob Daemmrich/The Image Works.

Chapter Five: **192,** John Coletti/The Picture Cube; **194,** Steve Greensberg; **195,** David Simson/Stock Boston; **196,** Shaun Egan/Tony Stone Images; **197,** Annie Hunter; **199,** Tate Gallery, London/Art Resource, NY; **202,** Roy Morsch/The Stock Market; **206,** © duomo; **207,** Pete Saloutos/The Stock Market; **210,** Michael Furman/The Stock Market; **213,** The Granger Collection; **216,** Antman/The Image Works; **219,** Joe Cornish/Tony Stone Images; **224,** Bob Daemmrich Photography; **225,** Abe Frajndlich/Sygma; **226,** Eon Productions; **230,** Comstock; **234,** Russ Lappa; **235 T,** U.S. Department of Justice, Federal Bureau of Investigation; **235 B,** William Whitehurst/The Stock Market; **239,** D & I MacDonald/PhotoEdit.

Chapter Six: **243,** Rick Maiman/Sygma; **248,** Peter Aitken/Photo Researchers, Inc.; **250 T,** David Madison/Bruce Coleman, Inc.; **250 B,** Courtesy, Joshua Gitersonke; **251,** Joe Towers/The Stock Market; **255,** From *The World Book Encyclopedia © 1993 World Book, Inc.* by permission of the publisher; **256,** Mike Kagan/Monkmeyer Press; **259,** Magnus Rietz/The Image Bank; **264,** Art Matrix from Rainbow; **272,** Rich Maiman/Sygma; **275,** Bob Daemmrich/The Image Works.

Chapter Seven: **278,** Steve Greenberg; **280,** Ken O'Donoghue; **282,** courtesy, Amanda Johnson; **283,** Cartoon: Joe Duffy, National Cartoonists Society, Photo by Russ Lappa; **286,** Bob Daemmrich Photography; **289,** Will/Deni McIntyre/Photo Researchers, Inc.; **290,** Christian Steiner/EMI; **291,** Bob Daemmrich/The Image Works; **298,** Nancy Bates/The Picture Cube; **303,** Courtesy, Western Wood Association; **307,** Bob Daemmrich Photography; **308,** Steve Greenberg; **310,** Bill Aron/PhotoEdit; **331,** J. Boeder/Allstock.

Chapter Eight: **314,** Richard Bowditch; **316,** Palmer/Kane; **318,** Comstock; **324,** Nicholas de Vore III/Bruce Coleman, Inc.; **333,** Llewellyn/The Picture Cube; **343,** Amy C. Etra/PhotoEdit; **347,** Will & Deni McIntyre/Photo Researchers, Inc.; **351 T,** Donald Johnson/The Stock Market; **351 M,** Berenholz/The Stock Market; **351 B,** Wes Thompson/The Stock Market; **354,** Courtesy,

Stacey Lomprey; **355 T,** The Stock Market; **355 B,** Gabe Palmer/The Stock Market; **358,** Frank Siteman/Monkmeyer Press.

Chapter Nine: **365,** Bob Daemmrich/Stock Boston; **366,** Jeffrey Markowitz/Sygma; **369,** UPI/Bettmann Newsphotos; **374,** David Doody/Tom Stack & Associates; **378,** Annie Hunter; **386,** The Granger Collection; **393,** Jacques Cochin/The Image Bank; **396,** David Young-Wolf/PhotoEdit; **398,** Bob Daemmrich/The Image Works; **399,** Ed Degginger/Bruce Coleman, Inc.; **400,** Annie Hunter; **402,** Hans Reinhard/Bruce Coleman, Inc.; **407 L,** Allan Tannenbaum/Sygma; **407 R,** Bettmann Archive; **409,** Bachmann/The Image Works; **410,** Dean Abramson.

Chapter Ten: **418,** Sandy Clark/The Stock Market; **419,** Frank Siteman/Stock Boston; **421,** Rob Tringali, Jr./Sportschrome; **422,** Arlene Collins/Monkmeyer Press; **425,** Courtesy, The National Weather Service; **432,** Lance V. Mion/The Picture Cube; **445,** NASA; **446,** Phil A. Dotson/Photo Researchers, Inc.; **447,** Mark W. Bolton/Bruce Coleman, Inc.; **449,** Bob Daemmrich/Stock Boston; **452,** PhotoEdit.

Chapter Eleven: **457,** Kenneth W. Fink/Bruce Coleman, Inc.; **458,** Gary Conner/PhotoEdit; **459,** The Granger Collection; **461,** John Madere/The Stock Market; **465,** Annie Hunter; **470,** Courtesy, Daniela Pisciuneri; **471,** Craig Hammell/The Stock Market; **474,** Gabe Palmer/The Stock Market; **476,** Courtesy, Kari Castle; **483,** Jericho Historical Society; **486 TR,** A. & F. Michler/Peter Arnold, Inc.; **486 BL,** John Shaw/Tom Stack & Associates; **486 BM,** Jerome Wexler/Photo Researchers, Inc.; **486 BR,** Charles Kennard/Stock Boston; **487 T, B,** Roy Morsch/The Stock Market; **489 T,** Foto World/The Image Bank; **489 B,** Rod Planck/Tom Stack & Associates; **492,** Kenneth W. Fink/Bruce Coleman, Inc.; **495,** Bob Daemmrich/The Image Works.

Photo Research: Toni Michaels

Contributing Author: Paul Curtis, Hollis Public Schools, Hollis NH

Editorial, Design, and Electronic Prepress Production, for the Teaching Resources:
The Wheetley Company

Editorial Services for the Teacher's Edition:
Publishers Resource Group, Inc.